Also by Martin L. Gross

THE BRAIN WATCHERS

The Doctors

The Doctors

by

Martin L. Gross

New York

Random House

To

My wife, Anita, for her work and wisdom

My daughters, Amy and Ellen; and my parents

ACKNOWLEDGMENT: A sincere acknowledgment to the many members of the medical community who aided significantly in the preparation of this book by giving generously of their specialized knowledge and openly of their opinions. The author is also grateful to those physicians who read this volume prior to its publication and offered helpful suggestions and comments.

CONTENTS

Part I: THE DOCTOR AND THE PATIENT

   I.   Introduction to the Modern Doctor:
       Man of Paradox   3

  II.   How Good Is His Art?:
       A Report on Medical Diagnosis   23

 III.   Modern Medical Practice versus the Patient:
       Arrogance, Availability
       and Assembly-Line Medicine   77

  IV.   The Doctor As a Scientist:
       The Fallacies of Doctor Erudition   100

   V.   Life and Death in His Hospitals:
       Surgery, Anesthesia, Obstetrics and Negligence 149

  VI.   Iatrogenic Disease:
       The Scourge of Doctor-Caused Illness   234

 VII.   Human Experimentation and the
       American Patient: *Failure at Nuremberg*   286

Part II: WHO ARE THE DOCTORS?

VIII.   The Doctor As a Person:
       The Non-Renaissance Physician, His
       Conspicuous Leisure and Declining Prestige   317

IX. The Doctor As a Businessman:
     The Golden Cult of Medical Economics   343

Part III: THE MAKING OF THE DOCTOR

X. Our Medical Colleges:
    "Trade Schools" in Need of a New Revolution   369

XI. Internes and Residents:
     From Innocence to Practice   402

Part IV: THE FAMILY DOCTORS

XII. The GP's: *Disappearing Family Doctor?*   419

XIII. The Pediatricians: *Grandma or Scientist?*   432

XIV. The Internists: *Tomorrow's GP's?*   441

XV. The Osteopaths: *Medical Manipulation*   450

Part V: THE DOCTOR AS A PROFESSIONAL

XVI. The American Medical Association:
      Our Most Potent "Labor Union"   463

XVII. The Doctor and His Drugs: *Ignorance,
       Detail Men and Four-Color Promotions*   483

XVIII. Malpractice: *The Patient's Recourse*   515

XIX. Disciplining the Doctors:
      A Conspiracy of Laxity   534

Part VI: CONCLUSION

XX. Which Way Caduceus?:
     A Scheme for Tomorrow   557

Notes and Bibliography   571

Index   601

Part I *The Doctor and the Patient*

Chapter I

Introduction
to the Modern
Doctor: Man of Paradox

It is not the purpose nor is it within the power of this book to destroy the reputation of the American doctor. It is not easy to undertake an analysis of the physician soon after one's own child has received a polio vaccine from the hand of a busy pediatrician, or after visiting a convalescent in the hospital, ruddy-faced and well after a successful operation. No one is immune to the fear of illness or death. Having learned—from day to day, through word and picture—that the doctor of medicine may be the only barrier between self and eternity, we find it painful to try to see the modern doctor as he really is. We have taught ourselves, instead, to view him through a prism of fear or hope.

We have seen the image of the doctor undergo a radical metamorphosis, from the kindly bearded "counselor-healer" portrayed in the sentimental painting "The Doctor," used so effectively by the American Medical Association, to the new, trimmer, shaven image. Our medical ancestor suffered, we are told, from a surfeit of love and a dearth of ability. The new "scientist-healer," however, deftly manipulates the armamentarium of modern medicine, ostensibly to keep Americans healthier and living longer. He may practice more swiftly and impersonally than his predecessor, but only, it is said, to cure more people in less time.

Not until the second decade of this century, the late Professor Lawrence J. Henderson of Harvard informed us, did a random patient taking a random ailment to a random doctor have even a 50–50 chance of "benefiting from the encounter." Today, a half century later, there is little doubt about the greater potential of medicine. But such a concept is abstract, while the doctor is quite concrete. "What of my doctor's skill?" the patient asks. How sure can any patient be that the stethoscope-draped physician is the philosophical descendant of the 2300-year-old Hippocrates—that his doctor is the true repository of the accumulated wisdom, art and science of medicine?

All such inquiries have been answered with a deafening paean of self-praise from the medical profession. "A tremendous distribution of quality medicine characterizes American medicine," Dr. Edward R. Annis, American Medical Association past president, recently assured the nation. "You can get fine medical care in other big cities of other countries; but in America you are in reach of fine medical care wherever you are . . . We can look forward to 90 to 100 years of enjoying life with our children." The theme is clarion-clear: there is little, if anything, that need concern the American patient if attended by a licensed American physician.

Despite a growing minority of public disenchantment, such constant accolades—both from within and outside the profession—have gained a pervasive hold on the American psyche. If not the outstanding folk hero, the American doctor is still the *primus* of professionals. A recent National Opinion Research Center survey confirms this: physicians rate at the apex of esteem, receiving 93 of a potential 100. They scored well ahead of lawyers, teachers, dentists, etc., and second only to U. S. Supreme Court Justices in national stature. For those inured to surveys, there is a more hard-headed index of his public acceptance as a professional: the typical patient presents himself and his body—voluntarily and unskeptically—to one of the nation's 276,156 physicians five times a year, twice as often as did the last generation.

The theory that sustains the modern doctor and the abiding faith in him is simple, if deceptively so. Medical "advances" emanate daily from the eighty-seven medical schools, several hundred university-hospital complexes and other research centers, adding to the prior body of information and forming a cohesive system of medical knowledge. The scientifically trained physician, according to popular belief, then applies this body of knowledge efficiently and intelligently to his patients as the modern healing balm.

Many of the so-called advances have been grievously exaggerated, but much of the medical revolution is of course significant. The polio and measles vaccines have added to a successful inventory of immunizing agents that have virtually eliminated diphtheria, smallpox and other former killers. American researchers have made practical the artificial kidney, invented in Holland; tetracyclines and other newer American antibiotics supplement the British-developed penicillin in controlling a variety of infections; mechanical heart-lung machines have advanced heart surgery pioneered by Dr. Robert Gross in Boston. Corneal transplants, aorta replacements, oral drugs for diabetics, modern neurosurgery, rehabilitative medicine, plastic and reconstructive surgery, among others, have given modern medicine a spectacular aura of technical brilliance.

The modern practitioner has lost little time in basking in its reflected image, developing confidence—what his detractors call "arrogance"—and an obvious distaste for criticism, especially from the layman. The late Dr. Alan Gregg of the Rockefeller Foundation, quoting an earlier source, put it bluntly: "A physician is so surrounded by frightened patients, adoring families and obsequious nurses that he will not brook criticisms by God or man." Dr. Gregg personally adds: "We behave as though we were a group set apart, and that attitude degenerates into professional provincialism."

It is the purpose of this book to attack that provincialism, and to probe the truth of the simplistic theory sustaining the modern doctor. Hopefully, this book will soundly pierce the God-man mystique that surrounds the doctor and reveal him—his foibles as well as his assets—more clearly to the public and his patients. In doing so, it will waive the exemption that the doctor has sought (and usually received) for himself from "challenge and education at the hands of disputatious laymen," as Dr. Gregg stated it. It is this book's intention to provide constructive answers to medical dilemmas and doctor ills. It will not, however, be done by invoking cookbook panaceas such as the ill-defined "socialized medicine" which—as Dr. Herbert Ratner of Stritch School of Medicine at Loyola University warns—would only distribute more efficiently all that is currently bad in American medicine.

It should be made abundantly clear that it is *not* the purpose of this book to deny or downgrade the achievements of modern medicine collectively, or those of the physician individually, but rather to use them as an effective and constructive yardstick for the profession as a whole. It would be foolish to deny that this book is written in the spirit of advocacy, but hopefully it will be shown that its client is the highest ideal and practice of the Hippocratic physician.

No layman, by himself, can make the incisive analysis envisaged here. As medical quality studies show, the patient is absolutely no judge of a doctor's ability, or even of his philosophy or dedication. Only the profession itself can provide the material for such an inquiry; by and large, only the doctor can reveal himself.

Fortunately for the American patient, a growing number of courageous physicians have been doing just that, in an undercurrent of professional criticism and discontent that has been virtually hidden from the public. Taking a reflective and flinty look at themselves and their colleagues, they describe a side of the medical condition that is far more pathologic than the one traditionally seen. It involves a doctor of considerably different dimension than the public, and much of the profession, has previously visualized.

This more tarnished side of the medical caduceus is tantalizingly hidden from the public, sometimes through doctor chicanery, more often simply because of the separateness of the doctor's world. The medical critiques that reveal it are not the mere prickings of a small and disillusioned minority but a sizable, rapidly accumulating body of criticism that exists in depth and documentation. It is found in leading medical journals such as the *New England Journal of Medicine,* the *Journal of the American Medical Association, Surgery, Gynecology & Obstetrics, Annals of Internal Medicine, American Journal of Surgery, American Journal of Public Health,* and scores of others; in uninhibited letters published in medical periodicals; and in candid personal interviews with medical educators, hospital administrators, medical scientists, and practicing physicians and surgeons—interviews that might not have been as frank only a few years ago.

The new medical dialogue is omnipresent: it appears in government surveys; medical association reports; quality control studies; Public Health Service reports; postgraduate symposia; hospital accreditations and investigations; community health surveys; hospital-tissue committee reports; and in many other professional sources. The most revealing material is often in the form of routine medical reports never intended as criticism. Common-sense interpretation, however, converts the doctor-accepted into grist for public annoyance, or worse.

It is the major purpose of this book to pull aside the gauze curtain of medical secrecy and make this private medical debate considerably more public. The story is often shocking, always enlightening, and usually in conflict with the established shibboleths and demimyths surrounding the American doctor, many of which we may have to re-examine or discard if we are to best advance health and medical care. (Throughout this book, the term "the doctor" or "the physician" is meant as a general phrase that excludes those physicians endowed with superior skills, integrity and introspection, as well as that minute segment of the medical community which lacks even rudimentary talent or dedication. The *doctor* refers to those physicians who provide the bulk of American medical care, whether they be called pediatricians, GP's, surgeons, internists, obstetricians or by other medical sub-definitions.)

The body of medical dissent contradicts scores of current medico-sociological theorems, including the venerable one stating that although doctors, like people, vary, medical care is sufficiently uniform in America to make doctor incompetence an almost nonexistent threat. Dr. Martin Cherkasky, director of Montefiore Hospital in New York, deflates this Pollyannish concept by describing current medical care as a commodity that ranges from "superb to terrible." It is, in effect, a sliding scale of life or death that, contrary to common prejudice, he contends, is usually unrelated to the cheap or prestigious price tag that accompanies it.

One of the many startling confirmations of this grave medical disparity emerges from an analytic in-the-doctor's-office study of general physicians in North Carolina conducted under the direction of Dr. Osler L. Peterson, then a staff member of the Rockefeller Foundation. The quality of care dispensed proved to have shocking extremes, with more than *60 percent* of the therapeutic treatment graded as below acceptable medical standards. Inasmuch as American medical education, training and quality vary little *geographically,* this North Carolina report, as we shall later see, is a representative index of at least family doctor frailty and ignorance throughout the nation.

The unprecedented "Trussell Reports," two penetrating studies conducted by the Columbia University School of Public Health and Administrative Medicine in 1962 and 1964 under the direction of Drs. Ray E. Trussell and M. A. Morehead, are other forceful rebuttals to the myth of uniform medical competence. The studies evaluated two samples of medical and surgical care provided by *both* specialists and family doctors in the New York area, by scrupulously surveying the medical and surgical care of hundreds of patients in some 100 co-operating hospitals—from giant medical-center complexes to doctor-owned profit-making proprietary hospitals.

"Appalling," "shocking case," "medical ignorance," "gross violation of medical ethics," "completely unjustified surgery," "sloppy performance, diagnostically and therapeutically" are just a sampling of the glossary of these medical quality studies, the results of which were both surprising and upsetting. Almost half of the care (43 percent) given patients was rated less than "good" by a group of outstanding doctor-auditors, including three internists, one pediatrician, one obstetrician-gynecologist, one pathologist, one surgeon. Almost a fourth of the patients (23 percent) received care of such low quality that it could only be described in the report as "poor." Statistics such as these openly refute the profession's traditional refusal to recognize any other than the "qualified," "licensed" physician.

Ironically, the patients were "overwhelmingly" satisfied with their treatment. Many thought that they were receiving the "best" of medical attention even when the report indicated "poor judgment on the part of the attending physician." Patients husband many misconceptions, including the comforting thought that time-tested diagnosis and treatment for specific ailments are almost a professional reflex for doctors. The reports, among others, bitterly shatter such faith. Diabetics, for example, are prone to early hardening of the arteries, and an accepted diagnostic test is to examine the retina of the eye and the arterial pulsations in the feet for early clues to this condition. Of forty-two diabetics being treated, the 1964 Trussell audit states melancholically: "the records of only 10 showed that an examination of the retina had been done; in only seven instances was there evidence that the pulsations in the feet had been recorded."

Other shocking discrepancies mar the supposed "uniform" medical image: major surgeries performed without standard laboratory tests; 20 percent of surgical cases unjustifiedly delayed for more than five days. Too often, the report indicates, "patients who required detailed and exhaustive study received only casual, symptomatic handling of their disease." In a tragic case in point, a young woman who was admitted to a hospital with rheumatic heart disease died suddenly, with evidence that the serious nature of her illness "was not appreciated" by her doctor. Says the medical surveyor about the doctor's performance: "Casual handling, lack of close cardiac observation such as recording of heart rate, blood pressure, color change."

Physicians have traditionally been casual about their serious shortcomings, accepting them as inevitable idiosyncrasies of the human animal. But objective critiques such as the Trussell audits startle the more sensitive doctors as much as they do the patient. "I had the opportunity of sitting in on a preview of what the report reveals," Dr. Martin Cherkasky told the assembled American Public Health Association in Detroit, "and some of the findings were shocking to me, even though I had spent my professional life in medical care, and knew some of its shortcomings. For example, Caesarean section where there was no need; out of 60 hysterectomies, in more than 20 there could not be any possible cause for doing them—and so on—errors of omission and commission, almost beyond belief. . . . Of course, the complications, misery, the pain, unhappiness, and the disability which followed upon this unnecessarily poor care will go on long after our discussions are over. If this was shocking to me, just imagine what it was to those lay people who place their lives in our hands.

"Since the doctors are the ones who know about quality care, and since despite too much bad care there are thousands and tens of thousands who practice good medicine, what leadership for change can we expect from organized medicine? The answer, unfortunately, is—not much."

What about the surgical level of excellence in our meticulous operating rooms, often so lavishly equipped with the chromium-new hardware of medical progress? The critical reviewer of current surgery sees a deep fissure of inconsistency in operative care that is taking a heavy toll in life. To him, the operating theater is not quite the scene of casual perfection that many of the 13,900,000 surgical patients each year (and their doctors) think or hope it is. Many undoubtedly receive new life, or ease at the hands of extremely competent surgeons, physicians and anesthetists. Physician-critics, however, place the inexcusable error in surgery as high as 40, 50 and even 90 percent of current surgical mishaps.

One Trussell report states that more than 40 percent of the surgery under study was less than "good." Some critics believe that this percentage of failure might be more awesomely applied to surgical *deaths* caused by lack of uniform competence. An estimated 100,000 to 150,000 patients die each year as surgical mortalities, a sizable if specifically unknown percentage of them in the operating room. Almost half of the latter group might have lived, states one critic, had the profession willed otherwise fiercely enough. Dr. Arthur James Mannix, Jr., a Fellow of the American College of Surgeons, states this highly provocative opinion in the *New York State Journal of Medicine:* "Errors in judgment or technic concerning either the anesthesia or the surgery, or a combination of the two, contribute close to 50 percent of the mortality in the operating room."

Writing in *Surgery, Gynecology & Obstetrics,* pediatric surgeon Dr. Edward G. Stanley-Brown of St. Luke's Hospital in New York reports that of twenty-one surgical deaths of infants and children that he and colleagues examined, 90 percent were the result of doctor error. His catalogue of fatal errors is commanding: errors in diagnosis, seven deaths; errors in management, five deaths; errors in technique, five deaths; errors in anesthesia, two deaths; errors in judgment, two deaths. Even though St. Luke's death rate in pediatric surgery is comparatively low, Dr. Stanley-Brown saw no excuse for preventable death. "To err is human," he states, "but when human error results in operative death, the patient is deprived of any opportunity he might have had to forgive, at least in this world."

Dr. Leroy H. Stahlgren of the Philadelphia General Hospital reveals that at least 40 percent of death in surgery of elderly patients may be avoidable. Of seventeen geriatric patients who died, he reports in *Surgery, Gynecology & Obstetrics,* "errors were committed in the surgical care of 7 of the 17."

The scene of surgery and much of medicine (the professional term for nonsurgical care) is of course the hospital, the doctor's workshop. To patients, best described as innocents, "hospital" is a word with a specific sense and meaning that generally evokes an image similar to the celebrated Massachusetts General in Boston or, at the least, a tightly supervised institution maintained by hordes of intent, white-gowned internes and residents, astute attending specialists, full-time department heads, and allied researchers and scientists. Many such institutions do of course exist. (Over four hundred hospitals are connected with teaching institutions; all, however, do not necessarily provide quality care.) But looking more closely into the corridors of the American hospital, we shall see that the reality of the nation's 7127 registered hospitals is far less bright than its image.

More than four out of every five American hospitals have no internes or residents (the "omnipresent" young men-in-white exist in only 1400 hospitals; internes in only 765 hospitals); almost 40 percent of hospitals do not even meet the minimum standards (and they *are* minimum) of the medical profession. Thousands of hospitals have no doctor at all, or only one or two foreign, often unlicensed, doctors, on the hospital premises—which may be a threat to the patient's life. In fact, when the Massachusetts House of Representatives recently introduced a bill requiring every hospital in the state to have at least one doctor on the premises at all times, the legislation was greeted with outrage by medical spokesmen, and blocked. Understandably, American hospitals vary greatly in the quality of care they dispense, in their infection and death rates, in their index of healthy tissue removed by surgeons, in the patient's very chances of cure, or even survival.

The hazards to the patient are not limited to the doctor's failures to heal, or his fatal or near-fatal omissions of modern diagnosis and therapy. Aroused medical critics are now warning the profession that the burgeoning medical technology is a two-edged twentieth century sword that cuts sharply both ways, for benefit or harm. Its unsophisticated use by doctors—including rash experimentation on patients, overcasual dispensing of potent drugs, and potentially dangerous diagnostic and therapeutic techniques—is *creating death and disease* at an alarming pace that, if not controlled, may more than counterbalance the physician's power to do good.

There is penetrating evidence that in addition to his healing power, the modern physician has already become one of man's most potent killers and cripplers. Dr. David M. Spain, clinical professor of pathology at Downstate Medical Center of the State University of New York in Brooklyn, warns that such doctor-caused, or *iatrogenic,* disease is, in effect, epidemic. "Unfortunately," states the prominent pathologist, "iatrogenic disease can now take its place almost as an equal alongside the bacteria as an important factor in the pathogenesis of human illness."

Iatrogenic disease, as well as other doctor failings that are creating medical heretics, is often related to the modern doctor's infatuation with the novel and the new, even when these "advances" are false, dangerous or premature. Exaggeration has virtually become an

American medical way of life. New medical and surgical "cures" are heralded daily, then later quietly discarded with unobtrusive majesty. As in the recent case of the gastric freezing treatment for stomach ulcers, which was first greeted with near-theatrical huzzahs, the patients trapped between the enthusiastic acceptance and the later rejection are the victims of the physician's seemingly uncontrollable impetuosity.

Soon after researchers announced the technique, many physicians throughout the nation were performing the supposedly simple and safe procedure for ulcer sufferers, often right in the doctor's office. Patients swallowed a balloon and tubing through which a freezing solution of ethyl alcohol at $-15°$ centigrade was circulated for forty-five minutes. The result? A recent survey of 826 of the patients subjected to the technique was published in the *Journal of the American Medical Association*. The toll was seventy cases of gastric bleeding evidenced by melena (stools colored black from altered blood), twenty-one cases of gastric ulcers *created* by the treatment, and an encyclopedia of complications, including death. Other recent surveys indicate such serious damage as hemorrhage and perforation of the stomach. Its value as an ulcer treatment? Says the *JAMA* article: "There seems to be no justification for its widespread clinical use."

Dr. William B. Bean, head of the department of medicine at the State University of Iowa, is one critic who enjoys throwing literate darts into this type of medical overexpansiveness. In an impressive piece of satire entitled "Recent Setbacks in Medicine," published in *Northwest Medicine,* Dr. Bean chides his fellow doctors: "With casual but touching optimism today's physician has almost come to believe what the layman says about the extravagant powers of science to banish pain and disease, to prolong life and to create panacea in something reminiscent of Ponce de Leon's fountain of youth—Hollywood style. In actual fact the physician's apparent worldly wisdom is a masquerade for intellectual innocence."

Once a probing catheter was dispatched into the body of the doctor, it was inevitable that the critics concerned would diagnose him not only as a physician, but as a man as well. Dr. Bean believes that many of his fellow physicians have "debased themselves" by "forsaking humanism and the feeling of continuity with history." Dr. Julian Price, former AMA Board of Trustees chairman, is perturbed by the modern doctor's overemphasis on money, which he describes as one of the "insidious trends" in American medicine. Other doctors, with less access to authoritative podiums, express their disillusionment through the letters columns of medical publications—with the exception of the typically neurotically censored county medical society publications.

A Washington (D.C.) physician who has been in practice for thirty-six years writes to *Medical World News:* "I am disgusted and fed up with the attitude of many physicians." Instead of dedicating themselves to "service and humanity," the annoyed physician says, "doctors by and large are worshiping the call of the golden fleece and totally unmindful of what their real function should properly be. They have their noses in the air and use their positions to seek status."

Another critic, assailing the "egoistic" and "money-grabbing" doctor whose character failings cause death and disability, saw fit to reveal all—except his name. (This cautious technique is a common ploy against professional countermeasures, and is not an idle doctor neurosis.) This anonymous physician, writing in a popular medical publication under the pen name "Dr. Michael V. Corio," invited *more* rather than less of the hated malpractice suits, which each year accost the pride and pocketbook of six thousand doctors, at a cost estimated as high as $50,000,000.

"If patients brought more malpractice suits against *all* guilty doctors—and against all guilty doctors only—the courts would probably be flooded with three times the number of such suits in litigation," the impassioned doctor wrote. "These are cases the plaintiffs would win, and it would be a good thing for every honest, ethical scrupulous doctor that they did . . . I'm talking about flagrant abuses of the right to practice medicine—abuses that lead to catastrophic results to the patient. We all know about such abuses. Too often we keep our mouths shut."

"Dr. Corio" relates several cases in which "egoistic" doctors have endangered patients' lives by refusing to recognize their own limits. A woman had the ominous symptoms of vomiting, pain and weight loss. Rather than send her to a radiologist, the doctor gave her the complex "GI (for 'gastrointestinal') Series" of X-rays—then informed her that the results were negative. The woman finally came to "Dr. Corio." "She had a gastric carcinoma [cancer], plainly visible on the films taken three months earlier. The doctor had missed it. This woman died." The doctor, he claims, was professionally over his head.

After describing another case, "Dr. Corio" makes a passionate indictment of a type of colleague: "Nobody gave him [the doctor] away, and the patient's family accepts this catastrophe as the will of God. I say it was the will of an irresponsible egoistic physician."

The doctor as a person, as seen by many critical sociologists—amateur and otherwise—is a scientifically oriented man who is becoming increasingly dehumanized by his training and type of practice —a defect that has been blamed for much of the current uneasiness between patient and doctor. Dr. Frank P. Pignataro, former president of the New Jersey Neuropsychiatric Association, states this increasingly common critique passionately. Writing in the *Journal of the*

Student American Medical Association, he warns: "I feel that the personality of today's physicians is deteriorating in an alarming fashion . . . I am prepared to maintain against all comers, that the majority of young men being graduated from medical schools today in this or any other country are not competently prepared (by attitude) to practice the healing art . . . they have little or no training whatsoever leading to the development of the personality which is absolutely indispensable to a true doctor of medicine."

This sampling of criticism—whether critiques of medical personality or surgical care—cannot, of course, make a cohesive argument in a few pages. The cumulative total of professional annoyance at the failings of the modern doctor, however, constitutes a bill of medical particulars that neither patient nor physician can safely ignore. It is one that must be ledgered alongside the more obvious and well-publicized gains of modern medicine.

Naturally, the charges of serious failings apply in varying degree to a varying number of physicians and cannot be considered a blanket indictment, either by doctor-critics or by the author. Such a disclaimer, however, should not impede the charge, and the important and sometimes subtle distinctions involved will, as we progress, be seen in perspective to the profession as a whole. Further, it should be remembered that the physician is in almost total control of American medical practice; virtually all that occurs in medicine is either to his credit or the result of his failings.

Doctor failings in care and treatment are at the core of the critique: his diagnostic inabilities that cost tens of thousands of lives; his carelessness in overlooking known lifesaving techniques; his dangerously immature use of rash, unproven therapies and surgical procedures; his inhuman experimentation on unknowing, trusting patients; his growing toll of iatrogenic death and disease; his tendency to use medical procedures beyond his training or ability; his abysmal neglect of preventive medicine; his neglect of the chronically sick, especially among the aged; his continued practice of unnecessary surgery despite professional and public rebuke.

There are giant gaps in the modern physician's vital knowledge and training. He is being accused of unwarranted ignorance of modern drugs; of unconscionable inattention to postgraduate education and failure to "keep up"; of failure to go beyond the Abraham Flexner reforms of 1910 and provide the adequate medical education needed to train today's healers; of serious failings in scientific thought; of fostering a dangerous imbalance favoring elegant research over inquiry into practical day-to-day care.

Of the doctor failings catalogued by his critics, his philosophical shortcomings are among the most serious. (Contrary to popular belief, many doctors never take the Hippocratic or any other oath of healing.) He has been charged with a casual, almost cynical acceptance of mediocrity in a profession that cries for excellence; with overindulgence in the money and business aspects of medicine; with a crass attempt to combine medicine and politics; with a tendency to exaggerate and make premature medical claims; with an egoistic failure to seek consultation from his colleagues; with maintaining an outdated guild relationship that endangers the public weal; with rationalizing all his shortcomings in the name of medicine; with knowingly, and in bad conscience, keeping the public ignorant of medical pitfalls, thus jeopardizing the health and lives of his patients; with creating medical-practice systems that fit his rather than his patients' needs; with contributing to the increasing failure of the health-insurance concept; with inability to comprehend the true essence of medical ethics as being related to the needs of his patients rather than to those of his fellow doctors.

The doctor has also been charged with being responsible for a serious lack of organization. He has been accused of mismanagement that has brought medical care to the brink of anarchy: of inadequate hospital supervision; of lack of supervision of private practitioners; of the travesty of so-called medical discipline; of failure to provide sufficient doctors in needed categories; of the existence of inferior hospital facilities; of the absence of overall planning for the health of the nation; of creating an impersonal, discontinuous brand of medical care.

Perhaps most important, the doctor should be cited for permitting the existence of such a large percentage of medical incompetence and insufficient competence—considerably more than the public or the profession had previously suspected. It is, in fact, a credit to the egocentricity or to the isolation of the typical doctor that this growing critique has not yet really affected him or his practice.

How can such an indictment be given credence when it so patently violates known medical catechism? How can these charges be consonant with the "fact" that medical care has increased our longevity fantastically?

Life expectancy has unfortunately become a medical numbers game that has been used by certain professional spokesmen to patronizingly remind the laity of the themes: "Many years have been added to life by medical care" and "We are living longer and longer every year." Life expectancy throughout the developed portion of the world has advanced rapidly in the past two generations, statistically increasing some twenty-three years in America since 1900. This vision of extended life rising in the near future, as one overenthusiast of modern medicine speculated, to a hundred years of doctor-given existence, is, however, a statistical and factual myth. The actual life span of the average American *adult* has been extended only a tantalizing fraction in the past three generations: a man of forty can expect to live only 3.7 years more than did his grandfather in 1900; the man of sixty can anticipate only an added 1.3 years, with no key to how much of this small gift can be credited to medicine or how much is attributable to better housing, sanitation and general living standards.

The *New England Journal of Medicine* sought to educate its confused doctor-readers on this statistical hope-trap, in an editorial entitled "Life Expectancy." The staid Boston journal chastised an immature "public service" advertisement by a pharmaceutical firm extolling medical care which prophesied 150 years of life by the year 2175. The historical increase, the *NEJM* explained patiently, is not due to "any material stretching out of the normal life span" but "rather to the improvement and ability to care for infants and for infections as well as other treatable diseases." Mathematically, the saving of an infant during childbirth or a small child from diphtheria adds years to a longevity table but not to a surviving adult's life. The normal life span 5000 years later, the journal reminds us, is still the Biblical "three score and ten."

The *NEJM* added the dour possibility that instead of a Nirvana of 150 years of existence, the life expectancy of seventy might actually decrease. This prophetic analysis has already borne melancholy fruit. The most recent HEW figures show that life expectancy, which reached its summit of 70.2 in 1961, decreased to 70 in 1962, and further declined to 69.8 in 1963—placing it back toward the 1959 level, when enthusiasts were militantly trumpeting the future. From a high of 67 years in 1961, life expectancy for males has *declined* to 66.6. In fact, the surviving life expectancy for a man of 65 has *decreased* since 1952!

A U. S. Public Health Service report, "The Change in Mortality Trend in the United States," sounds another discouraging note. The death rate, which had been declining since 1900, leveled off in 1953 and has not continued its original optimistic trend since. In fact, almost all the improvement in life expectancy figures in the last thirty-five years is traceable to the conquests—sanitary and medical—over most of the infectious and communicable diseases. Once the immunization and antibiotic revolutions had made their mark, the impetus of increased life was rudely halted. During the past decade, when supposed scientific-medical "advances" made such an indelible imprint on the American psyche, life expectancy made its most begrudging gain in history: a total of only one-third of a year, which itself may be only a tenuous and short-lived statistic.

In comparative national terms, American health statistics are not complimentary. Our infant mortality rate is eleventh highest of fifteen graded nations, with indications that if we could but match the record of the Netherlands, we would save forty-two thousand young lives each year. In longevity, United Nations demographic figures indicate that rather than the suspected highest life expectancy in the world, the American male rates twenty-first—ignominiously beaten out by the men of Sweden and the Netherlands by five years, and by almost as much by the males of just-emerging Israel.

Equally discouraging is the fact that our position has been weakening steadily: American male life expectancy, which is now 66.6 years at birth, was rated thirteenth in the world in 1963; eighteenth in 1964; twenty-first by 1965. (The American female does survive comparatively better—tenth place—but our combined male-female life expectancy is still only fourteenth in the world.) Those who would glibly ascribe longevity failure of the American male to the pervasive stress of our society should first consider several factors: it has not been proved that life stress of any variety is a killer; no one has found a method of evaluating American affluence-stress with Israeli state-survival or Czechoslovak Communist-created stress; managing executives, who are ostensibly subjected to the apex of American stress, have a death rate, according to National Vital Statistics, some 20 percent *lower* than union-protected plumbers!

The poor record of American life expectancy gain during the last decade does not, of course, indicate a hopelessness, nor is it an argument for medical nihilism. If there is a common denominator to the medical critic it is his concrete recognition of the *potential* of medicine, albeit limited, and the lesser reality of the modern doctor. It is a question of bridging the chasm, as medical lecturer Dr. Lester J. Evans recently stated to the University of Michigan Medical School, "between potential and performance."

The present potential is undoubtedly not the ninety to a hundred years that the American Medical Association's ebullient spokesman contemplates. Longer European life expectancies and examples of superior American performance, however, indicate that there is sizable room for health improvement and better medical care. Dr. George Rosen and Odin W. Anderson (Ph.D.), writing in a Health Information Foundation report, ask: "What are the possible levels of achievement?" In answer, they argue that a low death rate of 6.7 per one thousand versus the current 9.4 is definitely possible, because one state, Utah, actually recorded it in 1955. "Obviously if current knowledge were applied to the maximum," they comment, "the present death rate for the country as a whole could still be reduced appreciably." Dr. Iwao M. Mariyama of the Public Health Service estimates that if the "lowest age-sex specific death rate" of any country were matched here, "there would have been about 297,000 fewer deaths in the United States" in 1960.

Who is this American physician under scrutiny here, and by his colleagues? What can we say of his portrait, at least in tintype? First, he is 44.2 years of age, has had ten years of training since completing high school, and is one of the 80 percent of active doctors—other than internes and residents—who are in their own private medical practice-business, generally as individuals ("solo") or in partnership. A minority of eleven thousand physicians are in "group" practice with two or more fellow doctors.

The doctor operates a financially successful enterprise, one with no professional equal. He admits a gross median income of $44,060 a year, and a net of $28,380 after all deductions. Thirty percent of doctors who answered a recent survey admitted a net of $40,000 or more, with strong evidence of a doctor prosperity that far exceeds even such estimates.

Much of his affluence is a by-product of the doctor shortage and his ability to command a seller's market among the ill, a situation which organized medicine bemoans publicly but has been accused of winking at salaciously in private. The ratio of doctors to patients has remained a steady 130–140 per 100,000 during the past generation. Patient visits have doubled, and there has been a drain of physicians into residency training, teaching, administration, industrial positions and the armed forces, leaving only 90 doctors per 100,000 population in private practice, many of these in narrow subspecialties.

The fervor with which this scarce physician is courted by patients today has given him the spoiled prerogatives of an ante-bellum belle. The result, as we shall see, has been a quest for personal convenience and income that now ranks among the prime stimuli in modern medicine.

The modern doctor works less hours than his predecessor and sees many more patients. Many physicians do work hard, but the poignant image of drudgery, sleeplessness and abnormal working hours is now usually only perfumed nostalgia. The modern doctor works approximately a ten-hour day, or about fifty-eight hours a week, including sizable fringe time spent studying, at meetings, etc. As frantic patients have learned during certain evenings, weekends and all day Wednesday (the doctor's traditional "golf" day off in many areas), physicians' hours rival those of businessmen—many of whom, with commuting and homework, put in equivalent or more working time. In fact, a recent survey indicates that 26 percent of physicians now work forty-nine hours a week or less.

An Alfred Politz study reports another accelerating trend: 35 percent of doctors now work only five days a week or less. Just as persistent seven-day illness has been asked to conform to the doctor's new week, so twenty-four-hour illness may soon have to restrict itself to increasingly common nine-to-five hours.

This medical weekend-and-evening trauma has prompted warnings from responsible medical spokesmen who fear its effect on the professional "image" and its possible repercussions. Dr. Milton Helpern, on assuming the presidency of the Medical Society of the

County of New York, chastised some of his colleagues for "terminat-ing" their work at "4 or 5 o'clock." He then added: "My lay friends complain more and more that it is difficult, if not impossible, to obtain the services of their own physicians over weekends, par-ticularly in the summer months. The tendency for physicians to emulate their friends in business or other professions by disappearing to country homes and resorts, or to make themselves unavailable seems to be on the increase . . . It has become hazardous to develop a serious illness over a weekend or on a holiday, and now, even at night."

In the fewer hours he labors, the modern physician handles what weary waiting-room veterans consider an unchecked epidemic of patients. The typical doctor of the 1930's had a case load of 50 patients per week: today it is an admitted 124 patients for all doctors, 169 for the general practitioner, and almost 200 patients for the busiest twenty-five percent of physicians. Other studies, such as one conducted in Kalamazoo, Michigan, reports an even higher average figure of 31 patients a day, or about 175 a week. Even 40, 60 and more patients per day is apparently not unusual for some busy practitioners. One Kentucky family doctor recently boasted of handling 50 patients a day in a forty-hour work week!

Mathematics is a relatively inflexible discipline. With shorter working hours and more patients, the doctor obviously gives less and less time to each patient, to each diagnosis, to each therapy. Time has become such a carefully husbanded commodity for the modern physician that his chary dispensing of it has annoyed even his most loyal patients.

As most any parent knows, the doctor has virtually eliminated the "house call" under the sophistic argument that it is no longer medically necessary. In 1930 the typical practice consisted of 40 percent house calls; today it comprises less than 3 percent of the typical family doctor's practice. Despite the potential threat of mal-practice "abandonment" charges, many doctors, including pediatri-cians, refuse to make or avoid making house calls at all. A recent survey shows that the average specialist now makes only one house call per week; the typical pediatrician only three a week.

Just as the modern doctor has adjusted his work week to fit his rather than the community's constitution, so he has altered his year's work to fulfill the good life his professional ancestors sought in vain. The workingman's "two weeks with" was the envy of last generation's doctor. Today, three- to six-week trips to Europe and the far continents during lengthy summer vacations, and often an addi-tional winter vacation in the Caribbean, are almost as much the norm as the exception. A New York agency, "At Home Abroad," which rents luxurious villas on the Mediterranean between Barcelona and

Rome, is but one of the many leisure sellers who find doctors their best and most frequent customers.

This ubiquitous modern physician is either a specialist or a general practitioner (only one in four is a general practitioner). A recent survey of medical students indicates that only 18 percent intend to enter general practice after internship, while 78 percent expect to complete a two- to four-year residence and follow a specialty. The remaining 4 percent are interested in teaching and research.

Whatever his special calling, the doctor tends to be conservative-minded, although the ofttimes archaic views of the American Medical Association are only a crude nineteenth-century caricature of many doctors' true opinions. He is a registered Republican (a 1964 Presidential poll showed 71 percent of doctors favored the Republican Party); is the offspring of upper-middle-class families earning $10,000 or more; and has college-trained parents, with either a professional or executive background. His motivation for medicine includes several goals, especially money, prestige, science and humanitarianism, and in many cases all are probably an inseparable conglomeration in his mind.

There is increasing evidence, however, that the potentially damaging motivations—money and prestige—are beginning to outweigh humanitarianism as the professional *raison d'être*. A study by the Student American Medical Association, reported in *GP* magazine, surveyed 694 medical students, internes, residents and prospective students, with dismaying results. In response to the survey, which in effect asked: "What were the major reasons you chose medicine as a career?," 56 percent answered "income" or "prestige" rather than "humanitarianism." Dr. Frank P. Pignataro is one of many who are frankly concerned. "Their ambition is not achievement but financial security," he laments. "It bodes no good for the standards of our profession."

One item from the statistical wax figure of the modern doctor should stand out as pre-eminently vital in understanding medicine today: the fact that the American physician in private practice is an astonishingly free agent—what Dr. George A. Silver of New York disconsolately calls "a free-booter." Medicine has often termed itself "the most closely self-regulated profession," another medical myth with little substance or substantiation. In actuality the modern doctor, once licensed by his State Board of Medical Examiners, is a virtually uncontrolled soul who has lifetime prerogatives almost entirely outside the purview of the law or the medical profession, unless he commits a crime. Says Dr. Martin Cherkasky of New York of this modern *Homo medicus:* "In his characteristic fee-for-service solo-practice situation, he is the least supervised of any professional group."

It has been said that "doctors work best when other doctors are looking over their shoulders." In most situations, the modern doctor is unencumbered by this prying colleague. The doctor can choose his medical subcategory and even his patients (it is not true that a doctor must treat any person who presents himself); he can provide services in the location, time, and manner of his preference; he can associate with an admittedly inferior hospital and funnel his patients in, or seek affiliation with an efficient institution; he can provide medical care within the bounds of his training or legally pretend expertise in fields in which he has no qualifications and call himself a "specialist"; he can lie or be candid with his patients; he can be a proficient or dangerously incompetent practitioner.

Not only is he uncontrolled, but he has adopted what is almost a litany: that the "freedom" he so passionately seeks is intimately tied by mystique to medical quality; that the greater the medical anarchy, the more lives will be saved. The danger of this rationalization was underlined by Dr. Robert S. Myers, now executive assistant director of the American College of Surgeons. Writing in *Modern Hospital,* he says: "The prevailing belief of many physicians [is] that controls are undesirable and are an infringement on the freedom of practice. The American physician is a rugged individualist, conditioned by generations of public respect and confidence. He has become accustomed to believe that, in medical matters, each physician is a judge of his own capabilities and limitations. Unfortunately, few human beings are blessed with such insight . . ."

State licensing authorities do suspend and revoke medical licenses for such reasons as criminal abortion or use of narcotics. The so-called stringent regulation the profession speaks of, however, is virtually nonexistent. Infrequent censure generally involves so-called ethical complaints from other doctors about the lighting of a lawn shingle or patient-swiping. Except when abusively large fees, ungentlemanly conduct or the violation of a patient's confidence is involved, medical "regulation" has little to do with the patient, or with his medical protection.

Dr. Gerald D. Dorman, an AMA Trustee, has confirmed that getting doctors to discipline other doctors is difficult. Dr. William F. Quinn, a former member of the California Board of Medical Examiners, emphasizes this dearth of public protection: ". . . We have no jurisdiction over the unethical or incompetent doctor, unless he breaks the law or is found insane."

Not only the physician but American medical care in general is unsupervised and unmanaged, a miasma of often unrelated services through which the patient—and even the doctor—must cautiously grope his way to maintain his safety. Though most laymen have not delineated their relationship with medicine, they have a peripheral concept that medical care is overseen by some suprabody, perhaps the American Medical Association. The only overall "regulation" worth even the faintest definition of the word consists of two accreditations, one without enforcement, the other related only indirectly to the patient. The Joint Commission on Accreditation of Hospitals does check hospitals *if asked*, but has no power, professional or legal, to enforce its criticisms. The Council on Medical Education and Hospitals of the AMA (and, when appropriate, certain specialty boards) does approve the interne and resident training programs in the minority of hospitals that house them, but only to regulate postgraduate training, not as any standard of patient protection—although in *some* cases the patient does benefit indirectly. As Drs. Avedis and S. J. Axelrod of the University of Michigan School of Public Health state it: "It is apparent . . . that a major characteristic of the organization of medical care in this country is its lack of organization."

The unfortunate reality is a system of near-anarchy—of the magnificent, the mediocre, and the abysmal, side by side and publicly undifferentiated—in which the patient is at the mercy of the individual doctor's concept of himself, his skill and his conscience. To learn this salient fact may be the patient's best medical education and personal protection.

What has the laissez-faire physician done with his magnificent freedom of action? He has, it is obvious, created a new professional entity—the *scientist-businessman-healer*—a philosophical medical trinity with little precedent in history, and one that may yet prove to be an anachronism in modern society. There is seldom doubt expressed about the business proficiency of the private-practice doctor. However, what he brings to his crucial role as a scientist and healer is under heavy challenge.

Dr. Herbert Ratner of Loyola is one of this growing species of skeptics. Says he: ". . . Our much-vaunted claim [is] that physicians, pre-eminently by their years of arduous education, are masters of the scientific method. That, I think, is the biggest illusion held by medical educators today." Others, including Dr. John R. Ellis, leading British internist and educator, are concerned that the new physician is too often merely a "technician."

Whatever his scientific proficiency, the modern doctor faces the unenviable challenge of trussing it into the framework of his busy, tightly managed business-practice, where the complex demands of science, medicine and healing butt sharply up against the reality of time, money and even the doctor's new management consultant. How much science and healing art can, and should, a doctor dispense for this traditional $5 or $10 fee?

We shall observe this modern doctor (and his university and

research colleagues) in action. We shall study him as he works in the hospital, in his office, at medical school, in the laboratory, in the operating room, at home, with his patients, his associates and by himself—constantly testing the possibility that he is a man of paradox, a physician with more built-in conflicts than solutions. To this examination, on behalf of his almost 200,000,000 patients, this book is dedicated.

Chapter II

How Good Is His Art?:

A Report on Medical Diagnosis

The female patient was not medically unusual except for a history of chronic, unexplained aches and pains. On this visit to her regular physician she complained of a stomach ache. Checking her medical record, the physician noted a disposition to stomach aches plus the results of a battery of laboratory tests, all of which were negative. The busy doctor's mind quickly shifted into loose diagnostic gear and assumed that the prior material was accurate. His considered diagnosis: a general stomach malaise triggered by emotions. His therapy of a mild sedative was equally inconclusive.

A month later the patient returned, unsoothed by either the sedatives or the doctor's casual attitude. She was still suffering stomach pains complicated by soft stools. The diagnosis? Obviously the same, requiring still more sedative capsules. At the end of two months the patient—showing weight loss, with the same stomach ache but now accompanied by rectal bleeding—returned to her doctor's office. Faced with the reality of blood, the physician's clinical thermostat finally was alerted and he ordered a series of abdominal X-rays. The near-tragic diagnosis was cancer. The patient's cecum, the cul-de-sac in which the large intestine begins, was malignant.

This doctor's original abysmal failure, then tardy success, involved three of the one billion annual visits to the nation's physicians, perhaps half of which are the setting for the drama of medical diagnosis. Since even the healthiest eventually become ill, no physician can escape the constant challenge of finding and delineating illness among his patients, an imperfect art of detection that awes and excites the true medical mind. According to one survey of five hundred physicians, diagnosis is the most satisfying aspect of the profession, an opportunity—as some express it—for "sheer intellectual enjoyment," an exercise comparable to "putting a puzzle together."

The art of diagnosis antedates Hippocrates and has traditionally been a technique that requires the fullest use of the doctor's hands, eyes, ears, mind and intuition. The human being, in all his undressed glory, was the center of the ritual. The doctor circled his subject—mentally and physically—viewing, questioning, palpating (a laying on of his hands to examine the affected part, auscultating (listening to sounds of the heart and other organs) and percussing (firmly tapping the body). Despite current derisions of our medical ancestry, many last-generation doctors were so adept at physical examination that considering their limited knowledge, they often made "remarkable diagnoses," as Dr. Morris Fishbein, editor of *Medical World News,* emphasizes.

The best modern physicians have not deleted a medical *pas de deux* from this traditional performance, but much of the emphasis in modern diagnosis has shifted to the scientific-technological method and its exotic hardware: stereocinefluorography that permits diagnosis in three dimensions; catheter tubes to the heart and other organs; myelogram photos of the spinal cord; ultrasound to detect neurological disorders; radioisotopes for diagnosis of the brain, heart and gastrointestinal tracts; electroencephalogram to measure changes in the electrical potential of the brain, among others. In the wings of the scientific stage there is even a steel-plated diagnostic stand-in for the doctor himself, the unlicensed computer (no house calls either), which has already competed with man's diagnostic acumen with frightening—if erratic—success.

The modern diagnostician is also supported by an expanding battery of laboratory tests. Blood-glucose tests provide clues to diabetes; an enzyme, transaminase, helps reveal liver trouble; analysis of the spinal fluid authenticates a suspected encephalitis case; albumin (protein) in the urine may indicate kidney difficulty; a study of the leukocytes (white blood cells) helps diagnose leukemia; the sedimentation, or settling, rate of the blood can be a clue to rheumatic heart disease.

Surely, with such scientific elixirs overflowing from his black bag and with his remembrance of the traditional techniques, the modern M.D. must be that elusive wizard so desperately sought by public and profession—the Magnificent Diagnostician. Is it needless, then, to ask if the American physician's record as a diagnostician is as exemplary as might be expected?

In the new tan brick building of a New York medical center, a young faculty member and former senior resident of a leading hospital is far from sanguine about the modern diagnostician. Walking the corridors of the ward under his supervision, the assistant professor of medicine explained why he found it more reasonable to group many of his fellow doctors with the physician who so casually overlooked the malignancy of the cecum.

"As a resident and now as a medical educator, I have found entirely too many doctors in private practice signing in patients whom they had incorrectly diagnosed," relates the young medical educator. "I recall a case of a patient referred to us who had weakness and weight loss, an advanced state of what we call 'inanition.' The doctor had been treating the patient with vitamins. After a thorough diagnosis we found a massive cancer of the uterus, but it was too late.

"To what do I attribute the inferior state of diagnosis in the typical medical practice? I don't think that by and large it's a problem of stupidity. Basically it stems from a lack of thoroughness on the part of the doctor. He doesn't take the time to make a thorough examination, and sometimes doesn't want to charge the necessary costs for needed tests, so he passes them by. If a patient, for example, has a fever, weight loss and anemia, he could be suffering from a variety of ailments. History-taking alone should take between thirty to sixty minutes, and the physical examination fifteen to thirty minutes more. Anything less than an hour diagnosing such a patient is inadequate. How many doctors will give that much time for the fee they can get?"

The key to good diagnosis is dedication, states this critical physician. "Good medicine requires a doctor suffering from what I call the 'crazy man' syndrome—the starry-eyed individuals who are unique in personality and intellect," he argues. "We have too limited a supply of such men in medicine."

This discrepancy between the stringent requirements of modern diagnosis and the lesser effort expended by many doctors is increasingly heard in candid medical circles. "There is no doubt that we have the facilities for making modern diagnosis," says Dr. George A. Silver, former director of social medicine at Montefiore Hospital in New York, "but many physicians don't try. We have the medical capability, but often don't use it." Dr. Peter Rogatz, now director of the Long Island Jewish Hospital, adds his assent to the dissent. "If a doctor will just take the time to listen to the patient carefully and knows how to take a medical history, and then thinks about it objectively, he can make a diagnosis eighty to ninety percent of the time. This takes time, but many doctors don't have it, won't take it or won't make it. It is easier for them to write slips for lab studies. I think that diagnosis is often careless and sloppy."

Buttressed by a tradition of self-congratulation, physicians themselves are often not aware of the extent of their day-to-day failures.

Dr. L. Henry Garland of the University of California School of Medicine is one of those who seeks to remind his colleagues. "During the past fifteen years several investigations have revealed the fact that a surprising and clinically important degree of inaccuracy is to be expected in the interpretation or evaluation of many clinical and laboratory procedures used in everyday practice," he states. "The mere existence, far less the extent, of the ensuing diagnostic error is little appreciated."

What many critics consider the atrophying "art" of diagnosis is a near-magical amalgam of knowledge and intuition that possibly defies full definition. However, some, including Sir Russell Brain, have made reasonable attempts to describe the gift. "Diagnosis cannot be made by punch cards or computers," says the famed English physician. "It is founded on the skill of the observer, partly motor and sensory in the use of hands, eyes, ears and nose, partly interpretive. And the interpretation is only partly logical: it depends to an important extent on conscious memory, and even more, perhaps, upon the intuition, or the hunch, which springs from the unconscious memory."

The patient in the doctor's waiting room has dutifully carried out the first step: he has made the vital self-diagnosis that his body is not functioning correctly, or that it needs a preventive "checkup." After five or fifty minutes the patient rebuttoning his clothes is relieved to hear the physician's pleasant verdict: "You seem to be in good shape. I couldn't find a thing wrong with you." Unfortunately, documented medical evidence indicates that this welcome relief is often undeserved, that too many American physicians lack the diagnostic acumen necessary to correctly spot potentially deadly ailments. The relieved patient given a "clean bill of health" may only be the deluded victim of the doctor's clinical oversight.

Many doctors do, of course, skillfully diagnose ailments correctly and promptly, often pinpointing hernia, diabetes, pneumonia, fractures, cancer or other of the many diseases and abnormalities. But documented evidence, which is available but ignored by many ostrichlike physicians, indicates that he fails much too often. The resulting death and disability must not be chalked up to inevitable error. (Communities seem to tolerate doctor error but are not wont to be casual if every second bridge cascades into the sea.) The doctor's failures in diagnosis are not justifiable or unpreventable. They are tied to his shortcomings and to the inadequate methodology that viciously dogs too many medical practices.

The front-line of diagnosis is usually the general practitioner for adults and the pediatrician for children, with a secondary bulwark of general practitioners for children and board-certified internists for adults. Scores of comprehensive studies indict the ability of physicians as medical diagnosticians. One of the most penetrating involves a random sample of eighty-eight general practitioners in North Carolina. (Like many regional studies of medical performance, the North Carolina audit can be considered typical because of the *geographic* near-uniformity of American medicine and medical training. North Carolina, for example, contains three of the nation's eighty-seven medical schools: Duke University, Wake Forest and the University of North Carolina schools of medicine. This study involves general practitioners, but as we shall see, other material focuses as critically on specialists as well.)

The study is such a devastating indictment that it is subject to initial disbelief. Conducted by the Division of Health Affairs of the University of North Carolina under the direction of Dr. Osler L. Peterson, now visiting professor of public health at Harvard Medical School, the doctor-auditors observed their colleagues at close patient-range, but with the more discerning eye of the medical surveyor. For three full days they graded the doctors' work in the office, at the hospital, on house calls. It was scored on a 107 point scale, 90 of which were devoted to the diagnostic method: history-taking, the physical examination itself and the use of laboratory aids.

The revelations would gladden a chiropractor's envious heart. Some diagnostic results—such as the report that *45 percent* of physicians tried to examine their patients physically without asking them to remove any of their clothes—were bizarre. "Physicians were observed attempting to perform auscultation of the heart or lungs through several layers of clothing or dropping the stethoscope chest piece down through the open neck of the clothing in this attempt," say the study authors with noble restraint. "Similarly, several physicians failed to recognize the impossibility of feeling a soft, rounded liver edge through several layers of clothing."

The overall diagnostic score card is a faith-breaker for the type of patient who is content to gamble his existence solely on his physician's diagnostic judgment. Forty-four percent of the physicians were graded *below average* in performance, and almost 20 percent performed at a level that would have been, as Dr. Peterson states, "unsatisfactory in a senior medical student." Of a possible 100 percent score, three out of four physicians averaged only 30. The university-sheltered authors of the study were startled to learn what patients have long suspected: head-to-toe physicals for new patients, or for those not seen for some time, are the exception rather than the rule.

At the core of medical detection is the initial dialogue between patient and doctor, the painstaking unautomated technique of history-taking which by unraveling the patient's medical past can often reveal his present condition. "At least half of all diagnoses can be made solely by eliciting a thorough medical history from the patient.

We can't overemphasize the importance of history-taking in good medical practice," says Dr. Eli A. Friedman, assistant professor of medicine at Downstate Medical Center in Brooklyn. "The competent physician should take at least a half hour, or more, exploring a new patient's medical history back to his childhood, and up to the present, including facts about his diet, his habits, his life routine, his environment, his complaints. Almost as important are the pertinent medical facts about his family, as far back as he can remember. If the doctor does not get these exhaustive details, the diagnosis and the care of the patient could suffer."

Dr. Friedman gives concrete examples of diagnostic acumen gained from histories: a serious case of chest inflammation deduced from knowledge that the patient overused hair spray containing a potentially harmful ingredient; consistent clues to diabetes, tuberculosis, and bleeding and clotting disorders from history of the disease within the family; a lead to such ailments as polyposis (multiple polyps) of the colon after learning that a member of a family had died from the ailment.

How thorough are the nation's doctors at history-taking? Although it may be no revelation to the modern patient paced through a medical questioning as if it were a harness trial, the North Carolina surveyors found the typical doctor practices a truncated, uninspired brand of history-taking. Fifty-two of eighty-four doctors sampled were graded at the bottom rung of 0-10 in history-taking out of a potential 30, and only eight physicians received a top grade of 21–30. The failing majority were indicted for the cardinal sin in medical questioning: a lack of curiosity about the patient's past or about the patient as a whole man, the latter a concept that enjoys superlative lip service in medical quarters.

To illustrate doctor incompleteness, the report gave this example: "Almost no good histories dealing with anemia and hypertension were observed. The former was often regarded as a disease entity rather than a finding which may be produced by diverse causes . . . Historical data dealing with either the etiology [cause] or the effects of hypertension was only rarely obtained."

The meticulous, unhurried history-taking as the golden fulcrum of diagnosis is not debated by doctors, even if it is often ignored. "Doctors would learn a lot if they would only listen carefully to the patient when he speaks," a New York internist comments. The ability to listen carefully, however, requires patience, time, and respect for the speaker-patient, and critics see doctor deficiencies in all these areas.

Patient sophistication on once obscure medical regimens such as history-taking is undoubtedly on the rise. A Russell Sage Foundation study, "Patients Who Use Medical Practice," developed by sociologist Elliott Freidson, shows that patients want doctors who are thorough in history-taking (and examination) and who are not curt or abrupt.

Doctor abruptness in history-taking, which can set the pace for an incomplete, crudely organized diagnosis, may actually be developing as a well-honed modern medical skill. "How's Your History-Taking Technique?" a physician-author asks in a recent medical article. He answers his own question by suggesting that doctors "guide" and "organize" the vital doctor-patient discussion, not necessarily to let the patient talk out his true case history, but to get it over with as quickly as possible. "Wouldn't it be wonderful," this up-to-date doctor asks, "if, when taking a medical history, you could move the interview along at a fast clip—yet still leave the patient feeling he hadn't been hurried?" The patient who feels his next history-taking being speedily "organized" with doctor-provided "turning points" can assume he is a contemporary victim of the condensed medical history.

The doctor's ability to blend successfully the use of his hands, eyes and mind in the "physical examination" was also under careful scrutiny. Sixty percent of the doctors in the North Carolina sample never percussed the patient's chest, even when the patient obviously had a respiratory infection, and lung lesions might easily have been detected. Listening to the heart to locate heart murmurs or other irregularities was badly done by 65 percent of the doctors, most of whom checked only a single area of the organ, a technique guaranteed to leave important heart ailments undiscovered. Examination of the abdomen, which can provide a host of clues, was "perfunctory" 60 percent of the time. Even the threat of a mild local polio epidemic failed to stimulate 30 percent of the doctors to give a basic neurological exam.

The philosophical observer might have expected this result— that the traditional physical exam would suffer in this era of scientific obeisance. But even in the more modish area of laboratory examination, the doctor has illustrated that much of the medical revolution is still undigested. While performing somewhat better in this milieu, the sampled physicians scored an average of only 48 percent in the use of laboratory tests and aids.

White blood cell counts were not made in 45 percent of the cases indicated; 66 percent of the time, stools were not examined for parasites or occult (hidden) blood. The failure to take blood smears in 48 percent of the cases led the surveyors to a sharp indictment touched with anger: "Treatment of anemia is common in general practice, and study of erythrocyte morphology (red blood cell structure) should be an integral part of the investigation of anemia; yet this was not the case."

These doctors under careful scrutiny did understand the importance of doing a urinalysis. But even though the auditors found that 89 percent of the physicians used the test, they reported that most doctors were incapable of handling it intelligently. "Actual performance of the urinalysis was frequently improperly carried out," they state. Many doctors failed to obtain and examine the sediment of the specimen which is vital, or to insist that patients give them a fresh, clean-voided specimen.

To many sophisticated (and wealthier) patients, such dire report-age on the general practitioner is academic comment, for they have long since switched their medical allegiance to specialists, usually to the new "family" internist, who practices much like the GP, but at a higher fee. He is either board-certified, or has at least com-pleted a residency in internal medicine, with an additional diploma affixed to his office wall and to his ego. "My specialist," the patient may be heard to boast, "surely does a thorough job of examination and diagnosis."

He may well be the sage physician the impressed patient has conjured up. However, a leading internist and former chairman of the American Board of Internal Medicine, Dr. Howard P. Lewis, recently penetrated the myth that diagnostic prowess is conferred, sudden and genie-like, by postgraduate education, at least in the broad field of internal medicine. "High competence in physical examination is inherently implied in the title 'internist,'" says Dr. Lewis. However, he quickly adds: "Many candidates [for board certification] demonstrate indifferent, careless, or thoroughly in-adequate techniques in this skill: some because of a lack of training in this valuable art, some because they judge physical examination to be an unimportant part of the diagnostic evaluation of a patient. The board does not share this latter view."

Dr. Lewis' comment is considerably less disturbing if one has the mettle to consider the shocking information revealed by two medical educators: many doctors are never competently taught how to give a complete physical examination! Two faculty members of the Columbia University College of Physicians and Surgeons, Drs. David Seegal and Arthur R. Wertheim, report what they term "an alarming decrease in emphasis on the training of the medical student to perform with excellence the average comprehensive phys-ical examination."

Writing in the *Journal of the American Medical Association*, these candid educators explain how the fragmentation of specialist training has forced the student to absorb bits and pieces of the physical exam from perhaps a dozen different specialty courses, after which he is left to his own limited resources to assemble it— if he can or wishes—into a comprehensive exam for his future trusting patients. It is rare, they state, for a student at medical college ever to do even one complete physical examination that is supervised and graded by an instructor. "In point of fact," relate the Columbia doctors, "conversations over the past 15 years with members of house staffs graduated from some prominent medical schools indicate that *not one* [italics mine] of these individuals had ever been overseen by a senior instructor while performing a complete physical examination prior to receiving his medical degree."

Does this anarchistic anti-medicine improve when the young graduate becomes an interne? "But will his errors of commission and omission spontaneously disappear without supervision, and what assurances are there that he will receive such supervision?" the two New York educators ask. Their answer is not reassuring: "Sad to state, such supervision rarely takes place. The interne's deficiencies continue to be repeated until they are hardened into firm habits." Then—they fail to mention—the vigorous young physician buoyantly plunges into the private practice of medicine, zealous to put his unlearned examination techniques into use on his paying patients.

Why should modern doctors countenance such carelessness in themselves and leave their practices wide open to nosy, critical intervention by the public and their peers? The answers are complex, but one is surely the doctor's *low index of suspicion,* a deadly tendency to assume that the patient is "probably" well. This fatal non-neuroticism is nicely illustrated by a recent *Medical Tribune* cartoon. Pinned on the office wall, over a physician's smiling face, is the cheery epigram "YOU'LL LIVE." A suburban Long Island practitioner who, with his partner, processes some seventy or more patients a day, is one of the many contemporary physicians to whom the punch line represents a realistic practice philosophy. It is a philosophy based on the frivolous rewards of percentage-playing. "Eighty-five to ninety-five percent of the people we see aren't really sick, or have minor, self-limiting ailments," he says. "If we are worried that every patient we were seeing was about to die, or was really seriously ill, not only would we be wrong, but we would get too nervous to practice medicine."

This same low index of suspicion may protect the doctor's psyche from becoming ragged and permit him to run a speed-up medical system. But it surely dulls the doctor's diagnostic antennae, which many believe should be constantly extended and quivering, seeking out any significant signals emanating from the medical ether. Failure to detect many serious ailments is too often due to this low index of suspicion.

Pneumonia, according to medical folklore, has been "conquered" by modern medicine, especially by the antibiotic revolution. In fact, one doctor-worn quip, usually directed at a sniveling flu patient and delivered with a slightly devilish smile, goes as follows: "It's a shame you haven't got pneumonia. *That* we can cure." Last year over sixty thousand Americans died of this "curable" pneumonia, making it the fifth largest cause of death.

A case history of a missed pneumonia illustrates the danger of the assumptive diagnosis. A patient with a history of minor respiratory ailments complained to his physician that his chest "burned" and that he was feeling very tired. The doctor examined his chest with a stethoscope, then took his temperature. He could hear nothing significant in the patient's chest, and the temperature was normal. He prescribed the usual remedy of bed rest and aspirin. Two days later the patient returned, somewhat weaker, with a more aggravated chest burn, and feeling subjectively "feverish," but still without fever. The physician assuaged his "baseless" fears of pneumonia: "Don't worry, I'm sure it's just the flu that has been making the rounds. Take a day or two off, and I think you'll feel better." He was, however, dealing with a persistent patient, who returned a third time several evenings later with exacerbated symptoms but still without a fever. When the bland diagnosis was repeated, the patient's wife insisted on a chest X-ray. "If you want to throw away ten dollars," the physician said, "it's all right with me."

The next morning at seven-thirty, the bell rang frantically at the patient's front door. The physician, excitedly waving an X-ray photo in his hand, quickly made his apologies while embarrassedly explaining that the patient had an advanced case of pneumonia, covering most of his left lung and requiring immediate hospitalization.

The physician had been looking for the fever which usually accompanies a pneumonia case but which had been absent in this case. In fact, a consulting physician pointed out the possibility that the physician's prescription of around-the-clock aspirin therapy had probably dampened any fever that may have been present.

The assumptive diagnosis creates havoc because the doctor rapidly rules out a multitude of alternatives that might otherwise occur to him. One physician describes the case of an unconscious man brought into a hospital emergency room, smelling heavily of alcohol. The doctor on duty "assumed" he was unconscious because of intoxication, and omitted X-rays or other diagnostic tests. He turned the patient over to the police as a drunk. Two hours later the man died in jail, the victim not only of nine fractured ribs, several of which had punctured the chest cavity, but of one physician's low index of suspicion.

The more obvious the assumption is, the more awry can be the physician's misdiagnosis. Recently a pregnant woman described a pain in her abdomen to her obstetrician. Without examining her further, the obstetrician answered, "It's nothing but the baby kicking." The pain persisted for two weeks, when the patient finally sought the advice of another physician. The correct diagnosis involved a painful "kick" from a hematoma (solid blood clot) of the liver, not that of an aggressive fetus.

Overlooking illness because of a doctor prejudice that *statistically* one should not expect it is a current pseudoscientific obstacle to good medical diagnosis. Dr. Ernest L. Wynder of Memorial Hospital in New York attacks this prevalent medical rationalization that releases a doctor from checking a patient thoroughly for a specific ailment because certain diseases *probably* will not be found. He admits that in most any diagnostic procedure—whether checking the female breast for cancer, or even searching between a patient's toes for disease—"statistically speaking, chances are no abnormalities will be found." But, in effect, he warns his colleagues, playing such attractive odds may be a game of disguised diagnostic Russian roulette. "However, the physician should not apply statistical probability to the individual, but must think of all the patients he may examine in the future," he says in the excellent forum of the *Journal of the American Medical Association.* "It is thus apparent that statistical probability may mislead him into a false sense of security."

This false security also draws its power from the most dangerous of all modern doctor assumptions—the inner "feeling" that he is a competent diagnostician. Beginning with medical school, that comforting notion is so actively conditioned into the average doctor that he piously assumes its validity, about himself as well as his colleagues, and incorporates it into his prideful concept of self. As a "man of science," he is aware of the theoretical impossibility of 100 percent accuracy in an "art," and is willing to assume a 70 to 90 percent score in diagnosis, give or take a few unavoidable errors or omissions. As doctors are fond of modestly stating: "We are not infallible."

How accurate is this assumption of reasonably high diagnostic skill? The North Carolina study and others indicate doubts, but such a question can only be answered conclusively by a careful synthesis of all studies on medical diagnosis, a mammoth research task. Fortunately, the job has recently been accomplished by Barkev S. Sanders, Ph.D., a research consultant for the United States Public Health Service. His formidable document, "Completeness and Reliability of Diagnosis in Therapeutic Practice," covers hundreds of studies of hospitalized patients, undiagnosed ailments and executive routine examinations; screenings of large samples of patients in towns and cities; comparisons of diagnoses with proven autopsy results; reports of human errors and inconsistencies; and errors stemming from technical equipment.

His conclusions? "On the basis of available evidence," Sanders states, "I estimate if we regard all diagnosable diseases at a given time that are considered of significance for current health as *1,* the number of therapeutically determined diseases constitute numerically *0.4.* Of this 0.4 nearly half are conditions diagnosed incorrectly.

This suggests that correctly diagnosed diseases known to attending physicians represent *0.2* of the universe of diagnosable diseases of health significance."

It is inevitable that such a momentous piece of research should be expressed in the language of statisticians. What Dr. Sanders is eloquently shouting, at least from his medical mathematical rooftop, is actually quite simple. *Only 40 per cent of all human ailments are found and labeled by doctors, and 60 percent are missed. Of those that are ostensibly found, half are diagnosed in error.* Given an unknown ailment in the body of a patient, then, the chances of the American physician finding it and diagnosing it correctly are *one in five!*

Sanders believes, however, that the failing is not necessarily in the essential nature of the diagnostic beast. "With proper protocols and repeat examination, the level of precision could be raised to 0.7 and possibly 0.8," he states. The modern doctor's diagnostic efficiency—according to these figures—leaves a great deal to be accomplished, and an equal amount to be desired.

The undiagnosed sick among us harbor a majority of all the illness in the nation, the Sanders study shows. Some patients are victims of lack of medical attention. Many more patients have passed through their doctor's diagnostic screen undetected, and are the end products of a medical system that concentrates on *specific complaints* rather than on the health of the whole man. Whatever the causes, the existence of a vast plague of undiagnosed ailments has conclusively been proven by any number of studies of population samples put through extensive physical examinations. The resulting list of hidden illnesses, unknown to the patients or their doctors, is long enough to make the practitioner blanch and the patient gasp.

The villain is surely not the patient; he has not failed to present his body periodically to a licensed physician for examination. Americans, in fact, are compulsive doctor-visitors, making an average of five visits to physicians annually. A recent U.S. Public Health Service survey reveals that two out of three people have seen a doctor within the past year; 50 percent have been to the doctor within the past six months. Only 19 percent of the public have not sought out the services of a physician within the past two years. The American doctor thus has ample opportunity to find undiagnosed ailments among the general population. His reluctance or inability to assume scientific responsibility for the full medical diagnosis of his patients makes him the culpable party in the tragedy of undiscovered illness.

During a recent twelve-year period 10,709 apparently healthy adults, most between thirty and forty-nine years of age (97 percent of whom had their own private doctors), were put through the diagnostic hoop at the Tulane University Cancer Detection Clinic. The results were a diagnostic apocalypse: 77 had cancer, 444 had benign growths that might be premalignant; 804 had a variety of heart diseases; 1302 had vascular problems; thousands more had anemia, nephritis, prostatitis, arthritis, chronic asthma, pneumonia, active tuberculosis and other diseases.

Many other so-called multiphasic health screenings confirm the Tulane figures. Of a thousand employees of Grumman Aircraft over fifty years of age who were examined at the famed Strang Clinic in New York City, 104 had polyps (growths) of the colon and rectum that needed immediate excision. Ten of the growths proved to be malignant. Of 818 longshoremen in the San Francisco area, 265 were found to have formerly undiscovered diseases, while 323 more had ailments which were revealed in a follow-up examination. Of these men 12 percent had previously undiagnosed hypertensive heart disease; 2.8 percent had undiagnosed glaucoma (an eye condition that can lead to blindness); ninety-two men had unknown pulmonary diseases; and thirteen cases of lung lesions, including cancer, were found.

A study of 1513 executives put through extensive routine examinations at the University of Pennsylvania Diagnostic Clinic and reported by Dr. K. A. Elsom and colleagues in the *Journal of the American Medical Association* confirmed the other studies: that unknown disease is rampant. It showed that 612 of the men were found to have previously undiagnosed ailments—57 percent of which would result in death or major disability if not checked. An important study of 800 residents of Baltimore, in which each was asked to estimate the state of his health, and then examined thoroughly, turned up further diagnostic surprises. Of those with hypertensive disease, 60 percent were unaware of it, as were 80 percent of Baltimoreans with cataracts.

Since fatal chronic illness often begins its insidious advance in early middle age, the extent of illness was not the only revelation. It was the fact that most of these diagnoses were unknown to the patient's own doctor, even though he had had ample opportunity to diagnose the conditions himself. As these studies show, the lifesaving value of a routine physical examination should not be debated, unless the checkup is in the hands of a "routine" physician.

To the unsuspecting ranks of the undiagnosed, we must add the confused legions of the misdiagnosed. Dr. Sanders' survey concluded that aside from missed diagnoses, nearly 50 percent of all diagnoses actually made by doctors are incorrect, a figure primed to trigger angry rebuke from the most gentlemanly of the profession. A *New*

England Journal of Medicine report stating that the diagnosis of heart disease on death certificates is often wrong is one of many substantiations. A check of 911 death certificates in Pennsylvania showed that doctor diagnosis of heart disease was incorrect at least 27 percent of the time, and perhaps as often as 63 percent.

A mistake in diagnosis is an abscessed psychic sore to the prideful physician, who can more easily absorb the concept of a "missed" diagnosis. Mistakes, however, do occur, and in larger volume and greater variety than most doctors, or patients are willing to believe. A British medical educator, Dr. G. S. Kilpatrick, writing recently in the American publication *Journal of Medical Education,* nettled the profession on this question. "Many are skeptical that much error occurs in everyday medicine," he says, "but not a few experienced physicians and others of international repute have admitted that they too have been skeptical, if not overtly disbelieving, until they had taken part in what have come to be known as observer error trials. To quote several of them, 'we found it a very chastening experience.' "

As an example of this observer error and the lack of agreement among diagnosticians viewing the very same patients, he gives the now classic case of a thousand eleven-year-old American children who were diagnosed for tonsil disease. Of the youngsters, 611 had already undergone tonsillectomies. Of the remaining 389, all of whom were supposedly free of diseased tonsils, a group of physicians —with no vested interest in the matter—diagnosed an additional 174 as being in need of a tonsil operation. The remaining 215, who were diagnosed as having "healthy" tonsils, were then examined by still another group of physicians. The doctors diagnosed still ninety-nine more as requiring a tonsillectomy. The remaining eleven-year-olds, who had successfully passed two medical screens with their tonsils intact, were then examined by a third group of physicians. Again, many of the children—this time half—were diagnosed as having tonsil disease requiring surgical removal. "In the end," reports Dr. Kilpatrick, "only 65 of the original 1000 remained whose tonsils had not either been removed or recommended for removal. Fortunately, perhaps for them, the supply of physicians appeared to run out at this point."

Dr. L. Henry Garland, in a lecture before the Mayo Clinic on the accuracy on diagnosis, recalled several studies of medical observer error, including incorrect diagnosis of more than half the cases of myocardial infarction (heart attack causing damage to the myocardium, or heart muscle), violent statistical disagreement by five experienced pediatricians in the diagnosis of malnutrition, broad disagreement on interpretations of medical histories, and others.

When Dr. Garland relayed these uninspiring reports to his own hospital residents, he found that he was at first met with "incredulity." Later some of the residents even became "quite distressed," he says, uttering such dire pronouncements as "It's as though my world was cracked open." Their blind faith in medical science had been indecorously chipped. "They dislike thinking that specialists in a given field are not always expert in that field," Dr. Garland points out. He even reports the distressing anecdote of a well-known medical professor who expressed the hope that he had discontinued his investigations in this field because they were so "morale-disturbing."

No one volume can catalogue all the reasons why the doctor goes astray on medical diagnosis. Some physicians are not bright enough; some do not give enough time or concern to the art; others do not have sufficient experience to have seen a breadth of disease; some diagnose everything to relate to their particular medical interests; others insist on diagnosing cases of "this year's" ailment—whether it is hepatitis, mononucleosis or the Asian flu. The lack of professional supervision of what goes on in the sacrosanct enclave of a private medical office is another contributing factor, as is the frequent absence of strict and careful diagnostic methodology. The doctor often diagnoses by habit or prejudice, and in certain burgeoning practices, economic factors can dictate what the doctor does or does not do medically.

One pertinent, if sometimes overlooked, reason is the human tendency to consider the simple rather than the complex concept—or ailment. The late Dr. Samuel Levine of Harvard Medical School related the case of a patient being treated by a doctor with aspirin for a condition he had diagnosed simply as rheumatism. Actually, Dr. Levine revealed, the patient had a parathyroid tumor which caused an irreversible kidney insufficiency and, finally, death.

Dr. Levine made the point that the research that led to the diagnosis of hyperparathyroidism—by testing the amount of calcium and phosphorus in the blood of anyone with pains in the limbs who also has kidney stones—was done a decade ago, but that physicians need to be "taught again." Dr. Sanders of the Public Health Service underscores this expanding gap between what is known and what doctors know as another reason for faulty diagnosis. "With expansion of medical knowledge and diagnostic criteria, no individual is capable of carrying all the available knowledge in his memory," says Sanders. "Thus despite improvement in the training of physicians, it is conceivable that diagnostic acumen vis-à-vis expanding medical knowledge could be actually declining."

A humorous poet of some minor proportions, a Philadelphia doctor, created a literary image of another diagnostic dilemma: that doctors prefer to diagnose only one illness per patient, while the patient might have the effrontery to be host to several simultaneously. In his offering, "Multiple Diseases," in the *New England Journal of Medicine,* he rhymes:

> We must invariably display in a complicated way
> How everything harks back to just one malady . . .
> I maintain with all my might
> To the man who's got a right
> To have as many ailments as he pleases.

Few physicians are poets, but many consider themselves near-experts in human psychology. This is an unfortunate misevaluation of self that is another grave threat to the American patient and to accurate medical diagnosis. Each day, in thousands of medical examining rooms, harried and/or unknowing physicians unable or unwilling to exert the full force of medical art and science are childishly flirting with the role of Dr. Freud. In a frivolous imitation of their psychiatric colleagues (occasionally even with extended fingertips tenderly tapping against one another), the American physician has found a new diagnostic category which provides him with a socially accepted escape from the trying exigencies of organic diagnosis.

It is the often-inaccurate diagnosis of "functional illness," more commonly known as "imagined disease," whose seed is not in the soma (body) but in the patient's mind; hence the label of "psychoneurotic," which doctors often—erroneously—use interchangeably with the term "psychosomatic." The onerous appellations are thrown about by many doctors carelessly, leaving patients not only with their original complaints, but with new doubts about their mental as well as their physical stability.

Doctor infatuation with offhand psychology can sometimes be a relatively harmless immaturity that provides an escapist release from his trying work. A patient with stuffed sinus cavities begging for drainage who is immediately queried: "Are you getting along with your wife?" can shrug it off as another modern aberration and seek out a more intelligent practitioner. But medical evidence documents that there is a heightening wave of "psychological" diagnoses emanating from the doctor's office today, involving hundreds of thousands, if not millions, of patients. Diagnosed by their doctors as suffering from "nerves," "general malaise triggered by emotions," or as "neurotic" patients or "experienced psychoneurotics," or even "malingerers seeking attention," many of these seriously organically ill patients will have their autopsy certificates prematurely processed because of such inconscionable nonprofessionalism.

The lure for the physician is admittedly powerful. Rather than drop his carefully postured status guard and make the humble admission "I don't know" or "I can't find anything, but that doesn't mean you're not sick," the doctor has been able to weld psychological jargon to his needs. His concern with the psyche wins him approbation from certain *avant* groups, and enables him to dismiss the troublesome patient from his mind without further concern.

Dr. William F. Sheeley, in the *American Journal of Psychiatry,* warns that physicians who mistakenly label real organic illness as being psychiatric in origin are exposing their patients to needless suffering and even death. A similar warning, accompanied by a plea for full diagnostic work-ups and re-examinations rather than offhand psychoneurotic labels, has been issued by Dr. Phillip L. Rossman of Los Angeles, an internist at St. John's Hospital. Dr. Rossman has done a massive research job of cataloguing cases of patients suffering from serious physical illness who had mistakenly been diagnosed by their doctors as psychoneurotics. "Too often the doctors put the cart before the horse," Dr. Rossman stated recently when interviewed. "They fail to realize that people often appear to be, or are, neurotic because they are physically sick."

The wasteful nature of physician tendency to grasp at a "psychoneurotic" diagnosis rather than redouble his diagnostic efforts, was dramatized by a recent case of a thirty-year-old man who suffered repeated attacks of palpitation and sharp pains in his left chest, shortness of breath on climbing stairs, and anxiety and pallor. He had once been brought to the emergency room of his local hospital complaining of pain over the front of his chest and his left shoulder. His hand felt paralyzed and had developed a slight spasm. Emergency treatment of morphine and oxygen appeared to help.

The patient lived a classic existence of stress and anxiety. He worked days to support his five children, one of whom was blind, and went to night school to improve his lot. He drank sixteen cups of coffee a day, smoked two packs of cigarettes, and was consistently tired. His weariness convinced him he was going to die of a heart attack, just as his father had at the age of thirty-eight.

Supposedly complete examinations by several physicians indicated no abnormality. His chest X-ray, electrocardiogram, blood tests and urinalysis were normal. Because of his life stress, the opportunity for a "functional" or "psychoneurotic" tag was perfect, and the physician seized it. He referred the weary father of five to a psychiatrist, who concurred in the diagnosis of hysteria and anxiety. Shortly after, the man moved out of the community. Three years later his case was followed up by a medical investigator. After leaving the psychiatrist, the patient had been re-examined by still another physician, who located a hiatal hernia, a not uncommon hernia of the space near the esophagus involving a small part of the stomach. After it was repaired surgically, the harried patient's *neurotic* symptoms disappeared completely, including the spasm, the anxiety, the shortness of breath, the tiredness and the pain in the chest. The physical symptoms were all logical manifestations of such a hernia; the nervousness and anxiety were normal emotional reactions to his physical weariness and pain.

The misdiagnosis of serious organic illness by physicians as being purely "functional" or "psychoneurotic" is a natural outgrowth of society's general emphasis on psychology, and the banal attempts by much of the medical profession to replace some of the lost "art" of medicine with a curious admixture of science and psychology. The result is that for the first time in clinical medicine, doctors are attempting nonmedical *value judgments* of their patients, their demeanor, how they express their symptoms, how they speak and act.

From this, the doctor has somehow inexpertly concluded that he is in a position, intellectually and scientifically, to determine which, if any, of the patient's subjective symptoms he will concern himself with—"subjective" symptoms that are at the core of much of clinical diagnosis. Warmed-over freshman psychology in the form of articles such as "How to Sift Shirkers from the Sick" and a recent psychiatrist-authored *JAMA* article entitled "Discovering the Functional Illness in Interview" serve to Freudian-plate the doctor with a statuslike patina of psychology, but hardly increase his true diagnostic acumen.

Such articles are actually Lorelei calls for the tired physician who would just as soon chalk up idiopathic (unexplained) illness as being psychoneurotic. The siren is sweet: "It has long seemed desirable to be able to discover the functional illness without having recourse to numerous expensive, sometimes painful laboratory examinations," hints the *JAMA* psychiatrist-author, promising the doctor a short cut and danger-laden succor from the weary but necessary labors of medicine.

There is also intellectual confusion by doctors of the concepts of "psychosomatic" ailments and "functional" or "neurotic" symptoms, the former being organic changes ostensibly created by emotions, the other, emotional manifestations of nonexistent illness. The typical physician, being parochial in his views and often lost in nonmedical quicksand, is inept at sifting these philosophical abstractions into a firm mold. Given less than half a chance, he acts out the latest propaganda call to be the "front-line against mental illness," and proclaims a diagnosis of "neurosis," when he perhaps might have more accurately said "cancer."

Critics are making early stabs at piercing this fog-enveloped world of psychomedical diagnosis. They offer significant evidence and opinion that the physician is childishly wading in this psychological swamp as would any uneducated layman, hypnotized by the banal wonders of psychiatric television and cinema dramas. "I find a definite tendency of doctors to call everything 'psychoneurotic' that they don't understand, or are too lazy to find out about," says a West Coast psychologist. "This tendency almost cost my wife her life. There is of course always something in a person's present personal life or history that an M.D.—if he wants to—can blame the symptoms on. In my wife's case, I switched doctors after we got a psychoneurotic diagnosis. We told the new doctor to start running tests, and not to stop until he found the trouble or there were no more tests. He finally found a kidney infection. A certain antibiotic cured her almost overnight, after two years of progressive kidney damage. 'See a psychiatrist,' the first M.D. had said. Hogwash!"

Dr. George Silver sees the psychological orientation of many physicians as a "disservice of psychiatry" that is dulling medical skill. "There is a tendency, because of the popularization of psychiatry, for doctors to look for psychiatric diagnosis and blame the illness on subjective symptoms," he says. "They do not then look as hard for objective illness, which stands in the doctor's way of being the good scientist."

Andrew Salter, a Park Avenue psychologist, concurs, adding evidence of the danger of doctor-playing-psychologist. "When your doctor starts talking 'psychoneurotic' or 'functional' symptoms with you, it's usually time to look for another doctor," says Salter. "I had two recent cases where patients came to me after their doctors had told them their physical symptoms were the result of emotions, not organic illness. After a while it appeared to me that both of them were physically ill. I recommended other doctors to them, and after proper examination they proved to be physically sick, just as they had originally suspected.

"In one case, a young woman of 28 had to get out of bed every hour or two during the night to urinate. She complained to her regular physician, who sent her to a urologist for examination. The specialist could find nothing wrong with her, and suggested to her that the condition was 'mental' in origin. She came to see me, and after six sessions with her, I became convinced that the situation was not 'mental.' I refused to see her anymore until she saw another urologist. She did. He quickly found that her problem really was urinary, and treated it successfully."

Unfortunately, the psychological infection of medicine is deep and common-sense resistant. Roche Laboratories, for example, in an impressive two-page advertisement for their psychiatric drug Librium, attempts to "educate" the physician on the preponderance of "hypochondriacs" cluttering up their waiting rooms. It even dangerously advises the physician to avoid "overstudying" the hypochondriac, stating that "a long and unnecessarily detailed work-up alarms this already anxious individual. It also strengthens his conviction that there really is something wrong—the doctor just can't find it."

The bad seed such malingerer-mongering plants in the medical mind is shown by a Nevada GP who, in a medical publication, develops the argument that routine checkups are a waste of time, partially by mouthing the modern neurotic mythology. "It's clear that most of their complaints can safely be considered functional from the outset and treated as such with a minimum of diagnostic mumbo jumbo," the doctor claims.

In view of the simple statistical facts that chronic disease is increasing annually, that the male animal dies at the age of 66.6 years, and that fatal illness is often contracted twenty years or more prior to death, this pseudopsychological sophistry regarding "imaginary" ailments would be amusing if it did not have such a fearsome touch. Since it is impossible to know if the patient is "neurotic" or "hypochondriac" until a "detailed work-up" has been completed, an advance diagnosis of "hypochondriac" is nonmedical, to use the most charitable term for such doctor behavior.

The most impressive documentation of false psychoneurotic diagnoses is the work done by Dr. Rossman in Los Angeles. Entitled "Organic Diseases Simulating Functional Disorders" and reported in *GP,* the journal of the American Academy of General Practice, the study covers 115 patients who had been described by their doctors as neurotic, psychoneurotic or hysterical, and advised by their physicians—who could find no organic illness—to visit a psychiatrist instead.

Through colleagues, from his own files, and from those who learned of his study, Dr. Rossman accumulated 115 case histories of these supposed neurotics, *all of whom had proved to be organically ill.* The correct diagnoses were finally established by more astute physicians, by the disease coming to a head, and by death itself, and corroborated by re-examination, lab tests, surgery, biopsy and autopsy. Most of the supposed neuroses, Dr. Rossman found, were the result of the underlying physical condition.

The glossary of physical illness masquerading as neurosis was encyclopedic. Of the 115 "neurotics," thirty-one died of organic illness, including twenty-five from cancer. Of eight patients who were given electroshock for their "psychoneurotic" disturbances, three really proved to have hyperthyroidism, while the others had brucellosis (undulant fever), chronic pelvic inflammatory disease, drug intoxication, glioblastoma multiforme (tumor of the central nervous system), aortic aneurysm (balloonlike tumor of the main artery of the heart).

"Frequently such a patient's complaints go unheeded until a catastrophe occurs," warns Dr. Rossman. Addison's disease (adrenal insufficiency) seemed to resemble nervous systems reactions, including depression; malignant brain tumors simulated several neurotic disorders; thyrotoxicosis (hyperthyroidism) appeared as an unstable, anxious personality disorder. Patients with sexual symptoms were often misdiagnosed as neurotics when the actual causes proved to be Simmond's disease, Addison's disease, a diaphragm not properly fitted, pelvic inflammatory disease or a cyst of the seminal channels.

"What were the factors which caused the physicians to make diagnoses of functional disorders rather than of the true organic diseases?" Dr. Rossman asks. The answers relate to the patient's history and the kind of symptom. The complaining nervous patient, or one with a stressful life, who brings only vague generalized symptoms to his "scientific-oriented" doctor, is the most likely victim. As Dr. Rossman states it: "When environmental stress or vague symptoms were also part of the clinical picture, the diagnostic trap was set for a misdiagnosis of functional disease."

The "vague" symptoms varied from irritability and palpitations, dizziness, weakness and insomnia to such colorful ones as "chest-burning," "something moving inside." They were the trigger for the unfortunate medical accident, especially when the physician could find no laboratory confirmation. "The modern-day scientific approach to medicine makes the physician feel more secure in his diagnosis if he has laboratory support. In many cases, authentic symptoms were disregarded because this confirmation was lacking," says Dr. Rossman. As examples he cites cases of early abdominal pain of cancer being termed "neurotic" when the first X-rays showed no lesion. In another tragic case the headaches of brain tumors were disregarded as "functional."

Inadequate medical investigation, including incomplete histories, and physical and laboratory examinations, were outlined as other underlining causes of psychological misdiagnosis. A routine X-ray in several patients would have shifted the suspicion from the nervousness to cancer and aneurysms. The doctor-neurosis complex also appears to be contagious: several organically ill patients who had been diagnosed as "neurotic" by one doctor were accepted as such by other doctors who learned of the original diagnosis, welding a link of poor judgment into a solid chain of ignorance.

Dr. Rossman recalls the case of a young man who had been told by many other physicians that he was neurotic. "When he came to see me, I could see why other doctors had jumped to that conclusion," Dr. Rossman relates. "His demeanor was anxious; he seemed overly concerned with his health; and he was somewhat effeminate. He approached me with a straight deal. 'I want you to take it for granted that I'm not neurotic, and proceed from there,' he said, and I agreed. From time to time, I almost decided that he was neurotic, but I stuck to our original agreement, and kept looking for his organic problem. Finally, I found the cause—a polyp in his colon, something that other doctors had overlooked in twenty examinations."

Unfortunately, the doctor's opinion of his patient plays a feature role in the creation of the psychological-based misdiagnosis. This is especially true among so-called crank or nervous patients who consistently complain or telephone their physicians. When organic illness does strike, Dr. Rossman points out, their neurotic reputation helps set the stage for the physician to overlook real and serious sickness.

What does this augur for the patient who believes he is organically ill and is seeking an accurate diagnosis from his physician? Perhaps a word of practical advice is not out of place. In presenting your case to the typical doctor, give no hint of life stress or personal difficulty that might lead him to rationalize your complaints as psychological rather than organic. Present your symptoms calmly, straightforwardly and in the least colorful terms possible. Be specific: "I have a sharp pain about two and a half inches over my heart that persists for some fifteen minutes after I exercise." If you are anxious about your condition, do not let him know it. Do not exhibit nervousness or hysteria in front of your doctor; he may misunderstand its origin.

In the perplexing world of modern medicine, the calm, almost stoic patient is taken most seriously *organically.* You can possibly anticipate sympathy, common-sense psychology, even pseudopsychiatric advice or treatment from your doctor should you display your "neurotic" emotions when gravely ill. Tranquilizers and counseling, however, have never been known to cure cancer of the cervix. The patient generally will not go wrong underestimating the psychological maturity of the American diagnostician.

The comforting assumption that his patient is healthy rather than sick is symptomatic of the rushed, and rushing, American doctor, despite attempts to educate him otherwise. In a health survey of the town of Tecumseh, Michigan, conducted by the University of Michigan School of Public Health, nine investigators examined and re-examined 80 percent of the town of 10,000. Among residents in their fifties, for example, they found coronary heart disease in 12 percent of the men, 6 percent of the women; diabetes in 2 percent of the men, 3 percent of the women; rheumatoid arthritis in 1 percent of the men, 5 percent of the women; chronic bronchitis in 11 percent of the men; 2 percent of the women.

The hurried modern doctor may be academically aware of this epidemic of debilitation, but he has decided to carve out a career as medical "fireman," to concentrate on locating and putting out the medical fires of patients with clear, incontrovertible symptoms of advanced illness, such as extreme pain, fever, sudden weight loss and bleeding—from as many orifices as possible. This emphasis on the more obvious diagnosis is being done, say his most annoyed critics, at the expense of diagnosis of incipient diseases which yield much easier to treatment and cure in that early stage.

Early conditions may stimulate only vague symptoms, or none at all, what doctors call "asymptomatic." Unfortunately, dramatic ailments such as bleeding ulcers command the contemporary medical stage, and their treatment produces patient gratefulness at being saved at "death's very door." The pinpointing of the ulcer when it was first emerging, and more treatable, runs counter to the American actionist philosophy and is cursed with medical mundanity.

This dilemma of misplaced emphasis in diagnosis was sketched recently by Dr. George James, former New York City Commissioner of Health, who divided medicine into four stages. He assigned "Pre-clinical [before symptoms appear] Diseases" the rank of Stage Two, while labeling "Symptomatic Diseases," which now take most of our medical effort, as Stage Three. "This [Stage Two] is the stage when a health problem is developing but not yet far enough advanced to make the victim aware . . . In this second-stage detection is all-important. One must find these emerging problems before they develop into frank disease, or in any event, early enough for methods against them to be effective," Dr. James says. "How are doctors doing in Stage Two medicine? Again, not nearly as well as they should, considering what they know."

Incipient disease that is overlooked by one's doctor is especially galling when medicine has developed a cure, or at least a technique, for controlling it in its earliest stages. Cervical cancer, cancer of the rectum and colon, diabetes, glaucoma and tuberculosis are among the early curables or controllables that many doctors have elected to overlook diagnostically. "Each year 400 women die in New York City from cancer of the cervix [Note: 10,000 annually in the nation]," says Dr. James. "Caught early, nearly all these cases could be cured. Here if one waits for the patient to apply for symptomatic treatment, it is apt to be too late. This failure not only costs in pain and heartache, but also is a drain on the community since terminal care is more expensive than early surgery."

The medical case histories of overlooked early diagnosis are vast in number, and all compelling. A man in his late thirties who had gone into diabetic coma was hospitalized for twenty days, receiving excellent treatment for his diabetes. However, no chest X-ray was taken at the time of his admission or during his hospital stay. Eight months later, advanced tuberculosis was diagnosed, and the patient institutionalized. "If a chest film had been taken at the time of the initial hospitalization," says a report of his case, "it is possible that the disease would have been recognized earlier and

he would have had a more favorable prognosis for a rapid recovery."
In another case, a man admitted for pneumonia recorded higher
than normal in a blood-sugar test, a fact that was casually overlooked by his physician. A year and a half later he was stricken with
a diabetes condition that was "out of control."

On East 34th Street in Manhattan is one of the nation's foremost
advocates of improved second-stage medicine—the Strang Clinic. In
its modern, noninstitutional setting, each year over twenty-two thousand apparently healthy people pay a nominal fee of $40 for a
thorough diagnostic examination designed to spot early signs of cancer and other diseases. Strang's director, Dr. Emerson Day, has been
carrying on a lifelong fight for such preventive cancer examinations.
"With our current knowledge, more than ninety thousand lives a year
could be saved from cancer with earlier diagnosis," Dr. Day explained
in his new offices. "Forty-two thousand, for example, die of cancer
of the colon and rectum each year. Yet sixty-five percent of these
lives could be saved by early proctoscopic examination. In some
cases the cancer can actually be removed almost painlessly by
cauterization during the examination itself. It is a needless loss."

Dr. Day was referring to the ten-inch-long lighted metal probe,
the proctoscope, which is the doctor's most practical tool in diagnosing
serious rectal conditions. By fortunate coincidence, at least 60 percent of rectal or colon cancers begin in the lower twelve inches of the
bowel, where they can be seen by proctoscopic or sigmoidoscopic examination. The use of the proctoscope is routine at the Strang
Clinic, where it has helped doctors identify thousands of cancers
and other premalignant conditions in time for satisfactory treatment.
In this era of supposed technical worship, it is virtually ignored
by the bulk of the nation's physicians, who apparently prefer to
wait for rectal cancer to reach even greater lethal proportions before
considering it.

The danger of doctor neglect of this vital procedure is illustrated
by figures which confirm that early diagnosis is the only hope:
modern therapy is ineffective in curing the disease once symptoms
appear. "Today, as fifty years ago, nearly three quarters of symptomatic rectal cancer patients continue to die . . . in spite of substantial medical progress . . . The overall five-year cancer-free
survival rate [is] only 23 percent," says Dr. Victor A. Gilbertsen
of the University of Minnesota in *Surgery, Gynecology & Obstetrics*.
"By the time most symptomatic cancers are detected," he explained
on another occasion, "more than half have already spread beyond
the wall of the intestine, so that even with best available therapy
only a minority of patients are cured."

The clinical ignorance of diagnosis with the proctoscope was
recently illustrated by the remarks of a suburban practitioner. His
waiting room, filled to a near-crush, was evidence of the "success"

of his practice. "The proctoscope? I have one in the office, but to be honest, I haven't used it for some time," the doctor answered. "Actually, ninety-five percent of people with rectal complaints don't need such a detailed examination."

The doctor's failure to understand that clinical medicine is designed to diagnose and treat that deadly minority of disease, is unfortunately almost epidemic in the doctor community. The proctoscope, for example, is a virtually unused device except, of course, among "proctologists." One recent physician survey turned up the disturbing fact that only 22 percent of physicians use the lifesaving instrument in physical examinations, while 89 percent of physicians use digital rectal examination, a technique that will fail to discover many serious conditions. Dr. Roald N. Grant of the American Cancer Society estimates that digital examination will locate only 13 percent of asymptomatic rectal cancers, while the proctoscope is "at least 75 percent" effective. Here, once again, the physician specializes in the least medically profitable procedure at the expense of the most useful but more time-consuming technique. The patient, especially if over forty, would be cleverly hedging against a cancer threat by educating his own physician in the value of using this silvery inspection rod.

Doctor lassitude about using this tool of the trade, and the misdiagnosis that often results, recently drove one patient from doctor to doctor hopelessly seeking relief from what had been diagnosed as a "hemorrhoid" condition, complete with the traditional bleeding and "sitting" pains. Internist, then family doctor, then internist—finally a total of five doctors—made the usual cursory rectal digital examination and prescribed salves, balms, baths, suppositories, over-the-counter shrinkers and surgery. After five years of frustration and pain, the patient approached a sixth physician, who immediately prescribed a proctoscopic examination. It quickly revealed the true diagnosis: the supposed hemorrhoids were superficial and not at the seat of the trouble. The proctoscope revealed a deep internal fissure, which has been treated successfully.

Proper rectal examination of the male is a lifesaving procedure. Each year fourteen thousand men die of cancer of the prostate, a small male organ at the neck of the bladder which tends to enlarge with age. Autopsy examination of men over fifty indicates widespread prostate carcinoma, affecting from 14 to 16 percent of such men. The ailment is a diagnostic cliché: surgically curable *if* caught in time. Symptoms generally do not appear until too late, but by palpating the prostate in rectal examinations, then taking a small biopsy if suspect, the alert diagnostician can save many lives.

"All clinicians," Drs. Ralph J. Veenema and John K. Lattimer of the Institute of Cancer Research state in *JAMA,* "should develop a high degree of suspicion regarding any irregularity, asymmetry, or other areas of firmness in the prostate, and promptly undertake additional diagnostic steps to identify histologically (by tissue) what has been felt by the palpating finger through the rectum."

The American doctor is modern, from his multiple-patient processing to intracity computer billing. Yet inexplicably, he often ignores modern diagnostic techniques which may save patients' lives. In addition to the proctoscope, there are two other cancer-detection methods he has opted to ignore in varying degrees: the Pap smear test for cervical cancer, and the sputum cytology technique for diagnosing lung cancer while there is still some possibility of hope.

The Pap smear, a simple and painless method of detecting cancer of the cervix in women in its early, curable stage was developed in 1928 in New York City by Dr. George Papanicolaou. It was ignored by the profession until after World War II, when physicians finally realized its potential. This minute smear of cells from the womb, which can be taken from the patient in the physician's office, is—under the microscope—a clue to cancer long before the symptoms of irregular bleeding and unusual discharge appear. "Discovered and treated in the pre-invasive stage, cervical cancer is 100 percent curable," gynecologist Hugh J. Davis of Johns Hopkins University School of Medicine reminds us.

The incidence of cervical cancer among apparently healthy women is considerable, as demonstrated in a study of 108,000 women conducted by the University of Tennessee Medical School. Eight hundred cases were discovered, half in the very early stage, when almost all can be cured with radiation and surgery. Approximately the same incidence—six to eight cases per 1000 subjects—were found in asymptomatic women thirty to forty-five years of age (the high-risk group) by the Cytologic Screening Center of Johns Hopkins. Pap test diagnosis—technically known as exfoliative cytology—has helped cut the cervical cancer incidence 29 percent in a decade, but many doctors still fail to press its use, as the 40 percent mortality rate of those stricken so plaintively illustrates.

Its routine use by physicians, including gynecologists, is surprisingly uncommon. Two physicians from the Jackson Memorial Hospital in Miami who use it on all women in the hospital's delivery room, where they uncovered 261 cases in only two and a half years, recently felt obliged to remind their less alert colleagues that their procedure could be duplicated elsewhere.

Gynecologist Davis laments the diagnostic lag and the fact that only 10 percent of adult women (over 18–20) now receive the needed annual test. "Practitioners are 'too busy' to take routine smears; women are 'too busy' to seek prophylactic examination; hospital cytologic laboratories are 'too busy' to organize population screening services. Only the invasive cancer seem to have enough time to make themselves monotonously manifest," he argues persuasively.

In the Pap test, as in other diagnostic screens, considerable attention has been paid to "self-education." They are worthy projects, but have unfortunately been used by some medical spokesmen to shift the responsibility for diagnosis from the physician to the patient. The failure to administer the Pap test routinely, for example, was recently blamed not on negligent gynecologists and general practitioners, but on the fact that 40 percent of sampled women had never heard of it!

(Studies indicate that Jewish women in Israel have a very low incidence of cancer of the cervix, possibly because of the virtually universal circumcision of males in that country. Similarly, there is a low incidence of cancer of the penis in the United States in men circumcised at birth. Of 120 such cancer cases at the famed cancer treatment-research center, Memorial Hospital in New York, none of the patients had been circumcised in infancy. The seeming relationship between sexual relations and cancer of the cervix has apparently been confirmed by studies of celibate women. "It does not occur among nuns," says Dr. Sidney A. Gladstone of the New York Polyclinic Medical School.)

The profession's failure in early diagnosis of lung cancer, which kills forty-three thousand Americans annually, is even more regrettable, for late discovery of the disease is a virtual death sentence. Many physicians may mistakenly feel that in warning their patients not to smoke they are absolved of the responsibility of diagnosing *early lung cancer,* which represents the only possibility of curing the vile disease. "The hullabaloo about smoking and radical approaches to therapy with the attendant hopes for the future, have to some extent obscured the subject of diagnosis, or at least of early diagnosis," Dr. Haskell J. Weinstein of the University of Southern California School of Medicine recently admonished his fellow doctors. "The fact is that the only real hope for better results, right now in lung cancer treatment, lies in better and earlier discovery. Much more can and should be done, even with only our present tools, to detect lung cancer in its early stages, when the prognosis is so much more helpful."

Only one out of twenty victims of lung cancer that has spread now survive the disease for more than five years, a figure that at least one expert, pathologist William O. Russell of the University of Texas, feels could *now* be brought up to 34 percent—or better than one in three—with proper diagnostic work-ups. (Dr. Emerson Day of the Strang Clinic thinks this is overly optimistic, but does believe the survival rate could be tripled with early detection). Today, says Dr. Russell, "physicians generally discover the disease in a terminal, inoperable state." Dr. Robert S. Fontana of the Mayo Clinic concurs, stressing that "this gloomy prognosis can be improved, providing that the tumor can be discovered while it still is resectable."

How can lung cancer be diagnosed before blood-vessel invasion kills the host patient? Equally vital, why hasn't the American doctor been doing it?

Unfortunately, chest X-ray—the conventional pulmonary detective—is often inadequate, especially in detecting *early* lung cancer. "In spite of rather widespread acceptance" by doctors, says Dr. Victor A. Gilbertsen of the University of Minnesota, "there appears to be little evidence" of its value. The elusive lung lesion hides, sometimes behind other parts of the body until the cancer is massive and therapy impractical.

Clinical examination of the lungs is not generally rewarding because lung cancer is typically without specific symptoms in its early stages, and because, as Drs. Seymour M. Farber and Samuel L. Pharr of San Francisco point out, "of its ability to masquerade as other chest conditions." Dr. Emerson Day makes the same point, adding that the clinician should be suspicious because "occasionally" such a sign as a wheeze or an unresolving pneumonia "is the first evidence of a bronchial neoplasm."

Sputum cytology, however, is a virtually unused technique that *can* diagnose lung cancer, generally two out of three times, before definitive symptoms appear. It is based on approximately the same theory as the Pap test: that proper samples of specific body cells can reveal the presence of cancer before the patient feels it or the X-rays show it. The sample is generally taken from the chest sputum, produced for the doctor (if an interested one can be found) by a deep productive cough, or by sucking on an aerosol inhalator. The aerosol uses a mixture containing a saline solution (only weak concentrations for asthma and emphysema cases) and is inhaled for a period of fifteen minutes. At the Mayo Clinic the technique has been used in more than a thousand patients, and material suitable for testing has been obtained in 99 percent of the cases.

In a guest editorial in *Medical Tribune,* Dr. Russell appealed to his colleagues to make sputum cytology a routine office test, especially for men. "With this simple diagnostic tool every physician has both the means and the responsibility to detect the disease," says Dr. Russell. As the observant (nosy) patient can testify, however, the typical medical cupboard is bare of lung cancer detection equipment. As far as the doctor is concerned, detection of lung cancer—in time to save lives—is an academic question that he has relegated to speculative rather than diagnostic concern.

The doctor record on diagnosis of other cancers is somewhat better, but still far short of adequate, considering its current potential. Five-year-survival rates of the sixty-four thousand women who are new breast cancer victims each year is approximately 50 percent, generally after radical surgery of the breast and lymph nodes (mastectomy), a technique developed in 1894 by a Dr. William Stewart Halsted. (Controversy currently rages over whether this or simpler surgery is preferable.) These figures, however, include all levels of diagnosis, late and early, while Dr. H. T. Randall, medical director of Memorial Hospital, reports that of 2083 women whose breast cancer was diagnosed in the first stage—before it invaded the neighboring lymph nodes—the five-year survival was 80 percent! Dr. Edward F. Lewison of the Breast Clinic at Johns Hopkins Hospital reports in *JAMA* that such localized cases had a 25 percent higher five-year survival (66 percent against 41 percent) than breast cancers that had invaded the regional nodes.

What diagnostic procedures can be used to save an additional ten to fifteen thousand women a year from breast cancer death? The Strang Clinic has outlined a breast cancer examination, which can be done by any alert physician. The examination is basically in two parts. First, with the patient sitting facing the doctor, the breasts should be inspected for masses or other abnormalities with the patient's arms at her sides, then with her arms extended overhead. With the patient still seated, the doctor then palpates the axillae, or armpit areas, then the supraclavicular areas above the collarbones. Second, with the patient lying down, the breasts should be palpated with the patient's arms at her sides, and then with her arms behind her.

The failure to perform these breast examinations properly, or not to include them at all in routine exams, may soon injure doctors where some are the most vulnerable—in their pocketbooks. Attorney John H. Tovey, writing in *Medical Economics,* warned the profession about the probability of increased malpractice suits involving breast cancer diagnosis: "And plaintiff's lawyers I've talked with say it's just a matter of time before they start tagging OBG [Obstetrics and Gynecology] men and internists who fail to detect cancer of the breast during physicals."

The usual signs of cancer—unusual bleeding or discharge, hoarseness, unhealed sores, lumps or thickenings, change in a mole, difficulty in swallowing—are almost as well known to patients as to doctors. Many physicians seem sophomorically unaware, however, of the more subtle diagnostic cancer signs. In a schoolmarm-reminiscent editorial, the *New England Journal of Medicine* tried to jog medical memories by reminding doctor-readers that diagnosis and treatment of "iron deficiency anemia" avoids pinpointing the underlying cause, which might be cancer of the stomach or colon.

Such anemia, the *NEJM* lectures, is often the first clinical signs of these cancers. "It cannot be overemphasized that iron deficiency anemia is due to blood loss, and that in every case of iron deficiency anemia, one must look for the site of the bleeding," state the journal's editors. "No case of iron deficiency anemia can be considered appropriately treated until the cause has been demonstrated and treatment carried out to eliminate it. Obviously, iron therapy cannot cure cancer."

Certain cancers, such as stomach malignancy, are not usually subject to early detection, except perhaps by superior diagnosticians using the latest X-ray, radioisotope, photographic, enzyme and other laboratory techniques. Often little clue is given until the tragic symptoms appear, to patient and doctor, too late. Other cancers—such as that of the larynx, which kills twenty-five hundred (mostly men) a year—are amenable to detection, if doctors could be taught to look. The early cancer of the larynx can be seen by any observant doctor using a laryngoscope (actually a long-handle mirror) to view the vocal cords.

The technique should be an integral part of every routine examination; if not, the suspicious physician should at least check patients suffering from chronic hoarseness. In a recent case, the patient complained of hoarseness continually for three years, without provoking any reaction from his doctor—except advice to cut down his smoking. He complained again when his throat did not improve, but still could not arouse his doctor's clinical curiosity. He finally visited an otolaryngologist—an ear, nose and throat specialist—who performed a careful examination of his larynx. It proved to be an advanced cancerous condition. The vocal cords had to be surgically removed—destroying the man's normal speech—in order to save his life.

The disease mainly affects men in their fifties and sixties. If diagnosed early enough when only one vocal cord is involved, not only can it be cured, but 90 percent of such patients will regain their normal voice, according to a Public Health Service estimate. Unlike many other malignancies, cancer of the larynx does show early symptoms—hoarseness lasting for more than a few weeks, lump in the throat, change of voice pitch, coughing, difficulty in swallowing. Patient awareness is essential, but more physicians must of course be taught to look at the suspect voice box.

This seldom-considered nonprofessionalism of the American doctor permits many tragic but controllable ailments—tuberculosis, diabetes, glaucoma, and others—to conquer because of his diagnostic failure. Tuberculosis, which medical superstition says has been eliminated, kills 10,000 Americans each year and produces 55,000 new cases annually, 43,000 in the dangerous advanced stage. The doctor failure to diagnose TB—except in its advanced stages—is the prime cause of this unnecessary death. "All of these persons," corroborates Dr. J. Arthur Myers of the University of Minnesota School of Public Health, "could have had their disease diagnosed when the only evidence of its presence was a tuberculin test."

The virility of tuberculosis as a killer has been attenuated since the turn of the century when it was the leading cause of death, responsible for 150,000 lives a year. Its annual toll of 10,000 today, however, is a mockery of modern medical diagnosis, since physicians have methods of early detection and disease control which are valuable if used in time. Unfortunately, the nonconsumptive appearance of patients harboring an early invasion of tuberculosis bacilli lulls many physicians into inactivity. The mortality figures, however, should make the most sanguine physicians suspicious of any cough or chest difficulty—at least enough to take a chest X-ray or subject the patient's skin to a tuberculin test.

The chest X-ray may pick up strong, active cases of TB; the patient is then put on effective isoniazid-streptomycin, and PAS (para-amino-salicylic acid) drug therapy. Earlier TB cases, however, often evade the X-ray film, which throws many untutored physicians off the trail. The possible presence of TB can be initially surmised from a procedure such as the multipuncture TINE test. The doctor injects a purified derivative of the tuberculosis germ into the patient. The raising of an inflammation within eighteen to thirty-six hours, a so-called positive reaction, shows that the germ is currently present or that the patient had suffered a prior invasion. With this clue— and if faced with a patient with respiratory history, slight fever or cough or weight loss—the alert doctor can sample the patient's sputum, and have his colony of tuberculosis bacilli counted and identified in a medical laboratory. Even if the initial X-ray screening was negative, another X-ray should be taken. The methodology takes only moments of the diagnostician's time—ignored moments that now cost us up to ten thousand lives a year.

Routine tuberculin skin testing of all would be a beneficial health measure, but the most susceptible are in urgent need of such an inquiry. If a patient has an illness that "tends to allow a tuberculosis infection to escape" from body controls, a TB test is essential, advises Dr. William Russell. Dr. Myers stresses the testing of children, pointing out that we "are all born free from tubercle bacilli."

The current misadventure of medical diagnosis is too often in this category—in diseases that are not self-limiting, and where deterioration takes place simultaneously with diagnostic neglect.

Glaucoma, a disease of the eyes that now unknowingly affects a half millon Americans, is an undiagnosed tragedy that has already totally blinded fifty-four thousand, blinded one hundred thousand in one eye and impaired the vision of many more. Yet, with the proper technique and a competent doctor, it can be detected easily, almost painlessly, in seconds. If diagnosed early enough, glaucoma can be arrested in 50 to 80 percent of the cases.

In glaucoma, eye fluid fails to drain, building up the pressure and slowly damaging the internal structure and retina. Side vision is the first affected, and eventually blindness develops, sometimes without prior obvious symptoms. Doctor failure to diagnose glaucoma is common, for the sight destroyer is often confused with conjunctivitis, corneal ulcer and iritis. Supposed cases of "red eye," given conventional antibiotic treatment, have proven to be glaucoma. Tonometry, a simple test which measures the eyeball pressure, can differentiate the two—if utilized. Unfortunately, the test is almost completely restricted to eye-specialist practice, and not always sufficiently used there.

When glaucoma does evidence itself with severe symptoms, such as eye pain, the alert doctor should suspect the worst. One patient with severe headaches was under doctor care for over a year. Occasionally he also complained of eye pains, but the physician chose to disregard this symptom. When the eye pain became too excruciating, the patient visited an ophthalmologist of his own volition. The diagnosis was advanced glaucoma, which in two months took its toll in complete, permanent blindness.

Perhaps the most woeful and best-known victim of the doctor's diagnostic lapse is the diabetic. The American Diabetes Association laments the 1,400,000 unaware victims of the disease, whose health and life expectancy depend almost entirely on the illness being recognized. The Public Health Service, drawing on four studies—including virtual whole-town investigations of Sudbury, Massachusetts, and Tecumseh, Michigan—estimates the disease is even more widespread than prior estimates: some four million diabetics, more than half of whom are unknown. Many of these undiagnosed diabetics are being seen by their physicians today for other complaints, but apparently easily slip through his loose diagnostic net. Some physicians are not sufficiently alert to the disease; others use outdated methodology.

The by-products of this diagnostic nonregimen are many of the 33,100 annual diabetic deaths, helping to make it seventh in magnitude as a killer. Since diabetes complications such as cardiovascular disease are often listed as the actual cause of death, diabetes—and its inexorable body toll—is even more dangerous than statistics indicate. It is also a merciless defiler, causing blindness, fetal loss among pregnant women, vascular complications and coronary heart disease. As a hereditary disease, its spread through procreation is inexorable: five and a half million people living in America today will contract the disease during their lifetime.

The classic symptoms of diabetes—fatigue, thirst, excessive appetite, loss of weight—are absent too often to make them reliable clues. Doctors, too, weaken the detection screen by the use of insufficiently accurate tests. Typically, the doctor looks for diabetes with a fasting blood-sugar test and a urinalysis, which are not sensitive enough to trap many an overworked and underproducing pancreas. Dr. Glen W. McDonald, chief of the Diabetes and Arthritis Program of the U.S. Public Health Service, stresses this, and urges doctors to evoke more diagnostic suspicion about undiscovered adult diabetics, some of whom are walking about in imminent danger. (Many of the undiagnosed are overweight; a recent survey of government employees showed three times as many new cases of diabetes in men and women at least 20 percent overweight as in those of normal weight.) "Physicians should also be alert to the fact that fasting blood sugars or urine sugars will miss many mild diabetics," says Dr. McDonald, who advocates that doctors give patients postprandial *(after* eating) blood tests. The meal is either a measured one, or a known glucose load, often a flavored glucose-and-water drink.

The threat that the undetected mild case can degenerate into a severe diabetes if not found quickly prompted the *New England Journal of Medicine* to beseech its readers to properly screen patients without diabetic symptoms but with a diabetic family history, by using a little-used but more sensitive glucose-tolerance test. After the patient has ingested a glucose drink, his blood is sampled one, two, then three hours later, and the blood-sugar levels charted. The creation of a "diabetic curve" is the best available laboratory verification of diabetes. Like all tests, it has its weaknesses: a "diabetic" curve should be *rechecked* by having the patient go through the test a second time; the post-sixty-five group tend toward "abnormal" curves, which may make it a less conclusive screen for the aged. Despite these possible disadvantages, it is an essential lifesaver. From the doctor who practices less rigorous methods, such as the fasting blood-sugar or simple urine test, an "OK" next to diabetes on a routine exam chart can be a cataclysmic error of trust.

Medical authorities substantiate this abysmal failure of knowledge and interest in diabetes by the American physician. "In the experience of many of the members of the American Diabetes Association, the incidental diagnosis of diabetes has frequently been ignored and the patient has not been provided with adequate instruction," states Dr. George J. Hamwi of the Committee on Professional Education of the American Diabetes Association. "The fact that this occurs at some academic institutions where, theoretically, the standards are so high that they should serve as an example to the rest of the medical profession, is extremely disturbing."

The miracle of insulin therapy, developed by Banting and Best in Canada in 1922, makes diagnosis of diabetes the stirring first act in a continuing drama. Unfortunately, many other chronic ailments—including the major killer, heart disease—do not have similar magic bullets that convert diagnosis to cure, or even sure control. Despite this partial resignation, accurate and early diagnosis of heart disease can sometimes add years to life through drugs, preventive diet, rest and even surgery.

The preponderance of cardiac disease as a cause of death is well known, and perhaps quite logical: 980,000 deaths a year, some 54 percent of all fatalities, are due to cardiovascular disease—mainly myocardial infarction (the fearful "coronary" that destroys the heart muscle through sudden blood stoppage), hypertensive (high blood pressure) heart disease and rheumatic heart disease. That many of the aged should die of such a classic deficiency as heart and artery disease is perhaps fateful; the life of the species, and therefore this major organ system, may be limited by Nature. The quarter of a million deaths from heart disease in men and women under sixty-five, however, is perhaps less inevitable and should be treated less philosophically.

The extent of heart disease, especially among the middle-aged, is greater than previously anticipated or reported, and makes a broad and damning case against physician skill and dedication in heart disease diagnosis. A recent U.S. Public Health Service heart disease survey put 7710 persons, aged eighteen to seventy-nine, through a thorough physical examination, the results of which were published in 1964 as "Heart Disease in Adults," a compendium of rather startling statistics. Almost one in seven—14,621,000 adults—now suffer from "definite" heart disease, while another 12,979,000, or one in nine, are "suspect" victims—an average of one in four persons of all adult ages. In the fifty-five to sixty-five year group, the percentage rises to a combined 44.7 percent—or almost every other person.

Even at a relatively early age, such as the thirty-five to forty-four year group, of which the Public Health Service believes one in six may be current heart victims, the government estimate-incidence is much larger than heart disease already diagnosed. Why the discrepancy between apparent disease incidence and doctor diagnosis? The answers are complex, but the most obvious are that diagnosis of heart disease is generally performed poorly and inadequately; at best accurate diagnosis is quite difficult for the average physician to achieve.

A patient given an electrocardiogram examination which produces satisfying, normal curves from its stylus, prompts the doctor smilingly to assure the anxious examinee that his heart is "as sound as a dollar." The next week, the next day—in some cases while the patient is driving home from the doctor's office—a sudden pain strikes his chest, and the ostensibly "sound" heart stops almost instantly, killing its unsuspecting host. (Within twenty-four hours after an attack, one of four heart victims is dead; within three weeks the mortality rate is almost 39 percent.) As one physician describes it: "Sudden death due to electric disturbances that lead to ventricular fibrillation or standstill."

What methods should the physician use to diagnose heart ailments properly before "standstill" occurs? The Public Health Service heart examination is a model that family physicians might follow, in both design and technology, especially those doctors who are addicted to the three-minute tap-and-listen routine. After taking a medical history, three measurements were made of the blood pressure, followed by examination of the eyes in a darkened room with an ophthalmoscope, a sensitive clue to hypertension that is overlooked by many practicing doctors. The neck was then examined for enlargement of the veins, the arteries of hands and legs were inspected visually and manually, and the physician looked for telltale edemas (swellings) of the body's extremities. The examination naturally included the traditional listening to the heart through a stethoscope for unusual sounds including "murmurs."

The stethoscope was used with the examinee upright, first breathing normally, then holding his breath, then in expiration, then supine, then on his left side. Palpation (inspection by hand) of the heart area was done with the examinee sitting upright, then leaning forward—breathing both normally and holding his breath. To find actual enlargement of the heart, an especially important symptom in rheumatic heart disease, a chest X-ray was taken, followed by a "twelve-lead" electrocardiogram—six leads wired to the chest and six to the arms and one leg. (The technique did not include such esoteric and sometimes valuable methods as stereofluoroscopy, vectorcardiography, enzyme tests, catheterization to sample blood of the heart, angiocardiography or phonocardiography to record the heart sounds.)

Angina pectoris, a heart ailment that manifests itself by extreme chest pain, is diagnosed from the pain, plus the patient's medical history. The myocardial infarction is diagnosed after the first attack, generally with the aid of electrocardiogram readings, which show if a portion of the heart muscle has been damaged.

The doctor's invaluable heart diviner, the electrocardiogram, is touched with medical mystique, and even bears a sacred kinship with the physician's stethoscope. It is true that abnormal electrocardiogram readings can be a scientific clue to several heart ailments, *if* given and interpreted carefully and judiciously. Otherwise, the impressive device can become only a well-wired complex of deception.

The device is far from infallible, especially since interpreting its graphs involves fallible human skill. Nine cardiologists and one inexperienced doctor participated in a revealing EKG (doctor shorthand for electrocardiogram) accuracy study, in which they read a hundred tracings of EKG's—fifty myocardial infarctions, twenty-five normal hearts and twenty-five of other abnormalities. They disagreed on what they saw 20 percent of the time. "Diagnostic value of the single electrocardiogram may be much less than is generally realized," the report authors stated in the *British Heart Journal*.

The importance of proper electrocardiagram readings is underscored by the fact that many people suffer "silent" heart attacks that cause momentary pain and heart damage but are unknown to both patient and doctor. Undiagnosed, they make the patient considerably more vulnerable to future attacks and death. Dr. John J. Sampson, president of the American Heart Association, indicates that from 20 to 40 percent of scarring found in patients' hearts on autopsy cannot be correlated with their medical histories.

One reason for missing these "silent" myocardial infarction attacks —and thus losing the chance to place the victim on preventive management—is that the doctor may rely on a single EKG when the patient comes in with a complaint of chest pain, says Dr. Sampson. If the EKG is normal, the doctor may tell the patient that the pain is only indigestion, while an EKG taken several weeks later might have shown up the heart attack on the sensitive graph.

An EKG reading may also be erroneous because it was taken under artificial conditions, such as rest. An important safeguard— but one which suffers because of medical ignorance or nonobservance —is to give the electrical test after mild exercise. Dr. Arthur M. Master advises a two-step work-out, pointing out that EKG's taken afterward are far more "revelatory" than the typical test. The two-step test, he states, has been 95 percent accurate in detecting significant coronary disease in men. Studies on EKG efficiency show that the machine varies as low as 51 percent and up to 95 percent in diagnostic accuracy, with indications that the use of many EKG leads from the body to the measuring device—such as the government's use of twelve in their diagnosis project—can also increase its value considerably.

Aside from *underdiagnosis,* the heart diagnostician suffers from another fallibility—that of *overdiagnosing normal individuals* as suffering from heart disease, with all the concomitant, perhaps lifelong, psychological trauma. The government heart survey turned up 203 "false positive" electrocardiogram readings, including twenty-five nonexistent cases of myocardial infarction. Dr. Lawrence E. Hinkle, of Cornell University Medical College, recently warned the American College of Physicians that changes in the electrocardiograph complex of a person's heart occur so frequently "that it is hazardous to assume that they necessarily indicate the presence of a pathological process."

In a recent editorial re-evaluating the electrocardiogram, the *Journal of the American Medical Association* laments the tragedy of the resulting misdiagnosis. "Some patients who demonstrate normal EKG's may die from an acute attack within hours or even minutes," says *JAMA* candidly. "Other patients, who present clinical and laboratory evidence of myocardial infarction, may show no significant EKG changes for days. Still others, with the most grotesque EKG patterns, live for years without symptoms or signs, often defying their physicians' admonitions with impunity . . . Eccentricities of the EKG have occasionally led to errors in diagnosis and, even more serious from the patient's viewpoint, in prognosis. Such findings have forced men into retirement, only to have them live for years, healthy but frustrated." As a solution, *JAMA* asks for more "standardized" EKG methods, perhaps unaware that it is the official medical journal of the only group that could, if it believed in "standardization," possibly implement such goals.

The best prognosis for any heart disease is the hypertensive variety, for *if found in time* it can often be controlled with drug therapy. The cause, high blood pressure, so destroys the body organs by enlarging the heart, injuring the blood vessels and speeding up hardening of the arteries, that Metropolitan Life Insurance statistics show that a man of forty-five with a sustained blood pressure of 140/95 can expect six years less of life than average, while a thirty-five-year-old with 150/100 sustained pressure is robbed of sixteen years of life.

Again, however, the diagnosis must be meticulous to avoid the trauma of "false positives." As in electrocardiogram readings, single blood pressure measurements made by doctors can be misleading, for blood pressure can rise temporarily due to excitement or work. One specialist indicates that differences in blood pressure readings become more usual with advancing age, and that both patient's position and arm should be noted by the doctor so that subsequent measurements can be made under the same conditions. For added insurance, the physician should read the pressure in both arms.

At the core of heart disease detection is the doctor's stethoscope, a prized tool of his profession, and almost as symbolic of him as the caduceus. With it, he enters the world of auscultation, of sound detection of the body. It is invaluable in heart disease diagnosis for the malfunctioning heart produces eccentric noises such as the sound of leaks—"murmurs"—often from heart valves injured by rheumatic heart disease.

Since every physician possesses a stethoscope (usually the gift of a drug firm in medical school), and uses it routinely, is its effectiveness in detecting abnormal heart sounds close to 100 percent? Drs. Paul Y. Ertel and Aaron M. Stern of the University of Michigan Medical Center recently showed that no two stethoscopes perform alike, and that doctors may be overlooking important signs of illness because of built-in errors of some stethoscopes.

Dr. Dale Groom of the Medical College of South Carolina gathered up the stethoscopes of thirty-three of his colleagues at the Medical College Hospital in Charleston and checked them out. Two thirds of them proved to be defective, about as valuable to their owners as a rolled-up sheet of paper—which put them on a par with the original stethoscope invented in France in 1816. They contained leaks that let out wanted heart sounds and let in noise of the office; most were too long and too wide, and made of thin-skinned rubber; and some fit so badly that the specially slanted ear pieces had their openings completely shut off by the ear itself. A better stethoscope, more adeptly handled, plus a $500 soundproofing job in one room of the doctor's office, or in a hospital will make it possible, says Dr. Groom, to increase the physician's listening sensitivity twelvefold. Thus equipped, many physicians may finally hear what many believe they are listening to now.

One undiagnosed patient in particular is often more recognizable to friends and family than to his doctor. He has a constant nagging cough which sometimes produces phlegm, and is constantly tired, especially after exercising or working hard. To his doctor he is generally a slightly sick crank whose condition is common but hardly to be taken seriously.

Actually the patient may be seriously ill, a frustrating reject of diagnostic know-nothings. He may have chronic bronchitis, or the more serious chronic pulmonary emphysema, respiratory conditions that remain undiagnosed, and underappreciated by many physicians despite the more than twenty thousand lives they take each year. "The most common cause of inadequate therapy of chronic bronchitis is failure of recognition," comment Drs. Sanford Chodosh and Maurice S. Segal of Tufts University School of Medicine, and the Lung Station at Boston City Hospital. "There has been a reluctance to consider that the symptoms of chronic cough and phlegm production may add up to a disease worthy of concern."

It is a common mistake, the angry lung experts explain, for doctors to belittle the symptoms because clinical and X-ray evidence may be minimal or even completely lacking. Despite this, they state, the ailment "carries with it a real threat of significant chronic illness, with increased morbidity and shortening of life span." Even when diagnosis is made, argue the Lung Station specialists, there is a tendency for doctors to underestimate and undertreat it. "Furthermore," they add, "the therapeutic armamentarium available does not seem to be common knowledge."

These two diagnostically neglected ailments, chronic bronchitis and pulmonary emphysema, affect several million Americans, having quadrupled in intensity during the past decade. Emphysema is currently the second largest cause of disability among Social Security recipients. In addition to its direct death toll, these and other generalized respiratory ailments are said to hasten the death of an additional forty-two thousand people a year. This breakdown in the system, by which the many air sacs in the lungs supply oxygen to the blood and expel waste carbon dioxide, often begins with obstructions in the smaller bronchial tubes, producing a chronic cough. The situation becomes aggravated after a respiratory bout with pneumonia or influenza, and in time the patient finds himself short of breath and especially winded after mild exercise. Eventually it can lead to a suffocating death, often from a complication known as acute respiratory acidosis.

Detecting emphysema is especially difficult for the type of physician who insists on "specific" proof before his practice-dulled suspicion can be aroused. The illness, unfortunately, is not amenable to this mentality, and usually avoids showing itself on X-ray plates. "Generally a diagnosis of emphysema is established when the disease is quite advanced and already requires costly and time consuming procedures which can do little," comments Dr. Albert Haas of New York University.

In the hands of a responsive physician who can see the disease developing, the ailment can often be diagnosed in time, especially with the aid of pulmonary function tests, which measure the amount of breath a person exhales. A subnormal amount is a clue which can make the present diagnostic dilemma easier for the disbelieving physician seeking "objective" proof before he acts. If caught early enough, symptomatic treatment—with bronchial dilators, expectorants, positive pressure-breathing, inhalation of 32 to 40 percent oxygen from cylinders, and use of broad-spectrum antibiotics—is helpful. At the NYU Medical Center, Dr. Haas is developing a hopeful technique of rehabilitation based on breathing exercise and optimum use of the patient's breath that may be especially fruitful in cases that are not too deteriorated.

Drs. Theodore Rodman and Bernard H. Pastor of the Veterans Administration Hospital of Philadelphia reveal—with restrained annoyance—that the condition sometimes progresses to acute respiratory acidosis with cardiac failure, coma, then death, without the underlying obstructive emphysema ever having been diagnosed by physicians. The diagnosis, they state, "is frequently missed because of widespread misconceptions about diagnostic criteria." For the same reason, they add, "diagnosis is often made in patients who do not have this disease." Doctor failure, they believe, is a result of insisting on such textbook symptoms as "barrel chest" and audible wheezing, which may or may *not* be present. Single chest X-rays seeking signs of "hyperaeration" may be equally misleading. Drs. Rodman and Pastor instead advise more complex radiological studies of breathing and mechanical studies of pulmonary function that will show up airway obstruction. The deadly disease is apparently too complex for the meager diagnostic skill of most practicing physicians.

The sore throat is one of man's common afflictions, and often one of the most harmless and transient. However, this sore throat can also carry the core of another diagnostic dilemma that the modern physician has often sought to evade—with all the frightening results of medical abdication. Streptococcus-caused pharyngitis—the fierce "strep throat"—is on the increase, having doubled in the last decade to over a third of a million cases annually. (When the disease is accompanied by a rash it is called scarlet fever.) The illness in children and young adults is serious, mainly because of its possible aftermath: rheumatic fever, then lifelong rheumatic heart disease that now affects 1,270,000 adults alone, takes 16,000 lives a year. It also provides many of the patients for dramatic, but quite dangerous, open-heart surgery.

Despite the seriousness of "strep throat," physicians commonly misdiagnose the disease through ignorance or neglect. The strep throat can usually be bacteriologically cured in ten days with penicillin, and the rheumatic heart disease prevented, *if the streptococci bacteria are detected by taking a simple throat culture from the sick child.*

By some incredible confluence of ignorance and indifference, most percentage-playing American physicians—family doctors, internists, and pediatricians as well—*refuse* to take throat cultures of their sore-throat patients, despite the mortal danger involved in the missed diagnosis. "In spite of their value, throat cultures are used only infrequently by most physicians in their practice of medicine," lament several pediatricians from Harvard Medical School in a recent issue of the *New England Journal of Medicine*. By not practicing this prophylactic medicine, physicians are contributing to heart disease and death in youngsters, and a crippled adult life for many of those who survive.

A girl of seven with a slight (101°) fever, chills, nausea, and an aching sore throat is taken to the office of the family pediatrician. "Say 'Ah,'" the physician demands, and the child responds. "Nothing much to worry about," he assures the parent, who takes the child home to the prescribed therapy of bed rest, aspirin and throat gargles. Three days later, as per physician prediction, the child's malaise tapers off and she is back at her girlish activities. The mother expresses her gratitude for the pediatrician's medical advice— if somewhat prematurely.

Two weeks later, on returning home from school, the child suddenly feels feverish and is put to bed. An unusual skin rash and weakness prompt her physician to take several blood tests. The diagnosis: rheumatic fever, and finally, a damaged heart valve and the uncertain life of a rheumatic heart disease victim. In fact, the youngster was fortunate: death strikes 4 percent of all initial rheumatic fever victims.

Why? Surely, the pediatrician is not venal. Surely, he must understand the correlation between strep throat infections and subsequent rheumatic heart disease. The answers are wedded in a score of current medical diagnostic shortcomings. One of the most pertinent in this case is the modern physician's mistaken, even arrogant, evaluation of his own intuitive skill. "I can tell a strep throat by looking at it," is the pretentious boast made by many doctors, one which is refuted by experience and science. "Without a throat culture, the differentiation between viral and streptococcal pharyngitis is unsatisfactory," stresses Dr. Gene H. Stollerman of the Northwestern University Medical School.

Dr. Stollerman also berates those practitioners in the well-to-do suburbs of many large cities who have been unwilling to use chemotherapy on supposedly mild strep throats "for prevention of initial attacks of rheumatic fever." Considering the extent of rheumatic heart disease, Dr. Stollerman believes it best for these doctors to "err on the side of overtreatment." The Harvard Medical School pediatricians, perhaps weary of attempts to convince the profession to practice this good diagnostic medicine, have even suggested that patients *do their own* home throat cultures—offering a detailed description of this how-to medicine.

The parents of a child with a severe sore throat have a noble opportunity to educate their physician on the importance of throat cultures in the diagnosis of "strep throat." They can perhaps accent the point by having the American Heart Association send their doctor educational material on rheumatic heart disease and its causes. Failing this, the AMA's much-vaunted dictum of "free choice" of doctors should be put to good immediate use.

In his diagnostic tribulations, the doctor has the aid of two modern sorceries which make him a potential diviner of many body ills: the X-ray and the laboratory. To master both wisely, he must be as aware of their whims and failings as of their obvious assets. Radiology is becoming increasingly important in diagnosis—as is the radiologist, the specialist trained in the taking and interpretation of X-ray films. The barely visible shadings can spell the difference between health and disease; and as the inventory of disease entities increases with research, so do the complex radiologic methodologies and nuances of interpretations.

Many physicians are convinced that only a qualified radiologist should read X-ray films where serious illness is suspected. At the Strang Clinic for example, board-certified radiologists do all the X-ray interpretation, from simple chest shots to barium enema contrast studies of the lower intestine, and upper intestinal "GI Series."

Error is a natural component of any diagnostic procedure, and interpretation of roentgen-tube films is no exception, despite patient reverence. X-ray mistakes in diagnosing fractures are, as one malpractice attorney puts it, "more common than many physicians apparently care to admit." In one case, a greenstick fracture of the ulna (inner side of the forearm) was missed by a doctor, causing the bone to heal at an angle. Eventually the patient sought out an orthopedic specialist who rebroke the arm and set it. The doctor who missed the original diagnosis could not understand his error since the fracture showed plainly when he later took the film out of his files. His aide solved the mystery when she recalled that he had been rushing to catch a plane and had committed the medical gaucherie of reading the wet film in the darkroom.

A resident of a large metropolitan hospital relates a more serious X-ray failure. A patient with a supposed ulcer was admitted to the hospital for a subtotal gastrectomy (partial stomach removal). While examining the patient the resident noticed large lymph nodes on both sides of his neck. He ordered a chest X-ray, which revealed lung cancer. When he contacted the patient's attending physician, he learned that the doctor had taken a chest X-ray but had read it as being "normal."

Although better equipped at this highly sensitive art, radiologists, too, are far from omnipotent interpreters. Radiologist L. Henry Garland of the University of California School of Medicine presents eye-opening information on his colleagues' accuracy in a paper entitled "Studies on the Accuracy of Diagnostic Procedures," published in the *American Journal of Roentgenology*. He reports on several studies, including one in which five expert radiologists reading chest X-ray films missed 25 percent of the "positive" cases of pulmonary disease. Three months later the same five physicians read the very same plates and disagreed with their previous judgment 20 percent of the time.

For substantiation of his heretical comments on diagnostic accuracy, Garland details three additional studies with "underreading" errors of missed X-ray diagnoses ranging from 27 to 32 percent. In addition, there was a 2 percent error created by "finding" nonexistent pathology. When Dr. Garland confronted other radiologists with these dismaying statistics, the typical reaction was unsupported bravado: "If I took these tests, I would do better than those busy investigators."

In addition to the studies' myth-cracking value, they did establish that experienced radiologists can do up to five times better than inexperienced physicians. Perhaps most significant for a profession intent on improving: interpretation of the same film by *two doctors* significantly reduced the number of errors.

This general range of errors in diagnostic reading of X-rays was confirmed by Dr. Marcus J. Smith, a Santa Fe (New Mexico) radiologist who recently informed his colleagues that he found disagreement by physicians in the reading of 30 percent of three hundred consecutive X-ray examinations. Of a hundred errors in one radiologist's practice, he said that 72 percent could have been avoided by dual doctor interpretation.

The importance of accuracy in X-ray reading may rise geometrically as new roentgen and other radiology-like techniques are developed. Mammography, a new X-ray method used to film the female breast, may—says Dr. J. Gershon-Cohen, chief of radiology at the Albert Einstein Medical Center—greatly increase the salvage rate of breast cancer victims by early diagnosis. Using radioisotopes that target the disease site, some radiologists are now practicing nuclear medicine by taking scintillation-scan "pictures" of such inaccessible areas as the liver and the brain. Thermography is another potential diagnostic boom related to radiology. Instead of X-rays, however, still-experimental thermography uses infrared emissions from the body, creating a "heat photograph" in which inflamed areas show up differently from normal tissue. In all of these techniques, physician and patient understanding of the fallibility of doctor observation makes accurate diagnosis more probable.

The scientific orientation of the physician (even if he has little time for, or intellectual dedication to, the concept) can make him overdependent on the results of diagnostic tools, especially laboratory tests whose definitive numbers—so many milligrams of bilirubin per 100 cubic centimeters of blood, etc.—loom like immutable markers in his universe of reality. The modern laboratory has been an important adjunct to modern diagnosis, but like Dr. Faustus' bargain, it involves unseen ramifications the modern physician is often unaware of.

The wary physician knows that laboratory findings may be misleading or atypical, even if technically correct. But the nemesis threatening medical diagnosis today is the incredible inaccuracy of much laboratory work, and doctor naïveté in accepting and acting on erroneous laboratory reports. The state of laboratory testing is crucial because of the popularity and complexity of chemical and biological tests involved in modern diagnosis. A typical tuberculosis patient receives some fifty laboratory tests, and Dr. Sigmund L. Wilens, a leading pathologist, states that two hundred tests on a patient is not unusual—critically pointing out that "only a half dozen or so have any pertinence."

The threat of laboratory error is not sufficiently appreciated by many doctors, the famed internist Dr. Walter Alvarez warns, advising these naïve physicians to "repeat" tests before making definite diagnoses. "I hate to write about these things, but I feel I must—it is my duty," he states. "What disturbs me most is that all the mistakes of this type that I keep seeing today are not made by country doctors: they are made by able or even distinguished internists who apparently trusted implicitly to laboratory tests. This is one curse of medicine today."

Dr. Alvarez recalls several such calamitous errors based on false trust. A woman of thirty went to a "distinguished internist" for a premarital examination that included several laboratory tests. At the final interview the doctor noticed a blood-sugar reading of 171 mg., and told her that she was a "beginning diabetic." The girl had seen several relatives die a miserable death from the same disease, and panicked. When she came to see Dr. Alvarez, he had two further tests made, both of which showed considerably lower blood-sugar readings. "With this I got a hunch, and calling my friend long distance, I asked him to check the report in his laboratory," Dr. Alvarez relates. "In a few minutes he called back to say that the secretary who copied the report had reversed the figures, and actually, the original report was 117 mg.!"

Laboratory error integrated into the doctors' thinking without further checking had resulted, indicates Dr. Alvarez, in specious conclusions ranging from an incorrect diagnosis of hopeless cancer to a faulty blood-sedimentation report (110 mm. in an hour instead of 2 mm.!); a false diagnosis of venereal disease in an engaged girl, based on a spurious +4 on the Kahn test; an erroneous diagnosis of hyperthyroidism stemming from a basic metabolism rate of +35 instead of the correct readings of +12, −3, −12.

Medical literature is full of examples of such faulty laboratory reports. They have been the stimuli for mistaking leukemia for less serious blood disorders; other cancers have been missed by poor interpretation of simple smears; mismatched blood has sent patients into shock during transfusion, causing death. The possibility that such examples of inaccurate lab findings might be as much rule as exception was given credence after a recent public survey. The private laboratories in New York challenged the city's right to give free blood tests to mothers in prenatal care, setting off a return challenge by Dr. Morris Schaeffer, director of the city's Bureau of Laboratories, for them to prove their competence.

More than a hundred labs volunteered for an experiment in which they received blood samples to group. The result, says Dr. Schaeffer, was that 75 percent of them filed reports that were in error. Nettled by the results, Dr. Schaeffer and his twenty investigators initiated an unannounced survey of the 425 laboratories under his jurisdiction—150 in hospitals and 275 privately operated labs.

"The results were unbelievably appalling," says Dr. Schaeffer. "They revealed a situation that is both deplorable and shocking. A clinical lab with accuracy and quality proved to be the exception. Of the 425, only 100 labs were acceptable, and we found that almost one-third of them, 130, were bad enough to be closed down. Seventy percent of the labs failed to report accurately on simple blood-chemistry tests. Only in teaching and research centers were good labs the rule, and even there we found weak spots. I would say that in general there is a dangerously increasing amount of cheap inaccurate lab work."

Schaeffer found that some West Coast physicians were sending blood samples for sedimentation tests to New York commercial laboratories—who processed them even though a sample more than twenty-four hours old is virtually worthless. In another case, Schaeffer's investigators checked a laboratory technician doing a prothrombin time test for heart patients taking anticoagulants, a clotting factor test on whose accuracy the patient's life can depend. The test tube had no markings; the drug had come out of a bottle without a stopper. Most important, the technician's stop watch was broken, even though the test must be rigorously timed in seconds.

Dr. Schaeffer, who is a ten-year veteran of the United States Public Health Service, indicates the national scope of this problem. "These sad conditions in the laboratory are not especially peculiar to New York. It is worse there only because of its larger concentration of laboratories, but other communities suffer from a similar if not more critical blight."

The greatest fire has been directed at the 1783 profit-making laboratories in the nation who do the bulk of nonhospital tests for private doctors. A recent special report by *Chemical and Engineering News,* described what Dr. John G. Reinhold at the University of Pennsylvania refers to as a "pseudoprofessional underworld" composed of substandard laboratories whose reports the doctors unwisely use.

"Although they may disagree heatedly on some points," says the chemists' professional organ, "pathologists and clinical chemists are in complete agreement on at least one point—that a substantial number of independent clinical laboratories in the United States do incredibly bad work. . . . According to some estimates, more than 50 percent of the nation's independent clinical laboratories are definitely substandard. Many private labs, of course, do accurate, meticulous work. However, some, it seems, could hardly care less— a situation also true in too many hospital laboratories."

The failure is often due to inadequate training and faulty supervision, plus the aggravated profit motive. The 770 AMA-approved schools for medical technologists have trained thirty-three thousand MT's—medical technologists—with at least three years of college, who take a year's intensive laboratory training and pass a qualifying examination. These MT's make up only half of the needed labor force, however, and laboratories—private and hospital—are forced to take high school graduates who have taken quickie, unapproved training courses. As an example of lax admission standards, one school accepted a nineteen-year-old girl who had never taken a science course and who had flunked out of high school as a sophomore.

Although the local doctor is a hard, fast customer of the "lay labs" (a medical pejorative for laboratories run by nonphysicians— usually chemists or medical technologists), medical pathologists claim that the errors they detail are the outpourings of "lay" establishments, and that "high standards" are enforced in doctor-run laboratories. Dr. Victor B. Buhler, president of the College of American Pathologists, attacks the "fly-by-night" commercial laboratory as a "menace to the community," stating that only board-certified pathologists should be allowed to direct laboratories.

Physicians can and do make excellent lab directors, but medical propaganda that this singular fact will insure lab accuracy is baseless overconfidence. Inaccuracy appears to be the bane of almost any laboratory, doctor or lay-directed. One embarrassing substantiation of this evolved from the profession itself. As part of a quality study, the College of American Pathologists sent test material to several hundred pathologist-lab directors, then analyzed the results. According to the College's report "an unexpectedly large number of errors, some quite gross, were discovered."

The most distressing aspect of this situation is that physicians, pathologists included, have used their profession's lip service to high standards to enjoy additional income by *selling their names* as dummy heads of laboratories actually run by laymen. Dr. Omer E. Hagebush of the College of American Pathologists reveals that at least 135 of these lay laboratories have doctor "fronts," physicians who nominally head the laboratory but who do not in fact supervise its work. His disheartening indictment even implicates twenty-three board-certified pathologists.

Dr. Morris Schaeffer refers to the doctor who plays this blood-and-urine shell game as a "rubber stamp," illustrating with the case of one pathologist who was ostensibly in charge of six laboratories at one time, all of them actually run by technicians. Others have revealed that the going price for a "dummy" director runs as high as $8000 per year per laboratory.

The much-needed pathologist—often referred to by his colleagues as "the doctor's doctor" because of his critical and counseling mien—can be spread only so thin before he becomes a pseudopresence. There are only six thousand pathologists in the United States, while there are over seven thousand hospitals, most of which have labs to administer. In addition, there are thousands of private laboratories outside the hospital which require skilled directors.

Can the patient who has trusted his physician's sure nod that his blood was "OK," anticipate that conditions will improve? New York City, for one, has closed eighty inefficient laboratories. The responsibility must be exercised by cities and states; the qualifications for laboratory technicians must be high, the policing must be strict and samples must be tested periodically on an unannounced incognito basis.

The good physician, of course, has his own built-in safeguards. He can have his most vital tests split-sampled—that is, sent to two different labs simultaneously for corroboration. Before administering blood, he can have it matched twice, preferably by two different lab technicians. The physician can refuse to believe a test, then recheck it if it seems to disagree with his own diagnostic opinion; and he can spend more on lab work (still less than the patient pays him) by selecting the most closely supervised laboratory that will protect his patients' interests and lives.

The importance of physician skepticism toward all unchecked lab reports that conflict with clinical symptoms and with his own sensory judgments was underscored by the tragic case of an Rh baby. The tests ordered by the pediatrician showed the baby's Rh factor as negative, which weakened his diagnostic guard. The doctor ordered no follow-up serum bilirubin or hemoglobin tests on the child. Characteristic jaundice of an Rh baby appeared, but the negative lab report still loomed Gibraltar-like in the doctor's mind. The jaundice continued, followed by convulsions. Eventually the worried mother sought out a neurologist, who had the unenviable job of telling her that the child's brain had already been damaged.

The laboratory of the future, automated and computerized, may offer some hope of eliminating these gross human errors. The early beginning of such a situation are analyzing machines that do forty to sixty tests an hour. The "no hands" laboratory of the future has many advocates, but critics still point out the need for skilled programers and repairmen to maintain the machines and their accuracy.

The medical-computer revolution—the new adventure generally known as biomathematics—has created both awe and fear in the doctor psyche. The physician is entranced by the current experiments in computer medicine—especially in diagnosis. As one dimension of him welcomes this electronic aid, another sees in it the possibility of added deterioration of doctor image. Just as the drug revolution (albeit exaggerated) appeared to diminish his godlike qualities, some physicians are concerned that the electronic transistor memory could relegate him to the role of medical programer, a diploma-laden IBM technician.

Rather than a twenty-first-century visualization, computer medicine is a reality involved in serious experimentation. The primary medical use of computers, thus far, has been to keep medical records available for instant recall. Such a computer unit, capable of printing 108,000 characters a minute, was recently installed in New York's Montefiore Hospital. "Physicians will be able to know more about a patient's condition and know it more quickly," says the hospital director.

At the Palo Alto Veterans Administration Hospital, psychiatrists now prescribe drugs for patients via a computer located more than a thousand miles away, at Kansas State University. Computers have been used in dozens of diagnostic experiments, attempting to duplicate the complex problem-solving methodology that goes on inside an alert physician's head, and occasionally striving beyond this human capability. At Tulane University, biomedical engineers and radiologists have developed a system in which an electronic scanner hooked to a computer can "read" X-rays and make limited heart diagnoses based on heart size. The computer measures the distance between the outlines of the heart and the rib cage. If the distance is more than usual, the computer prints a warning—"cardiothoracic enlargement"—which alerts the radiologist.

Electrocardiograms have been converted into digital form and then fed into a computer which makes an analysis based on prior EKG pattern material. According to Dr. Hubert V. Pipberger of the Veterans Administration Eastern Research Support Center, the system has been tested with 90 to 95 percent accuracy—greater, he claims, than would be possible for a physician unaided by the computer. The method has a futuristic touch: results from three EKG leads are transmitted by regular dial telephone to the computer, which analyzes it for twenty-seven factors, and flashes back the answer in six seconds.

The Soviet Union has been active in this area, reporting that their computer system at the Moscow Institute of Surgery has correctly diagnosed between 80 and 90 percent of two hundred cases of congenital heart disease. In several cases where the machine diagnosis did not coincide with the physician's opinion, says the institute, surgery proved the machine's judgment to be superior to the doctor's. The machines were able, say the Soviet scientists, to take into account a large number of minor symptoms whose significance was not assessed by the doctors. Corroboration comes from the Latter Day Saints Hospital in Salt Lake City, where a computer system has been doing a similar diagnostic job on congenital heart disease. According to Dr. Homer Warner, the machine consistently diagnoses as accurately as a panel of experts and outperforms them as individuals.

Cardiology seems the best present possibility for computer diagnosis or diagnostic aid, but work is going on in other areas, albeit with irregular results. At the Henry Ford Hospital in Detroit, information on 204 patients with stomach complaints and known diagnoses was programed into a computer. The computer was then used to diagnose ninety-eight other patients with stomach complaints, by asking each patient eight crucial questions. Considering the limited situation, the results were interesting: 73 percent accuracy in diagnosing hiatus hernia; 75 percent accuracy in spotting gallstones; but only 27 percent success on gastric ulcer, and 33 percent with gastric cancer.

Better diagnostic results with computers have been achieved in other specialties, including obstetrics. At the University of Cincinnati Medical Computing Center, a condition known as placenta previa (a displaced placenta obstructing the birth canal) which can produce serious hemorrhaging during labor, was supposedly accurately diagnosed in forty-nine out of fifty cases by a computer system, while the judgment of residents in radiology proved wrong three times out of ten.

Despite its undeniable glamour, computer medicine has its vocal skeptics. Dr. Murray Eden, associate professor of electrical engineering at MIT, believes that its potential is overrated. "Diagnosis is closer to a pattern-recognition operation than to a computer's mathematical function," he says. "Because so little is known about pattern recognition in the human brain—and even less about how to make a computer perform a comparable function—the possibility that machines will one day supply useful diagnoses is extremely dim."

Other observers, including the editors of *Medical Tribune,* are more sanguine, pointing out that the computer "has been tested in medical diagnosis and has done at least as well as the majority of physicians," especially in the reading of "EKG's, and for that matter any curve, set of variables, diagrams, and what have you." They are concerned, however, about its possible abuse by doctors, just as has partially happened with the laboratory revolution. "The sense of unease so many of us experience about the computer in medicine of the future relates to a suspicion that what is sought is the replacement of the physician and not the mere provision of a tool. We think, however, that if computers turn out to be replacements, the onus will fall upon physicians, and not upon the electrical designers. Too often diagnostic aids, as, for example, laboratory tests, cease being mere aids and become the final judge because the physician has abrogated his role. There are no replacements for a proper history and the performance of a proper physical examination."

The horrifying potential that the machine represents to some as an extension of the current trend toward dehumanized medicine was best portrayed by a sarcastic physician who used the computer to berate his supramodern colleagues. "Among the electronic gadgets for your future office, you forgot one thing—the patient scanner," the wary doctor writes in a letter to a medical periodical. "As the patient walks by this gadget, it records pertinent data (such as findings, diagnosis, and indicated therapy) on a magnetic tape. The doctor receives the information on the golf course through his pocket audio viewer: a red light flashes, indicating his lawyer's OK. Back at the office, the bill is tucked into the patient's pocket on his way out."

The debate on computer diagnosis will undoubtedly mushroom in proportion, but the serious observer of medicine should always consider the inherent value of an electronic aide—not replacement —for the doctor. No arrangement of transistors can destroy the acumen of the true physician, yet a competent machine can surely suggest differential diagnostic possibilities to many physicians whose circuitry is considerably less well tuned than that of the computer.

Until the millennium arrives with its transistorized certainty, what can the contemporary patient do to get proper, accurate medical diagnosis? There is little alternative except to patronize a physician. If the ailment is obviously localized, there is a temptation to seek out the obvious subspecialist—cardiologist, urologist, etc. This can be successful, but visiting an internist or general practitioner first has certain advantages: he can examine you, then recommend a subspecialist. This enables you to have two doctors involved in a forced consultation with you as the subject, for the subspecialist will generally refer your diagnosis back to your regular doctor. In addition, there is always the possibility that the condition may not be as localized as expected. It might also be appropriate to consult several physicians on a serious ailment—investing time and money in the hope of cutting perhaps extravagant error.

By the profession's own standards, an internist is more qualified as a diagnostician than the general practitioner, and the generalization is a worthwhile one. However, there has been a tendency to overpublicize the internist as a supradoctor touched with divinity, which he is not. Incompetence and mediocrity cut rudely across all medical lines, and many general practitioners may have the talent for diagnostic detective work, plus the sensitive nose for suspect soma that is missing in many a board-certified internist. If diplomas were panaceas for inferior diagnosis, the problem would be considerably less complex.

The astute patient knows that he need not be in an emergency condition (bleeding, weight loss, extreme pain) to be suffering the early, or even developing, stages of a serious chronic ailment. What he requires is a thorough-going examination, the legendary head-to-toe checkup. Unfortunately, getting such an examination calls for considerably more ingenuity than the typical patient possesses. Organized medicine has tried to make it a frivolous, light-hearted pursuit by simply advising: "See your doctor once a year for a checkup."

The truth of the thorough examination is that it is rarely available. If it is available, it is often at prohibitive cost to the medical consumer who considers $25 a high diagnostic fee. Dr. Walter C. Alvarez tried to nudge the profession closer to crude reality recently when he commented in *Modern Medicine:* "Certainly, it seems that if we are going to keep telling people to get a yearly checkup, we should face the fact that many of them cannot find a man who will do a good job and do it quickly—not in a hospital—and for a fee that can be paid."

Aside from the diagnostic pitfalls already sketched, the patient is faced with an equally formidable economic obstacle, about which his physician may not be candid. The doctor calculates his time at between $30 to $50 gross an hour, with most internists at the upper figure. A "complete checkup" takes at least a full hour, and with laboratory tests, will run between $50 to $100. Rather than demand such a fee from most patients, or find the time in his busy practice, the typical physician will agree to the physical, but cut out necessary time and money-consuming procedures. Dr. Alvarez comments on this embarrassing point: "Many other laymen have written to say, 'When I insisted on having an examination, my doctor gave me what he called a "complete checkup," but I know it wasn't that. He listened to my heart and my lungs and poked at my abdomen for a few seconds; he looked for ruptures; he took my blood pressure, and he examined my urine, and that was about all. Surely, a good general checkup consists of much more than that. Please write and tell me where in my neighborhood I can go to get the sort of checkup which you say I should have.'" Confesses Dr. Alvarez: "What distresses me is that I usually do not know what the person can do."

Given the willing physician, and the patient's ability to pay, what should a so-called complete physical include? There are no limits to diagnostic probing, but the following is a reasonable list of procedures that should be part of a classic head-to-toe checkup: 1. Complete medical history. 2. Physical examination, including (not in a particular order) visual and hearing tests; blood-pressure readings; examination of the heart, chest, abdomen, eyes, ears, nose, mouth, throat, larynx, skin; examination for viewable cancers; use of the ophthalmoscope; basic neurological exam. 3. Proctoscopic examination of the rectum. 4. Blood counts. 5. Specific blood chemistries. 6. Postprandial (after eating) blood-glucose or glucose-tolerance test for diabetes. 7. Tuberculosis skin test. 8. Urinalysis. 9. Pap vaginal smear for adult women. 10. Chest X-ray. 11. Resting and exercise electrocardiogram for patients thirty-five and over. 12. Simple pulmonary function tests. 13. Tonometry test for glaucoma if indicated. 14. For smokers, or ex-smokers, the checkup should include cytological examination of the sputum. 15. X-rays of the gastrointestinal tract, gall bladder and breasts should be made if indicated by examination or history.

If the search for a competent physician with the time and inclination is fruitless, where can the determined examinee go? By conspiring to have an internist check him into a university hospital for a three-day diagnostic travail, much can be accomplished diagnostically. In a teaching institution, as a *paying patient,* one has the use of his own attending doctor and the house staff, all of whom feel the necessity to complete the hospital chart with some definitive diagnosis, a compulsion the totally unsupervised private doctor can dismiss.

The diagnostic hospital patient, however, must be willing to accept the risk of hospital hazards and to forego his Blue Cross benefits. Despite the proven lifesaving value of early diagnosis, diagnostic admissions are exempt from Blue Cross benefits in most states. Some doctors fudge the admission slip in a health-and-mouse game with Blue Cross, but alert medical bureaucrats tagged some sixteen thousand patients in New York City alone in one year, and surprised them with a laundry-list-long hospital bill for diagnosis— payable in cash. Lifesaving diagnosis can be more than elusive: apparently it can be a near-crime.

Many diagnostic clinics, some of them world-famed, do excellent work-ups, a few of them inexpensively. The Strang Clinic in New York, for example, will give asymptomatic (apparently healthy) patients a one-hour cancer detection examination for $40. The exam is primarily cancer-oriented, but other ailments that make themselves known are duly noted. The PMX (Preventive Medical Examination) Group in New York City, composed of several top specialists, gives a full three-hour examination, plus a return visit, for $150. The Mayo Clinic in Rochester, Minnesota, offers a complete work-up, as does the Lahey Clinic in Boston, and the Cleveland Clinic in Cleveland, but these are not small-budget procedures. At the Mayo Clinic, for example, the examination is a three- to five-day ambulatory study that costs an average of $150 to $200, and can run higher depending on the number of tests. (Mayo is booked three to four months in advance on diagnostic examinations). The Cleveland Clinic charges only $35 for the basic physical, but with tests and specialty consultations it runs an average of $75 to $125 for the two- to four-day work-up. The Greenbrier Clinic in West Virginia gives an "executive" diagnostic examination—often at corporate expense—that fills three mornings, after which the patient can recuperate on the golf links of this posh resort.

Those who favor some form of private medicine (including many advocates of improved health care) are distraught at the present gap evidenced by lack of sufficient and thorough routine examinations in regular medical practice. The exceptions, too, are often special and privileged situations. At the Kaiser Foundation Health Plan in the San Francisco Bay Area, for example, thirty thousand adults a year receive an extremely thorough physical "Multiphasic Health Checkup," which is partially supported by a United States Public Health Service research grant.

The complete examination is, of course, only one part of the complex art of disease detection. Diagnosis is the most intimate aspect of medicine, and goes on incessantly in all medical practices at all stages of illness. Whatever the auspices or the geography of that practice, the query "How good is the art?" eventually devolves on the individual doctor and his competence and philosophy. As we have seen, his inadequacy as a medical detective—despite his laboratory and scientific assists—is becoming increasingly obvious, in individual cases and disturbing statistics.

What, may we ask, goes on inside the mind of the doctor who has abrogated much, or part, of his diagnostic responsibility? The pressure of patient load destroys some doctors' fine compulsive instinct to know all. He may be mesmerized by the necessity to get the flood of humanity out of his office and back into their homes. Others rely heavily on the weight of percentage, hopeful that the patient who presents the formidable challenge is not really sick, or will eventually find succor in another doctor's office. Or, inured to a steady whine of patient complaint, the doctor may no longer be actively seeking definitive answers.

His practice is free and uncontrolled, and the quality of his diagnosis—which is life and death to his patients—is, at present, a matter of personal conscience. The problem will have to be adjudicated between the physician and his Maker, or the rules of this medical art may have to be drastically revised.

Chapter III

Modern Medical Practice versus the Patient:
Arrogance, Availability and Assembly-Line Medicine

The ear, nose and throat specialist's office was a paradigm of modern medical efficiency. Patients were placed in separate examining rooms, and one even waited in a hallway at a miniature desk no larger than a serving tray which had been pressed into service as a "patient station." The specialist maintained a hurried gait, and manner to match, as he scurried from one room to the other, dispensing his technical skill in concise doses.

In one cubicle, a patient suffering from fatigue, sweating and "stuffed" sinuses awaited attention. The physician glanced briefly at the patient's medical record, then probed into his nose. The examination was a model of brevity and ostensible surety. Without undressing the patient, the doctor completed his diagnosis and scribbled a prescription for a popular steroid to reduce the sinus inflammation.

Three days later the patient's condition not only had not improved, but had worsened considerably. Sleep was now difficult, the sweating more persistent. In desperation, the patient lifted himself out of bed and visited a local physician, who conducted a less harried interview and examination. His conclusion was that the steroid therapy, although effective for the sinuses, was making sleep almost impossible. Underlying was a case of influenza which was getting progressively worse with lack of sleep. The successful therapy: eliminate all treatment and go back to bed for a week.

The assembly-line medicine that had produced the first unfortunate result is not the sole prerogative of board-certified specialists. Increasingly the typical community practitioner has initiated similar medical procedures, complete with vinyl hallways punctuated by examining-room doors. Where once he sat and contemplated patients one at a time, many a contemporary physician now commutes at a rapid pace among his examining cubicles, all part of a pressurized, clinical atmosphere calculated to impress and dispatch his patients. Not every physician has succumbed to assembly-line medicine, but only a stubborn minority resist the "progress" of modern medical methodology.

A visit to the suburban practice of two medical partners is an unsettling introduction to the new speed-up technology. Patient names are announced by a "nurse" (a doctor euphemism for high school graduates dramatically garbed in professional white) who leads the patient to a barren antiseptic cubicle. The patient's medical file is inserted in a metal-door sleeve. Its geometry—open end up, open end down, or vertical—is a key to whether the patient asked for Dr. A or B or if it involves a new patient with no doctor preference. The patient undresses and waits.

The physician, having just applied a cast to a fracture in one examining room, hurries down the hallway to one of the closed examining-room doors, slowing his gait perceptibly as he enters the cubicle. Patients known to him are greeted with a friendly gesture or word. Others are cued in by the medical folder. "Hello . . . Mrs. Taylor. What seems to trouble you?" Propped against the door, the physician digests the medical history with obvious dispatch as the patient recites her problem. The patient's tale of symptoms inevitably comes out seriously truncated in a respectful concession to the military-like, abridged medical operation.

After examining the patient, the doctor reaches for a wall buzzer, on which his fingers dance a meaningful tattoo. The message has been received in code by the "nurse," who enters with disposable hypodermics already loaded with medications, and test tubes color-coded for blood-test processing by an automated laboratory. After a cursory discussion, the writing of a prescription and instructions to return next week, the patient departs and another anxious patient enters the medical maze. The physician has meanwhile diverted his mind once again, resuming his frenetic traffic pattern to another cubicle, the X-ray room or back to his private office.

The suburban doctor operates this medical factory with admirable energy. If quizzically asked about the propriety of such an operation, he reassures the skeptical. "I know it looks very hurried, but when I'm in the examining room with the patient, even for a few minutes, I'm concentrating very hard."

This punctilious routine, with its unfortunate Chaplinesque overtones, has euphemistically been termed "Multiple Patient Processing." It is only one of the innovations of the doctor's "Practice Management" that—falsely, in the name of science—exert strict control over patients while carefully husbanding the doctor's time, energy, income and emotions. It has revolutionized medical care by removing the patient from the doctor, both psychically and physically. In the eyes of astute patient and critical physician alike, it has strained the doctor-patient relationship to the breaking point. It has set the stage for failings of the medical art and has more often made patients its victims than its beneficiaries.

Its method is impeccable; its implications are antimedicine; its instincts are antipatient. Its goals are increased patient loads and larger incomes for doctors, along with the apparently paradoxical aims of more free time for physicians and increased detachment from patients constantly seeking attention, information, succor, reassurance and medication. Its success is a credit to many doctors' determination not to sacrifice themselves for their profession, and a monument to the pliability, fear and supineness of the patient public. Not to be overlooked are the many quasi-medical legions who have come between the patient and his doctor, from aides to medical management consultants.

The doctor's success in shaping his medical practice for his convenience—and the resulting deterioration in doctor-patient relationship—is an outgrowth of the multitude of barriers that he has erected in the specious guise of "better" and "modern" medicine.

Some of the barriers have been physical: phone answering services which doggedly "protect" the doctor from patient intrusion; physician isolation after hours, on weekends and on the midweek day off; "unlisted" home phone numbers; aides who shield doctors from "pestering" patients; virtual elimination of house calls, even in emergency situations, thus cutting the physician off from large groups of the ill; increased doctor absence during vacation periods in summer and winter; active discouragement of phone calls to report illness and seek advice; the decrease in evening office hours; and the less time and concentration afforded each patient.

Other barriers between doctor and patient that can maim the healing process are less tangible, but no less real. So-called modern medical practice has made doctor-patient communication a difficult, even hazardous operation. Many physicians fail to keep patients fully informed on their ailment or its treatment; others fail to follow up initial visits; physicians too often adopt a patronizing, superior attitude toward today's educated patients; many doctors find it difficult to react with compassion to the sick; and in an attempt to keep the patient in his "place," certain physicians have become near-expert in the not overly subtle art of intimidation. Instead of a partnership of healing, modern medicine has too often become a joust, an unfair contest in which the patient is almost inevitably the weaker participant.

In the extreme, it might be said that patients no longer have doctors, and conversely, that doctors no longer have patients. Instead, those who are sick, or believe they are sick, purchase medical advice and therapy by the minute or by the visit from a practitioner legally licensed to sell his training.

Organized medicine merchandises the false theory that impersonality, speed and unconcern are somehow related to medical science. "We have neglected to explain to our patients why we do the things we do," a leading AMA spokesman recently argued. "We haven't told patients often enough that their welfare is important to us. Modern medicine isn't just one person; it involves many people. The modern physician is different from 'Old Doc.' He is more skilled. He must see more patients in less time. He must have them come to him because his office is where the tests and the tools are."

The argument that the modern doctor has sacrificed warmth and proper attention as an offering to the god Science is lacking in observable truth. In fact, there is no significant proof that the external trappings of "progress" are even related to medical science, except perhaps negatively. More likely, the doctor may have sacrificed himself and his patients for the tinsel trappings of modern "practice management" with little in return—except personal comfort and affluence.

A glimpse into the dehumanized (yet not necessarily scientific) medical future is afforded by a practice in a small Midwestern community. Three physicians have created an electronic marvel for the multiple processing of a hundred patients a day, complete with ten examining rooms, panels of colored flashing lights, and portable short-wave beepers. The $800 communications setup uses colored lights to "speed" the doctors through their chores "without the usual wasted motion," according to a description of the modern practice. It adds, most significantly, that it is all done with a "minimum" of conversation.

After examining one female patient, the physician presses designated signals for red and white lights which flash on a master panel at the nurse's station, indicating a pelvic examination preparation. A yellow light would summon a lab technician; a clear light, a nurse for an injection. While that patient is being prepared, the physician re-enters the hallway to search out more business by looking for a white light over one of the ten examining room doors.

The typical physician cannot boast such extravagant technique, but he still manages to expedite patients efficiently. Many patients are not consciously aware of being "processed," but as a recent *Medical Economics* survey reveals, a strong minority have become cognizant of the less than adequate medical attention involved in multiple-patient processing. "He always has four or five patients in different treatment rooms," one patient complained. "I think he should take one patient at a time and finish with him, instead of skipping from one to another and back again. That way he could understand more of what is the matter with his individual patients," says a critical patient. Still another patient-commentator described his doctor as less than composed during such multiple therapy: "When he runs from one patient to another it makes him breathless and me nervous, so neither one of us is able to concentrate on the health matter at hand."

Many disenchanted patients believe that doctor curtness inhibits their questions—answers to which could provide diagnostic clues. "You get the feeling that you are being hurried through an office visit before all the questions you have in mind have been answered," states a surveyed patient. Another makes the common complaint that the hurried purveyor of assembly-line medicine is a bad listener: "He occasionally does not appear to listen long enough. That is, I may have something more to say but he cuts in . . ."

An annoyed New Jersey internist agrees with this view of rampant medical curtness and illustrates one of its many dangers. He admonishes his colleagues to "listen to what the patient says" while examining him. "I learned from my mother's experience with doctors," the physician recalls in a medical publication. "She went from one doctor to another for years, until she finally found one who would let her finish a sentence. He listened long enough to learn that she had massive hemorrhages."

In no area as in the virtual elimination of the house call—taking the patient out of the sickbed for the doctor's convenience—has the physician been so successful in suppressing the patient's true needs, often with grave consequences. A graph of house calls made by the typical doctor is a descending line of clifflike proportions. Thirty years ago four out of ten medical visits were made in the home. By 1957 the typical physician made only twelve house calls a week; by 1962 he visited only six patients at home; by 1963 it was an insignificant three. A survey of a thousand doctors, conducted by *Medical Tribune,* showed that one-fourth made no house calls at all, and 60 percent of the physicians made between one and five house calls a week. The most recent survey indicates that the typical specialist makes an incredible one house call per week, the pediatrician three, and the GP only five.

The rationale that his office "equipment" is needed for proper diagnosis and treatment has been the doctor's specious argument against the traditional home visit. In fact, one New Jersey pediatrician, Dr. Phoebe Hudson, has adamantly advocated the end of house calls "as outdated as the horse and buggy" and "medically unsound"—except in such emergencies as croup, convulsions, or accidents. This new philosophy has been so successful that the comment, "Take an aspirin and come to the office," has become a near-reflex in many practices. Dr. Hudson is undoubtedly sincere, but the evidence indicates that once again many physicians have created a makeshift scrim to disguise their true and quite uninspired motives.

The results of such behavior have only been documented in fragments, albeit frightening ones. "A friend of mine called a doctor to come to his home because of his mother," a patient recounts in the *Medical Economics* survey. "The doctor said he wouldn't come. My friend's mother died." Speaking of her doctor's house-call policy, another patient states: "If you can creep, you go to his office—or else."

An angry, embarrassed minority of physicians are just as irate as some patients over this wholesale abdication of medical responsibility. Dr. A. S. Rogoff of Detroit is one physician who faces the issue straightforwardly. "It's a doctor's duty to serve his patients even if it is inconvenient and financially unsound for him," he states in a medical publication. "Maybe our public image wouldn't be as dim as it is if we were more careful to respect the obligation to serve our patients as we should."

Dr. John S. DeTar, former head of the American Academy of General Practice, was once prompted, on returning from a 2 A.M. house call, to draft an angry note to his colleagues about their neglect of the sick at their sickbed. He had originally been called in by an aged couple when their plaintive phone call at 1:30 A.M. was turned aside by their regular doctor's wife with the terse comment that the doctor was "not available."

Dr. DeTar offers little support for his colleagues. He writes in a popular medical publication: "Berating the profession on this score has become a favorite cocktail-party pastime. And I for one can offer no defense for the doctor—be he family doctor, specialist or sub-specialist . . . If the patient requests a house call, the onus is on the physician to prove to himself that the call is not required—or to answer to his own conscience for his refusal."

Many mothers futilely explain to their doctors that they will not take a sick child out of a warm bed into freezing temperatures. Pediatricians and general practitioners usually counter with the false argument that zero temperatures are not dangerous for sick children.

This refusal of many pediatricians to make house calls has created a deranged, even surrealistic medical situation. The higher-priced, better-trained pediatric specialist cares for the child while he is well, while any doctor who will respond to a parent's plea cares for children too ill to be taken to the pediatrician's office. "It is a peculiar fact," says Dr. Herbert Ratner of Oak Park, Illinois, "that most of the sick children in this country are handled by the GP and most of the well babies by the pediatrician. It should be the reverse."

Why? Is the doctor sincere when he states that the best medical practice is available only in his office and not at the bedside—even for potential pneumonia victims? A knowing physician-critic in Webster, Massachusetts, is skeptical of this thin motivation. "Any doctor knows you can see four patients in your office in the time it takes for one house call," he writes. "So at the end of the year, the doctor who sees all his patients in the office will obviously have more money in the bank. But should that be the primary consideration of practicing medicine?"

The hoary specter of "false alarms" turned in by near-hysterical patients at the first run of a sniffle is inevitably brought up. Medical testimony indicates quite the contrary: most house calls are medically necessary and not the provocation of cranks. A *Medical Tribune* "Pulse" survey of almost a thousand doctors revealed that the average physician believes that more than half of his house calls were necessary—a miraculously high proportion considering that he, not the ailing patient, was making the determination. The false-alarm hypothesis was supported *by less than one fourth* of the participating doctors.

The anti-house-call physician conveniently overlooks the danger to those already ill that some medical critics believe can pervade physicians' offices. Dr. Anna W. Perkins of Westerlo, New York, raises this pertinent, if scrupulously ignored common-sense point in a leading medical publication. "A not impossible result of the 'bring him to the office' technique," she warns, "might be the close and happy association of the following: a child in the beginning stages of 'regular' measles; another with whooping cough who has had the triple toxoid 'shots'; an adult with 'walking' pneumonia; a child with a 'strep' throat; and a woman who is two months pregnant, sitting next to a baby with a fever of currently unknown origin who in a day or two will lose his fever and blossom forth with the rash of German measles!"

The doctor's reluctance to make house calls has been accepted by many docile patients who assume that it is the doctor's prerogative to say "no" capriciously. In actuality, the physician has been abusing the patient's ignorance of his own rights, for although the doctor has great latitude under the law, he does not have this unlimited right. He must make all reasonable house calls for any of his sick patients, or risk being charged with "abandonment."

Charles Kramer, a prominent New York malpractice lawyer, outlines the doctor's responsibility in his monograph "Medical Mal-practice" with a quote from the case of Becker v. Janinski, an early precedent for abandonment cases. "When a physician engages . . . to attend a patient . . . without limitation of time he cannot cease his visits except *first,* with the consent of the patient, or *secondly,* upon giving the patient timely notice so that he may employ another doctor, or *thirdly,* when the condition of the patient is such as no longer to require medical treatment, and of that condition the physician must be the judge at his own peril."

Some members may ignore their responsibility, but the AMA is concrete on the subject. "A physician may choose whom he will serve," says the AMA *Principles of Medical Ethics,* Section 5. "Having undertaken the care of the patient, he may not neglect him, and unless he has been discharged he may discontinue his services *only after giving adequate notice* [italics mine]." In a classic case a southern physician was sued for abandonment for refusing to visit the patient's home, even though the patient became gravely ill *as a result of an injection given him by the doctor himself.* In another case a doctor was sued for refusal to attend a pregnant woman when summoned by her husband.

"I'm trying to stop making them [house calls], but some patients still ask me to come to their homes," one anxious physician told a medical-publication consultant. "Can I be charged with abandonment if I refuse?" The consultant's response was straightforward: "You can—and the charge may stick unless you can prove that you *never* make house calls and that the patient knew this when he first came to you for treatment."

Although unknown to most, the patient obviously has stronger recourse against "unavailable" physicians than cocktail-party cynicism. The unwritten doctor-patient contract automatically binds the doctor to *full* responsibility, seven days a week, twenty-four hours a day. His only opportunity for limited coverage, either in working hours or place of practice, is by virtue of his specialty, or any other limitations announced *in advance and to all his patients.* The many doctors who luxuriate in the financial half of the sacred doctor-patient contract, might well be reminded by their patients of the stern requirements of the other half.

Fortunately, there is a conscientious minority of physicians who need not be cajoled or threatened in order to perform their duty, a minority that could be an effective guide for their errant colleagues.

One can easily recall when much of the doctor's office work was done in the evening, a common-sense precept that fits the simple fact that most people work in the daytime. Today's practice management, wedded to doctor convenience, is gradually eliminating the evening hours along with the house call, making nine-to-five medicine a virile trend. Many doctors consider evening office hours a practice builder for the neophyte physician, a service that is gradually eliminated once the practice is built.

The "conspiracy" of modern doctors to make patients conform—undoubtedly to the detriment of the medical art—has prompted the wrath of many commentators. "A prominent one [attitude] held by many physicians is that they should refuse to be led around by their patients as if by a ring in the nose," says Dean William L. Prosser of the University of California School of Law. "A comparison attitude is that the physician should train his patients to adhere to a pattern in their requests for his services—indeed in the timing of their illnesses! Such attitudes, which run counter to the human need for individualization, may make for certain businesslike efficiency, but they do not promote the historic essential of good medical practice—truly personal service."

The modern physician's obsessive desire to depart from medical tradition and convert the doctor's life into an orderly, normal existence is too often at the expense of his medical responsibility. The "night call"—which medical propagandists once used as a symbol of doctor dedication—is an early casualty of the doctor's *Krieg* against demanding patients.

A recent anecdote underscores the bitterness that can be provoked in doctors by patients who interrupt their new restrictive medicine. A male patient allergic to penicillin was given another antibiotic for a suspected infection. The physician reassured the worried patient about a possible reaction: "Don't worry; just call me and I'll take care of it." The following evening, at midnight, the patient took an antibiotic capsule and went to bed. Within moments his body started itching, and by 1 A.M. a rash had broken out on his arms, legs and stomach. Moments later the serious symptom of a "choking" feeling indicated that a potentially fatal edema of the larynx that could stop the flow of breath was possibly beginning.

The patient's wife dialed the doctor frantically, only to receive the answering service, who reminded her that *"it is one o'clock in the morning."* After several phone calls the operator finally agreed that it might be an emergency. Fifteen minutes later an angry physician got on the phone and confirmed that it was a potentially serious reaction. His suggestion: antihistamine by mouth or an immediate visit to the hospital emergency room for a shot of Benedryl. A night call was out of the question. The high-priced practitioner was available during the day for costly treatment commensurate with his training, but had no qualms referring the patient to a green interne when complications set in after office hours.

Some angered patients have stated that it takes a police call in their community to get a doctor at night. However, documentation indicates that even that drastic action can prove futile. In Suffolk County, Long Island, firemen desperately tried to help a forty-one-year-old engineer who had collapsed of a heart attack. The police telephoned nineteen different doctors, but by the time one could be secured, the patient was dead.

The frenetic shopping about to find a doctor during emergencies has created another jagged wedge between patient and physician. The alarming unavailability of doctors on Wednesday (or Thursday) in many communities where physicians have suspended doctoring in a midweek siesta and retreated *en masse* to their golf courses or rose gardens, has exacerbated an already chaotic situation, creating frayed relations and sometimes even leading to death.

In the burgeoning suburb of Massapequa, Long Island, the doctor's day off was at the core of a simmering unresolved crisis. "You didn't dare get sick, have an accident, or a heart attack on Wednesday in Massapequa," says Ira L. Cahn, editor and publisher of the *Massapequa Post,* the local weekly newspaper. "We had a series of incidents in which patients just couldn't get their own or any other doctors. The phone services and the doctors started blaming each other. People would call the service, find that their doctor was off for the day and unreachable, and that the doctor who was supposed to be covering wasn't in, or was busy with his own patients. At least one person died, and several had heart attacks without being able to get a doctor, before the situation came to a head."

The incident, which triggered a *Massepequa Post* prize-winning editorial campaign, was the death of a four-month-old infant on a Wednesday. Seeing her child stricken with a choking fit while in its carriage, the mother frantically called for a physician, then another, but without success. Meanwhile neighbors were calling other physicians, all of them simultaneously reaching the same answering services. Forty minutes later the surgeon for the fire district was reached by the local police and responded immediately, but only in time to pronounce the child dead.

"We immediately started a campaign clamoring that either the doctors would have to clean house in this town or face real trouble," says Mr. Cahn. "We ran an all-out campaign, with news stories and editorials, and it finally brought results."

The climax of the newspaper's crusade was a devastating editorial entitled "For Shame!" which expressed the community's disgust. "A baby lay gasping for breath as adults frantically tried to reach a doctor this past Wednesday," Mr. Cahn wrote in an editorial that won the New York State Press Association Award. "The baby died. Our heart-felt sympathy goes out to the parents, not only because of the tragedy that has entered their lives, but because they are among the victims of a medical profession that refuses to awaken to a need for a better system of emergency notification . . . But all that is forthcoming from the medical profession is outraged indignation that a mere layman dares to criticize the lofty MD. This doesn't cut any ice with this newspaper. Until the doctors themselves come up with a program that will prevent incidents like this past Wednesday's, then they are guilty of not having the welfare of the community at heart . . . In the name of Hippocrates, we plead with the doctors of our community to allay this situation before the people lose all respect for their physicians."

"As a result of our campaign, we received a call from the public relations man of the county medical society, and two local physicians started to organize the other doctors," says Mr. Cahn. Dr. Steve Schmeiser, Jr., who helped lead the doctor movement, describes that effort. "We met and set up an emergency panel consisting of about thirty local doctors. Each man was assigned emergency duty for a day, and a full calendar with the doctors' names was given to the local police and to the two phone answering services in town. Our instructions to the phone service are that if a person cannot reach his regular doctor, or his associate, or if they have no doctor, the physician on emergency service is to be called immediately. There are now telephone answering boards for the doctors alone, and calls to us are not mixed in with those for oil dealers."

This emergency-panel system has been attempted by other communities—often under the stimulus of death—but with mixed success. The suburban community of Syosset, Long Island, established a physician panel which functioned for two years before collapsing. "It had too many built-in problems," says a local internist. "We have two phone answering services in town. But for all practical purposes, they don't speak to each other, which created a problem in co-ordinating after-hour calls. Then, of all the doctors in town we could only get co-operation from those willing to make house calls—which narrowed our choice to internists, general practitioners and pediatricians. The other specialists either did not feel qualified to do general emergency work or stated that they did not make house calls. Even among the doctors we had, there were bones of contention. A pediatrician, for example, might be concerned about making an emergency house call on an adult with a heart attack. He felt he might be vulnerable to a malpractice suit. Eventually, all of these problems proved too much to overcome and the panel stopped functioning."

It was in Syosset that a young boy fell from a bicycle on a Wednesday and bled to death internally before medical help could be secured. In the local paper, the *Syosset Tribune,* where a debate raged over doctors' day off and failure of coverage, a letter appeared with a plaintive account of the futile attempt to secure a doctor: "When the accident occurred, the family doctor was called . . . The answering service informed the mother at this time that the doctor was in Manhattan that particular day. There was a doctor covering for him, however, who would be available at about 6:00 P.M. . . . .

Unfortunately in the ensuing minutes the child became terribly uncomfortable, and it was only then that immediate aid was sought by scouring the town for an available doctor. Even the police submitted three additional names to contact . . . The doctor covering for the family doctor had since returned and was again called to come immediately to the home. The nurse said he could not. A call was then placed to the Nassau Medical Society, who claimed that they would send a doctor out and call back within five minutes to inform the mother what to do until the doctor arrived. The call was never returned, nor did a physician appear. The family and friends who mourn for this boy would be somewhat comforted to know that something like this might never happen again. I'm in a good position to say this. I'm the mother . . ."

Such a stark recitation becomes overwhelming drama when juxtaposed with the remark of an official of the Westchester Country Club in suburban New York. "Our busiest days on the golf course are Saturday, Sunday and Wednesday," he stated in answer to a query. "Why Wednesday? In our county, that's the doctor's day off."

The tragedies in Syosset and Massapequa both involve burgeoning Nassau County, New York, whose medical society now boasts an emergency service which they claim is "85 percent" effective, and can deliver a doctor to a home within forty minutes—a job they are called on to do after hours some sixty times a week. Other communities are establishing emergency panels, and the best ones—unlike Nassau County's—use physicians who do not have regular office hours concurrently with emergency duty.

The gap in medical coverage has been widened further by the modern doctor's relaxing propensities. The admonishment to have a "regular" physician does not anticipate the lengthy vacation leaves of the contemporary physician, a leisure-lover of unparalleled proportions.

The discontinuity of care due to long vacations is supposedly offset by providing a "covering" doctor, but patients have learned that this is often an unsatisfactory arrangement. One pediatrician left for his country home for a full six weeks, placing his practice in the hands of another physician. When a child became ill, the mother called the covering physician, whom she found unsatisfactory but settled for on a temporary basis. The dislike was academic, for two weeks later the covering doctor left on a European tour, leaving his practice—and the practice he was covering for—in the hands of a subcoverer. At this point the patient extracted her child from this medical spiral, which apparently had no theoretical end.

The vacationing physician may feel carefree at his lake-front dockside, but his obligation to his patients is ever-present. Should the doctor covering for him fail to respond to one of his patients' calls, the pleasure-bound physician may find himself guilty of the serious charge of medical abandonment. Legal authorities point out that the covering doctor's obligation does not begin until after he has seen the patient; until then the vacationing doctor is still responsible. One California GP suggests that his colleagues apply "a little balm" on their return by phoning patients seen by the substitute. Such a public relations policy would, he says, keep patients from feeling that "you've left them in the lurch."

The telephone is another major instrument of frustration in the new aggravated doctor-patient relationship. The doctor sits insulated from its electronic grasp by unlisted phone numbers, protective secretaries and overindulgent if unintelligent phone answering services, many of whom masquerade with the salutation: "Dr. Jones's office." Many a modern doctor at home lives a relatively calm existence while his public front bristles with messages from anxious patients. A recent visit to a successful suburban practitioner, for example, began one afternoon in the "back yard" of his spacious home. The doctor relaxed on a porch chair in the middle of a busy day, between office hours, while the phone on the wall— whose number was unknown to his most seriously ill patients—remained significantly silent.

The typical physician, according to a Michigan survey, handles fourteen telephone calls a day, and in many practices he approaches each one with an admixture of trepidation and annoyance. "The phone is a horror," says one metropolitan doctor. One in ten physicians even charges for telephone advice in an unsuccessful effort to ward off callers. Yet the telephone is the life line between patient and doctor. Despite this central importance, getting past the doctor's aide, or the phone service, can be a study in frustration.

Many phone services (hired for from $30 to $50 a month) are insensitive message centers who often handle patient calls as if they were from commercial customers. In fact, many answering services handle not only physicians but plumbers and other commercial clients. The admonition to "Hold on, please!" in answer to an urgent medical call for help is all the more disconcerting when the answering service operator has pressed the hold button to speak to someone about a deficient television set.

Phone answering services, though not a formal part of the medical team, often take an unwarranted "pride" in protecting what they interpret as the doctor's interests. This can be medically deadly when combined with the assumption that they can decide which calls are clinically urgent.

In one case a worried parent called her regular pediatrician when a wasp bit her one-year-old baby, a situation that can cause anaphylactic shock, and death. The phone service answered the call, informing the mother that it was Wednesday, the doctor's day off, and she preferred not to disturb him. "What's wrong?" the telephone girl asked with her most professional aplomb. When the mother supplied the details, the phone service felt vindicated. "Why, that's no emergency! Just wash it with brown soap," she said. After six such calls to the phone answering services of physicians throughout town, all of whom were off for the weekly Wednesday "holiday," a doctor finally responded and insisted on seeing the child immediately.

The tardiness, presumption and inaccuracy of many phone services can be equally irksome to the concerned doctor. A cardiologist learned this when one of his regular heart patients tried to call him in the midst of a heart attack. The doctor was not in the office, and the single operator on duty in the phone service answered, then kept the ailing patient waiting. She finally got on the line and brusquely told the patient that the doctor wasn't in, and to call back the following day! Fortunately, the patient reached another cardiologist immediately after.

The constant interposition of a phone service between himself and his patients is a major reason why a New York physician left private medical practice to become a public health doctor. "I couldn't tolerate the phone service situation and I wasn't willing to be available twenty-four hours a day."

Another doctor-critic avoids such extreme action by eliminating the phone answering service. He takes his after-hours and weekend calls personally at home, lightening the burden by alternating the after-hours coverage with his partners. "The important thing is that my patients and I decide how important each call is and then deal with it directly," writes Denver pediatrician Lawrence M. Bugbee. "Major problems are not inadvertently screened out by a girl at the answering service."

Unlike the phone answering service, the doctor's aide *is* a member of the medical team. This added barrier between doctor and patient varies from a high school girl with a smattering of typing to a registered nurse legally capable of giving intravenous injections. Although *two of every three aides are not nurses or trained technicians,* they are nevertheless the nerve center of the modern medical office. Doctors no longer answer their own office phones, and the aide who does usually erects—with the doctor's blessings—a medical Berlin wall. The medical quandary is how a layman aide can screen phone calls for emergencies without error. As some doctors are belatedly learning, it is a toying with medical fate that invites patient strain, malpractice suits and crippling illness.

The difference between an inquiry addressed to a physician and one addressed to his aide cannot be overstated. A woman patient was examined by a radiologist at a hospital outpatient clinic. Fearing cancer, she called the radiologist's private office for a particular afternoon appointment to discuss her case. The doctor's aide answered the phone and informed the woman that he did not see patients then. Without suggesting another date, she hung up. With typical human frailty, the woman did not call back. She neglected her condition, and eventually it worsened, requiring surgery. She sued the doctor for abandonment, on the correct assumption that the phone call to the doctor's office was sufficient to establish the doctor-patient contract, even though—through no fault of her own—she never reached the physician personally.

It cannot be denied that with the emergence of overloaded modern practices, the modern doctor needs help. The danger in the medical "aide" situation is the growing power being assumed by the quarter of a million medical assistants.

Her value to the patient is arbitrary—and probably nonexistent. It increases medical impersonality and the distance between doctor and patient. It shifts responsibility for doctor knowledge of his patients as people into nonmedical employee hands. It has another awesome danger: the tendency for medical aides to function almost as "subpractitioners."

What is a medical assistant, and what training must one have to qualify? The shocking situation is reminiscent of many others in chaotic modern medicine: it is left almost exclusively to the doctor's whim. Some physicians hire registered nurses; others hire high school girls whom they "train" themselves; others are graduates of medical-assistant "institutes." The American Association of Medical Assistants has established a certification examination, but thus far, only a handful of the nation's doctor aides have taken and passed it.

In the crush of their assembly-line practices, many physicians are bending the law and medical ethics by not strictly limiting their aides' responsibility. In one recent case a pediatrician's aide attempted a medical diagnosis with a fatal result. A mother called the doctor's office and relayed a description of her baby's rash and fever to the aide. "Measles," the aide answered in her most professional tone. "There's a lot of it around. I'll have the doctor stop by this afternoon." Unfortunately, it wasn't measles. The baby had meningococcal meningitis, inflammation of the brain membranes. Within hours, before the pediatrician got to the house, the child was dead.

The wholesale administration of injections by meagerly trained doctor's aides is commonplace, although unsuspected by many patients who believe every peak-capped assistant to be a bona-fide nurse. Dire results, including intramuscular injections delivered into a vein, paralysis, infections, severe inflammations and growths have resulted from this lax policy.

Only a doctor or an R.N. can legally give intravenous injections, but intramuscular injections—such as administration of antibiotics—are in a judicial never-land. Such injections given by aides—some of whom are "trained" by learning to shoot hypodermics filled with water into an orange—are commonplace today. They have generally been held legal if ordered by the doctor and administered by an aide who has been "competently trained." A California court, however, has ruled that doctors cannot delegate any medical tasks, including injections, to assistants not authorized by law to do them.

In such situations the wary patient can hardly hope to roll back the wave of impersonal medicine all by himself. He can, however, insist that no one but a doctor or at the very least a registered nurse tamper with his body.

Doctors too may benefit from restricting the ambitious activity of some aides. A woman undergoing a series of injections to reduce came to the doctor's office for her regular visit, only to find him out. The doctor's aide took it upon herself to give the injection, entering it on the patient's record. A serious swelling developed over the injection site, and it was finally necessary to cut out the mass that had developed. It had cost the patient injury and the doctor $3400 for allowing his aide to practice medicine without a license.

The imperfect art of medicine can be calamitous in the most expert hands. Relying on nonmedical opinion may increase the opportunity for catastrophe. A case recently reported by the law department of the American Medical Association underlined this fact. The morning a child became ill in a southeastern town, his mother brought him to the doctor's office, where the physician diagnosed it as nasopharyngitis (generalized nose or throat ailment) and had his nurse administer penicillin. Two hours later the mother returned with a critically ill child, unconscious and breathing abnormally. She told the nurse she thought the child was having convulsions and might be dying. The nurse phoned the doctor, who was home for lunch, and relayed the mother's message—but added her own opinion that the child seemed in the same condition as in the morning. The physician said he would return to the office after lunch.

Meanwhile the nurse too left for lunch. Minutes later the child vomited and his breathing became faint. The receptionist called the doctor, who arrived twenty-five minutes later, a few moments after the child had died. The cause of death was either the overwhelming virus or the aspiration of vomitus, the latter a condition that might have been handled. The doctor was held liable for the nurse's negligence in leaving the child unattended.

The ever-busy, sometimes underinterested doctor has alienated the patient relationship with still another "modern" method: his failure to keep the patient fully informed. The modern doctor is typically casual about dispensing information, often assuming that the patient need not be overly cognizant of the details of his own illness. Rather than a partnership between patient and doctor, modern medical practice is too often an exercise in patronization, of doctor failure to dispense information along with his supposed scientific therapy.

The doctor's one-time masterful art of putting pen to paper to list "do's" and "don'ts" for the sick—whether the complex management of a colostomy (artificial anus) or keeping the windows open or closed during a flu attack—has become virtually vestigial. Motivational researcher Dr. Ernest Dichter, writing in *Medical Annals of the District of Columbia,* discusses the patient's frustrated desire to know, which, he says, has crystallized as "resentment" against the doctor. "The patient wants not only understanding and sympathy but the right to participate in his treatment, by knowing scientifically what is wrong and how it should be handled."

In a letter to a medical publication a physician from Danbury, Connecticut, speaks of the "arrogance" of doctors who can't take time to explain a patient's condition. "Many people go to clinics simply because they give each patient a complete report and then interpret the report for him," he says. Another physician, from Oklahoma, ascribes the "deterioration of the doctor's image" greatly to "failure to explain things to them."

Dr. I. P. Frohman of Washington, D.C., offers wise counsel: to be *specific* with the patient. "When a patient is in my office, shirt off, brow furrowed, and wondering how his blood pressure is, I don't put him off with some vague phrase such as 'pretty good.' I tell him, '128 over 88,'" he writes in a medical publication. "I give him the numbers because they're specific. Then I explain the numbers and offer whatever reassurance is necessary." His admonishments to use reference books openly in the presence of patients, to admit ignorance honestly, to follow up prior treatment and to have "patience, patience and more patience" with patients is a revolutionary if untested prescription for better medical relations.

A National Institute of Health-sponsored study substantiates that patients usually want to know more about their ills and treatment than doctors are willing to divulge. According to the study, the complaint that "the doctor won't take time to explain things to me" expresses a recurring patient frustration that can interfere with his ability to handle the stress of illness.

Is the American doctor secretive or merely inarticulate? Possibly both. Some physicians who have not yet absorbed the fact that many patients' intellectual capacity is equal or superior to their own, falsely believe that the patient may not be able to understand the treatment or diagnosis, even if explained. If he is not fairly certain of his diagnosis, his prognosis or his treatment, the doctor fears—states the NIH study—the loss of patient respect if he is in error.

A University of Michigan law professor, Marcus L. Plant, warns the profession that this right to know is not an arbitrary one. Doctors, he stresses, have a legal obligation to speak to their patient in plain English, and "never to misrepresent by words or silence the nature and character of the medical procedure he proposes to undertake." Communication is an "absolute duty" on the doctor's part, he points out, because it involves "an absolute right on the part of the patient to choose whether or not he will submit to the medical procedure."

When some doctors do speak to patients, it can be an exercise in tiresome patronization, a soliloquy in speaking down. This "father knows best" attitude, warns Dr. Myron E. Wegman, dean of the University of Michigan School of Public Health, should be avoided at all costs. "The average layman will be thoroughly annoyed," says Dean Wegman, "if he is given a pat on the shoulder and told the subject is too complex for him to understand, and that he should take the doctor's advice and do as he is told. If our convictions are based on sound facts, we ought to be smart enough to interpret those facts in a way which will convince the public."

One New York patient represents the new species of sophisticates who insists on full information and is not adverse to putting a doctor through a medical third degree. "If the doctor does not treat me as an intelligent human being I just discharge him," he states. Atherton Bean, president of the Board of Carleton College, visualizes a not-too-distant time when this medically sophisticated patient will be typical. "You will not be able to treat my grandson with that superior air that implies that he does not know anything medical," says Mr. Bean. "If you try to obscure your ignorance or your indecision with elaborate phraseology, he will find you out," because, he adds, "he will either understand you and recognize the ignorance and indecision, or he will demand a simpler explanation and learn it then."

Industrialist Bean warned a group of doctors-in-the-making that it will be upsetting to "the traditional doctor-patient relationship to have your medical judgments—I repeat, your medical judgments —challenged not merely by your peers but by your patients. But I think in the long run it will be a good thing."

An unpublicized report of the Committee on Medical Practices of the American Medical Association, chaired by West Coast physician Dr. Stanley R. Truman, echoed this sentiment in an uncommonly frank AMA document, which (not surprisingly) was published in *Northwest Medicine* rather than in *JAMA,* the AMA's own journal. "For one thing," says the report, "the American Medical Association is well aware that patients regret deeply the loss of personal element in doctor-patient relations."

This critical, unpublicized Truman Report interviewed hundreds of doctors and patients. It warns that the medical habits of lack of frankness, of claiming near-infallibility and of not admitting limitations or ignorance are dangerous to the profession and to the doctor-patient relationship. "He [the doctor] thinks that in order to keep his patient's confidence he must live up to a superman role, and build the illusion that medicine is an exact science and doctors infallible," says the bold report. "If the profession permits itself to slip into a belief that all patients have to have their doctors appear infallible—and their drugs 'wonder' and their cures 'miraculous' and their operations 'lifesaving'—they are placing themselves in a vulnerable position because they cannot deliver the goods."

The Truman Report describes the all-too-recognizable doctor who will invent, falter, hedge or lie, but will never admit his ignorance to the patient. "The doctor who says, 'If you tell them you don't know, they lose faith in you,' is not looking far enough ahead," say the AMA committeemen. "He forgets that if you don't tell them and they find out, they not only lose faith; they are disillusioned and even vindictive."

The doctor's God-complex and his reluctance to admit any failings prompted one physician interviewed by the AMA committee to state that most doctors can't handle the role of *Übermensch*. "I have often thought, in connection with this, that while the patient is somewhat to blame for this attitude, the medical professional is more to blame for it. They have set themselves up as being superhuman but they have not taken the trouble to screen their people well enough to admit to practice only those capable of handling such situations." One disillusioned patient, quoted by the AMA committee on the doctor's Olympian pretensions, was much ruder: "They pass themselves off as being a part of a loftier profession . . . Other endeavors—where there is just as much service given—give it with more understanding and plain honesty."

Playing the patronizing *Übermensch* is one of the subtlest aspects of doctor manipulation of patients, a near-game skillfully engaged in by many practitioners. The goal of the *jeu* is to keep patients ever so faintly off-center, sufficiently askew to remind them that the physician is master of the doctor-patient relationship. As the patient becomes more educated, he keeps abreast—albeit superficially—with medical news and thus presents a greater challenge. One physician, a busy general practitioner in a lower-middle-income suburb, maintains a facile upper hand by refusing to practice in an upper-middle-class area. "The kind of patient you get in those sections thinks he knows as much as I do," the doctor complains. "Here I'm the boss. I'll tell the patients what I think, and I get no arguments."

Among the upper-middle and middle class, where the college-educated patient is the norm, the physician faces his greatest test of patient-squelching. Satirist Stephen Potter, who coined the combative term "upmanship," describes some of the clever ploys used by physicians, and the patient counter-ploys, in his essay on "Doctorship."

Potter, in a critical sense, is intrigued by physicians and their "one-upmanship" methodology, much of which, he contends, is aimed at making the patient the fool. "Above all professions," states the British humorist, "except perhaps that of the expert in commercial law, the Box Office manager, and the man whose special job it is to advise people about having their cars decarbonized, doctors have shown themselves to be apt and natural Lifemen, and their careers are built on a well-sprung framework of ploys and gambiting."

The patient is the perfect foil, says Potter, because of his natural "one-downness," which is magnificently accentuated by the skilled physician. In answering the phone, for example, the doctor can use a "paralysingly brisk voice" to "suggest that Doctor is busier than Patient in normal life, and in a more important way." Even the failure to listen to the patient—a commonly observed phenomenon that has been considered sheer neglect—is premeditated, says the upmanship scholar. "Doctor may, *under certain circumstances,* ask Patient his symptoms," says Potter. "But he will let it be seen that he is not listening to what Patient is saying, and may place his hand on Patient's wrist, or, better, stomach, as if to suggest that he as Doctor can tell more through the sensitive tip of one finger than from listening to the layman's self-deceiving, ill-observed, and hysterically redundant *impressions* of what is wrong with him."

The patient is not without counsel. Potter catalogues a list of patient counter-ploys, including the traditional gambit: "Would [he] mind bringing in another opinion?" If the physician hints that the patient is not really sick and asks if the symptoms have a "psychological basis," Potter suggests a cutting retort: "I had no idea that was one of your subjects. I have always wanted a good psychotherapist." If Doctor stammers that he is not really a trained psychiatrist, says Potter, the patient should ignore his humility and insist that he will send all his troubled friends to him.

The necessity of ploys, of upmanship on either side, is an unfortunate truth, an accelerating failing in communication between patient and doctor. One of the most destructive failings is the lack of phone follow-up of sick patients, a courtesy and medical caution that seems beneath many prideful doctors. Physicians too often assume that the patient is in a position to determine his own condition and medical needs; that the patient would call him if the situation warranted it. "Phone follow-up of patients is almost never done today," a young internist-researcher in New York comments. "But if I open a medical practice of my own, I intend to have a rotating card file of all my patients. If a sick person doesn't call me within a specified time, I intend to call him."

The ranks of critical physicians who consider much of modern doctoring an impersonal, episodic affair are multiplying. Medical educator Dr. Lester J. Evans makes a call for a "new dimension" for the M.D. which would make it more than just a license to practice, and which would prepare the medical student for "his primary task of human service" rather than that of just a technician. The medical student today, he stresses, lives in "a predominantly biological setting which, unfortunately, often lacks the human aspect."

The failure of the human aspect of medicine is a bleeding wound to the sensitive physician, and he describes it, laments it, analyzes it and even tries to wish it away. Dr. Zale Yanof, in *JAMA,* writes sensitively and eloquently of the need for the "personal physician," the almost nonexistent expert in the art of close, comprehensive medical care. *JAMA* supports the premise, if almost acknowledging that it is a hopelesss one in today's overcommercialized, detached medicine. "The words 'personal physician' are appealing and thoroughly descriptive in a time when physicians are under attack— justly or unjustly—for failure to provide sufficient comprehensive and continuing responsibility for their patients," the *Journal* says longingly. "We would welcome their re-entry into our vocabulary and ranks."

Motivational researcher Dr. Ernest Dichter has asked: "How can we make the patient love his doctor?" His question is left unanswered by the medical profession intent on developing increasingly dehumanized methods. Can the patient love the physician who finds it inefficient to talk to his patients, boasting in a popular medical publication: "I Let My Tape Machine Do The Talking"? This internist saves the time of repeating instructions for such patients as diabetics who need instruction on diets and blood-sugar levels, coronary patients who need tutoring in the use of anticoagulants. The enterprising doctor puts the patient in a room with a tape machine and turns on the prerecorded "doctor," while he leaves to handle another patient. "Do the patients object to this automation?" he asks. His answer of "no" is a signal compliment to the "practice management" of the modern doctor and the spineless nature of his supine patient.

"The practical arts of medicine are nourished by altruism," says astute philosopher Dr. William Bennett Bean of the State University of Iowa. Altruism, expressed either in selflessness or devotion to

Sir William Osler's magic word, "Work," is not often used to describe today's physician. The self-centered doctor is surely today's child, an offspring who might find it taxing to fulfill that portion of the Declaration of Geneva, a doctor oath developed by the World Medical Association, which states: "I solemnly pledge myself . . . the health of my patient will be my first consideration."

Certain modern medical practices are making the Geneva oath a hollow document. In fact, the modern doctor's failure to disguise that *his* self-interest is now paramount in the doctor-patient relationship is no longer even shocking or hidden. One physician queries a medical-magazine consultant: "I'm plagued by a patient who won't pay for past services but continues to come in for treatment. Can I refuse to treat him?" The pragmatic American doctor might do well to absorb the warning of enlightened management consultant Horace Cotton. "Once a patient suspects that you're more interested in your own well-being than in his well-being," he writes, "you can be sure you've gone too far in your practice management."

In some cases, as Dr. Herbert Ratner of the Stritch School of Medicine indicates, this failure of medical idealism is manifested by the "veterinarian" approach—treating men as if they were goats. "If modern medicine is to make its contribution to the preservation of civilization and if it is to be characterized as a profession and not a trade," he warns, "it must reorient itself to the common good of mankind rather than to the self-good and glorification of the physician . . ."

Critical doctors recognize this loss of idealism; some attributing it, perhaps as a rationalization, to a national spiritual anemia. One knowledgeable physician, an East Side Manhattan internist agrees, but warns that this is less than an exoneration. "I'm afraid we're living in a world where no one cares as much any more about the things that used to be important in life," says this doctor. "It is just as true of the lawyer and the teacher as it is of the doctor. The only difference, and it's a vital one, is that the doctor's responsibility to life is much greater. I'm afraid that some doctors don't understand that distinction."

The distinction is apparently being recognized less each year. As the physician strives for a "normal" existence through modern practice management, he resents the time away from family, children, investments, friends, leisure and hobbies—an estrangement from traditional dedication that no longer even embarrasses him. A "Special Report on New York Doctors" published by Blue Shield features a day with a suburban general practitioner, in which the doctor candidly states: "I hate the phone" and "What I resent is the time I have to take away from my family . . ."

The doctor who has mastered modern medical practices and stifled his idealism can actually find the patient an intrusion, a commodity that is, unfortunately, necessary to maintain his business. To him, as one commentator ironically states, the best patients are "inert, anesthetized, or even dead." In such a state, the patient can neither chafe at the doctor nor worry him, nor demand, nor probe, nor challenge. Perhaps only then will the doctor-patient relationship have achieved the modern physician's concept of sociological perfection.

The patient too has a Utopian if uncrystallized concept of what this relationship should be. Converting today's doctor into this patient wish, however, would require a forceful counterrevolution against the form and spirit of modern medical practice. It would demand a frustrated-patient uprising, one that the overconfident physician obviously has no intention of permitting.

Chapter IV

The Doctor
As a Scientist:
The Fallacies of Doctor Erudition

It has been difficult for most Americans to direct their wrath at physicians for any failing in personal attitude or lack of anticipated empathy or warmth, for it has seemed only reasonable to apply different criteria to the trained "scientist." In the folk culture of science, a wide variance of behavior and manner is permitted the practitioner of the provable, for his wizardry depends not on his relation to his fellow man but to his command of the finite truths of his discipline. By logical extrapolation, the modern doctor is sustained by his reputation (oft self-proclaimed) as a "scientist" educated in the calculable truths of cytology, biology, immunology, anatomy, statistics, chemotherapy and bacteriology.

The theory of the contemporary scientist-doctor is an attractive one, both for the grateful recipients of his scientific salve and for the doctor himself. In an era of false sociological, psychological and political messiahs, how much better to feel the strong underpinnings of measurable fact, and sell and buy that hard commodity in the market place rather than pious and ephemeral speculations.

The image of this meticulous science worker, the clinical Martin Arrowsmith, is carefully sustained by professional propaganda, and by and large, has been successfully implanted in the mind of the patient public. There is little doubt that the revolution in scientific education of the doctor accomplished by the Abraham Flexner report of 1910 has produced a new, mutant physician, more conversant with the theory and parlance of the sciences—from the DNA of biogenetics to the "chi square" of statistical significance. There need be no speculation about the possibilities for scientific method within the medical profession, especially in the research complexes of giant universities.

The leap from esoteric research to the habits of the American physician, however, is a philosophical arabesque that has been accomplished with considerably more style than substance. Increasingly, the well-hued portrait of the American physician as an impeccably trained, disciplined scientist faultlessly prescribing the biological truths of modern medicine is being revealed as an almost artless pencil caricature.

Skeptical medical voices, aware of the persistent chasm between medical hope and ministrations, are increasingly disappointed in the scientific prowess of the practicing doctor—as a scholar, as a continuing student and as a knowledgeable interested party in a still greatly unfulfilled medico-scientific revolution. He has more scientific therapy at his disposal than the physician of prior generations, but often lacks the scholarship to implement it. Reluctant to improve his knowledge by "keeping up" with significant new knowledge, he is sure of his prejudices and slow to discard them. Often a naïve enthusiast, he can be an impetuous supporter of new and outlandish therapy, which he defends spiritedly until fashion passes it by. Meanwhile, too often the truly scientific of medicine and healing escapes him.

His academic colleague maintains a keener sense of medical intellect, but he too can stray from the bounds of science, especially by his overconcern for personal or institutional medical stardom. Such nondetachment may result in scientific abuse in the form of premature claims or by overuse of flamboyant or unproven therapies.

A massive case history in current anti-knowledge—of extreme medical activity based on ignorance—involves more than a million youthful patients, most under ten years of age. Bedded down in thousands of hospitals, the youngsters will be prepared this year for major surgery. They will be placed under general anesthesia even at the susceptible age of two or three, and have two globular organs—the tonsils—removed by a surgeon's scalpel.

An overwhelming majority of the youngsters will survive this historic tonsillectomy, but upwards of 20 percent will experience postsurgical complications. Some, like an unsuspecting three-year-old on Long Island, will be less fortunate. Examined by a local physician, the youngster fit the classical "textbook" syndrome of enlarged tonsils ostensibly contributing to frequent colds and sore throats. The remedy: their excision. The parents were assured that the surgery was "routine," and the small child underwent the operation, and was returned to his bed. Shortly afterward a generations-old complication presented itself: the child started to hemorrhage. An hour later the hospital called the parents. Their only son was dead.

This tragedy of medical non-science, of macabre doctor non-sense, is inexorably played over again, for years and generations, despite the known result that thousands of well children will have been killed, not by the benign "hypertrophy of the tonsils" but by doctor's ostensible science. The National Health Survey reports 139 deaths from tonsillectomies in one year, while the *Canadian Medical Association Journal,* safely ensconced across the border, reports a greater toll of tonsillectomy death—1805 youngsters in the United States killed by tonsillectomy during a recent five-year period. (Tragically, death is more frequent in the youngest age groups.) An estimate of twenty-thousand child fatalities from tonsillectomy since the turn of the century would probably err on the side of conservatism.

The routine surgical removal of tonsils is one of the modern practitioner's replacements for "bloodletting," one of the irrational medical acts enshrined by time, and such prior "scientists" as Dr. Benjamin Rush of Philadelphia. The Canadian medical journal speaks melancholically about the unnecessary death: "Most of these were normal healthy children who underwent the operation to relieve a self-limiting condition." Children apparently do not die of tonsillitis, but they can, and do, perish from the physician's tonsillectomy.

With the fervor of modern public relations, the medical profession has recently been telling the community that this pharyngeal bloodletting is diminishing. "We don't do tonsillectomies very often today," a physician recently informed a child's parent. The comment is laudable but illusionary, for there is substantial proof that the orgy of pediacide is unabated. The federal figures indicate more than a million tonsillectomies done a year. The Commission on Professional and Hospital Activities which co-ordinates information from 316 hospitals in thirty-nine states shows that, aside from childbirth, removal of tonsils is currently the largest single reason for admission of patients into American hospitals!

"Hypertrophy (enlargement) of tonsils and adenoids," and subsequent tonsillectomy and/or adenoidectomy currently involves 6.67 of all non-maternity patients, or 1,600,000 (rather than the U.S. Government's estimate of 1,063,000) children a year. The killer-tonsillectomy, which takes as many lives as many nationally publicized diseases for which millions are spent seeking a cure, is the generally useless remedy for a condition which experts consider either a nondisease, or a self-limiting condition which corrects itself within a short time. In most cases, the child outgrows the "ailment" or if necessary, it can be safely treated with antibiotics.

To the unknowledgeable physician, the child's enlarged tonsils present an opportunity to awe mother with their "giant" size and the promise of a cold-free or sore-throat-free existence afterward. Their excision may benefit his purse and the parent's insecurity but, says Dr. William B. Bean of the State University of Iowa College of Medicine, it is a dangerous procedure for *tonsillitis*.

In his essay "Surgical Error: Lo The Poor Tonsils!" Dr. Bean chastises the innocent in mind among doctors for the superstition of tonsillectomy, offering several reasons for its ridiculously widespread practice. "(1) Tonsillectomy removes an organ whose function is practically unknown," says Dr. Bean. "Thus neither judge, jury, coroner, fellow physician, or carping patient can say it caused any specific harm or did any good. (2) The turnover is quick. Candidates are readily available. Beds are not cluttered up long. (3) Tonsillectomy can be done for any clinical condition *except* acute tonsillitis which seems to be the only contraindication. In fact, it is best to do it in perfectly healthy people."

Tonsils and adenoids in children do get enlarged, especially during throat infection, which appears to be their normal function in helping to protect the young body. The biology of the tonsils makes their enlargement a temporary manifestation that almost always begs for neglect. By the time the child is twelve, the tonsils begin a spontaneous atrophy and virtually disappear in adulthood. Knowledge of its natural self-limiting enlargement is not a new phenomenon that up-to-date physicians can boast of. In 1885 a pediatrician, Dr. Goodhart, summarized the scientific facts on tonsil hypertrophy for posterity. "It is comparatively seldom that an operation is necessary . . . children generally grow out of it; at fourteen or fifteen years of age the condition ceases to be a disease of any importance," he stated.

Is avoidance of such knowledge eighty years hence the excess of only the undereducated general practitioner? Hardly. The neobiology of modern tonsillar medicine is widespread. Almost half (48 percent) of all tonsillectomies are performed by otolaryngologists (ear, nose and throat specialists), who ostensibly should know better.

The scientific frivolity of doctors in routinely removing "enlarged" tonsils is corroborated by an assistant professor of pediatrics at Babies Hospital in New York. "Enlarged tonsils seems to be a normal state of development and is no reason for tonsillectomy," he points out. "Some follow-up studies seem to show no appreciable difference in colds or sore throats in children with or without their tonsils. I would suggest tonsillectomy only if the tonsils were creating a mechanical difficulty in blocking the child's breathing, or in case of constant middle ear infections that were not easily controlled by antibiotics." Other physicians add the rare conditions of cancer and tuberculosis of the tonsils, quinsy (abscess of the tonsils), and recurring tonsillitis causing convulsions or exacerbation of renal or rheumatic disease, as legitimate reasons for surgery.

Tonsillectomy is proffered by many doctors under the medical cant that it is a miraculous respiratory cure in youngsters. A study by Dr. W. J. E. McKee in Britain shattered this hoary myth. He studied 413 children with recurring respiratory or throat infections, half of whom were advised to have their tonsils and adenoids removed while the other half acted as a "control" group. All the youngsters were checked every two months for a period of two years, and their records compared. The results definitively showed that the T & A removal had no beneficial respiratory effect—that it did not reduce the prevalence of colds, flu, bronchitis or other respiratory illnesses. (Physicians and parents who notice respiratory improvement in children in the years following tonsillectomy are being fooled by a coincidence of nature. Most youngsters get fewer respiratory ailments as they grow older.)

Among this *special minority of infection-prone youngsters,* tonsillectomy did have a slight effect in reducing the number of sore throats, while adenoid removal reduced the number of middle-ear infections—but the benefits were short-lived. By the time the children under study were eight years old, natural immunity had usually developed spontaneously and there was virtually no difference between the groups. (Significantly, the non-tonsillectomized group was left in the care of individual practitioners and not given specified antibiotic therapy.) In children five to seven years of age with recurring sore throats, the advantage of tonsillectomy is so temporary, states the Canadian medical journal, commenting on the McKee study, that "if there is a long waiting list at the local hospital, many of these children will outgrow the need for operation before their turn is reached." In view of "the risk from tonsillectomy and the probability of benefit for little more than a year," the *Journal* concludes, medical treatment is a reasonable alternative.

The McKee report indicates that tonsillectomy can be useful in special cases: children under five who have had three or more infected throats within a year. The surgical price for this possible benefit was substantial: one in four of the children in the study suffered complications, including hemorrhaging in every thirtieth child. Not surprisingly, postoperative complications were twice as common after the combined T & A removal as after adenoidectomy alone. Since adenoid removal itself seemed to provide the protection against otitis media (middle-ear infection), the *CMAJ* was prompted to comment: "It seems clear that tonsillectomy should not be undertaken routinely when only the adenoids need to be removed."

How many special cases are there in which tonsillectomy is a necessary intervention? How many tonsillectomies are surgically

justified? The *CMAJ* uses the term "few." Studying tonsillectomies
performed in one California hospital, the late Dr. Paul Lembcke
of the UCLA Medical School translated that skepticism into statistics. He reported the ratio of superstition to science, the percentage
of unneeded to needed tonsillectomies, as 98 to 2. The 1,600,000
tonsillectomies performed each year might thus be reduced to *32,000,*
with the concomitant saving of young life. If Dr. Lembcke were wrong
by a factor of *twenty,* there would still be one million unneeded tonsillectomies.

Much of the research work on tonsils has been done by British
physicians, one of whom, Dr. J. A. Glover, reminds us that the
enlarged size of the child's tonsils is usually not—as anxious American physicians believe—an indication of "infected tonsils." Neither,
he explains in the *Archives of Disease in Childhood,* can the physician
tell, by looking, that a tonsil is diseased—not by its size, its color,
nor its appearance. The enlarged tonsil the doctor feels compelled to
cut out may just be a sign of "immunological duty well done."

The medical profession's "useless" tonsil may turn out to be
less than vestigial after all, and well worth saving. The immunological
function of the tonsil was noted as early as 1943 by the eminent
British journal *Lancet.* "It now seems probable," they stated in
this neglected editorial, "that the tonsil, by trapping pathogenic
bacteria, not only may act as a front-line guard against infection,
but may also contribute to the production of antibodies specific
against the invading microorganisms." American researchers have
just rediscovered the fact, and advanced the theoretical possibility
that the tonsils may be more vital than even *Lancet* suspected.

Dr. Robert Good, professor of microbiology at the University
of Minnesota, postulates that the tonsils may complement the
thymus in the body's basic immunological work, including protection
against malignancies in the lymphoid system. Others believe it is a
vital side of an immunological triangle composed of the also "vestigial" appendix, the tonsils and the thymus. The non-science of
excision of a child's tonsils at the age of three may hinder his antibody production at thirty.

The doctor's exultation about the curative powers of tonsillectomy
is not an isolated sally against science and sense. Although he will
rapidly embrace any new therapies that seem to be touched with
medical stardust, he will sometimes ignore valued remedies if they
appear mundane, or older than his professional life span. The
present state of the treatment of the pneumonias is a case in point.

The physician entrusted with antibiotics is as awed by its performance as the layman who demands a "shot." In his daily practice
the physician fearlessly sees the common pneumonia strike (3,026,-
000 cases a year). At home or in the hospital he calmly treats the

situation with penicillin, tetracyclines and other antibiotics, or combinations, and can usually observe his patients recover. If he handles fifty cases a year and loses two or three, the "isolated" incidents fail to weaken his faith in his therapy. As any medical plebe knows, antibiotics cure pneumonia.

Unfortunately, the physician knows this catechism of half-truth too well, and his absence of fear in approaching his pneumonia victims is ill-developed science. It may well be one of the reasons why this "conquered" disease—after sixty-five years of warfare—has only fallen from the third to fifth place on the infamous list of major killers. The current toll of 62,650 pneumonia deaths may not cause the medical mind to flinch, but it staggers the nonmedical imagination.

Much of the scientific information about pneumonia is known to medicine, but evidence indicates that it is often scrupulously avoided by many medical practitioners. Pneumonia is caused by a variety of agents: viruses, microorganisms such as Mycoplasma pneumoniae or Eaton agent (a PPLO, or pleuropneumonia-like organism), and various bacteria, including staphylococcus and E. coli as well as pneumococcus, a versatile and onerous bug with a genealogy of several score types.

The pneumococcus is the most common cause of bacterial pneumonia cases, and is reportedly responsible for one quarter to one half of pneumonia deaths. According to medical superstition, simple antibiotic therapy easily destroys this germ. But scientific evidence indicates the contrary—that the pneumococcus can be quite virulent and is often unperturbed by current therapies. Despite antibiotics, it kills an estimated one in eight to one in twenty of its victims, not as a result of "drug resistance" but because of the deadly qualities physicians were confident they had conquered.

Dr. Robert Austrian, now a research professor at the University of Pennsylvania, studied 454 cases of pneumococcal pneumonia with bacteremia (bacteria in the blood) at Downstate Medical Center in Brooklyn. Eighty-nine died, even though 437 were on antibiotic therapy, the great majority on penicillin. In all cases the pneumococcus was typed beforehand (from 1 to 72), a generations-old procedure that the "scientific" modern doctor usually ignores. "Regrettably," says Dr. Hobart A. Reimann, another pneumonia authority, "type determination, so helpful in diagnosis, prognosis and epidemiology, largely is abandoned."

Dr. Austrian showed in his studies that six pneumococcus types —1, 3, 4, 7, 8, 12—produced 60 percent of all deaths. Type 3 is the virulent killer, causing death in approximately 20 percent of all those it attacks despite the most modern antibiotic therapy. In fact, says Austrian, "the data suggests that antimicrobial therapy has little or no effect upon the outcome of the infection among those destined, at the onset of illness, to die within five days."

Criticism of modern pneumonia treatment has paradoxically been increasing simultaneously with practicing doctor confidence in his current techniques. Dr. Donald B. Louria of Cornell University Medical School has shown that instead of massive antibiotic doses, often given to patients in mixtures (penicillin, chloramphenicol, tetracycline, etc.), the *smallest possible dose of a single well-chosen antibiotic* is usually the most effective, in both treatment of respiratory disease and the prevention of modern superinfection.

A most revealing study of current doctor "errors and hazards" in pneumonia treatment has been compiled by Dr. Jonas A. Schulman and colleagues at the University of Washington School of Medicine in Seattle. The study reveals several doctor failings, including inadequate diagnosis of the pneumonia, improper use of antibiotics, and overreliance on them as the sole therapeutic methods. Rather than the modern propensity to give an indiscriminate "shot," learning the cause of the pneumonia is essential to treatment. "The importance of making an etiologic diagnosis rapidly cannot be over-emphasized," states Dr. Schulman.

Diagnosis of which agent is causing the pneumonia is generally made by analyzing the patient's coughed-up (samples from the throat containing saliva are misleading) sputum, a technique which few physicians seem to master. "The frequency with which the etiologic agent is missed on Gram smears of sputum" is a major error in the handling of bacterial pneumonia, the candid physicians comment in the *Annals of Internal Medicine. "Although the problem of a misinterpreted sputum smear is infrequently raised, at the King County Hospital the majority of patients with Gram-negative pneumonias have had their initial sputum smear misinterpreted by competent, conscientious physicians* [italics mine]."

Only by identifying the bacteria responsible is an intelligent choice of antibiotic possible. The properly diagnosed "resistant" staphylococcus pneumonia, for example, can best be treated with the new resistant-staph fighters, such as oxacillin and methicillin, rather than with the traditional penicillin. A typical mistake of a misread pneumonia made by these "competent" physicians is described by the Washington doctors. A fifty-two-year-old woman was admitted with shaking chills and severe cyanosis (insufficient oxygen in the blood causing blueness on the lips and extremities). Chest X-ray showed pneumonia in both lungs. A sputum smear was taken, which supposedly revealed only "normal flora." Based on that information, the patient was treated with penicillin-G, but her "condition deteriorated rapidly." *Two days later* the error was found. Proper interpretation of a smear showed the bacterial villain to be *H. influenzae,* a Gram-negative bacterium. "After administration of tetracycline the patient rapidly improved," state the authors.

Choosing and using the right antibiotic can be lifesaving, but the modern doctor may too often imperiously reject other pneumonia remedies as "old-fashioned." Prior to the antibiotic revolution, the physician could only labor to improve the pneumonia patient's breathing, and to clear his lungs and respiratory tract as well as possible. Today, say critics, this *sound* therapy is often ignored, and the mechanical aspects of pneumonia therapy, such as drainage, may be needlessly forsaken. "In addition to appropriate antibiotics, therapy in sick patients with pneumonias must include adequate ventilation, drainage of secretions, and correction of other factors . . ." the Washington doctor-critics stress.

Modern physicians may also be overlooking the most scientific of all pneumonia treatments, one prominent researcher believes. Dr. Robert Austrian, in both interview and medical journals, states that between ten thousand and twenty thousand pneumonia deaths a year caused by antibiotic-intractable pneumococci may be needless. This loss of life, especially in the high-risk over-50 group, may be a sacrifice to the doctors' indifference to pneumonia preventatives.

A vaccine against several major types of pneumococci has already been developed, but has been ignored by the antibiotic-mesmerized physicians. "A sizable body of data has been developed which points to the efficiency of vaccination with pneumococcal capsular polysaccharides as a means of preventing pneumococcal infection," says Dr. Austrian. "Vaccines of this type were available commercially after World War II, but were not used widely because of misconceptions about pneumococcal infections resulting from failure to study them adequately. As a consequence they were withdrawn from the market."

The basic research on the pneumonia vaccine was accomplished at an Air Force base during World War II, where inoculated soldiers were effectively protected against various types of pneumococcal pneumonia. A subsequent study on 5750 subjects, most of them over fifty, published in *Archives of Internal Medicine,* substantiated the effectiveness of a vaccine at approximately 90 percent, a performance that ranks with the Salk polio vaccine. Modern-physician attitude has unfortunately made the statistic a wasted academic correlation.

"A vaccine to prevent the pneumococcal pneumonia caused by the half dozen most common types is practical right now," Dr. Austrian stated during an interview, "and I'm hopeful that a drug firm will try again within a year or so." Not every observer shares Dr. Austrian's optimism about the number of lives that can be saved, even though the prior studies seem to support his critical viewpoint. But in any event, the physician who with disdain waved aside the available vaccine in the late 1940's as he reached for a hypodermic to treat a dying Type 3 pneumococcus victim with often ineffective antibiotics, may have thwarted science in pneumonia treatment for a generation. More telling, a quarter of a million patients may have perished needlessly through this lack of doctor perception.

Those seeking a pattern of doctor failure in scientific erudition and performance will have to adjust to less than sociological perfection and settle for the physician's random unpredictability. While the doctor's excessive belief in penicillin may have deterred specific pneumonia therapies, his massive withholding of the antibiotic has caused ill-needed mayhem in the prophylactic treatment of rheumatic heart disease.

The non-science involved in the failure of doctors to diagnose "strep throat" has already been demonstrated, a lapse of erudition that has resulted in failure to administer ten successive days of penicillin which can ward off rheumatic fever. That debacle has still another unworthy chapter, one whose origins are difficult to decipher. The group A beta-hemolytic streptococci bacteria is the "strep throat" agent that brings on rheumatic fever, then proceeds—by a still unknown method—to attack the heart, damaging the myocardial muscle and the mitral, aortic and other valves that help the heart to pump efficiently. The damage done is called rheumatic heart disease, a victory of doctor non-science that permanently afflicts over 1,200,000 Americans and kills 16,000 a year.

Faced with the first attack of rheumatic fever, the scientific physician can do more than wring his hands and comfort the apprehensive parent. "Rheumatic heart disease can be eradicated," states an editorial in *Michigan Medicine,* adding that it requires "physician education." The child that survives the first attack of rheumatic fever—and most do—can be effectively treated against future damaging attacks, to which he is susceptible. If he is placed on regular prophylaxis, the chances of warding off crippling heart disease are excellent.

It has been known for some time that daily oral doses of penicillin, maintained until the youngster is twenty-one, are reasonably effective in preventing subsequent "strep throats" and heart damage. A monthly injection with benzathine penicillin (Bicillin) has recently been reported both more effective and practical. At Irvington House, a children's heart institution, Dr. Alvan Feinstein conducted a survey on acute rheumatic fever patients, aged five to sixteen years, which showed that while the oral penicillin was quite valuable, monthly injections were a superior barrier to future attacks.

In evaluating the scientific acumen of the modern doctor, should he be judged by how speedily he has implemented this new regimen? This might be a harsh, presumptuous indictment of those physicians cautious in accepting new remedies. A more accurate standard would be to establish what percentage of physicians have placed youngsters with a history of rheumatic fever on heart-saving antibacterial prophylaxis of any type.

This has been done and the result is a seemingly improbable statistic of medical negligence or ignorance, neither expected from the doctor-scientist. Dr. Michael DeBakey, chairman of the President's Commission on Heart Disease, Cancer and Stroke, gave the answer in his initial report to the President, compiled after sixty-five hearings. Does the scientific prophylaxis-treatment rate approach 100 percent? Do half the physicians use this proven methodology? Under the heading "Unnecessary suffering and death," the DeBakey group made their educated and shocking estimate: *Only one in twenty children who had suffered rheumatic fever attacks were receiving antibiotic prophylaxis to prevent subsequent attacks and heart damage!*

This avoidance of proven scientific therapy is not an isolated incident; there are innumerable examples of the failure of erudition in the medical community. Despite the existence of a toxoid that is almost 100 percent preventive against tetanus, for example, the ugly "lockjaw" continues to kill—an incomprehensible failure in scientific proficiency. World War II was a giant field trial for the ten million immunized soldiers who developed almost as many minor and major injuries, yet contracted fewer than twenty cases of tetanus. The current failure is due to the doctor's neglect to immunize his patients, a shortcoming that was only recently inventoried by a spot check of 465 Army recruits from various sections of the country. The results revealed our national susceptibility: *43.4 percent of the men were unprotected* against tetanus.

The organism *Clostridium tetani* is invaluable to man in its natural earth habitat, where it converts organic waste into fertile soil material. Festering in a wound of man, however, it is a punishing evil. Hippocrates, 2300 years ago, spoke of the master of a ship who had mashed his right index finger with the anchor: "Seven days later a somewhat foul discharge appeared; then trouble with his tongue . . . his jaws became pressed together; his teeth locked . . . on the third day opisthotonos occurred with sweating . . . six days later he died."

This same calamity still befalls hundreds of Americans each year, 60 percent of whom die despite every combination of medical therapy. In a typical recent year, the death toll was 256. Paradoxically, the therapy often given an injured person to block potential tetanus creates equally ghastly morbidity and further death.

The failure is the end product of illogical medical thought. If the person has a history of prior tetanus immunization, a safe "toxoid" booster shot given soon after injury is sufficient to prevent tetanus.

But since immunization by physicians is spotty, many physicians assume nonimmunization and administer horse tetanus "antitoxin," a fierce biologic that makes approximately one person in ten ill with serum sickness. More than one million such antitoxin shots are given each year, and according to the late Dr. Champ Lyons of Birmingham, Alabama, twenty-five thousand people are hospitalized each year with the aftereffects of tetanus antitoxin, which can include rash, fever and even a form of palsy. The ultimate result is several hundred more deaths caused by the antitoxin, a toll as great as that of tetanus itself.

The medical profession is abstractly aware of the irrational situation they have created: of underimmunization and subsequent overtreatment. The AMA and the American Academy of General Practice have instituted "drives" to convince physicians to immunize all their patients and administer occasional boosters over a patient's lifetime. The campaigns have had no discernible effect. The neglect has its occult origins in the physician's nonscientific psyche: when seeing a patient for another ailment, he assumes that the patient *has had his tetanus toxoid immunization*. When the same person presents himself with a tetanus-potential wound, the same doctor then assumes the opposite: that the patient *does not have his immunization*. He must then tardily protect him, not with the safe toxoid booster, but with the terrifying, sometimes fatal horse antitoxin. (Fortunately, a new human antitoxin has been developed which, although expensive and in limited supply, has proven to be considerably safer than the horse biologic.)

In good pediatric practice, young children receive tetanus immunization routinely; much of the lag is in protection of older children and adults. Dr. Geoffrey Edsall of the Harvard School of Public Health advises that adults be given a whole series of tetanus toxoid injections and a booster immunization every five years.

Proper tetanus immunization is simple: two injections a few weeks apart followed by a third shot six months to a year later. Research indicates that boosters may last ten to twenty years each, but for safety, physicians should give adults boosters as per Dr. Edsall's suggestion.

The blessings of general immunization cannot be overstated, and neither can doctor neglect of inoculation, and ignorance of its subtleties. A Bureau of Census survey reveals that four million children under five have not received a single injection against diphtheria or whooping cough. A survey of thirty thousand first grade Pennsylvania children showed that only 39 percent were completely protected. Although vanquished as a mass danger, diphtheria strikes over four hundred of these nonimmunized children a year.

The whooping cough incidence of *seventeen thousand cases a year* is a graphic and massive testimonial to doctor scientific inadequacy. Widely administered by many physicians, *it is often given to young infants too late!* Dr. James L. Goddard, then of the U. S. Communicable Disease Center, places the blame on individual doctor ignorance. "Because there is no maternal transfer of antibodies and because pertussis [whooping cough] is such a threat to the young infant, it has been recommended that immunization begin as early in life as six weeks," he explains in *JAMA*. "This has been accepted as a pediatric principle, but analysis of survey results in several communities across the country indicates that this is not happening. Too often immunizations are started at six months rather than six weeks, and most deaths from whooping cough in the past three years have occurred under the age of six months."

Failure of doctor erudition is perhaps nowhere as pronounced as in the current fiasco of tuberculosis control. The modern physician, in a plethora of non-thought, has virtually paralyzed himself in this area, leaving the harvest of ten thousand lives annually to the tuberculosis bacilli. It is unquestionably our most deadly contemporary communicable disease.

There are two approaches to blunting the disease which annually strikes fifty-five thousand Americans—including many relapses from prior TB infections. One is detection and treatment, the other prevention. Twenty million preschool children, thirty-seven million school children ages five to fourteen can be tested with the Mantoux or tine test—tuberculin skin tests which indicate if the body contains an active tuberculosis infection or has harbored one in the past. (The concentration on young people is due to the smaller percentage of "positive" reactions, and the hope of detecting TB cases at earliest opportunity.)

Those with "positive" reactions require detailed chest X-rays and sputum analysis, and may need to be placed on a daily long-term prophylaxis of chemotherapy (isoniazid, etc.) to prevent the infection from flaring up. Those with active tuberculosis are given full chemotherapy (isoniazid, PAS and streptomycin) until the condition is alleviated. With the present inadequate implementation of detection, however, three fourths of newly found cases are advanced; many are incurable. Critics of this control route consider the amount of testing, plus annual retests, a too-mammoth task. They also shudder at the number of people who might require preventive chemotherapy to hold the infection in check, and the difficulty of assuring daily intake of antibacterials in the low-income areas, where TB flourishes.

A second and possibly concurrent approach involves *immunization* with BCG (Bacille Calmette Guerin), a highly debated vaccine which is reported to be 80 percent effective in preventing tuberculosis for a period of at least five years. The vaccine has been used in other nations and has had sporadic tests here. There is opposition to the BCG vaccine in some medical circles because it ostensibly voids the tuberculin skin test among the vaccinated, and because its permanent value is unproven.

Countercritics deny both charges. Recent test vaccination of four groups in the Chicago area with BCG, reports Dr. Roy Rosenthal of the Institute for Tuberculosis Research of the University of Illinois, *has resulted in a 75 to 100 percent reduction in the disease incidence.* The rate was cut 100 percent as compared to nonvaccinated persons in certain areas of the city, and was almost as effective—75 to 80 percent reduction—in crowded slum areas, where tuberculosis is most rampant. The opposition to BCG as a biologic despoiler of the tuberculin skin test is denied by Dr. William R. Barclay, recent president of the American Thoracic Society (medical section of the National Tuberculosis Association), who says that the assumption "is not valid."

Dr. Barclay is one of many proponents of BCG as one of the important answers to eventual tuberculosis eradication. Citing that Chicago alone had three thousand new TB cases and three hundred deaths in a recent year, he states: "It's the height of idiocy to subject children to polio and smallpox vaccination and ignore tuberculosis." BCG, he adds, "is a well-developed technique; the research has been done; the vaccine is standardized, safe, effective, and available." The National Health Education Committee concurs, reporting that since 1952, when isoniazid was introduced, TB cases have only dropped from 109,837 a year to 54,381 a decade later; polio vaccine, meanwhile, cut the polio incidence from 57,679 to 910 during the same period. Had BCG been as widely used, says Mrs. Albert T. Lasker, the committee chairman, the TB incidence might have been cut by 80 percent.

The National Tuberculosis Association recently recommended BCG *only* for certain tuberculin-negative persons in high-risk (congested) areas, especially young people. Unlike Dr. Barclay, they feel that BCG does harm the tuberculosis skin test, which they feel should be used on a widespread basis.

The American doctor has heard samplings of both arguments. How does he react scientifically? It can conservatively be stated that most physicians *do not* give annual tuberculin skin tests to patients, *nor* follow up the "positives" with further X-ray and sputum testing, and prophylactic chemotherapy for a year or more. *Nor,* it must be added, does he offer his patients the BCG vaccine. More typically, his policy is one of scientific abdication of the issue, relinquishing it—and its ten thousand yearly deaths—to some future generation's concern. The *American Review of Respiratory Diseases,* in an understated editorial by Dr. Carl Muschenheim, recently summed up the depressing situation among practicing physicians: ". . . tuberculosis has engaged the attention of physicians specializing in internal medicine so much less than its prevalence, its clinical fascination and its scientific interest would seem to indicate."

The recent Presidential inquiry into cerebral "stroke" illustrates another case of scientific knowledge that has been painstakingly avoided by physicians. "Stroke has been a tragically neglected disease," medical rehabilitation expert Dr. Howard A. Rusk reports in the *New York Times*. "The health professions have not been interested in stroke. The public is resigned to the view that nothing can be done. This is not true."

Stroke is a generalized term for cerebral vascular disease—ailments resulting from injury and clots in the blood vessels of the brain. Two million Americans are affected, and the condition took 201,166 lives in 1963 alone. It strikes mostly in the aged, but it also prematurely killed 38,411 victims under sixty-five years of age that same year. Eight out of ten survive the initial stroke, but often in a semi-invalid condition, with loss of speech or memory, ability to walk, and sometimes even loss of control of bodily functions.

The medical neglect is evidenced by the fact, says the report of the President's Commission on Heart Disease, Cancer and Stroke, that "three out of four patients with occlusive stroke have symptoms that forewarn of a disabling attack," symptoms that should bring prompt medical attention. (A national stroke conference estimated that there are nineteen signs and symptoms.) Secondly, the report states, modern rehabilitative care is not being provided by the medical profession even though "as many as 80 percent of stroke survivors" can be brought back to relatively active, near-normal lives.

An estimated nine in ten hemiplegic (one-side paralysis) victims can be taught to walk again, and three in ten can be sufficiently rehabilitated to return to work. "A well-defined and tested program of medical rehabilitation has been developed, which, if started early enough and carried through, can make the difference between total dependency and self-sufficiency," the commission states. "A few such programs are under way, but they are reaching pathetically few of the thousands who can benefit from them." Modern rehabilitation is a complex job which involves not just physiotherapy of the affected arm and leg, but often retraining of the power of speech. Early rehabilitation is preferable, but authorities believe "it is never too late." It is of course hoped that the federal centers to be established by the new legislation resulting from the DeBakey report will be a positive influence in both treatment and doctor education.

Is neglect of the "modern" the typical medical reaction, an antediluvian syndrome in the body medical? Sometimes, yes, but often quite the opposite is true. The contemporary doctor is often a fervid worshiper of the new, the involved, the glamorous, the technique that jogs the doctor out of his daily ennui and conjures up images of miracle medicine, a pleasing imitation of the vivid medical art he sees in television drama. Unfortunately, true medical progress is not the major key to piquing his "scientific" interest. Too often, the "new" must be packaged in tinsel and heralded nationally, capable of stimulating medical corridor conversation more telling than his latest pneumonia case.

Gastric freezing for peptic ulcers, a technique with all the components for doctor excitation, was rushed into use as stomach-defiling therapy by thousands of American doctors. The debacle we have already witnessed has obviously not reached its culmination, as indicated by the comment of a malpractice lawyer who should be knowledgeable about doctor shortcomings. Months after published conclusive evidence showed that the technique was capable of triggering stomach danger, the attorney was boasting to his friends that his minor peptic ulcer was about to be "frozen right in the doctor's office." He complimented his physician for his acumen in "keeping up" with the latest in science.

The tendency to equate the dramatic in medicine with the most curative drains considerable medical energies at all levels. The sizable hospitals and research institutions are not immune: they can be just as susceptible to the items of "scientific" fashion which are often phased out as impetuous exaggerations after a brief medical showing. The hyperbaric oxygen chamber, in which oxygen is available to the body under heavy pressure, was initially heralded as a virtual medical panacea for dozens of diseases. Although large installations were made at great cost, hyperbaric therapy is now being slowly "depressurized" after a period of promise, much of it apparently false.

Reports from Holland indicating cures in rare gas-gangrene cases prompted American interest in the therapy of high-pressure rooms. In hyperbaric oxygen, the patient is placed in a steel chamber, or walk-in room, where the pressure is adjusted to two to four times the normal atmosphere, a condition similar to that found under the sea. In the case of gas gangrene, the anerobic (non-air-using) bacteria causing the ailment yielded to the oxygen forced into the patient's blood by the high-pressure situation. Within a short time the complex hyperbaric oxygen chambers that could hold an entire surgical team—and looking not unlike massive diving bells—were being swung into place in a dozen American medical institutions. Medical personnel were examined to see if their constitutions could stand the strain of working at 2 or 3 "atmospheres."

The early enthusiasm was limitless. Research papers poured forth from these chambers with claims of superior therapy: in curing tetanus, prevention of amputations, superior survival in almost every phase of surgery. A symposium on "H.P.O." drew a "standing room only" response from intrigued physicians in New York. As is often the cycle with premature scientism, the reactions now setting in among many medical researchers are as critical, and subtly biting, as was the original acceptance.

Dr. William F. Bernhard, clinical associate in surgery at Harvard Medical School, sums up the current disconsolate opinion. "Although logic dictates that many pathologic processes characterized by diffuse tissue hypoxia should be benefitted by hyperbaric oxygen ventilation, little scientific evidence supports such a broad therapeutic concept," says Dr. Bernhard in the *New England Journal of Medicine*. "It is evident from a complexity of factors necessary to maintain normal tissue homeostasis, that sweeping clinical recommendations for hyperbaric oxygen therapy are neither possible nor appropriate at this time."

Dr. Robert E. Smith, chief of anesthesia at Children's Hospital Medical Center in Boston, concurs. "There are very few areas where anything definitely good can be said about hyperbaric oxygenation," he states. He lists the areas where premature claims were followed by disappointment. Follow-up studies have failed to confirm value of H.P.O. in tetanus, shock, severe cerebral oxygen starvation following cardiac arrest, vascular diseases or hyaline membrane disease in premature children.

The news of a hyperbaric "cure" of tetanus was reported in *JAMA* after experimenters at St. James Hospital in Chicago saved all nine stricken patients. According to other researchers, this experiment is an isolated bright incident in a still-bleak situation. "No one else has been able to get similar results on tetanus," Dr. Smith stated when interviewed. "Most of the experience has been quite unsuccessful. By and large, we've pretty much given it up." Dr. John Adriani, head of anesthesiology at Tulane University School of Medicine, is equally skeptical. "I personally do not think that excessive oxygen has any beneficial effect on these [tetanus] patients."

The hyperbaric program, for all its flamboyant early claims, should not be totally discontinued, Dr. Smith stresses in Boston, but should be tempered with realistic, scientific appraisal. The bulky spacelike chambers have helped in controlling cases of gas gangrene, and according to Children's Hospital claims, have been valuable in improving the survival rate in children undergoing heart surgery.

Other critics stress the unknown dangers to a human body—patient and personnel—subjected to high pressure for a considerable time. Dr. Charles B. Pittinger of the University of Tennessee School of Medicine raises the "profound and unsettled questions concerning oxygen toxicity and the possibility of adverse effects on the central nervous system under conditions of increasing oxygen tension." Dr. Adriani warns of the possible danger to personnel, which could include all the ill effects that befall deep-sea divers. A study at Duke University Medical Center, reported in *JAMA*, confirms that hazard: of fifty-two medical personnel working in chambers, eleven members felt that nitrogen narcosis (popularly known as "rapture of the deep") had caused them to make an error, a potential danger to their hyperbaric patients.

Prominent scientists have been quick to chastise the lay press for their "excitable" treatment of new methods, such as the hyperbaric oxygen chamber. They are justifiably chagrined by the overpublicizing of premature results. Few medical journalists would deny their anxiety to announce important medical discoveries as early and as dramatically as possible. The journalist is often culpable; however, he is usually only the interpreter. The demeanor of his exaggerated report too often reflects the publicity-proneness of many modern doctors.

The accolades awarded men such as Jonas Salk have not been lost on a generation of physician-researchers, many of whom seek the warm spotlight of approbation. The traditional image of the scientist as an absurdly retiring soul who feared personal publicity as damaging to the integrity of his work, is now a spiritual waxwork. Some, of course, struggle against the pressures for public exposure. But despite constant demurs to the contrary, many physicians involved in research—whether university academicians or practicing specialists—have become near-expert in publicity: in quietly but effectively promoting themselves and their work to their colleagues and the public as "ethically" as possible. This tendency is fed by an insatiable public desire for medical "breakthroughs," and is the prime stimulus for premature claims of "cures" that are still experimental or possibly without any value.

"Doctors like to pretend that they are reticent about publicity, but most of them really are not. They enjoy the spotlight," says the former medical editor of a large consumer magazine. "We writers are somewhat at fault, but we couldn't report what we do without the co-operation of physicians. If he has already published a paper on the subject, he will talk freely and will amply supply you with reprints. If the work is still unpublished, some physicians will refuse to talk. But many others will say 'it's still experimental' and they can't talk about it too much. They say they are concerned their colleagues might think they are advertising themselves. But, they often add, if I speak to the hospital or university public relations man, and it's okay with him, they'll co-operate. The hospital PR man's comment? 'Why, by all means!' "

The drive for medical stardom is the stimulus for much premature scientific material. The ancient scientific instinct to eschew personal glorification may still be in the latent consciousness of the doctor, but this medical journalist explains how the more demanding drive for public recognition often wins out, with only the slightest encouragement.

"A lot of medical men look for stardom, but won't admit it," says the experienced medical editor-writer. "When I come to see them, the first thing I hear is: 'I'm a scientist, and I'm not looking for publicity.' I quickly agree, and brush that aside because I know it's not true. I repeat the theme back to them by stating: 'Doctor, you're a scientist, and I know that your major concern is not personal publicity, but that your work is reported accurately.' When I reassure them of my journalistic competence and offer them the right to check my manuscript, this generally achieves the result. They are no longer worried about my distorting their story, and they will receive the publicity they really want."

The swamped desk top of any medical journalist, piled to overabundance with publicity releases from medical schools, hospitals, medical associations, clinics, with dramatic accounts of the activities of their associated physicians, is sufficient proof of the nonreticence of this generation's doctor. Although the doctor is bound by ethics from sending out his own publicity, the John Alden testimonials serve him equally well.

A classic case of medical impetuosity combined with professional superpublicity is the recent tumultuous, but premature, welcome given to organ transplantation. Within limits, the implantation of *artificial* parts within the body can qualify as a legitimate medical miracle. Electric pacemakers placed under the abdominal skin and attached to the heart muscle help maintain regular heartbeats in patients with Stokes-Adams disease; plastic tubes replace worn aortas and other blood vessels; artificial plastic and silicone valves have replaced worn natural heart parts; artificial tubes drain fluids from the brain of a hydrocephalic (water on the brain) child. Even some natural parts have been successfully used in transplantation. Both human and calves' bone material have been used in thousands of bone replacement operations, as have transplanted human corneas in the eyes.

The leap from such replacement parts to the transplantation of entire human organs, may, medical critics contend, be a current joust with the premature. Overwhelmed by the "miracle" results emanating from the surgical suites where kidneys (successfully on some occasions), hearts, lungs, livers (all unsuccessfully) were being transplanted from one human to another or from a cadaver to a living human, the scientific discretion of many physicians has been diluted, even destroyed. In the brouhaha of worldwide attention focused on the transplantation of organs, the simple fact that the work is important experimentally—but basically a therapeutic failure—has been lost on an entranced nation, including both its laymen and physicians.

In a typical case a young lady stricken with chronic renal failure was hooked into the hemodialysis machine, the stainless-steel tank with cellophane guts that serves as an artificial kidney. She was connected at the wrist to the apparatus (invented by a former Dutch physician, Willem Kolff, who brought it to America after World War II) and reclined in bed as the machine pumped her blood through the cavern of transparent tubes and washed out the impurities the defunct kidneys could no longer handle. Twice weekly the machine maintained her life, permitting her a near-normal existence the rest of the week. Her life expectancy on the artificial kidney could not be anticipated, for the technique has only been in continuous use for about six years. Not every dialysis patient (most of whom would otherwise die) survives, but units at the University of Washington in Seattle, Downstate Medical Center in Brooklyn and elsewhere have excellent survival records, including up to six years at the older Seattle unit.

In the hope of a "permanent" solution—a new kidney to replace the old—the young lady was taken off the artificial kidney. She and one of her parents were prepared for simultaneous surgery. Both diseased kidneys were removed from the girl, and a "bed" (a site in the abdomen) was prepared for the donor kidney. It had just been cut out of the parent, who could—unless unforetold circumstances arose—get by with one kidney. The surgery was "successful," and the next day the newly functioning kidney permitted a massive passage of normal urine. To keep the foreign tissue of the parent's kidney from being rejected by the body, she was given immune-suppressive drugs (such as azathioprine) which would lower the body's natural resistance and keep antibodies from rejecting the kidney.

To the probing medical eye, the young lady had been cured by transplant surgery, and for a while she was busy leading a normal life. A few months later she was dead. A typical statement on such deaths—hoping to soften the impact of failure—reads: "At the time of death, the transplanted kidney was still functioning." The death is obviously not a coincidence, and is probably caused by other malfunctions brought on by purposely weakening the body in order to maintain the kidney. The patient was the victim of a poor scientific bargain, expertly rationalized by a press release.

Ever since the miracle of the first transplantation, in 1954, of a kidney from healthy identical twin Ronald Herrick into his fatally ill brother Richard (who had been living intermittently on artificial-kidney therapy) researchers have been hoping to solve the riddle of the individual's rejection of foreign tissue. The identical twin, who survived for nine years, was in a biologic sense the same person as his brother, and such transfer therefore made both theoretical and therapeutic sense. Current attempts to transplant nonidentical kidneys are being made without an acceptable theory of how to keep them from being rejected by most patients.

The results of kidney transplantation are not as optimistic as the enthusiasm of some of the researchers. "In our present state of knowledge this is certainly a highly experimental procedure. It's not therapeutic," is the sobering comment of Dr. Joseph Murray of Peter Bent Brigham Hospital in Boston, a leader in transplant surgery. The latest figures on kidney transplant survival are maintained by the Registry in Human Kidney Transplantation and published in *Transplantation*. The cold statistics on length of life after surgery hardly match the extravagant claims or inferences made for the procedure.

The Registry has compiled a follow-up on 495 patients who had received kidney transplants through September, 1964. Thirty-three were identical twins and were expected to perform reasonably well. Of the total, 307 died: 199 in the first month; fifty-nine more within the next two months; nineteen more between the third and sixth month; and seven before the year end. Of the 462 transplants other than identical twins, there were 298 deaths. The remaining are unfortunately not "successes," but include many new transplants not yet tested by time. Only approximately thirty nonmonozygotic (nonidentical twin) patients have lived for one year or more with a kidney transplant, and only four for more than two years.

(Had they not received transplants, their anticipated survival on the better-established artificial kidney machine is not known, for not every case is adaptable to the machine. Those that are adaptable appear to have an excellent chance for survival. The National Kidney Disease Foundation estimates thousands of more lives could be saved each year with the installation of additional artificial kidneys and more trained personnel.)

Despite this high percentage of failure, medical bewitchment with the concept has accelerated the transplant attempts and spread the interest to institutions throughout the nation. Peter Bent Brigham surgeons have been forced to complain about the traffic of visiting surgeons who expect to learn the process in three days in Boston! Rather than hesitate and re-examine the scientific premise, transplant physicians have expanded into increasingly unscientific activity, including the transfer of organs more complex than kidneys, and of organs of different species into man.

At a hospital in New Orleans a team of doctors took a young married woman off the artificial kidney machine and surgically inserted two kidneys from a twenty-five-pound male rhesus monkey into her body. The event was headlined in the press: "The first reported successful kidney transplantation between animal and a human was announced yesterday by a medical team from Tulane University Medical School." Ten days after the operation the "successful" monkey transplant, now endangering her life, was removed from the patient. In a large Minneapolis institution, a similar attempt was made: a kidney from a male baboon was grafted into a woman. "It worked just beautifully for five days but then, very suddenly, was rejected," the chief surgeon states—as if this were a scientific surprise.

Unsuccessful attempts to transplant livers and lungs, even hearts, have been made, with anticipated body rejection and death. With an unscientific demeanor, transplant surgeons have been issuing unrealistic statements of "double-think" justification for these failures. One patient who received a transplanted liver in Denver died eight days later from pneumonia brought on by the immunosuppressive drugs. Despite this, the surgeons announced almost triumphantly: "The transplanted liver functioned normally until shortly before death." A liver transplant attempt in which the patient died from pneumonia in twenty-two days, drew this macabre optimism from the doctors: "Liver function had improved steadily until shortly before death."

Lung and heart transplants have stimulated the same "upbeat" communiqués, almost as disclaimers of responsibility. After one fatal lung transplant, authorities stated: "The patient died shortly after from an *unrelated* [italics mine] disorder." When a patient died eighteen days after receiving a transplanted lung, a university spokesman stated straight-facedly that they were "entirely satisfied with the lung transplant as such."

This postoperative sophistry has irritated some medical spokesmen, including Dr. J. Russell Elkinton, editor of the *Annals of Internal Medicine*. He believes a distortedly rosy portrait has been drawn of kidney transplants, with success still eluding us because of failure to solve the basic problems of organ rejection. He attacks the false hopes stimulated in patients, and their families, by euphoric statements and publicity in which "the smiling young woman with the transplanted liver was up and about and, by implication, ready to go on living." In contrast, her death notice will be buried ignominiously on the back pages of the newspaper.

Dr. Elkinton includes the physician in his indictment: "The moral responsibility for this unfortunate situation must be shared by the experimenting physicians and surgeons," he states angrily. "To the extent that the referring physician derives his primary medical information from the less critical and nonprofessional press, he is also responsible." (Other critics stress the possible danger to the "donor," both in surgery and afterward, when the absence of a "spare" kidney could prove dangerous.)

The premature monkey-to-man attempts, such as the chimpanzee heart placed in a human body for one hour, also receive just censure. In an understatement, Dr. Elkinton finds that their clinical use "appears to have outstripped the experimental preparations for the procedure." Doctor circumlocution to avoid responsibility for failure makes equally vulnerable targets. "Is it right," Dr. Elkinton asks, "to emphasize that the transplanted kidneys were functioning fully at the time the patient died from a pneumonia that was almost surely contributed to by the requisite immunosuppressive therapy?"

A critical spokesman, Dr. Ralph A. Deterling Jr., chief surgeon at Tufts-New England Medical Center, decries the theatrical braggadocio connected with the work. "I deplore the haste of otherwise responsible institutions and individuals to get into the limelight," Dr. Deterling stated recently. "It's time to call a halt to unwarranted clinical claims."

Unwarranted claims are only one aspect of a neoscientific atmosphere that pervades too large a part of the medical population. The current non-science, where it does exist, nurtures the false impression (immaculately served up to public and patients) that all contemporary medical practices are implicitly "scientific" and based on strict reason rather than hunch, habit or hope—what science refers to as "a priori" information.

From this attractive rationale comes the current pervasive faith in medical science as a supposedly unlimited cupboard of esoteric knowledge that can be freely drawn upon and applied, like a poultice, to *any* situation in need of therapy. This theory tends to create the distorted impression that little is healed by itself, nature is basically secondary, and common sense and health management are outdated concepts. Only the blatant headline on the obituary page, or the ill-considered therapy, or the surgical death or complication visited on friend or relative causes a reflection—even if momentary—on the seeming infallibility of current medical science.

The patient is not the only one gulled by the myth of medical omnipotence. The physician too is a willing foil. He has been mesmerized about the scientific nature of all his regimens and concepts, no matter how ancient, unproven or racked with superstition. Examples are plentiful, from bloodletting to radiation of the thymus to tonsillectomy. When physicians laughed at mothers who put children's burned fingers under the cold-water faucet (now the *scientific* therapy), their useless invocation of butterfat was persuasively served up in the awesome name of science. The current and often crippling drug orgy has been offered up to obliging patients in the same hallowed vein.

The cause and treatment of ulcers are a poignant or, one might say, burning case in point. This acid hole in the stomach or duodenum (the first ten inches of the small intestine) is a commonly recurring ailment of man, one that has been extensively discussed in medical literature since Hippocrates and Galen. It is harbored in the body of several million Americans, hospitalizes over four hundred thousand a year and kills twelve thousand annually. Clichés about it have been ennobled by doctor and patient: it is ostensibly caused by nerves, stress, smoking, bad food, whiskey and evil ways. Its "cures" are legion, from milk diet to complex drugs, antacids, tranquilizers and elaborate surgery, and the willing patient is plied with exotic admixtures of them all.

In actuality, say authorities, science knows little about ulcer etiology or therapy, and the practicing physician knows considerably less. "The remarkable advances made in medicine do not include the cause and cure of peptic ulcer," says Dr. Joseph B. Kirsner of the University of Chicago Medical School. "Treatment continues to be dominated by speculation, insufficient awareness of the 'spontaneous' remissions and exacerbations . . ." Dr. Basil I. Hirschowitz of the Medical College of Alabama underscores the lack of science currently attending ulcer treatment. "Every few months we witness the launching of a new 'cure' for peptic ulcer and daily we are deluged by advertisements claiming miracles for a new drug or a combination of old drugs," he states in *GP*. "Unfortunately, none has stood the test of time and currently there is no cure-all for peptic ulcer."

The internist-professor adds a further skeptical note: "There is no evidence that medical therapy does more than relieve symptoms and allow an ulcer to heal. It does not afford protection against further flare-ups, and the incidence or relapse in patients on a 'good medical regimen' is no lower than that in patients not following such a program." He documents his point with a sample of male ulcer patients treated in a hospital for a full year. They suffered the same recurrence and complication rate five years later as a control group that was hospitalized for less than two weeks.

As sound skeptics—but definitely not medical nihilists—physician-critics are attempting to codify what we know and do not know about ulcers and their treatment. Although they differ somewhat (physicians are generally less agreed on their "scientific" facts than patients are led to believe), they are hoping to bring a more scientific perspective to ulcers. Dr. Kirsner, for one, warns his colleagues: "Insufficient knowledge or disinterest by the physician may lead to ineffective measures or to no treatment."

Fallacies are the mainstays of many a doctor's ulcer therapies. Diet is a prime abused therapy. Physicians are masters at devising occult diets ranging from extracts of soy beans, sweet almonds and anti-ulcer "u" factor to the famed milk therapy. Critics do not deny that certain *individuals* suffering from ulcers find certain foods irritating, but the concept of foods both causing and curing ulcers is apparently scientifically unfounded. "There is no conclusive evidence either implicating coarse or seasoned foods in the development of chronicity of peptic ulcer or demonstrating enhanced healing of peptic ulcer during a soft diet," Dr. Kirsner states emphatically in *JAMA*. (Nothing feeds medical superstition more nutritionally than a miraculous "cure" accomplished by a self-healing ulcer in the presence of an esoteric diet lavishly concocted by the "scientific" practitioner.)

The antacid concept of ulcer therapy probably makes scientific sense, but not in the way critics say it is often administered. Current theory holds that ulcers are created by some unknown process which decreases the stomach and intestinal linings' usually fierce resistance to the normal secretions of hydrochloric acid. While it is true that ulcers can heal in the presence of the acid, pain is relieved and cure facilitated if the acidity is somewhat neutralized, say knowledgeable physicians.

The problem is in current therapeutic methods used by many doctors. Antacid value is limited to its short period of action, Dr. Kirsner states, adding: "Unless taken at frequent intervals for long periods, they can hardly be expected to influence the course of peptic ulcer significantly. The common practice of occasional use of antacids, 'one teaspoon or one tablet after meals' is worthless." Proper antacid therapy, he states, would require the use of a sizable dose *every hour,* preferably in liquid or powdered form, rather than tablets. If nocturnal pain is present, antacid should be taken every two hours during the night. "Truly effective antacid therapy prevents ulcer pain continuously," Dr. Kirsner states, pointing out that "the occurrence of pain, though occasional, signifies an inadequate neutralizing program." (Some studies have shown no proven superiority of popular aluminum and magnesium antacid compounds.)

The ulcer can cure itself, but can also craftily resist man's therapy. Several commentators warn of danger in excessive antacid therapy. If too much alkali is absorbed and the original neutralization point is passed (stomach is temporarily no longer acid), the parietal cells that secrete acid are probably stimulated to begin their work again, "neutralizing" the neutralizing therapy. Excessive intake of alkaline plus milk (more than two quarts of milk a day plus too much bicarbonate or calcium carbonate) can create the milk-alkali syndrome, often more serious than the ulcer itself. Unless caught in time and reversed, this calcification damage to the kidneys may prove fatal, warn medical observers.

For the past several years many doctors were convinced of another "miracle," the use of drugs known as anticholinergics, which decrease the secretion of gastric juices by their effect on the controlling vagus nerve. It may have some value, but like many supposed pharmaceutical boons, this one has apparently not fulfilled its promise. "Prospects for the development of a superior anticholinergic compound capable of suppressing gastric acidity for long periods after oral administration without development of tolerance and with minimal or no side effects seem less favorable today than a decade ago," states Dr. Kirsner.

The prognosis is generally cloudy for specific positive treatment of ulcers. Judging from expressed medical opinion, there is little agreement except on three basic points: the need for rest (in bed during severe attacks); antacid (neither too little nor too much); and frequent, if not sizable, feedings. Beyond these, each therapy has a detractor—a less than satisfactory scientific situation.

Milk, the symbol of a benign ulcer diet prescribed for centuries, appears to be the center of an ulcerogenic storm. In a letter to the *New England Journal of Medicine,* several California physicians, Drs. Rowe, Kahn and Uyeyama, argue that a milk diet in a beginning ulcer can cause an "allergic" flare-up that *aggravates* the intestinal sore. A similar heretical view has been proposed by Dr. S. C. Truelove of Radcliffe Infirmary, Oxford, who found that thirteen of his ulcer patients showed marked improvement as soon as milk was *eliminated* from their diet.

One villain who may have been blasphemed without cause is the "nervous personality," so often blamed by doctors as cause or contributor to ulcers. The "ulcerous" type is so implicit in the folk culture of medicine that it would be naïve to think that science, experiment or skepticism could ever banish it from the medical psyche. Yet several contemporary critics point to "nerves" as being more ulcer mythology than etiology.

Because the vagus nerve of the parasympathetic system stimulates the acid flow of the stomach, physicians have for ages made the casual jump to the idea that "nervous" people make their own ulcers. This bearded concept is now being re-explored and exploded as possible nonsense.

"The view that civilization has brought with it such an increase in general anxiety that it has led to a high incidence of duodenal ulceration is not confirmed on critical examination," states world-famed gastroenterologist Dr. Thomas C. Hunt of St. Mary's Hospital in London and author of the text *Pathophysiology of Peptic Ulcer.* "Many fail to show any correlation between ulcer incidence and stressful situations in a world survey of forty countries."

Dr. Hunt backed his skepticism with his own study of sixty-one duodenal ulcer patients, finding little sustenance for the theory that intestinal holes can be cured with psychotherapy. He found both "neurotics" and "nonneurotics" numbered among the victims, with the stable dominating. Although such measurements are subjective (as is the ulcer-nervousness theory), he regarded only fifteen of the forty-nine male ulcer patients and only four of the twelve women patients as being "neurotic."

Dr. Hirschowitz also dismisses the hoary tale of ulcers as a psychogenic disease. "While much is written about the personality of duodenal ulcer patients, there is no common ground between the successful hard-driving executives who are supposedly characteristic and the poorest workers in India, Nigeria, and other areas who show a great prevalence of duodenal ulcer." The popular tranquilizer-sedative regimen often fed to ulcer patients today probably has a more salutary effect on the anxious doctor. "Neither type of drug [sedatives and tranquilizers] has any pharmacologic effect on the stomach," Dr. Hirschowitz reminds us.

If such medical myths deserve further comment, a statement by a prominent Boston surgeon, Dr. Francis D. Moore, bears repeating: "For the great majority of patients with ulcer at the present time, the only thing that sets him apart from his fellow man, either physiologically or biochemically, is the fact that he does indeed have an ulcer," he writes. "Factors of psychology, adrenocortical function, environmental stress, may all be present in the background, but they exist to an equal degree in other patients who do not have duodenal ulcer."

Although it is difficult to make conclusive "scientific" statements about ulcer therapy, there is a growing medical belief that there has been an excessive and ill-advised history of stomach removal and attendant death and complications connected with its therapy. An examination of medical opinion on ulcer surgery (such as Dr. Claude E. Welch's impressive roundup on abdominal surgery in the *New England Journal of Medicine*) reveals an overwhelming discord between gastroenterologist and surgeon, and even between surgeon and surgeon. Arguments over the science of health are beneficial to the patient. This debate, however, is unsettling, for generations may have suffered from failure of swifter insight.

The classical operation for peptic ulcer has been the subtotal gastrectomy, a three-generation-old indelicate procedure that removes some 50 to 85 percent of the human stomach. The operation has a relatively high mortality, an average of about 2 to 3 percent for elective surgery and 20 percent or more for emergency bleeding ulcers, for an average death rate of 5 to 6 percent. (In good institutions, elective ulcer surgery may be less than 1 percent, but up to 3 percent or more in other hospitals.) Its complications appear to be sizable, and underrated by many doctors. Perhaps most important, after all these years and hundreds of thousands of subjects, its scientific rationale is being challenged.

The traditional signs for ulcer surgery have been scarring obstruction and ulcers—including bleeding ulcers—that do not yield to medical management and are thus considered "intractable." One of the apparent difficulties in deciding on ulcer surgery has been the definition of *intractable*. "I'm afraid that the label of intractability in ulcers is sometimes used improperly by both medical men and surgeons, leading to premature surgery," Dr. Joseph Kirsner stated in a recent interview. "I've had ulcer patients come to me who had been advised that they needed surgery. But I found after treatment that their lack of response was due to inadequate medical management and that surgery was unnecessary. I'd hardly call normal response to inadequate treatment 'intractability.' "

The danger of avoidable error is always present in any ulcer surgery, as indicated by a malpractice judgment for $150,000 against a Midwestern surgeon who improperly connected the patient's stomach to the intestines. The unavoidable dangers are also significant, and the gastrectomy operation has more than its share of complications. After stomach removal, many patients may be ulcer- and symptom-free, but others may first become afflicted with new difficulties including the "dumping syndrome" during and after eating, malnutrition problems, weight loss and even new ulcers.

A fifty-year-old woman who had 70 percent of her stomach removed for a duodenal ulcer, suffered such typical complications. Within two years after her operation she lost 15 percent of her weight and was down to a hundred pounds. (Others have recorded weight loss down to eighty-seven pounds in women five feet five inches in height.) Fifteen minutes after eating, she experienced the distressing dumping syndrome, with episodes of light-headedness, sweating and palpitation, forcing her to lie down. She was classified by physicians as having a 30 percent impairment of activity, more than some and less than others with gastrectomy complications. Other dumping syndrome victims also report nausea, diarrhea, cramps and even stomach distension.

Ulcers actually created after gastrectomy are, say some critics, considerably more common than ebullient physicians believe. Dr. Hirschowitz believes there may be new ulcers involved in one out of every four stomach removals. "In 250 postgastrectomy patients with various complaints seen in the past three years," he says, "no fewer than 60 marginal ulcers were found by fiberscope gastroscopy . . ."

Other surgical surveyors report an even heavier physiological booty extracted by the commonplace stomach resection. A study of 604 consecutive ulcer-surgery patients at the University of Mississippi Medical Center, most of whom had subtotal gastrectomies, was reported in the *American Journal of Surgery*. There were complications in 362, or 60 percent, of the cases: thirty-seven deaths; twenty-nine hemorrhages; fifty-five infections; twenty-nine dumping syndromes; twenty-eight severe cases of malnutrition; ten ulcers; fifty-four pulmonary ailments, among others.

Careful scientific investigation is now raising doubt whether there has not been a superior or safer method of surgically treating ulcers. In a widely discussed classic piece, "Surgery in Search of a Rationale," published in the *American Journal of Surgery,* surgeon Dr. Francis D. Moore of the Harvard Medical School and Peter Bent Brigham Hospital, defines the gastrectomy operation as "crippling." "Surgeons and patients favor rational operations," states Dr. Moore. "The removal of a large segment of grossly and histologically normal stomach for a disease in the proximal duodenum is not only crippling, but wanting in elegance of rationale."

The rationale given for subtotal gastrectomy from its beginnings in the second decade of this century was that it surgically removed the acid-producing cells of the stomach. As recently as 1955, Dr. Moore reports, it was possible to gather a group of young surgeons who would confidently explain that gastrectomy helped duodenal ulcer patients because it removed the "parietal cell-bearing part of that organ and thus 'reduced acidity.'" The fact that this is pure medical mythology has been known since 1915, patiently states Dr. Moore, who then explains the fallacy: "These [acid-producing] cells are in the upper portion of the stomach surrounding the fundus and residing precisely in that part of the stomach left in place in the classic subtotal gastrectomy."

Increasingly, leading surgeons throughout the nation are proposing a more logical surgical procedure for ulcers (when and if necessary). The technique has been receiving increasing attention in the past few years, even though it was first developed in 1923, then promptly forgotten by the profession for a generation. The operation is vagotomy, a much more conservative procedure for ulcers which keeps the stomach intact but selectively cuts the vagus nerves that control the acid secretion in the stomach. Vagotomy is now being done along with either of two other procedures, pyloroplasty and gastrojejunostomy, which help eliminate retention of material in the stomach after the vagus nerves have been sliced. In cases of bleeding ulcers, the bleeding spot is sutured. (Some surgeons prefer vagatomy *plus* antrectomy, which is actually the removal of the lower portion of the stomach.)

The results have been encouraging. Mortality is cut to one-fifth of that resulting from subtotal gastrectomy, and most digestive and nutritional crippling such as the dumping syndrome and malnutrition is eliminated. Like most surgical processes, it has its own host of complications, including a 10–15 percent ulcer-recurrence rate. However, several comparative studies of its safety are overwhelmingly convincing. One in Spokane, Washington, by Dr. C. P. Schlicke, chief of surgery at Rockwood Clinic, shows only two deaths in 228 vagotomy operations as against fourteen deaths in 244 gastrectomies.

Its advantage seems even more dramatic and widely accepted in poor-risk surgical patients and emergency ulcer bleeding, where gastrectomy death is as high as from 20 to 30 percent in the best institutions. At Memorial Hospital in Worcester, Massachusetts, the subtotal gastrectomy operative death rate in emergency cases of massive ulcer bleeding was a typical 26.3 percent—more than one in four patients died. By using the long-forgotten vagotomy (plus pyloroplasty) instead, on the last twenty-eight consecutive cases of emergency ulcer hemorrhage, the death rate has been cut to 3.6 percent—the loss of only one patient! It is painful to ponder how many thousands of lives of bleeding-ulcer victims have been lost during the past forty years.

The history of surgery has been a continuous, if erratic search for a science of tissue repair and removal, to make man's physical intervention in the human body more than a meddling joust with nature. The progress in technique has been estimable, in complex technology and surgical skills that permit six-hour open-heart surgery and deep neurosurgical probes into the brain. The barber-surgeon of the fourteenth century, inferior to the medical doctor of his time, is a long-past image. The modern surgeon epitomizes medicine today, in its most luminous, as both an artist of personal skill and a scientist of methodology.

Within that scientific discipline, misplaced enthusiasm can be the victor over careful study and sense. The generations-long un-examined gastrectomy is a case in point. Equally significant are dramatic operations for which mankind is not, and should not be, ready. For several years, ligation (tying off) of the mammary arteries of the chest was done to cure the pain of a heart condition, angina pectoris. After a flurry of wishfulness, the operation is being discarded as worthless.

Exotic operations, performed on many without proof of their efficacy, are popular surgical phenomena. The pattern of novel surgery begins with an enthusiastic original study, either from here or abroad, which catches medical fancy. The procedure is rapidly adopted and performed on thousands, *after* which a skeptical medical voice, or two, indicates that the fury may not have been worth the storm. This cycle of nonscientific enchantment, then disenchant-ment, is now virtually complete on an operation known as glomectomy, which was developed for the relief of chronic bronchial asthma. In the operation, a rice-size nodule, the carotid body, is removed from either side of the neck. The operation was designed to change the chemoneural responses of breathing to the brain, which are thought to be partially controlled by the carotid bodies.

The original impetus for this new procedure came from Japan when a surgeon, Dr. Komei Nakayama, had removed four thousand of these granules and reported that 80 percent of the asthma patients were cured or improved after six months, with 58 percent maintaining good results after five years. The news sent American surgeons in a frenetic carotid chase, which has resulted in thousands of similar procedures done here.

Although some report that Nakayama was ostensibly correct, many experts believe that the procedure is worthless. Dr. C. Thomas Read, chief of surgery at St. Joseph's Hospital in Phoenix, Arizona, is one of the critical skeptics who would add glomectomy to the pile of surgical discards. "The longer the patients are observed, the less are the number improved," says Dr. Read. "It is apparent that the enthusiast obtains good results from the operation, but the skeptics do not . . . The overwhelming evidence is that it does not do what it purports to do."

At the University of California Center for the Health Sciences three asthma patients were given glomectomies and five received "sham" operations with nothing more than an incision. All the survivors (one patient died) except one thought that the glomectomy "operation" helped them, even though four of them never received it! Perhaps more telling, their physicians judged patients 5, 6 and 7— none of whom had received glomectomies—to be improved after surgery. The general improvement has been attributed to temporary "placebo" benefits of a well-publicized technique. But some of it, stress the study authors, could be due to "increased activeness in management of the patients" that was a side benefit of the study.

Another devastating study of glomectomy, conducted at the Tufts University Lung Station at Boston City Hospital, showed that fifteen consecutive cases of carotid-body removal "demonstrated no objective beneficial effect." In fact, the skeptical surveyors scored nine of the fifteen as "worse" after the surgery.

The decision for surgical intervention in many illnesses is often wise, sometimes the only possible therapeutic intervention. Other times it is a travesty of science. That travesty is occasionally intentional, and motivated by greed. More often it is a reflection of the fact that the decision to operate is among the least scientifically defined aspects of modern medicine. "It is a veritable swamp," confides one leading surgeon. In some cases that decision is clear. Even when it is not, physicians are expert at staring straight-facedly at the patient and stating: "We must operate."

Incorrect diagnosis is one prime prompter of irrational surgery. Surgical impetuosity is an even more elusive enemy of science. The natural inclination of surgeons to "cut," to want to use their intensive training, may too often be involved in surgical decision. In such cases, protection against the scalpel can be one of man's most effective immunizations. A middle-aged woman on a visit to the clinic of a university hospital in New York learned this when she was advised by a surgical resident that her leg cyst needed surgery, which he immediately scheduled by phone for the following day. When a friend advised her to see an orthopedic specialist before agreeing, she learned that despite its size, the cyst was of minor importance and did not require surgery. It would (and did) yield to simple medical management.

In another case history, a man in his thirties was advised that he had an anal fissure and that rectal surgery was necessary. The concerned patient asked if there was any other course possible. He was reluctantly informed that the doctor might try simple cauterization with silver nitrate, a therapy that proved quite effective.

During our generation's concerted effort to perfect surgical techniques, insufficient scientific effort has been exerted in the area of surgical decision-making. When is it best to "cut," and when is it best to risk more on medical management and nature? There is an increasingly large critical school of doctors who preach a more "conservative" attitude toward certain surgical therapies until more is known. They are part of a logical counterrevolution against expansive claims and unfulfilled great expectations.

Aggressive surgery for certain adult heart ailments has come under critical investigation from a group of Los Angeles physicians who heretically ask whether in certain cases nonintervention may not be a reasonable alternative. Drs. Mark, Escher, and Young studied 237 adults with congenital heart ailments at Montefiore Hospital. Few single surveys are definitive, but they concluded that despite their ailments, "these patients have an ability to live productive lives"—even including the stress of pregnancy and military service. These heart patients, they stated, "must be identified and supervised, but not overprotected, except against bacterial endocarditis [heart infection] and perhaps at times the scalpel." The figures emphasize their last admonishment. Of thirty-seven deaths in the group, nineteen were as a direct result of surgery or its complications.

The disturbing Los Angeles report, given at a meeting of the American College of Cardiology, became the stimulus for a *Medical Tribune* editorial entitled "Science and Art" which eloquently asked for medical sagacity in weighing the risk of surgical interference. "The adaptive capacities of the living organism to adverse circumstances whether in the external environment or the internal, are an unending wonder," the editorial comments. "It is often the better part of valor to leave well enough alone rather than tamper with the anatomic abnormalities a particular patient may exhibit. The cost of attempting may far exceed the price of judicious neglect." The closing comment is a challenge to all physicians who would aspire to science: "But prognosis untouched by the scalpel must be weighed against the hazards of surgery, and the task is not an easy one."

The actionist surgical philosophy can be a vital lifesaver where the diagnosis is clear, the technique tested and statistics obviously on the side of survival. Lack of caution in approaching a less codified situation can, say critics, result in surgical overtreatment and its ugly complications. This path between intelligent, conservative management and the nontreatment of nihilism can sometimes be a narrow one, but one that the scientific physician and the sophisticated patient must nevertheless tread.

Dr. Paul Lahvis of Gowanda, New York, reminded his colleagues of the "surgical misjudgments" that come from attempts to excise portions of the body when the diagnosis, and the prognosis, is not clear. He describes the patient with segmental neuritis and accompanying "root pain" and local tenderness for whom impetuous surgery is often the answer. The doctor seeks out a site in the human body to explain the pain and, says Dr. Lahvis, the body usually accommodates him. "A great many human organs show deviations or evidence of some pathology which may or may not be pathogenic," he states. "The incidence is close to 100 percent in the adult. The X-ray finds the low kidney, the polyp, the diverticulum [sac or pouch], and lately, more and more, the hiatal hernia. The palpating finger locates the small cyst, the one-inch fibroid."

Having found this deviation, the physician is likely to advise or perform surgery. "The defect is corrected by repair or excision," Dr. Lahvis continues, "and the patient is happy because the rest in bed and the convalescence have eliminated the pain for a while." The pain often returns, warns Dr. Lahvis, and "the search starts anew, quite likely in another doctor's office, and a resected ovarian cyst is followed by an appendectomy and a cholecystectomy [gall bladder removal]. Lately, repair of hiatal hernia has been added to the repertoire . . . Finally, our patient develops obstructive adhesions or incisional hernias. He now is in real trouble and faces a life of partial disability, restricted employability, noninsurability, or worse." And, he adds, the patient "still has segmental pain and local tenderness."

Heralded procedures of surgery, when subjected to scientific scrutiny, sometimes do less well than anticipated, and not particularly better or worse than nonsurgery despite the dramatic changes made in the body's make-up. At a meeting of the American Academy of Neurology, Dr. Raymond B. Bauer of Wayne State University in Detroit reported on a comparative study of surgical and medical approaches to occlusive cerebrovascular disease, which causes stroke by obstructing the carotid arteries in the neck. Of 109 patients, all of whom had agreed to reconstructive surgery of the involved artery, fifty-seven were given medical treatment alone, and fifty-two received both medical and surgical treatment.

The results showed the surgery to have no significant superior value over medical treatment. Of the surgical patients, seven died; twenty-four were improved; ten became worse; and eleven were unchanged. Of those treated medically only, six died; eighteen were improved; eleven were worse; and twenty-two were unchanged. Using a point system, the two techniques approximately balanced out. Of those who died or got worse, the surgical patients declined more: 37.4 points to 26.7. Of those who improved, the surgical patients led 16.7 to 10.5.

"There is a greater degree and slightly higher incidence of improvement in the surgical group and there is also a greater degree of worsening," Dr. Bauer states. The necessity for extreme caution in choosing candidates for such serious surgery is shown by the fact that among those who died in surgery were "patients with minimal neurological impairment" whereas the medically treated who expired had a "severe deficit."

Surgical gain may too often be assumed, rather than scientifically analyzed. This is indicated by another critical study of an accepted surgical procedure—transventricular aortic commissurotomy, a form of heart surgery to repair damaged aortic valves. Dr. Willard P. Johnson of the University of Washington studied the survival statistics of thirty-eight patients who had undergone this complex surgery. The operations were done between January, 1955, and February, 1960, with an original operative mortality of 10.5 percent. By March, 1962, however, 76 percent of all patients were dead. "From these data, it seems dubious whether this operation prolongs life significantly beyond what might be expected without surgery," says the candid Dr. Johnson. The negative report does not conclusively prove the lack of efficacy, but raises scientific skepticism which the astute physician must carefully consider.

Those who believe that scientific inquiry will one day make medicine and surgery almost exact sciences are destined for disappointment. The necessity for scientific inquiry into the problem of when to operate is crucial today, however. Knowing the inventory of success and failure of an operation can help the punctilious doctor make reasonably intelligent decisions whether the risk of surgery is justified for his patient. If nothing else, he can candidly inform the patient of the realistic (not propagandistic) chances of surviving the scalpel in an improved state. Unfortunately, the trying problem of evaluating surgery is complicated by the euphoric air that surrounds some modern "miracle" techniques, whose mere imagery can dispel hard-headed attempts at scientific evaluation.

Three surgeons at UCLA are among those careful physicians attempting a reasoned look at this contemporary dilemma, using graft replacement of aortic aneurysms (balloonlike distentions of the aortic artery) as their case material. Of a hundred case histories, Drs. Van de Water, Cannon and Baker found the decision to operate simple in thirty-four patients in whom the aneurysm had already ruptured. Although not notably successful (60 percent died), surgery was the only known alternative. Another criterion for immediate surgery, they reasoned, was back pain, which, in the case of aneurysms, is interpreted as a sign of progressive expansion. When these two signs were absent, the decision was based on the size of the "balloon." If larger than seven centimeters (three inches), they felt that the risk of rupture was too great and that surgery was called for. If under that size, they reasoned from experience that surgery was not justified. The 15 percent risk of operative mortality then loomed statistically larger than the hazard of rupture.

No technique could be more symbolic of surgical advance than open-heart surgery, whose heart-lung machine replacement for the human heart during the operation is a living legend. With the publicized atmosphere of optimism that it promises, it is difficult—but still necessary—for doctor (and patient) to be familiar with the statistics of risk in open-heart surgery.

A recent Mayo Clinic study on mitral-valve surgery indicates that while often lifesaving, open-heart surgery is not the carefree miracle of contemporary folklore. The mitral valve is actually two cusps between the left atrium (upper chamber of the heart, which receives the blood returned from the pulmonary system) and the left ventricle (lower heart chamber, which forces the blood out of the heart). It does the important job of permitting the blood to flow into the ventricle but prevents its backflow into the atrium. Debilitation of the mitral valve—usually as an aftereffect of rheumatic fever—causes a "stenosis," or narrowing, that prevents its complete opening and closing, and can cause an "insufficiency" that permits an unwanted backflow of blood. In simplest terms, it is a "leaky valve," often identified by its "murmur." Patients with diseased mitral valves have had varied prognoses: some live out a full life expectancy, while others die at a premature age. Some are obviously handicapped; others participate in normal or near-normal activity.

The recent Mayo Clinic results give the doctor (and patient) a statistical opportunity to evaluate survival after three modern open-heart-surgery procedures. From 1955 through 1963, eighty-seven patients had operations to reconstruct the diseased mitral valve in which blood was backflowing. Of the eight-seven patients, thirteen died in the hospital and twelve more died in a follow-up period averaging two and three-quarter years. Fifteen more were not improved, and forty-seven were. The totals: almost 30 percent deaths; 17 percent not improved; 54 percent improved.

In the same period, open-heart reconstruction for mitral stenosis was done on fifty-six patients, nine of whom died in the hospital. Fourteen more died in a follow-up averaging two and one-third years; twenty-two were improved; and nine not improved. The totals: 41 percent deaths; 16 percent not improved; and 39 percent improved. The most recent results for valve replacement (the years 1962 and 1963) were also included: 28 percent deaths in the hospital or on follow-up, and 67 percent improvement. The overall open-heart mitral-valve-surgery score at the excellent Mayo Clinic: deaths in hospital, 16 percent; deaths on follow-up, 16 percent; not improved, 12 percent; improved, 56 percent. (There have been reports of both superior and inferior performances, but the Mayo Clinic is representative of better surgical treatment.)

For doctor and patient who understand such risk, and are willing to exchange it for the hope of improvement, open-heart surgery is truly a "miracle." Warnings against extravagant faith, however, especially when not performed by seasoned experts, are being made by mature medical sources. A recent editorial in *Circulation,* the American Heart Association journal, authored by two University of Kentucky Medical Center surgeons, warns of excessive reliance on the potentially dangerous procedure. "Many factors still push individuals and institutions into the field of open-heart surgery. Unfortunately, it maintains a totally undeserved role as a professional status symbol," they state candidly. "Fortunately, as its more lethal, complex, and expensive features become appreciated by surgeons and their critical referring cardiologists, the compulsions to get into open-heart surgery begin to wane. The grief and heartaches to both patient and surgeon become appreciated along with the occasional spectacular triumphs."

The trying process of weighing surgery against nature or medicine is difficult enough. To it is added the liability that many physicians and patients are wont to believe that surgery is as simplistic as arithmetic—that 2 plus 2 universally equals 4 in surgical results, whether in Boston or Dubuque. In this ostensibly scientific but inordinately inaccurate philosophy, the referring doctor, the patient and the surgeon himself may falsely believe that duplicating the amazing results of stellar surgical performers is merely a matter of modern technology and equipment.

Published reports on the Duke of Windsor's operation for abdominal aortic aneurysm accurately indicated the outstanding success of surgeon Dr. Michael DeBakey of Baylor University College of Medicine. He has performed eighteen hundred such operations with a mortality of 7 percent—and only 1 percent in a group with no other disease complication. The figures may be specific, but Dr. DeBakey is singular, not plural, and his genius is not available universally.

Other published reports on this type of operation show that in *good* hands, expected mortality is 10 to 15 percent and higher, indicating that faith in the risk of a particular surgical procedure may be less than scientific. It may be justified faith in the skill of an *individual doctor,* whose brain and dexterity can influence others, but is not generally available to the average patient. A urologist at a medical school in Brooklyn reportedly has had only six mortalities in his last one thousand prostatectomies. But like Dr. DeBakey, he too is indivisible.

The scientific decision-making of medicine is inextricably involved in the understanding of such numbers, in a sophisticated statistical skill that permits the scientist-doctor to escape traps of false hopes and false cures. The three thousand medical journals in the world publish tons of original articles from which the serious physician can extract a great deal of scientific value. He must also be able to recognize the medical fallacies, couched in shiny but erroneous numbers, scattered liberally throughout these same journals.

There is considerable evidence that physician fluency with numbers is stronger in medical economics than in understanding medical research. He may be an apt sucker for the enthusiastic journal article whose summary begins: "It appears evident from the results that this procedure should prove of significant value in the treatment of . . ." Similarly, physicians who write medical papers and who abjure the strict statistical method are in grave danger of mesmerizing themselves with their sleight of hand, blissfully interpreting failure as success with the help of myopic mathematics.

A grave physician error both in reporting medical studies and in interpreting them is the use of percentages (survival, cure, etc.) that only *seem* to be finite and definite. The small sample is often the gremlin. In the not uncommon survey of ten to twenty patients, the physician often forgets the "confidence limits." They may indicate that the miraculous new "cure" that seemed to improve almost every case could theoretically prove to be a hazard under further, larger sampling. "Since a percentage is always calculated on a finite number of cases," warns a statistical report of the Commission on Professional and Hospital Activities, "it must be used with caution as an estimate of the 'true' or 'long-term' percentage.

"For example, suppose a physician finds no adverse effects (0 percent) in the first ten patients treated with a new medicine," the report continues. "It is entirely possible that 0 percent is not the percentage that would show in the long run . . . The table of 95 percent Confidence Limits in this report specifies that the true percentage, in the example given, is most likely to lie between *0 percent and 30.8 percent.*" From a harmless drug with a 100 percent safety, it can potentially shift to one with deviltry for almost one in three patients, a probability situation that could only be checked out with much more extensive work. Until such time, the true physician-scientist must keep his skepticism ready and his doubt dry.

A biostatistician, Dr. Hugo Muench of Boston, recently felt compelled to inform two prominent Boston surgeons that their ostensible improvement in survival after surgery on ruptured aneurysms was possibly more apparent than real. The doctors had reported that three "died" and three "survived" during their first two years of experience, for a mortality score of 50 percent. For the last three years, however, they reported higher survival—fourteen in nineteen cases. The results appear hopeful, but Dr. Muench reminds them that statistically the results could just as well have been due to chance as better surgical technique. Says the skeptical statistician in a rebuff in the *New England Journal of Medicine*: ". . . two samples showing at least this much difference would happen by sampling accident at least half the time."

To the medical profession, the reputability of the published clinical report is vital to intelligent scientific decision. Several medical critics warn that it is sometimes of primrose quality. They reveal the existence of statistically "fudged" reports, which are either done by doctors with the malice of pride in mind or by the simple indirection of statistical ignorance. Research workers at the U. S. Armed Forces Institute of Pathology believe that many of the enthusiastic follow-up surveys of surgical or medical patients are subject to major error and distortion—including head counts on who is alive or dead.

Immortalized in a published scientific article, the statistical errors may stimulate false therapy. The typical follow-up of treatment, they point out, is a patient questionnaire that has the built-in distortion of those who do not respond. By using a more thorough system of multiple follow-ups, including hospital records, U. S. Public Health Service files, relatives, friends, Bureau of Vital Statistics, etc., the Institute of Pathology was able to show wide discrepancy between published results of treatment and what actually happened.

The results of the second count were often grimmer, and less flattering to medical treatment. In one study, questionnaire replies indicated that 5 percent of patients were dead, 41 percent ill and 54 percent well. A subsequent search by the Institute showed that only 39 percent were well, 34 percent were ill, and *27 percent of the patients, instead of 5 percent, were dead!*

The *initial* report on a group of patients with cancer showed results of unparalleled success. With a partial response from the patients, the survey results showed not a single fatality and that half of the patients were now well. When a full follow-up study of the *entire* group was made, the actual therapeutic results were dreary: 25 percent were still ill, 30 percent were better and, "alarmingly," *45 percent were dead!*

Such statistical loopholes prompt raised eyebrows from concerned patients and doctors. But it is a minor danger to health and science when compared to the report that is openly manipulated by the author, as a few apparently are. Surgeon George E. Moore of Buffalo, New York, in a whimsical, yet impassioned editorial in *Surgery, Gynecology & Obstetrics,* reveals the ugly physician practice of "doctoring" results to make them appear more favorable than they are. It is part of an apparent modern-physician necessity to produce a successful report to match public confidence in medicine. Moore believes this nonmethod is commonplace. "It is my personal opinion," states this Fellow of the American College of Surgeons, "that 80 to 90 percent of all articles relating personal, departmental, or institutional 'experiences,' whether by surgeons or by physicians in general, are of little or no value." He adds the warning that misreported series of treatments, by being "misleading," can "encourage the use of dangerous clinical procedures."

The outspoken physician offers, in effect, a satiric handbook for fudging physicians. "With a little experience one can become a superb paper surgeon," he suggests. "Some years ago, the literary and lecture mortality rates for pulmonary resection, total gastrectomy, and repair of hiatal hernias were becoming so low and the survival rates so good that it seemed that the secret of eternal life had been found."

Dr. Moore describes the technology of making a fake superior report, indicating that the secret lies in careful "patient selection." "For example," he illustrates, "the well-known surgeon or clinic treats only patients who have been previously screened before referral for therapy." Eager hospital residents who have been assigned the task of reviewing the charts for an upcoming report find it easy to eliminate certain dead patients who would dampen the study. Often it is on the grounds that they are "not eligible" for the series because they had a previous biopsy or a second disease.

Embarrassing complications and deaths can also be discarded by the technique of disease "classification," he points out. As an example he uses the gastric cancer patient whose tumor extended to the liver and who eventually died of peritonitis, qualifying him for elimination from the series. He catalogues other surgical Machiavellians that can liven an otherwise deadly report: using an elastic definition of "hospital deaths" so that patients who die from postoperative wound opening or pulmonary emboli (fragments of a blood clot) after discharge need not be included, and ignoring patients who die of a disease unrelated to the surgical procedure.

The art of excluding un-co-operative (i.e., dead) patients from such studies appears to be unlimited. Dr. Moore advises, with a twist of irony, that the doctor's "batting average" in a large series of cancer operations can be raised enormously by the simple expedient of including "a large number of relatively benign lesions—

grade ½—which help the survival rate enormously." He points out that when the record-keeping was standardized in the Surgical Adjuvant Chemotherapy Studies and was delegated to statisticians— rather than to involved doctors—"it was found that many patients died within 30 days after extensive operative procedures."

Dr. Moore's suggestion for improvement of scientific thought and attitude among physicians? He makes a plea for more objective and appropriate use of statistical knowledge. "More of our diagnostic and therapeutic methods must be evaluated by modern statistical techniques, by using results obtained by groups of co-operating clinicians with adequate numbers of patients," he states. "Perhaps then we will avoid ligating arteries for portal hypertension, cutting things for asthma, performing radical surgery without evidence of its effectiveness . . ."

The current use and misuse of statistics in medical literature is raised in a *JAMA* series on "Statistics, Science, and Sense," authored by Dr. Sidney Shindell (M.D. and LL.B.) of the University of Pittsburgh. Dr. Shindell comments on the various fallacies found in some medical articles, including case histories that reveal a shocking rudimentary failure of intellect.

He dissects a report published in the *American Journal of Cardiology* in which physicians stated that improvement took place in thirty-four of fifty patients with angina pectoris (chest pain from the heart) who had been given a fadlike surgical procedure—ligation of certain chest arteries—in an attempt to improve circulatory channels to the heart area. The report, however, failed to ask a significant logical query, says Dr. Shindell: "What else might this mean?" Two subsequent surgical surveys, including one in the *New England Journal of Medicine,* satisfactorily answered the question. A control group was given a "sham" operation, with only a skin incision rather than full artery surgery. On follow-up, the control group professed to have the same transient improvement in their angina as did a group who actually underwent surgery.

A revealing error in statistical logic is taken from a *JAMA* medical report which dourly reviewed the life span of 82,441 physicians who had died between 1930 and 1954. From this material the doctor-authors statistically concluded that radiologists were short-lived because of occupational hazard. "Radiologists die on the average 5.2 years earlier than do other physicians," they stated. "It may be concluded that exposure to ionizing radiation is the predisposing factor in this shortening of life."

A later article in the same journal reminded the doctors that they had been snared by one of the scientific traps for the uninitiated. Since "there are fewer elderly radiologists," they pointed out, "it is obvious that radiologists on the average would be expected to die at younger ages." Stated statistically, "the average age of death is misleading as an index of comparative longevity in groups having variable age composition."

Simple errors in statistics are sometimes the most tragic, for they convince others for years to come that there is a rightness about a wrong or unproven medical procedure. Printed numbers seem to have an indelibility that will survive later "letters to the editor" and corrections by the baleful, should they ever be printed by a magnanimous journal editor.

A recent such error in the April 15, 1965 issue of the excellent *New England Journal of Medicine* may be miseducating a generation of surgeons on the efficacy of a kidney transplant technique—with little hope that the truth will ever catch up with the flamboyant numbers. In an article on "Survival Data on Renal Transplantation in Patients," a table of otherwise gloomy survival figures on kidney transplants (except for identical twins) is suddenly illuminated by a statistic showing one group with a *miraculous 58 percent survival several years after transplant.* The shining number was in effect claiming that almost six in ten of dying renal-disease patients receiving a certain type of donor kidney have lived six years and could conceivably live longer. Such a statistic, if it were true, could mean life for scores of thousands of people, perhaps even more. At first study, the holy grail—a cure for kidney failure—appeared at hand.

The article, however, was a secondary source, having retabulated the figures from the "Third Report of the Human Kidney Transplant Registry," printed in *Transplantation* magazine, and covering 495 transplantations up through September 1964. Checking the original tables, it soon became obvious that the "grail" was a porous vessel, incapable of holding truth.

The transplant group with miraculous survival was listed as receiving donor kidneys from "sister, brother, other blood relative, or nonidentical twin." Comparing the figures with the original, it soon became obvious that the .58 survival was chimerical. There were only thirteen transplantations done in this group prior to March, 1962, and nine were now dead! Excluding the two-for-two success of twins, *nine of the eleven* transplants in the group have not survived, a survival rate of *18 percent* rather than 58 percent. The period of survival for the two were two and a half and three and a half years rather than six.

The highly creative (and optimistic) results stated in the article were evolved through numerical gymnastics with no rationale in common sense, science or statistics. Although there is no record of survival as indicated, the author created the euphoric percentage by using the recent better short-term (several months) survivals in this group, then magically extrapolating them out into a nonexistent two, three, four, five and six years, producing kidney transplant survivals that do not exist. A leading transplant surgeon in Boston privately concurred that the report was in error, adding that he might note it in a letter to the editor. The readership of the "letters" sections in medical journals is an unknown quantity. Meanwhile the American surgical community may be busily whetting the cutlery to perform unproven kidney transplants that have been falsely "documented" as lifesaving in a reputable medical journal.

The medical journal is a vital core of doctor postgraduate education or, as it is now called, "continuing" doctor education, a comment on the fact that it is ideally never-ending. The quality of these journals varies from excellent to poor, and even the very best —as we have noticed—incorporate the foibles of its authors. Some physician-critics are annoyed at literary limitations of the American physician and the poor quality of his article output. The literate internist Dr. William B. Bean of Iowa, for example, states: "I am inclined to agree with Alan Gregg's views that poor 'medical and scientific writing in our professional books and journals constitutes the most serious internal limitations to medical education and research.' "

With the floodgates of research opened by massive federal spending, it was inevitable that the production of medical articles should increase almost exponentially, which it has. *Index Medicus* lists twenty-five hundred journals, and 163,000 articles are published yearly. In the haste of this explosion, say some physician-editors, scientific quality is forsaken in the academic doctor scramble dominated by the edict of "publish or perish."

Medical journals "are embarrassed by the arrival of manuscripts prepared by well-meaning investigators without any control measures," states the editor of *Industrial Medicine* in an editorial. In making therapeutic claims, the vexed editor asserts, many physician-authors have been giving no thought to whether "in the absence of any treatment the majority might have been cured or improved . . ." In an unprecedented tongue-lashing of colleagues, he terms such results "not other than the prostitution of science."

Physician compulsion to author a "paper" for publication or for reading at a medical meeting has become the subject for satire, both light-hearted and acerbic. Dr. Arthur W. Proetz of St. Louis, editor of *Annals of Otolaryngology,* recalled that while Einstein used five pages to describe the theory of relativity that upset modern physics, many papers presented at meetings are five times that length and upset nothing more than the listener's sleep. This type of nonconsequential paper, he complains, typically concludes with the following disclaimer: "This present series is admittedly too small to permit of any conclusions, and further work will have to be done before . . ."

In his satirical paper "How to Smother an Idea," Dr. Proetz hypothesizes fourteen reasons why a doctor writes a paper: "1. To contribute a new idea. 2. To repeat an old idea. 3. To repeat an old idea for the 40th time. 4. To report an interesting case. 5. To report an uninteresting case. 6. To oblige a secretary (program secretary) with a program to fill. 7. To summarize a subject. 8. To get a job. 9. To get a grant. 10. To try to keep a grant. 11. To advertise a product. 12. To advertise himself. 13. To get money for it. 14. To retract a previous statement. (Rare)." The logical conclusion that science may be lost in this clash of motivations is made by Dr. Proetz. "Only four of these reasons are for science," he says. "Seven are just as clearly for the individual. Most of the latter papers are harmless, except that they pile up and give the impression of progress where none exists."

The philosophical key to much of this criticism is the consistent omission of the word "scholar" in the description of the contemporary doctor. In or out of the university, no endeavor requires a higher degree of continuing scholarship than medicine, and the opportunities to use scholarship are ever-present, whether at a rural bedside or in a laboratory of pathology. As Dr. Bernard V. Dryer of Cleveland, study director of the Joint Study in Continuing Medical Education, reminds us, the need is enormous. "By now most of us are in agreement that there is a widening gap between available medical knowledge and its application in medical practice," he says.

The scholarship of the practicing doctor has loosely been called "keeping up," and lately, by the more euphemistic term "continuing education." The possibilities of scholarship for the practicing physician are many. His intimate view of disease entities and their therapies theoretically enable him to make significant comments on medical treatment. A practitioner in Australia, Dr. N. M. Gregg, used personal observation to relate the cataracts of infants to the German measles their mothers had contracted during the first three months of pregnancy; an English general practitioner, Dr. Pickles, conducted an exceptional epidemiologic study on his own country practice.

In 1864 Dr. William Read, city physician of Boston, was confronted with a cholera epidemic soon after he was appointed. Read believed that cholera was contagious, but was opposed by his colleagues. As a lifelong "student" of medicine, Read went to the library and read John Snow's account of a cholera epidemic in London, including proof that the source was the Broad Street pump. With this evidence, he convinced his colleagues that cholera was contagious and that they could prevent its further spread. (The failure of such on-the-spot observation by current practicing doctors is painful by contrast.)

"He had to ferret out the facts based upon his experience and that of others. He did what every student of medicine must do," Dr. Wesley W. Spink of Minneapolis remarked of Read. "All this knowledge is available to the physician, but it implies that he must pursue the sources of this information, and having found them, must possess the intellectual discipline for critical evaluation. In other words, the physician must be a continuing student of medical science."

How well does the modern practicing physician "keep up"? How good a continuing student of medical science is he? Equally pertinent, how well does the medical profession provide the proper environment for continuous scholarship?

All these inquiries have been researched by the profession, and there is a near-unanimity to their critical conclusions. Despite the sincere efforts of many physicians and institutions, and the myriad of programs to educate the practicing physician, *the continuing education of the American doctor has been a failure.* It is a victim of doctor complacency and his inability to perceive the requirements of science. Like other breakdowns of medical performance, its seed is also in the incredible chaos of American medical organization. In the words of the former president of the Arizona Medical Association, Dr. Lindsay E. Beaton, continuing education for the would-be doctor-scientist has been "too little and too late." Adds this prominent medical spokesman: "I have doubts about continuing medical education. I have doubts about the desire of practitioners for true education."

The New York State Committee on Medical Education, after stressing the need for continuing doctor scholarship, admonished in a report to Governor Rockefeller: "But while its need is vital and self-evident, efforts to fulfill the need have been sporadic, disjointed, and largely unsuccessful." Dr. Beaton adds: "And sometimes like Ambrose Bierce's opinion of water as a drink—cheap but not good."

The educational offerings to the doctor seem impressive, if taken at face validity. The Continuing Education issue of *JAMA* catalogues 1569 courses given in 1964–65 by 251 institutions and organizations, most of them at hospitals and schools of medicine. The curricula vary from a one-day session in Aerospace Medicine to a year-long course in Adolescent Medicine at the Harvard Medical School "Courses for Graduates."

Closer examination of the *JAMA* schedule reveals a hint of why continuing education attracts critical comment. Approximately 60 percent of these "courses" are really packaged seminars of one to three days in length, rather than traditional continuous instruction on a weekly basis. Such an arrangement may seem to mesh with medical pragmatics, but can hardly be described as ideal scholastically.

"Keeping up," like seasonal flu, manifests itself in dozens of forms: taped lectures which doctors play in their cars; medical radio stations which transmit music for waiting patients, and medical news for the doctor's office; closed-circuit television lectures; ultra-high-frequency television shows which also permit the public to peek; medical journals and books; clinical meetings of specialty groups; county and state medical society lectures; programed instruction courses, such as one on hypertension in *GP;* lecture series by voluntary health agencies; scientific assemblies of the AMA. Some physicians travel hundreds of miles for their instruction; in New Jersey, Academy of Medicine circuit-riding teachers bring the material to local doctors.

The University of Michigan conducts courses in hospitals in twenty cities and has enrolled eighteen hundred doctors. Some postgraduate work envisions a community of scholars, albeit a temporary one. At the University of Minnesota, the Center for Continuation Study houses up to sixty doctors, who live, eat and learn together for a period of a few days to a week. The frivolous, too, is represented: the medical ocean-cruise meeting which cuts through the beneficent waters of the Mediterranean or Caribbean aboard a modern ocean liner while doctors supposedly "learn."

Individual aspects of continuing education have incontestable value. The American Academy of General Practice, the nationwide organization of family doctors, requires that its "generalists" complete 150 hours of postgraduate education every three years. Doctors receive ten points of credit for an original medical article, or scientific exhibit, or paper given verbally at a medical meeting. Some programs, such as the University of California School of Medicine's Continuing Education Program, reach a considerable number of physicians: twelve thousand doctors attended 106 courses in one year, most of them two-day weekend seminars.

With such apparent breadth of programing, why then have critics been carping at continuing doctor education? Its immensity has evidently disguised the simple fact that *most American doctors are oblivious to true continuing education.* The American Medical Association itself, in a report by D. D. Vollan, found that only a minority of doctors participated in continued studies. Speaking of the "physician's apparent lack of motivation," the American Heart Association Committee on Professional Education, states bluntly: "Despite the effort and manpower expended on continuing education, a limited number of physicians are reached." The enrollment of the American Academy of General Practice, whose organizational theme is continuing education, shows participation by a decided minority of all GP's. Surgeons are equally culpable. Dr. Edward R. Pickney reports that a recent survey showed that 40 percent of surgeons have not taken a postgraduate course in the past five years. The total attendance of physicians in university postgraduate courses in a recent year was 57,530—or only one in five doctors—a figure further diminished by the fact that many doctors enrolled in more than one course.

The appearance of "crowds" of doctors at meetings, say critical observers, is misleading. "In spite of the crowds that now seem to have exceeded the resources of all but the largest convention cities," states Dr. George E. Miller of the University of Illinois College of Medicine, "alarm is regularly expressed that those who most need the education are not attending meetings either large or small." The situation may deteriorate further. A survey of senior medical students at the Medical College of Virginia showed a significant failure of interest in continuing education.

The medical meeting, convention or scientific assembly, at which much of the doctor's opportunity to "keep up" is concentrated, is criticized as considerably less than contemplative. Anyone who has attended a medical convention, where theater tickets are as pertinent as science, knows the inherent handicap of education *en masse*. "Lifetime Learning for Physicians," a report sponsored by the AMA and seven other national groups, warned that "conferences and cocktails are not substitutes for a good curriculum."

The medical convention, with its semicarnival air, has taken on the aspects of a drug company give-away party, a propagandizing opportunity for medical politicians and a jamboree rather than a serious scientific gathering. One candid physician, Dr. Edwin A. Lee of Springfield, Illinois, feels that the white sand beaches and other inducements of convention cities might provide unfair competition. "Cities such as Miami Beach and Atlantic City offer many attractions which often tempt doctors to spend more time seeing the sights than at the actual work of the convention," he told the *Medical Tribune*.

A Michigan physician, in a letter to *GP* magazine, expressed his contempt for the oversocial aspects of certain continuing education assemblies, pointing out that he does not "care for the damn advertising no matter if they do pay the way." He takes equal umbrage at the "mink-coated diamond-studded wives," who are inevitable adjuncts to such affairs. "This started out to be a teaching outfit, not a social function," says the annoyed physician. "If you want hard-core general practitioners to attend the meeting, throw out all the above 'crap' and let us plan a real postgraduate study for four to five days away from all social events. Let's roll up our sleeves and get out the notebooks."

The *quality* of continuing doctor education has been under critical fusillade. Too many courses, charges Dr. Francis Lederer of the University of Illinois College of Medicine lack "sophistication." More critics comment on the impractical and disjointed nature of the material. The practicing physician, explains Dr. Herman K.

Hellerstein, needs postgraduate work that stresses "what the physician needs to know at the patient's bedside," rather than courses of the "medical student" species. The Western Reserve University cardiologist gives the bedside treatment of myocardial infarction (heart attack) as an example of the "working answer" postgraduate knowledge the physician desperately needs but is not now receiving.

A Seattle, Washington, physician also deplores courses which concentrate on esoterica at the expense of pressing daily medical needs. After commenting that "most physicians lack even rudimentary knowledge of how to deal with common, easily cured skin disorders," Dr. Arthur Bobroff complains in the columns of *Medical Economics* that typical postgraduate skin seminars are virtually worthless. "And when a knowledge-thirsty practitioner attends a refresher course, he pays tuition, travel and hotel expenses, incurs overhead costs in his unused office and foregoes his earnings to spend several days grappling with theoretical discussions of rare, unimportant dermatoses," he points out. "Then he returns home with nothing to show for the sacrifices he made . . ."

Dr. George Miller snipes at the typical postgraduate training for its infatuation with "transmission of up-to-the-minute information" at the jeopardy of more solid material currently missing from physician knowledge. He adds "that it may not be necessary or even desirable for every physician at every crossroad to know at once about the enzyme with which even the most distinguished investigator is currently enhanced." Instead he asks for a "better organized and more thorough application of existing knowledge."

The curriculum has been criticized for its aimlessness, lack of cohesion, and direction, with small expectation that the doctor who takes fifty or even five hundred hours of current continuing education will have absorbed much of concrete value. This tendency for continuing education to be external to the needs of the mature physician and scientist prompted a criticism from Dr. Bernard V. Dryer, planning consultant to the Association of American Medical Colleges. Continuing education's current lack of "a long-range, organized, sequential plan of participative learning," he says, is the result of the absence of "a modern curriculum."

This "capricious" handling of postgraduate education, as Dr. Irvine H. Page, editor of *Modern Medicine* terms it, is the penalty for what some physicians call occupational "freedom," and others view as extravagant chaos. In *JAMA*, Dr. Leland S. McKittrick of Boston cites this abysmal lack of co-ordination in attempts to keep up. "Unlike education at the medical school level, there is no central authority with the responsibility to stimulate, develop and coordinate the tremendous effort necessary to assure success, and to evaluate the results."

Concurrent with lack of planning has been the lack of money:

continuing education is operated out of medical petty cash. "Millions of dollars are poured into medical research that contributes new discoveries, technics and drugs; only a pittance is expended on the continuing education of those doctors who must apply this new knowledge," says Dr. Laurence B. Ellis, clinical professor of medicine at Harvard Medical School. Dr. Ellis then adds his spleen to those of his critical colleagues: "Too much of so-called postgraduate education is in an outdated era of teaching—didactic lectures on poorly selected subjects, not co-ordinated in an overall program, and reaching but a fraction of the potential audience."

Behind this failure is a sociological ulcer of modern medicine, one which doctors stubbornly refuse to treat: the "Town and Gown" syndrome, a pathological antagonism between the medical school and the practitioner. Although the general controversy has its antecedent in the scholar-community conflicts of the medieval age, it is now vestigial—except in medicine.

"Lawyers do not appear to trade blows with law schools; dental schools do not seem to have difficulties with dentists," says Dr. W. Clarke Wescoe, former chairman of the AMA Council on Medical Education. "Only in our professional field do the schools that gave the profession birth come under fire from their offspring; only in medicine does alma mater appear to lose common touch with her sons."

Through insularity and even disinterest (or disregard) for the day-to-day practice of medicine outside their ivied walls, the medical university has inbred an academic spirit that downgrades the community physician, GP or specialist. The same man they had trained only a few years before becomes a virtual pariah who need only be identified by the letters "LMD," local medical doctor. To the community physician, ostracized from the hospitals who decreasingly appoint practicing clinical men, the academic physician operates in a grant-surfeited ivory tower, apathetic to other doctors' needs or aspirations.

There is merit in both their disdains. The local medical doctor has too often cut himself from the scholarly impetus of medicine. The medical college—insistent on maintaining what it believes are the high standards of its university hospital—is of inconsequential assistance to the physicians of the community it serves. The mutual disenchantment has tragic scientific consequences for both, including the failure of continuing education. "Each physician must remain always a member of the medical college," says Dr. Lindsay Beaton, visualizing a compact not presently viable in medicine's disorganized state. "Closed-circuit television, traveling teams of medical school instructors, even publications, do not keep the practicing physician young in his learning. I want the practicing physician to remain an integral part of the chosen source of his profession . . .

at once a member of the college's faculty and of its student body."

This one achievement will not transmute the unprepared contemporary physician into the *compleat* scientist, but it would be an exciting beginning for the conscientious doctor and his concerned patients. Such expectations require medical revolutions as yet generally undreamed of. One potential reform that has been broached is compulsory continuing education. "Medical societies may soon insist that every member take postgraduate courses," says Dr. Fred M. Richardson of the Pennsylvania Hospital in Philadelphia. "They'll have to find ways to evaluate each doctor's practice in terms of his continuing knowledge. If medicine doesn't do this for itself, the law will eventually do it for medicine."

A general practitioner who praises the American Academy of General Practice attempt (overgenerously) chastises the American Medical Association for doing "little except talk." In a prominent medical publication Dr. I. Sternlieb of New York suggests more positive action to insist on physicians maintaining medical knowledge. "It [the AMA] should prod specialty boards into forcing diplomates to continue their education."

Meanwhile the typical physician is unperturbed by the dialogue about his failings in scientific attitude and proficiency. He lives comfortably on the crest of public enthusiasm for science, having falsely convinced the mass of unskeptical patients that he is born to the wave.

Chapter V

Life and Death in His Hospitals:

Surgery, Anesthesia, Obstetrics and Negligence

The chief of surgery shook his head sadly. Having been appointed to improve the surgical system of this large eastern hospital, he had replaced the community physicians, many of whom were general practitioners, with highly qualified members of the American College of Surgeons. Some had been appointed as full-time staff members, while others were named on a part-time basis.

"The surgical quality of this hospital has improved considerably as a result, but that's not all there is to a hospital," the surgical chief recounted. "We had one case recently in which a highly skilled team of surgeons operated for hours to save a critical case. After the operation, the patient was put back in the ward and placed on a Bird respirator. At five in the afternoon we went to look at him and we were proud because he was alive and doing well. When I came in to see the patient again the next morning, he was dead. The nurse had forgotten to replace the oxygen tank for the respirator. The nursing care in this hospital is abysmal."

Patients daily learn, through hazardous experience, what veteran physicians are well aware of: the hospital is a complex entity with failings and pitfalls of uneasiness that bedevil quality medical care. The image of a smooth-running centurion of health smashing illness has been well propagated by the profession through various vehicles from Blue Cross to Dr. Kildare. The sophisticated patient should be cognizant of the more accurate portrait—one of perpetual unsureness, shortcomings in using known medical knowledge and more than occasional negligence. Within this reservation, there are gradations of varying quality from hospital to hospital, some of which will hopefully become more obvious.

We shall soon, at close range, view the catastrophe, inadvertent and negligent, of doctor-made hazards. These therapeutic misadventures are only part of the medical interventions the patient must survive if the hospital is to be as intended, a place of true healing. Between the wish and the result there are problems of anesthesia, blood-transfusion reactions, poor surgery, unnecessary surgery, surgical complication, medication errors, hospital-bred infection, faulty diagnostic work-up, cardiac arrest, inappropriate therapy, negligent nursing care, callous nursing care, poor ambulance and emergency systems, sponges left in wounds, and even patients falling out of bed.

In addition to the medical hazards, there are unseen sociological pitfalls that vary from the profit-making motive of proprietary hospitals, to the simple absence of doctors in some hospitals. In this societal domain, the patient can be the victim of a weak hospital-accreditation system, lack of medical consultations, untrained internes, lack of internes, absence of registered nurses, distorted hospitalization-insurance principles, control of the hospital by ineffectual overseers, staff morale, lack of outside audit or control, and the "board" qualifications of staff doctors. In the chaotic environment known today as the "American hospital," its successes are more surprising than its many failings.

The potential errors of the generally unstandardized treatment in an American hospital vary from slight to grave, from routine to outlandish. The error of slight oversight in the hospital is commonplace. A middle-aged man admitted to the hospital was given a urine test, which showed that he was suffering from diabetes mellitus. The finding was ignored, and for three days nothing was done for him. Finally, out of the bureaucratic morass of hospital life, an order came to place him on insulin therapy. An equally simple, but more calamitous error resulted after a routine cholecystectomy operation (removal of the gall bladder). The patient was discharged from the hospital by his surgeon on the nurse's word that the incision had only a "slight drainage." Several hours later in the comfort of home, the surgical wound opened, causing death.

Other times the patient may be the subject of more bizarre hospital frenzy, the victim of a horrific chain of negligence. The verbatim report of one such case is most revealing: "A middle-aged man had a history of hernia which he had been able to reduce [push back in] manually in the past. He was admitted to the hospital after two days, during which the reduction of the hernia had been impossible. The house staff tried to reduce the hernia manually, and two days later it was necessary to operate for a perforated cecum [rupture of the cul-de-sac beginning of the large intestine]. The surgical surveyor noted: 'Manual manipulation of an incarcerated hernia forty-eight hours after sudden incarceration is a dangerous procedure. He should have been operated on at once. The two-day delay may have to do with the fact that the patient entered the hospital on the Fourth of July. The manual manipulation either caused the perforation or at least spilled the contents of the cecum. Furthermore, the operative procedure that was done did not include excision of the entire infected area of the intestine; this resulted in a fistula that required two subsequent operations and hospitalizations.'

"In one of the subsequent admissions there was an inexplicable delay of ten days prior to closure of the colostomy [artificial anus made in the abdominal wall]," the report of calamity continues. "Three or four days are adequate for preparation for surgery; and in this case even the administration of antibiotics to reduce the likelihood of infection was not done." A probably simple hernia case, complicated by a medical holiday and ineptness, resulted in a perforated cecum, an infected intestine, an operation to remove the diseased intestine, a fistula as a result of incomplete surgery, the surgical creation of an artificial anus, an operation to close the colostomy and a total of three hospitalizations with attendant pain, discomfort and danger.

The typical patient faces innumerable medical hurdles during his hospital stay, including the conquest of hospital bacteria. To the patient, and especially to the casual visitor, the American hospital seems the quintessence of cleanliness. The white-robed nurses, the pungent, purifying smell of antiseptic cleansers, the shined chromium accessories and neatly arranged beds conjure images of sanitation—the key to aseptic modern medicine.

In actuality, the American hospital is a dirty place. Its ostensibly aseptic halls, wards and operating rooms as well as the patients and permanent personnel provide a warm, convivial environment for the bacteria—staphylococcus, E. coli, Proteus vulgaris, Pseudomonas aeruginosa—that inhabit its every recess. In comparison to the American home, where the patient is safe among better asepsis and generally isolated from contagion, the germ-ridden American hospital is a challenge to the system and antibodies of the patient. It is a conflict in which the hostile bacteria often vanquish.

Without being properly alerted to the danger or protected from it, the sick patient is placed in this environment. He soon becomes exposed to a massive infection chain from hospital-housed bacteria that each year strikes well over a million surgical, medical, maternity and pediatric patients. Once home, those who survive spread the contamination even further to their families and the community.

The dizzying incidence of one segment of hospital contamination —postoperative infection that sets in three days to a month after surgery—was confirmed by a recent report by the National Academy of Sciences-National Research Council. Investigating the operating-room results of five university medical centers over a period of twenty-seven months, they studied 15,613 operations on 14,854 patients, 1157 of whom contracted "definite" infections within twenty-eight days.

Using the 10,250,000 non-maternity surgical operations performed each year as a guide, this yields a bacterial harvest of over 750,000 hospital-acquired surgical infections. When added to the medical, maternity and pediatric patients who acquire infections in the hospital, it reaches well over the million mark. Few diseases, iatrogenic or natural, can rival its enormity.

Hospital infections are not inevitable, but are invariably a result of loose hospital aseptic standards and procedures. The bacterial spread may be a result of unclean instruments, improper laundering, inadequate autoclave sterilization, faulty housekeeping, old surgical facilities, improper patient isolation, faulty surgical gloves, improperly washed hands, unidentified nurse and doctor "carriers" and "shedders," patient "carriers," the presence of antibiotic dust, dirty kitchens, contamination between septic child and mother, and vice versa, "cutdowns" for intravenous fluids and catheters.

A major cause of hospital infection, critics believe, is the casual but faulty assumption that in this age of antibiotics a clean, compulsively sterile hospital environment is somehow less essential. Dr. Harry B. Harding of Northwestern University School of Medicine blames hospital personnel for this oversight. "Workers have tended to lapse their aseptic techniques, believing that antibiotics would cover for these lapses," he warns. In fact, the indiscriminate use of antibiotics, especially penicillin, is greatly responsible, Dr. Harding believes, for the growth of resistant strains of staphylococci that now inhabit hospital halls, having *superinfected* the atmosphere after their weaker bacterial cousins were killed off.

The typical surgical patient who becomes infected has pus develop at the wound site, may feel feverish and have other early clinical signs of infection. The faith in antibiotics may keep the patient cheerful, but hospital-acquired infections are often too virulent for chemotherapy. Some of the newer antibiotics—especially the British-developed oxacillin, methicillin and cloxacillin—have power against hospital staphs, but assuring rumors of their victories tend to be exaggerated.

At Boston City Hospital, a group of eighty-four patients with severe hospital-acquired staphylococcus infections—deep abscesses, bacteremia (bacteria in the blood), skin infections, endocarditis (infection of the heart) and tracheobronchitis—were treated with one of the newest antibiotics, oxacillin. Of the eighty-four infected patients, thirty-one died despite the antibiotic treatment, some from the infection, others from their underlying disease. Treatment with two other supergermicides, methicillin and diphenicillin, performed with even higher mortality rates. (This high toll of up to 50 percent death is lower than before the introduction of these new staph killers.)

Not only are staph infections still resilient and deadly, but those acquired in the conducive hospital environment appear to be especially virulent. Dr. Maxwell Finland of Harvard reports on a survey at Boston City Hospital in which the relatively new antibiotic nafcillin was used on staphylococcus-infected patients. Sixty percent of the patients had acquired the infection in the hospital, and their death rate (48 percent) was twice as high as those admitted in the infected state.

The added lethalness of hospital-acquired infections was demonstrated by a ten-year study of Veterans Administration hospitals. Of a sample of eighty-five patients with bacterial endocarditis (infected hearts), seventeen had contracted the infection in the hospital. Although 45 percent of the others survived, fourteen of the seventeen hospital-infected victims died. "Host" factors such as the patient's age and debilitated condition contribute to the virulence of hospital-acquired infections, which makes hospital bacterial control all the more important.

Some hospitals are bacterially dirtier than others. Infection rates vary widely from hospital to hospital and even within the hospital itself. In the five university medical centers surveyed for surgical infections, the infection rate varied widely from 3 percent in one to a medically indecent 11.7 percent in another! Other reports have shown postsurgical infection varying from a low of 1 percent to a high of almost 20 percent in one institution. In Boston, for example, recent reports reveal the disparity between institutions. Of two university-connected hospitals in the city, one has a surgical infection rate of 3 percent, while the other has reported a staggering incidence of over 19 percent!

A survey of hip-surgery fracture at the State University of New York (Upstate Medical School) showed twenty postoperative infections in 316 operations (6.3 percent), including eight deaths "as a direct result of the infection." A survey of a pediatric hospital showed that 6.5 percent of 17,836 children developed infections following admission, "most" of which were hospital-acquired. Infection survival is obviously dependent on the bacterial dirtiness of the hospital the patient chooses, or is directed to, for his "recovery."

Infection breakouts involve every ward and cranny of the American hospital. A diarrhea-infection outbreak in the newborn nursery of an Indiana county hospital was traced to water baths used to warm the bottles. The baths "were grossly contaminated with Gram-negative bacteria." University of Virginia Medical School investigators traced one infection epidemic in a hospital newborn nursery to a heavy growth of bacteria *in five plastic bottles used to apply salve solution to the umbilical cords of infants.* One new hospital in Illinois, Lutheran General, which has not been infested with sizable colonies of "hospital flora," was dismayed over occasional "showers" of Staphylococcus aureus. They found the source to be the air-circulator units which had been the convivial host for staph. New filters treated with chemical disinfectant may well have saved the hospital from being permanently "dirty."

At New Rochelle Hospital in suburban Westchester, New York, three patients all underwent "open reduction" (with incision) of fractures on one weekend, only to have two of the patients die within forty-eight hours of septicemia [bacterial poisoning of the blood stream]. It was traced to a strep germ, Streptococcus faecalis, which is usually harmless but which had now appeared in a virulent form.

The ever-present danger from almost any hospital bacteria—no matter how apparently quiescent—was shown at the San Francisco General Hospital recently when an epidemic struck fifty-seven patients, sixteen of whom died. Their incidence of surgical infections—staphylococcal pneumonia, and especially staphylococcal enterocolitis (infection of the small intestine and colon)—soared during one four-month fall period. A forty-four-year-old man with cirrhosis was on neomycin therapy for a week when he suddenly had an onset of diarrhea, the first symptom of enterocolitis. He soon went into hepatorenal (liver and kidney) failure, and started bleeding in the upper GI area. Soon staphylococcal sepsis overtook his entire body, and he died. He was one of fifteen patients who contracted staphylococcal enterocolitis, four of whom passed away.

When the "bug" was isolated it was found to be a "new" hospital staph, whose presence was detected in almost every ward. Examination of both the patients' records and the outpatient population proved that this strain of staphylococcus was hospital-born, and that 14 percent of the hospital personnel had become carriers. A troubled *JAMA* editorialized on the incident, stressing that new hospital-acquired staph germs unidentifiable by previous coding systems "have appeared with increasing frequency in the United States, Canada and Great Britain," and appear similar to those isolated in Cincinnati, Boston and San Francisco. We well might, says *JAMA,* be dealing with a new virulent hospital threat. If so, it may make its most comfortable home in the bacterially dirtier of hospitals.

Modern medical technology, badly applied, may also lend itself to infection. Urinary-tract infections from catheters are a case in point, as are "venous cutdowns." The vein is cut, then sutured, after a plastic catheter tube is put into the vein to facilitate intravenous medication. The site is infection-prone if not handled scrupulously, as a Boston City Hospital survey shows. Of eighty-nine cutdowns on the Tufts Service of the hospital, eight developed purulent (with pus) infections, and there were five serious cases of septicemia.

The report in the *New England Journal of Medicine* (which showed that antibiotic treatment helped reduce the infection rate) described one awesome infection complication of this ostensibly "simple" procedure. A fifty-six-year-old man who underwent an operation for duodenal ulcer required prolonged intravenous therapy. A catheter was inserted, and fever developed three days later. On the fifth day, when clinical phlebitis (inflammation of the vein) was obvious, the catheter was removed. His blood showed Staphylococcus aureus. Antibiotics were given for ten days after which he was discharged.

The tragic aftermath of the septic incident is reported by the physician-authors. "In the cardiology clinic several months later, clubbing and a basilar diastolic murmur were found to have developed, and aortic insufficiency was diagnosed. He was readmitted to the hospital on June 12, 1964, with complaints of weakness and dyspnea (shortness of breath) on exertion. Further studies, including numerous blood cultures, were negative, and he was thought by cardiac and infectious-disease consultants to have aortic insufficiency due to healed endocarditis [heart infection], *caused by the cutdown septicemia six months previously* [italics mine]."

A hospital's history of unsanitary conditions, its layout or insufficient vigilance may make eradication of excessive infection impossible. Once staphylococcus, E. coli, and others, have become indigenous hospital bacteria, tenaciously pervading the corridors and operating room, only a new environment may destroy the infection chain. Deaconess Hospital in Spokane, Washington, learned this a few years ago when it replaced operating rooms dating back to 1908. The old surgical suites were high-ceilinged rooms branching off to a central corridor. Surgeons and nurses scrubbed up at the end of the corridor, then had to walk through the halls to their operating theaters. The surgical infection rate was a high 12 percent on gastric patients, and *27 percent* on surgery of the colon. The new suites were opened in September, 1961. Within two years the infection rates were cut in half.

Asepsis in the operating room should be undisputed catechism, but simple errors in logic and concern often make it bacterially "dirty." *The American Surgeon* recently reminded doctors of what should be gospel: meticulous clipping and cleaning of the nail beds, and the care and length of time devoted to the scrub are vital. Two surgeons, reporting in the *American Journal of Surgery,* found that *most* of the dramatic-looking face masks intended to protect the opened patients from the doctor's own germs are inefficient. Some of the masks currently in use, they found, had only 15 percent efficiency in screening out a particular test bacteria! (The authors believe a disposable mask made of spun glass is the most efficient.)

The surgeon's rubber gloves, put on with a flourish, have become the symbol of modern hospital sterility. Their job is to protect the patient's open body from bacteria that survive the surgeon's hand scrub. Actually, the barrier is less impressive in fact. "In the preparation of the surgeon's hands," say Drs. Peter Dineen and G. Hildick-Smith of Cornell Medical Center and the University of Pennsylvania, respectively, "every effort must be made to render them free of bacteria and prevent the escape of bacteria into the tissues via the breaks in surgeons' gloves which occur in approximately 30 percent of gloves worn at operations." Dr. Ira S. Goldenberg of Yale speaks of "the frequency with which small holes and tears occur in the surgeon's gloves during an operation," terming them "pathways of infection."

Frances Ginsberg, R.N., hospital asepsis consultant and columnist for *Modern Hospital,* is concerned about the surgeon's gloves as a source of contamination, advocating sterile disposable gloves, thrown away at the end of the operation, as a possible answer. Their universal use, she reveals, is being held up by hospital penny-foolishness. Charging that "too few hospitals are using them," she adds that those that do "are attempting to reprocess them in a misguided effort to save money."

Perusal of the hospital literature can unearth disturbing cases of doctor disinterest in surgical cleanliness. "We have a disagreement in our operating room on the need to remove gowns and gloves in the room where the case is done," a reader writes *Modern Hospital.* "The surgeons believe that keeping on gown and gloves saves time between cases, since they do not have to do a complete scrub. Nurses believe that this practice is poor technic. What is your opinion?" Consultant Ginsberg answered with what seems controlled fury: "Gown and gloves should be removed in the room in which the surgery is done, and discarded for treatment and disposal along with other supplies. *Wearing gowns and gloves from room to room results in spreading bacteria from the gown and contaminating whatever is touched by the gloves* [italics mine]." Another hospital worker wrote: "Our surgeons' shoes are disgracefully covered with dirt, blood, and debris and they are unconcerned about this!"

The current aseptic failure has led some medical researchers to reconsider the problem seriously. "Thus, ever since Pasteur and Lister, surgeons have been striving to develop methods and techniques which would permit them to operate under sterile conditions. That this goal has not been achieved is reflected in the fact that clean elective operations too commonly result in wound infections, some of which are caused by contamination of the wound during operation by exogenous microorganisms. We have pointed out elsewhere that descriptions of 'operating aseptically' upon man has been a wishful fancy, not an accomplished reality."

This statement, made in the *American Journal of Surgery,* is the candid comment of physicians at both Albert Einstein College of Medicine at Yeshiva University and Walter Reed Army Institute of Research, who have been experimenting with the development of a true germ-free hospital environment. (Not surprisingly, we as a nation are vitally concerned about eliminating possible contamination of the planets with our spaceships, and have developed magnificent "clean rooms" and advanced sterilization techniques for space vehicles.) The group has developed a plastic "tent" system for operations in a sterile environment and for isolation of susceptible and already infected patients. During the operation only sterile air, the doctor's gloved hands and the wound are in contact, a closed unit achieved by gluing the plastic isolator to the patient's body. The rest of the patient, the doctors, the staff and the equipment are outside the thin plastic isolator. Spacelike transparent-vinyl helmet-jackets for the surgical team are attached to the plastic isolator and doctors can slip in and out of them at will without breaking the sterile environment. Supplies enter the operating room through a sterile-lock isolator. Surgery conducted first on animals, then on four volunteer patients in the isolator proved its practicality: all the wounds were sterile after operation.

A similar nonsurgical system has been contrived to isolate infected or infection-prone patients such as those who are burned, in shock, who have been treated with defense-reducing drugs such as steroids, patients with open wounds and those with respiratory infections. Double-door ports make it possible to remove waste and dirty linen without contamination. Supplies and food can be introduced through sterile locks. The system can be applied around a bed or on only part of the patient's body, or to a full sterile room.

The first sterile hospital ward has already been installed at Fulham Hospital in London for treatment of rare type of cancer, chorioepithelioma, in which patients are highly susceptible to infection. The staff enters only through a changing room where special clothing is put on after a thorough wash-down. Air conditioning filters out particles down to ½ micron, and special hatches are used to bring sterile supplies in and remove used materials.

The London and Walter Reed concepts could profitably change infection-prone American hospitals. A seventeen-bed sterile isolation unit for staph victims was recently established at the University of Minnesota Hospitals. Their nursing staff is double the usual complement, and duty personnel are required to change uniforms and shoes before entering. When in intimate contact with patients, personnel are required to wear cap, mask and gown, plus gloves if the dressing is to be changed. Doors of complex cases are kept closed, and the shoes of personnel and wheels of carts are sprayed with phenolic detergent to avoid contaminating other sections.

Not all hospital-infection problems can be solved by unique isolation systems. Some hospital personnel, for example, carry infection as inveterate "staph shedders." The Typhoid Mary of history has been replaced by "Staphylococcus Peter" who actually "sheds" bacteria from his (or her) body. One such "Staph Peter" was a surgical-suite technician who shed his infective bacteria to patients despite cap, mask, gown and gloves.

Microbiologist John Ulrich, Ph.D., of the Mayo Clinic describes a series of surgical infections traced to a surgeon "shedder." Three patients from one surgical service in a clinic-connected local hospital developed postoperative infections within a week, all contaminated with Staphylococcus aureus 54/75, a strain uncommon to hospitals. Every member of the surgical team was tested, until a colony of the staph 54/75 was found *on the jaw* of one member! He was removed from the surgical team for six weeks until he stopped "shedding."

"We have developed a technique that allows us to successfully track down the shedders among the members of surgical teams, including surgeons, nurses, anesthetists, and technicians. I would like to see this simple method used routinely in other hospitals," states microbiologist Ulrich. The method is quite simple: infections found after surgery are related back to the surgical team involved. If in one week more than two infections of the same phage type are contracted by patients operated on by a particular surgical team, the members of that team are examined (nose and skin) to learn who is carrying the organism. If a carrier is found, he (or she) is given a shedding test.

He is placed alone in a small room with sampling devices which collect the "shed" bacteria. If the amount of staphylococci is significant, the team member is considered a "shedder" and is taken off duty so that he can be "cleaned up." This requires three to five weeks, and is presently being done with autogenous vaccines, injections of the shedder's own organisms.

Dr. Ulrich's work raises a most pertinent point in hospital surgery: it is possible that a particular minority of surgeons (and anesthetists, surgical nurses and technicians) should not be in that field of medicine. Although "shedding," like a cold, comes and goes, some surgeons (and surgical team members) have "bad skin" that is constantly subject to boils and outbreaks, and *may* dispose them to shedding, Dr. Ulrich believes. Those of them who are frequent staph shedders are "bad risks" in the operating room, and might well be bacteriologically identified and directed to other fields of medicine before they help to create an excessive number of surgical infections in patients.

Not all carriers are "shedders," but a California survey indicates the high incidence of carriers: one in every five hospital personnel. This is a segment of hospital population that should be carefully checked for "shedding," and temporarily (or permanently) suspended for duty by the "clean" hospital. Those who work closest with the patient are most apt to be contaminated, and the effect of medication dust increases the incidence. The Alfred Hospital in Australia found that *47 percent* of staff members who worked in operating rooms and wards were nasal carriers of antibiotic-resistant Staphylococcus aureus, while only 2 percent of the administrative and maintenance personnel were similarly potentially dangerous.

The jeopardy of hospital negligence is not absorbed solely by the patient. His family and community may also be victimized once he returns home. The "hopscotch" pattern of a hospital-acquired infection let loose—"staphylogistics"—is described in a drug company publication, *Spectrum*. Infant Johnny came home from the hospital nursery with staphylococcal impetigo. A few months later his three-year-old sister Mary had a staph throat infection. Following that, the father of the children contracted cellulitis, a severe staph skin infection, which put him in bed for a week. The pace then quickened. Mary was rushed to the hospital with another staph infection, paronychia (a deep infection around the nail) with the threat of septicemic blood poisoning; Mother contracted a perineal (around genital area) staphylococcus abscess; brother Bobby kept developing sties during the year. Fourteen months after returning home, Johnny himself had a painful staph boil.

In the spring of 1957 an outbreak of staphylococcal impetigo took place in the nursery of the University of California Medical Center. The following year hospital researchers investigated ninety-four of the families involved and found that 65 percent had either become "infected" with disease or had become carriers. A follow-up *five years later* revealed that there was still a lingering effect of the staphylococcus brought home from the hospital. As late as 1962, one of the families had two hospitalizations for staph—the infant (now five) and an older child, for both sties and impetigo. In other families, both the mother and father were plagued with recurrent boils.

Maintaining bacterial cleanliness in the hospital requires constant vigilance and a compulsion for sterility. An infection control committee is the first essential. Dr. Kenneth B. Babcock, former director of the Joint Commission on Accreditation of Hospitals, suggests that "dirty" (infected) cases can be scheduled at the end of the operating day, to provide time for thorough cleaning and airing of the surgical suite. Insufficient cleaning between operations in the over-busy operating room is possibly the explanation for an infection phenomenon observed by two Scottish surgeons.

They studied 595 patients classified as sepsis-free, and found that the infection rate was not related to age or length of surgery, or severity of incision. It was, they state in *Lancet,* mainly related to the time of day! The patients first on the operating list, when the room was clean and unused, had the least risk of purulence: one infection in 264 operations. Ten of the 331 patients scheduled for later in the day became infected. The surgeons suggest that there is a break in sterility—that aseptic technique "is not so meticulously observed by the surgical or nursing staff as the theater list progresses." The onslaught of uncontrolled bacteria during the day is another possible factor. "Increased contamination from theater clothing, decreased effectiveness of surgical masks, and dust from the hospital corridors" also take their toll. This conclusion makes the sterile hospital an even-more pressing need. (The NAS-NRC study disagrees on the significance of time of day.)

Lancet has reported a study of the movement of staphylococci during surgery—with intriguing results for concerned hospitals. Men sent out more bacteria than women; shedding by both men and women was more profuse below the waist; it was increased by body movement; and *it was not reduced by surgeons' cotton gowns or by cotton sheets covering the patients.* Disposable paper wrappings for the patient did, however, cut down on bacterial dispersal.

The meticulous washing of hands by doctors and nurses after each patient contact should not have to be stressed, but it is apparently often overlooked in the careless hospital. An anonymous but medically knowledgeable patient took careful inventory of the actions of nurses who cared for him, and recorded his experience in *Modern Hospital* in a controversial essay, "Patient Gives Needle Back to Nurses." Their unsterile habits drew his biliously critical comment. "The majority of nurses and aides did not wash their hands in the patient's room," he writes angrily. "Since the patient's room was the most distant from the nursing station, it is hard to believe that they always returned to the nurses' station to wash their hands before seeing another patient." A sterility-conscious hospital, consultant Frances Ginsberg points out, should have an open sink—with knee or foot controls—in the patient's room, to be used by doctors and nurses "after every patient contact."

The newborn child is an attractive host to hospital bacteria. Despite antibiotics and modern sterile techniques, infections are still a major threat to the newborn infant, Dr. Heinz F. Eichenwald, professor of pediatrics at Cornell, reminds us. The infant's infection-proneness should be protected through nursery isolation and sterile care, which are too often haphazard. If he becomes infected, there is the added risk he will contaminate his mother. "Prevention of colonization of the newborn infant during the first few days of life," states Dr. Leighton Cluff of Johns Hopkins, "can prevent staphylococcus disease in this group that is so highly susceptible to infection." In one of several hospital studies, 51 percent of a group of infants either contracted staphylococcus lesions or transmitted clinical infection to their mothers. One prime site of this infection is the umbilical-cord stump, says Dr. John P. Fairchild, who offers advice on controlling it: ligate (tie off) the stump by instrument, avoid handling it, use sterile dressings on the stump, and antiseptic foam instead of plain alcohol.

Two concerned pediatricians, Drs. Gluck and Wood, suggest in the *New England Journal of Medicine* that washing of the infant with antiseptic detergent can make the difference. The children in the study were given antiseptic umbilical-cord and skin care right in the delivery room, then were sent to the nursery in a sterile wrapper. They were then washed again carefully with the detergent, a procedure that was repeated every day. On discharge, only 6 percent of these children showed staphylococcus organisms, as against some 30 percent of those not treated with detergent. The threat of advanced infection in infants, septicemia, makes any precaution sensible. In *Pediatrics,* Drs. Johnston and Pell report a 38 percent death rate among such stricken newborns.

The delivery-nursery area is prone to infection epidemic unless it is isolated from the hospital and overseen with compulsiveness, say most observers. At the new Baptist Memorial Hospital in Memphis, the newborn are even protected from the passing staff by the purposeful omission of corridor doors: newborn children are handed into the nursery through a pass-through window.

Hospital housekeeping cannot compete with surgical skill in community status, but it may be almost as vital to patient survival. The housekeeper of the Cleveland Clinic stresses that even the cleaning equipment should be isolated. "Housekeeping employees must have three sets of cleaning equipment: one set for the patient rooms, another for the nurseries, and still another for the isolation rooms," she says in *Modern Hospital.* "Gowns, masks and caps must be changed to clean ones when the employees enter nurseries or labor and delivery rooms." Even the changing of shoes is required at the clinic whenever the employee enters the nursery area from another part of the hospital.

The former executive housekeeper of a Grand Rapids, Michigan, hospital insists that all staff members assigned to the floor "from the top down to garbage men" should have chest films and stool examinations every six months for signs of infection. Although it rings mundane, hospital-infection control requires sterile laundry arrangements, constant wet-mopping of germ-ridden floors with germicides, wall wash-downs and "fogging" of contaminated rooms.

The Joint Commission on Accreditation of Hospitals has asked hospitals to take active steps to investigate infections, and suggestions have been made for a maximum 2 percent infection rate. Even this might seem intolerable to the patient, but it would be a great improvement over the present survival course through hospital bacterial contamination.

One survival experience common to almost 50 percent of all hospital patients is the intake of anesthesia, the pain-killer or insensate creator administered to the 13,900,000 patients who undergo surgery and childbirth each year. The use of ether in the mid-1800's by William T. G. Morton as an anesthetic permanently changed the face of surgery from a near-savage art in which the bleeding patient howled himself into unconsciousness. In the process of making surgery practical (sometimes seemingly too practical) for all, anesthesia has added an attendant risk to hospitalization. This is especially true when its powers are wielded unwisely or unknowingly, as is apparently too often the case.

The danger to heart, lungs, brain and life from anesthesia are among the least discussed hazards of hospitalization. Rather than a rare occurrence, death from anesthesia is excessively common, more than most physicians prefer to believe. Estimates of its toll vary from 9,000 to 33,000 lives a year, with painful evidence that the larger, jarring figure may be more realistic. One of the most exhaustive studies of hospital anesthesia death was made by Dr. Robert D. Dripps and his colleagues at the University of Pennsylvania, and reported in *JAMA* in 1961.

The university anesthetists carefully analyzed 33,224 cases of surgery from 1947 to 1957, and found that eighty deaths could be attributed to anesthesia, as either the "definite" or "possible" cause. The failures of the hospital or the anesthetist, listed as "inadequate" anesthesia care or as physician "inexperience" and "error," are collectively implicated as the major cause of death. If the University of Pennsylvania is an accurate sample of anesthesia casualties among the 13,900,000 subjects, then as many as 33,000 lives are lost each year because of anesthesia—half of these tragedies "definite."

This toll is admittedly much higher than that usually reported. Estimates of anesthesia death usually vary from one in a thousand operations to one in two thousand, with one in fifteen hundred— 9,000 deaths a year—the most common. This figure is sufficiently awesome, but underreporting of negative medical facts is part of the American medical tradition. Death certificates, for example, severely understate the anesthesia problem. "In assigning the cause of death on a death certificate, anesthesia rarely was entered, except in those circumstances where the contribution was major and unequivocal," the University of Pennsylvania anesthesiologists confirm.

The Pennsylvania survey may show higher anesthesia mortality simply because of the authors' annoyance with typical fudging away of uneasy truths. "There is nothing to be gained in a mortality study by omitting a particular death merely to lower a statistical death rate," Dr. Dripps comments. "Avoiding responsibility or taking refuge in the fact that a patient was desperately ill prior to anesthesia and operation may improve one's mortality figures, but it will not advance general knowledge or change one's own practices."

There is also the grim possibility that the higher figure is conservative. This alarm is based on the common-sense observation that the University of Pennsylvania, where specially trained physicians administer the anesthesia, is a more capable setting than the typical hospital in which one of the many nurse-anesthetists who do more than half the anesthesia work in America may officiate over the patient's surgical sleep.

The apparent ease of administration and the miraculous absence of pain involved in anesthesia belie its serious depressant effects on the human body, effects made more dangerous by unskilled anesthetic care, but possible even when negligence is not involved. It is thought that general anesthesia works because it depresses the ascending activating system in the brain stem. While doing this, it also depresses other bodily functions, including the respiratory system, often the circulatory system and even the metabolic systems. The result to the patient can be anoxia (deficiency of oxygen), underventilation, (the failure of oxygenation of blood by the lungs), respiratory obstruction, heartbeat irregularities and circulatory collapse. The eventual result of any of these can be cardiac arrest—stoppage of the heart.

A six-year-old healthy child scheduled for an eye-corrective operation was placed under general anesthesia. During the administration of the anesthesia, the depressing effect of the gas on the child ended in cardiac arrest. The anesthetist refilled the bag with oxygen and attempted to restore the heart action by external massage, without success. A surgeon preparing for surgery was rushed in, and he opened the child's chest. Massage of the exposed heart by hand started it pumping again, but too late to save the blood-starved brain intact. The child became a blind mute, spastic quadriplegic and was confined to a state hospital. The cortical cells can exist for less than four minutes without oxygen-blood nourishment, after which damage is permanent, generally condemning the patient to a "vegetable" state.

Anesthesia death is a hydra-headed threat, occurring because of preoperative omission or error, operative anesthesia dangers and postoperative inattention. Anesthesia is a more virulent threat in the presence of debilitating illness: the weakened body is less able to offset its repressive interference. Dr. J. S. Denson of the University of Southern California School of Medicine believes, for example, that when an anemic patient is anesthetized, the chance of his suffering permanent brain damage from anoxia is two to four times greater than in a normal anesthetized patient.

Even a slight cold or feverishness, especially in a small child, may trigger tragic results in otherwise routine surgery. A young child of twenty months undergoing a harelip correction initially had his surgery delayed because of a cold. When the operation was rescheduled, his temperature was only slightly elevated, but he was taken into surgery and put "asleep" by the nurse-anesthetist. What should have been a routine repair became a biological debacle as the child's temperature soared, the fever destroying the brain tissue irreparably. The interference of the anesthesia on a healthy child had left the youngster blind, deaf and dumb.

Many patients, especially women in delivery, die simply because they vomit food while under anesthesia and then aspirate it into their respiratory system, blocking the airways. This "aspiration of vomitus," as it is called, is incriminated in several hundred maternity deaths a year in America. In one study of a thousand cases, vomiting accounted for 18.6 percent of the deaths from anesthesia. Women about to deliver are the most prone because of the chance that they may have eaten shortly before the sudden onset of labor.

Under anesthesia, the laryngeal reflex that closes off the airway to the lungs from the stomach pipe stops working. Regurgitated food comes up from the stomach through the esophagus, but slips over into the airway instead of up into the mouth. The patient either chokes to death, is "drowned" by the material in his lungs, or suffers chemical pneumonia from the thrown-up gastric acids, which burn his lungs. In one malpractice case, in which a judgment was delivered against the obstetrician, the administration of anesthesia by a nurse to a mother with a full stomach was held to be the cause of death. She choked on her own vomitus.

The uneasiness surrounding these deaths is that they are usually preventable, and most often caused by anesthetist error or oversight, as the University of Pennsylvania survey shows. Many board-certified anesthesiologists point to the undertrained anesthetist as a major culprit. Without stating it publicly, they have tagged much of the needless death as being related to a unique medical tradition in which nurses, rather than doctors, handle much of the anesthesia of American patients. Once considered a technician's job, it has now so grown in complexity that medical critics believe only the most intensively trained physician can properly handle the anesthesia emergency.

"There are approximately seventy-five hundred doctor-members of the American Society of Anesthesiology," a Columbia Presbyterian Hospital anesthesia specialist points out. "Three thousand of us are board-certified men, and the others are physicians with varying degrees of training and interest in the field. There are about an equal number of nurse and technician anesthetists, who handle about half of all the operations in the country. [Non-doctors administer *most*—57 percent—of all anesthesia.] Ideally, we would like to see physicians doing all the anesthesiology work. If a hospital hires a nurse-anesthetist, I believe they should have a physician-anesthetist supervise her work." Another colleague at Presbyterian agrees, adding that the nurse-anesthetist may be able to handle 85 percent of all cases adequately but that the remaining percentage harbors the potential for danger.

The disparity between the two groups, in training and competence, is well illustrated by Dr. Henry K. Beecher of the Anesthesia Laboratory at Massachusetts General Hospital: "By his medical training he [the physician-anesthetist] is in an entirely different position from that of the nurse-anesthetist, who can be no more than a technician subject to the orders of the surgeon."

The acute physician shortage in anesthesiology is a reflection of the specialty's undeservedly low prestige in medical quarters, a status game that injures the patient. "Anesthesia *looks* like a technician's business," the American Society of Anesthesiology has reported. "There are not enough residents in anesthesia today because of the historical attitude toward anesthesia," says Dr. John B. Dillon of the UCLA School of Medicine, in *JAMA*. "Many students finish medical school today without any exposure to anesthesia at all. This situation is a result of the most archaic thinking by medicine and by medical educators." He lampoons suggestions that the short-supply anesthesiologist handle the difficult surgeries and that the nurse-anesthesiologist be left for the "routine" matters. "Any anesthesiologist who has been in the operating room knows that the anesthesia for an incision and drainage of an abscess may well be more complicated than the anesthesia for a craniotomy, and there is no such thing as a simple or routine case."

The most routine case can be dangerous if only because certain anesthesia complications are implicit in the anesthetic itself—whether nitrous oxide, cyclopropane, ether, halothane, spinal or local anesthetic agents. Respiratory ailments are an obvious common aftereffect of anesthesia, as shown by a Public Health Service study of 514 patients given either general or spinal anesthesia for hernia repair in a Staten Island, New York, hospital. Forty-two of the patients developed respiratory complications, including twenty-one cases of bronchitis, four cases of pneumonia, and two victims of atelectasis (lung collapse) caused by the spinal anesthesia. In addition, almost one in three patients suffered urinary retention, almost all had some minor gastrointestinal distress and one in seven had headaches. Backache is considered by some a routine complication of spinal anesthesia, but almost as many with "general" anesthesia had the same gnawing complaint—17 percent and 24 percent of the patients, respectively.

Since anesthesia is a "drug," we should expect such reactions, and others. Ether and cyclopropane have been known to explode in the operating room, with tragic results. To avoid this, many anesthetists have been using nonflammables such as halothane, an efficient chloroform-like agent. Halothane has many advantages, including quick-sleep induction and equally quick recovery, but after more than 10,000,000 uses in hospitals, reports have implicated it in subsequent liver disease, including twenty-three such deaths.

Debate rages over the charge. One Canadian survey blames the increased postoperative jaundice on other causes, including blood transfusions. Drs. Herber and Sprecht in Los Angeles, however, surveyed a five-year record of liver dysfunction after operation, and are convinced that not only is halothane at fault but that jaundice occurs once in every eight hundred uses. Further studies are in progress; halothane's manufacturer meanwhile warns against its use in most obstetrical cases and in patients with liver disease. Astute physicians also keep patients from taking the gas twice within a short period.

Despite such possible built-in calamity, most anesthesia deaths are apparently due to human—physician or nurse—error. A physician writing in the journal *Anaesthesia* believes mortality is generally due to an inexplicable departure from good standard practice in the operating room, and after. The precautions against anesthesia death are not occult, and have been painstakingly delineated by American doctors for their colleagues' (and nurses') edification.

Hyperthermia, a rapid temperature rise that may occur during anesthesia, is one preventable cause of death. A twelve-year-old girl was admitted to the hospital for an adenoid operation. Her temperature prior to surgery was normal, and she was given premedication of Demerol and scopolamine. She was put to "sleep" with a combination of nitrous oxide and oxygen, and halothane. Five minutes after anesthesia had been administered, her breathing was affected and her abdominal and jaw muscles became "stiff." Anesthesia was discontinued and the patient "ventilated" with oxygen.

When she seemed back to normal, she was anesthetized again. The physician described the events that followed. "Once again a marked fall in chest compliance was noted after five minutes of anesthesia, which was again discontinued, and the child ventilated with oxygen. Five minutes later the child had a generalized seizure. Temperature at this time was found to be 104F (40.C.), and within fifteen minutes it rose to 108F (42.2C). Pupils were dilated [enlarged] and fixed. Alcohol sponging was ineffective in lowering the temperature, and direct application of ice was subsequently used. The temperature drifted down to 90F (31.1C) and she was warmed to 98F (36.7C). A tracheotomy was done. The patient remained comatose with dilated, fixed pupils for the following five days at which time she died."

Hyperthermia may result suddenly from a poorly air-conditioned operating room, hot operating-room lights, surgical drapes that restrict evaporation, belladonna drugs and even a defect in the patient's hypothalamus, the body's temperature-control gland. The room conditions should be watched carefully, and hospitals without sufficient air conditioning should be investigated by municipal and state authorities. The doctor's role in preventing death from the fever scourge is stated by Drs. Saidman, Harvard and Eger of the University of California. "We would say that a slight rise in temperature in an anesthetized patient must be regarded as being potentially very hazardous to the patient, and immediate attempts should be made to find and correct the cause and to prevent a further rise," they caution in *JAMA*.

Their recommendations should be remembered. Patients and doctors should avoid elective surgery in patients with any fever. If the fever is part of the illness (an abscess, for example), preoperative attempts should be made to lower it, say the California doctors. If this is unsuccessful, direct cooling should be maintained on the patient during the operation, plus the use of sparse surgical drapes. Belladonna drugs should be avoided in such patients, and temperature control of the operating room must be watched at all times. Most important, they warn that *immediate* cooling must begin with any temperature rise. It appears equally obvious that if a patient shows any sign of hyperthermic difficulty—as in the case history of the now dead twelve-year-old—the operation should, whenever possible, be called off and the child not resubjected to the killing anesthesia.

Anesthesia death from aspiration of vomit—food, blood, small bowel contents, gastric juices—is also preventable medical mayhem. Dr. Daniel C. Weaver of Yale University School of Medicine believes that widespread medical ignorance exists on the subject, and that "many physicians are largely unaware that regurgitation and vomiting are increased with the use of general anesthetics for emergency procedures because patients may have a 'full stomach.'" Writing in a prominent medical journal, Dr. Weaver adds the revelation that physicians may ignorantly think the tragedy is inevitable. "Nor are many physicians conscious that they may play a role, early in a patient's care, in preventing aspiration and vomiting," he says. "Most of these anticipated 238 deaths [his estimate] will be unnecessary!"

If not a pregnant woman, the "full stomach" patient is generally an emergency case, for patients should have been carefully warned about eating before surgery. Delaying surgery for a few hours may help, but Dr. Weaver warns that labor, pain or medication slows down digestion and the stomach may still not be empty, a fact often overlooked by physicians. Dr. David M. Little, Jr., of Hartford (Connecticut) Hospital states that even though four hours is considered normal stomach-emptying time, the emergency patient should be considered not to have an empty stomach for up to ten hours following injury. The stomach of a mother-to-be should not be considered empty until twelve hours after admission!

To prevent the vomiting tragedy, Dr. Weaver suggests the use of regional anesthetics (nerve blocks) in such emergency cases, if specialized talent is available to administer them. He believes that stomach-emptying and induced vomiting are not reliable enough, because they may leave some contents behind. The consensus appears to be that placing a special tube in the windpipe to maintain an open airway is the answer if surgery cannot be delayed sufficiently. Dr. Weaver believes this "endotracheal intubation" should be done in the awake patient with the help of a topical anesthetic. Others believe that such a tube, with an inflatable "balloon" that seals off the stomach pipe from the airway, can be inserted while the patient is under anesthesia.

Dr. Lester C. Mark of Columbia Presbyterian uses the forum of an excellent publication, *Hospital Medicine* (surprisingly, published by a drug firm), to give detailed instructions for preventing "vomiting, aspiration death" in case the accident takes place during the operation. He stresses that to avoid tragedy the anesthetist should constantly watch for early signs of vomiting. "Premonitory movements of the tongue and pharyngeal [throat] structures can usually be detected by the anesthesiologist's fingers supporting the patient's chin and the floor of his mouth," states Dr. Mark. "It is then imperative to lift the mask at once and inspect for the presence of vomitus." If vomiting occurs, he explains, the doctor should turn the patient's face to the side and place him in a head-down position. The vomitus should be removed carefully from the throat, the larynx and the trachea tube by a suction tube. The anesthesia should be lightened and oxygen given so that the cough reflex returns to the patient and he responds with a vigorous, perhaps life-saving cough.

To prevent recurring aspiration of the vomitus, a tube is inserted into the windpipe, with the cuff sealing it off from the esophagus, which leads to the stomach. A soft rubber catheter placed in the tube should be used to suction out any material that has been aspirated. Dr. Mark also makes the sensible suggestion that in the case of minor emergencies—suturing a laceration, manipulating a fracture, normal delivery, dental extraction—that the light inhalation of gas anesthesia will deaden the pain but will maintain the patient's lifesaving "cough" in case he (or she) vomits.

Such complexities explode the nonsensical concept that it is a "technician's job." The necessity of superb skill is illustrated by a recent tragedy in Kansas. A patient with a mastoid condition was awaiting surgery. The head anesthesiologist at the hospital had a resident-in-training aid him. The young doctor administered the anesthesia, then inserted an endotracheal tube into the patient to carry oxygen to his lungs during the operation. But instead of placing it in his patient's windpipe, the resident placed it in the esophagus. No one noticed his bluish, cyanotic condition caused by the lack of oxygen. The result of this failure of skill was a patient unable to see, talk, walk or perform his bodily functions.

Not just skilled anesthesiologists, but *all doctors* can prevent anesthesia death if they are aware of controllable factors, believes Dr. Little of Hartford. "Mere awareness of the existence of these situations would often be sufficient to safeguard the patient," he states in *Hospital Medicine*. "Widespread dissemination of knowledge of these problems can therefore be expected to prevent a considerable number of anesthetic tragedies." In addition to the "full stomach" problem, he claims that anesthesia is causing deaths in patients who are being "rushed to the operating room with little or no preoperative preparation." In this frightening category he includes the sick, fevered child with a ruptured appendix who should be receiving intravenous fluids and body cooling to "forestall convulsions and death" in anesthesia.

Eliminating anesthesia death also requires that doctors know the drug intake of their patients, many of which can precipitate deadly anesthesia accidents. The phenothiazine tranquilizers have an effect on the peripheral nerve endings, causing possible low blood pressure; despite this they are often used in preoperative medication. Anesthesia has the same blood effect, making the combination dangerous. "Patients who have been receiving phenothiazine therapy should not be given the drug before surgery," categorically say U.S. Army physicians Drs. Clark and Maier in *GP*. The same restriction is placed against certain antidepressants, whose use should be curtailed up to a week before surgery.

Reserpine and most types of anesthesia do not mix. Discontinuation of the common antihypertensive (high blood pressure) drug is advised for two full weeks before surgery, lest it trigger a fatal collapse. The common thiazide diuretics also augment undesired low blood pressure during anesthesia. They make the patient more susceptible to muscle relaxants used with anesthesia, producing prolonged respiratory depression when least needed.

Patients who have taken steroids present a severe anesthesia problem, for the stress may be multiplied exponentially because of adrenal insufficiency produced by the drug. The result of the gland failure during anesthesia and surgery, says Dr. Clark, is "hypotension [low blood pressure] and shock," which do not respond to transfusions or other medications, followed by death. Rather than cease steroid therapy, it is sometimes necessary to give cortisone derivatives to such patients, before, during and after surgery.

The electronic monitors in the modern operating room, which convert the patient's heart and other bodily functions into visible graphs, are valuable additional aids to medicine. Overreliance on the automated blips to the point of not reacting to flesh-and-blood symptoms may, however, invite disaster. Dr. Valentino D. B. Mazzia, chairman of anesthesiology at New York University School of Medicine, examined twenty-one anesthesia deaths. He concluded that the electrocardioscope monitor "did not help to predict the chain of events early enough to reverse them," and that it "was of no value in avoiding a lethal overdose of anesthetic agent." (The lightest possible anesthesia to do the job is usually considered best for the patient.)

Dr. Mazzia describes cases in which the patient showed initial symptoms of physical failure—falling blood pressure, slow pulse (bradycardia), and peripheal blue, cyanotic appearance—without changing the monitored ECG configuration. "If vital sign changes had been accepted at face value and immediate closed-chest massage begun," Dr. Mazzia lamented, "it is most likely that resuscitation would have been achieved." Dr. Carolyn H. Ziegler of Memorial Hospital in Marysville, Ohio, makes the same caveat: that the "gadget" should not receive more attention than the patient.

Spinal anesthesia has its advocates and detractors; statistical evidence indicates approximately the same safety as general anesthesia, but a somewhat different set of problems. The drugs are administered in the spinal column at various locations, to destroy feeling temporarily below those areas of the body. Paralysis can result from "spinal" mismanagement and is estimated to occur once in three hundred thousand operations—possibly an overoptimistic figure.

Aside from postoperative complaints of headaches and backache, nerve damage and paralysis are the most common ill effects of the badly done "spinal." A patient in a New Jersey hospital received a spinal anesthesia for a gall bladder operation. Afterward he suffered adhesive ascending arachnoiditis (inflammation of the spinal membrane) along with a resulting malfunctioning "neurogenic" bladder. In California, a mother became permanently paralyzed in both legs after the negligent administration of a "spinal" for childbirth. As with a general anesthetic, brain damage is also possible. A forty-nine-year-old mother of two who entered a New York hospital for a minor gynecological procedure was given a spinal anesthesia. She suffered severe brain damage, reducing her to an alleged "state of vegetation." The obvious damage from the anesthesia was sufficient for a jury to award her $317,000.

"Spinal" has received an unwarrantedly bad name among patients because of such accidents, some doctors believe, holding that the procedure may be as safe as—or safer than—general anesthesia. "The problem is not the technique, but who administers it," Dr. Robert Epstein of Columbia Presbyterian has stated.

The risk of anesthesia does not end in the operating room. Despite the fact that postoperative vigilance is crucial for survival, recovery-room observation of the patient is sometimes insufficient, or even negligent. Too often, observers point out, this period of care is left to a nurse rather than to close anesthesiologist supervision. "This [immediate postoperative period] has been a no man's land, at least from the patient's standpoint, if only he could know it," Dr. Henry K. Beecher and colleagues of Massachusetts General Hospital state in *JAMA*. "A period of great hazard comes when the surgeon removes his gloves and the anesthetist his endotracheal tube and the patient is placed in bed."

One deadly postoperative risk involves the way the still unconscious patient is placed back in bed in the recovery room! "One of the most common causes of anesthetic deaths is nursing the unconscious patient in a faulty position," says Dr. C. Brudzynski in *Annals of Western Medicine and Surgery*. "The problem is one of simple mechanics. With the patient lying on his back, if the jaw is left unsupported, the tongue will fall back and occlude the airway. This is an elementary fact which generations of instructors in anesthesia have drilled into their students over and over again. When the operation ends, this danger remains unchanged. And yet, for some unknown reason, the anesthetist may turn over the unconscious patient to an attendant who puts the patient flat on his back in bed and leaves him unsupervised, often for considerable periods."

Proper anesthesia aftercare has many subtle ramifications that can be vital to patient survival in the hospital. Dr. Mark Ravin of Columbia Presbyterian Hospital suggests one simple technique: if patients are told to take five deep breaths after they awake in the recovery room, the air sacs collapsed by anesthesia will "pop" open again. Duke anesthetists C. Ronald Stephen and Inger Talton believe that hypoxemia (insufficient oxygen in the blood) "may be present more than often believed" after anesthesia, and advise the use of oxygen in the recovery room, now an only occasional method. "All patients in the postoperative period should receive supplemental oxygen if hypoxemia is to be avoided," they state in *JAMA*.

In the second Trussell report, released in 1964 by the Columbia University School of Public Health and Administrative Medicine, Case No. 119 describes the death of a forty-year-old man involving unsatisfactory postanesthesia care that may have contributed to his death. "Operation for bullous emphysema. Expired 3 days postoperative," the report describes cryptically. "Preoperative evaluation consisted of bronchoscopy only. Inadequate postoperative ventillatory care."

The patient can lower the risk of many glaring anesthesia dangers by insisting on skilled hands putting him "to sleep." A board-certified anesthesiologist is preferable, a non-board physician-anesthetist next, and the nurse-anesthetist in an emergency only. The nurse-anesthetist is an anachronism in an era when the demands of surgery are stricter, more surgery is done on poor-risk patients and complications are more complex and challenging. Her role is a substantial medical one, yet she has no license to practice medicine. She acts as a "servant of the surgeon," yet in the operating-room complex he is busy enough without also assuming the titular role of anesthetist.

There are eighty-three hundred of these abnormal appendages to the medical arts in practice. Some nurses are undoubtedly skilled, but overall national health demands their retirement—simultaneously with stimulated replacement by an equal number of physicians. Meanwhile the patient can patronize the highly trained anesthesiologist *exclusively,* willingly paying the additional fee. The profession's own attitude is clear: many university hospitals use physicians exclusively, while most patients elsewhere receive anesthesia from non-doctors.

The physician-anesthetist is in limbo between private and hospital practice. His work is hospital-centered, but organized medicine's cries of "corporate medicine" usually restrain him from being a hospital employee. He is rather a contract physician, receiving a percentage of the fees taken in, or working on a "guarantee," a medical euphemism for salary. The fees in anesthesia are not as awesome as the surgeon's, but they are often not covered by hospitalization policies. As a rough rule of thumb, the anesthesia fee is approximately one-fourth the surgical fee. The anesthesia fee schedule of one prominent New York voluntary hospital is reasonably typical: appendectomy, $55; gall bladder, $80; open-heart surgery, $175; tonsils, $35.

"Choosing the anesthetist is as important as choosing the surgeon," says a hospital administrator. He is undoubtedly correct, but the patient is deprived of this choice and generally takes whom he is given. The prerogative is usually that of the hospital or the surgeon, some of whom favor particular anesthetists. The patient may be assigned a resident-in-training, or in case of emergencies, the low "man" on the anesthesiology status pole—generally a nurse or interne.

Even personally hiring the anesthetist may not always ensure that he will be standing over you in the operating room. Dr. Victor J. Tofany, past president of the New York State Society of Anesthesiologists, has explained that his organization is fighting to curb "ghost" anesthesia, a nefarious practice among some doctor-anesthetists. The patient pays the full fee for a trained man, but he is actually anesthetized by an unlicensed foreign doctor who receives only a nominal amount for his ghostly medical activity.

Anesthesia is only one determinant of hospital quality care, a broader commodity composed of an infinite number of components for survival. One of the most significant is whether the patient can be transfused with blood when needed and survive without costly aftereffects, or being killed. Two and a half million patients receive transfused whole blood yearly, and most live to discuss it. But the toll of blood-transfusion accidents and biological contamination is outlandishly high: a minimum of 3000 die every year, and a difficult-to-estimate 10,000 to 75,000 hospitalized patients contract hepatitis as a result of transfusions; thousands more suffer other serious reactions, including hemorrhage, gangrene, blood hemolysis (red cell destruction), kidney disease and even heart attacks.

Critics are convinced that most of the death is needless, that it originates in hospital negligence and physician ignorance or indifference. Explaining that blood has been transfused ever since 1788, when Italian physicians Rosa and Scarpa used donors' blood to treat anemia, an editorial in the *Annals of Internal Medicine* admonishes unknowing physicians about complacency in the use of what has been called "one of our most dangerous drugs"—human blood.

"Yet this very essential procedure is still beset with many controversial problems, and is subject to misuse and abuse on the part of misinformed physicians," says the *Annals*. "Some of these difficulties stem from the apparent simplicity of blood transfusion as it was performed in the early 1930's and from ignorance of the risks involved. Such misconceptions have created a very unfortunate state of complacency on the part of many physicians, a state which persists despite the increasing knowledge of the risk of possible severe, even fatal, results. . . ."

Dr. Leon Sussman, hematologist (blood specialist) at Beth Israel Hospital in New York, is convinced that preventable "human failure" in the hospital accounts for at least 50 percent of blood-transfusion accidents. The tales of such negligence fill the malpractice courts and hospital records. In New York a nurse produced a bottle of blood during an operation and handed it to the anesthetist for a transfusion. Without checking, the anesthetist asked the surgeon if he should give it to the patient, a twenty-five-year-old-mother of two children. The busy surgeon nodded his assent without asking how the blood got there, even though the hospital had a sage (but obviously neglected) regulation requiring a written order by the surgeon for blood. The blood proved to be the wrong type, killing the mother.

Keeping incompatible foreign blood out of the human body is essential. The reckless transfusion of such blood is a dramatic portrait in trauma. Almost immediately after the blood has begun to flow out of the plastic bag into the patient's veins, he complains first of backache, then chest pain. With only an ounce or two of donor's incompatible blood in him, the peripheries of his body start to turn blue and he becomes restless. Inside of his body the donor's red cells are being destroyed, at a fierce toll to the patient's body.

"If the transfusion is interrupted at this point, there are seldom any serious after-effects," Dr. Sussman states in *Trauma.* "However, if continued, the reaction gets worse, with chills and fever and severe prostration. (If the patient is under the effect of a general anesthesia these symptoms may not be recognized.) The symptoms progress rapidly and soon pulmonary edema [filling of the lungs with fluid and blood] may appear, followed rapidly by death." The patient may bleed excessively, and destroyed blood can damage the kidney tubules and cause uremic poisoning.

Does this tragedy require excessive amounts of incompatible blood? In one study of incompatible transfusions, those who died had received between 250 and 1000 cc. of the blood, but others survived equally large incompatible transfusions.

The typing and crossmatching of blood by hospital personnel is an attempt to predict, then avoid, such cataclysmic reactions. Almost all blood is divided into four major groups: A, B, AB and O. Typing is done by checking a sample of the blood with a typed "antiserum." If the diluted blood sample agglutinates (clumps) with anti-A, the blood is typed as A; similarly with B. If, however, the blood agglutinates with both anti-A and anti-B, the blood is typed as AB; if with neither, as O. In addition, the Rh factor of blood is essential; all blood is also typed Rh negative or Rh positive.

Unfortunately, being "blood-typed" is not enough. Ninety-five percent of patient and donor blood of the same ABO-Rh type will match, but the subtle nuances of nature have created at least thirteen identified blood groups—including MN, P, Kell, Kidd and Lewis—which must be taken into account. "Crossmatching" samples of the patient's and donor's blood, a process that should be reflex in the good hospital, is the only safeguard. The red cells of the donor are mixed with the serum (liquid) of the patient's blood and vice versa. The mixtures are watched carefully for telltale signs of clotting, an ominous warning that the transfusion will be a threat to the patient's life.

Despite such science, the permutations of transfusion mistakes in the hospital are staggering, an infinite complex of deadly buffoonery. Bottles of blood are mislabeled; donors are not correctly identified; units of blood are delivered to the wrong patients (a special danger when two patients in a hospital have the same name); blood is mismatched; bottles crack and become contaminated; the patient is improperly identified; a sample of his blood is typed, then placed under someone else's name.

The incidence of such error is less rare than the overassured hospital or physician would like the patient to believe. In a large Southern hospital a technician correctly identified the blood of two patients as Type 2 and Type 4 (hospital code), but mislabeled the bottles. The female patient, a Type 4, was mistakenly given 700 cc. of Type 2 blood during an abdominal operation. Her hands and fingernails turned blue, then ashen gray as her blood pressure dropped from 110 to 60, her pulse increased from 120 to 150, then was too faint to feel. Diverted into believing it was being caused by internal bleeding, the surgeon quickly reopened the wound, but then closed it abruptly when he realized that that was not the cause. A subsequent transfusion with the correctly typed blood was of no avail: the patient expired the next day.

Hospital blood mix-ups are possible because of easy assumptions made by medical personnel, and these simple human errors can result in potential horror. A thirty-one-year-old mother of four was admitted to a Michigan hospital for a total hysterectomy. On the evening she was admitted, a hospital technician drew blood for a sample *without marking the patient's name* on the tube. "She simply dropped a slip of paper around the tube," it was later revealed. After typing the blood, the technician later confused the patient's blood sample and identification slip with two other samples. The patient's blood was labeled A-Rh positive instead of the correct type of O-Rh positive.

The following morning the incompatible A-Rh blood was transfused into her body during the operation, starting the deleterious reaction of blood destruction. The transfusion caused hemorrhagic diathesis (abnormal bleeding), resulting in kidney shutdown and death. "She lingered during 13 days of complicated treatment and was in constant pain until the final hours of her life," a legal report on the case relates, "when 'she was thrashing, pulling her hair and screaming in pain to the point where the husband could stand it no longer and was forced to leave the hospital room.'"

The hospital must learn to protect the patient against such deadly confusion. The sophisticated patient, too, should be surveillant and aware of proper safety protocols. "The person who draws the blood sample in our hospital must write down the patient's name in front of him, and then initial it himself," says a blood bank spokesman at New York Hospital-Cornell Medical Center. "If a sample comes in here without a name on it we will not accept it, nor that person's word who it is from." Identification of the patient receiving the blood transfusion is equally important. "This frequently means simply asking the patient's name and comparing it with the name on the bottle label," says Dr. Sussman. "If the patient is unconscious, it is now the practice to affix to the patient's wrist a name plate for the purpose of identification."

Patient interest may intensify the hospitals' desire to keep him from being victim of incompatibility. Learning one's own blood type, and *insisting* that all samples bear his name before the nurse leaves the bedside, can only add to the patient's safety.

The most frustrating factor in blood death is that many of the transfusions given in American hospitals are totally unnecessary. Many add little to the patient's recovery and considerable to his life risk. In complex surgery, up to twenty-three pints (and probably more) of blood have been administered to one patient, and complete exchange transfusions have saved the lives of many Rh babies.

Against this backdrop of necessary, lifesaving transfusion is a plethora of unnecessary transfusion, done more for medical mode than necessity. Of thirty incompatible blood transfusions studied by Dr. Lee Binder and colleagues at the Kings County Hospital in Brooklyn, sixteen were judged to have been unnecessary and, ironically, the most lethal. "Clearly, the morbidity from blood-transfusion reactions would have been reduced by more than half and the mortality almost to *zero* [italics mine] were there greater appreciation for the indications for the use of blood," the doctors state in *Surgery, Gynecology & Obstetrics.*

Dr. Robert S. Myers, executive assistant director of the American College of Surgeons, also cites several operations "in which blood transfusions have been used in excessive amounts," including the surgeons' perennial love, the hysterectomy, where, he says, there is usually little need for transfusion. (In the last few years, goaded by such critics, doctors have dropped the transfusion rate in hysterectomy from 43 to 32 percent.)

The hospitalized patient must also survive medical dilettantism, which may involve him in "single pint" blood transfusion, which often accrues more risk than gain. The Commission on Professional and Hospital Activities (CPHA) in Ann Arbor, Michigan, reveals that in five common operations, including appendectomy, gall bladder removal and hysterectomy, almost half (49 percent) of transfusions were single pints, an amount the body can usually make up for by itself.

"One-Pint Transfusions May Not Be Worth The Risk," Dr. Robert

Myers warns in *Modern Hospital,* stating that the patient "would be safer if he were denied transfusion" in certain cases, especially current "routine" single-pint transfusions in surgery and as a "tonic" for slightly debilitated patients. "Here the anticipated benefits of transfusion are not great enough to justify its risk," he says. (Dr. Max Strumia of the University of Pennsylvania believes *some* single-pint transfusions, especially in surgery on cardiac cases and in the aged cardiovascular patient, are legitimate.)

The ultimate folly of some one-pint transfusions is illustrated by the biologic crippling of a patient on the eve of his discharge. The sixty-year-old man had been successfully operated on for an enlarged prostate. The day before his discharge he was given a pint of blood as a "pickup tonic" for a mild anemia that convalescence would naturally correct.

"During the transfusion a severe reaction with chills, fever and backache occurred," the report in *Trauma* states. "In addition, rather severe bleeding from the site of the prostatic surgery began. The transfusion reaction was not recognized as such, and the attention of the surgeon was directed toward the local bleeding. The patient was taken to the operating room where the wound was reopened and futile attempts made to control the bleeding, which became more profuse at each attempt to stem the flow. More blood was given (a total of nine pints) with inadequate crossmatching because of the patient's rapidly deteriorating condition. In spite of (or perhaps because of) these heroic measures, the patient succumbed on the operating table."

The aftermath showed that the patient's blood was sensitive to a minor subgroup of the Rh factor, which had caused the supposedly "compatible" blood to start the chain of untoward, then tragic reactions. An attempt to "pick up" an about-to-be-discharged convalescing patient had become a medical finale.

Hepatitis is the most widespread transfusion danger for the hospital patient, the result of contaminated blood. Its exact toll is elusive, but *JAMA* has editorially indicated that the hepatitis transfusion problem is significant and considerably more prevalent than previously thought. "It has been reliably shown," says *JAMA* worriedly, "that an essential therapeutic measure, blood transfusion, causes death in approximately one of every 150 transfusions in persons over 40 years of age as a result of serum hepatitis. Since this is the age group to which most blood transfusions are given, and since many hundreds are given daily, such a high fatality rate becomes a problem."

Key area studies—in Chicago, New Jersey, Philadelphia, Los Angeles and Baltimore—which have carefully followed up transfused patients are discouraging. The hepatitis scourge, they show, strikes about one in twenty-five to fifty patients, with sizable death rates of up to 20 percent in those stricken. "It appears that the incidence of hepatitis after blood transfusion is greater than prior estimates have indicated," states Dr. John R. Senior, a Philadelphia researcher. Dr. Garrott Allen of Chicago has reported hepatitis danger so extensive that it surprised the most inured of the profession: 3.6 percent of all transfused hospital patients later contracted the disease. (The risk rises with the number of units transfused.) Judging from these samples, there may be seventy-five thousand cases of hepatitis yearly, with almost ten thousand deaths!

More optimistic statistics have been garnered in Boston, by Tufts University School of Medicine researchers with a hopeful transfusion rationale for the future. A twelve-year study of the nine Boston teaching hospitals has produced only 171 patients rehospitalized for posttransfusion hepatitis, 12 percent of whom died. Since their total study represents about 5 percent of the nation's one-year blood use, we might thus expect thirty-five hundred cases nationally. The actual toll of blood transfusion hepatitis is possibly between the extremes of the Boston and Chicago studies.

One of the main keys to preventing hepatitis after transfusion, the Boston physicians found, was in the careful checking of the source of the blood. The epidemic-like hepatitis in other cities, they believe, is a direct result of pre-bottled blood supplied by commercial sources: 40 percent of the blood in the Chicago sample was bought and more than 75 percent of the blood in the Baltimore group was commercial. *In the teaching hospitals of Boston, conversely, none of the blood is purchased from commercial blood firms.*

"No matter what method of case finding was used, the lowest incidence of posttransfusion hepatitis was seen when commercially supplied blood was avoided," state Drs. Grady and Chalmers of Tufts University. The astute patient could do no less, refusing whenever possible to accept pre-bottled blood supplied to the hospital from a commercial blood bank, where screening of donors can never be as thorough as the good voluntary agency. On a societal level, it is apparent that the legal elimination of the business of blood will save thousands of lives a year from serum hepatitis.

Transfusion error and hepatitis rightly command our attention. But there are further blood-transfusion safeguards the cognizant doctor and patient cognoscenti should be aware of. In the *Annals of Internal Medicine* hematologist Dr. Lawrence E. Young makes several suggestions, including special sensitivity tests for patients who have been pregnant or who have received previous transfusions. Transfusion of women with the blood of their husband or husband's close relatives should be avoided, he says, because of the involvement of husband's and wife's blood cells during pregnancy through the fetus. He adds that universal donors (Type O) are not really "universal" and should not be used in that context except when other, properly typed blood is not available. Dr. Young stresses another caveat: severely anemic patients should not be transfused too rapidly, for they are susceptible to heart failure under such conditions.

The transfused patient may have to have his blood crossmatched *again* if he waits for forty-eight hours between transfusions, warns Dr. Sussman of Beth Israel. The first transfusion may actually have altered his antibody system. Dr. Sussman makes two other valued suggestions: a trained observer watching the patient's reaction carefully during the critical first two ounces of all transfusions can halt the procedure while there is still time to make amends. The blood bank, too, can aid by discarding stored blood if it is turning purple or shows signs of hemolysis—red cell breakdown.

Some concerned hematologists (blood specialists) and pathologists believe that the greatest safety in typing can come only by a *double* crossmatch of blood samples conducted by *two different technicians.* (One of the new techniques, autologus transfusion, eliminates blood-typing error. It uses the good surgical risk's *own blood,* taken from him three weeks before elective surgery.) Perhaps the best of all cautions comes from Dr. Young: "The surest way to minimize risks is to avoid unnecessary transfusions."

As the scene of much that is complex in medicine, whether blood transfusion or involved surgery, the modern hospital is determinedly dogged by error, seemingly on an individual basis, but cumulatively oppressive. One of the modern hospital's most widespread errors involves the carrying out of doctor orders—such as the common nursing error in the dispensing of drugs.

The dispensing of medication in proper dosage, at the proper time, to the proper patient is apparently too severe an effort for many hospital staffs. Medication error is now the leading cause of accidents in hospitals, says George F. Archambault, former chief hospital pharmacist of the U.S. Public Health Service. Sister Mary M. Gerald, chief pharmacist at St. Joseph's Hospital in Hamilton, Ontario, affirmed this point, telling a meeting of hospital administrators that there has been "an alarming increase" in medication error, forcing it ahead of the misplaced sponge as the leading cause of hospital accidents.

The hospital medication error in progress is a tale of sorrowful mischance. A patient who was supposed to have received intravenous glucose feeding (water and glucose), received instead 1000 cc. of distilled water from his nurse. The water coursing through his blood stream resulted in blood hemolysis (the breakdown of the red cells) and irreparable damage to the heart.

At a university-connected hospital in New York, giant hand-printed capital letters on both the patient's admission sheet and doctor's order sheet read: ALLERGIC TO PEN [penicillin]. Despite the double caution, penicillin was injected into the patient, who predictably died following anaphylactic shock. In Rochester, a similar medication error killed a fifty-two-year-old patient. Undergoing allergy tests at a local hospital, the patient was given a 20-unit test dose of penicillin. He reacted violently even to this minute dose, and was recovering when the nurse injected a normal, full dose of 600,000 units of penicillin into him. He died, stated the medical examiner, of an "acute reaction from penicillin." The hospital director later reportedly stated that the fatal dose resulted from a misunderstanding, both in the transmission of the verbal medication order from doctor to nurse, and the nurse's verbal reconfirmation.

The exact extent to which medication error has infused itself into the daily habit of the American hospital is difficult to assess, but sample surveys hint at a suspiciously high, and deadly, incidence. Many errors originate with the nurse, dispensing wrong medications and dosages, along with her supposed brisk efficiency. A seven-month study by Johns Hopkins researchers in an 1100-bed hospital showed that 178 medication errors were *reported* by the nursing staff during a seven-month period. A study at another general hospital uncovered 360 medication errors during a twelve-month period. These three-digit figures are deceptive, since they each represent only two hospitals (albeit large) of the nation's more than seven thousand. On a national scale they symbolize well over a hundred thousand hospital medication errors a year!

As Brobdingnagian as these six-figure statistics may seem, they represent only a particle of the problem. The Johns Hopkins survey relied entirely on the nursing staff to record their own follies. The logical conclusion that self-flagellation is not indigenous to the medical community occurred to two other researchers, Kenneth Barker and Warren E. McConnell, who set up a disguised observation system in a university-affiliated hospital in Florida. The *known,* recorded medication errors in the hospital that year numbered thirty-six. The medical sleuths unearthed a projected *51,200* medication-dispensing mistakes!

Thirty-seven percent were omissions—drugs ordered but not given the patient; 18 percent involved nursing overinitiative—drugs given but not ordered; 13 percent were underdoses; 10 percent were extra doses; 8 percent were overdoses; 10 percent involved medication given at the wrong time; 4 percent were the wrong dosage form. Extrapolation of this secret survey defies patient grasp: over *100,000,000 hospital medication errors* a year nationally, enough to ply each hospital patient with four pharmaceutical mistakes during his short stay in a hospital. "The average nurse," their *Modern*

Hospital report states, made "one error for every six medications given." Since the typical hospital patient received six to eight medication doses a day, each one could expect to be the subject of error at least once every day.

The results of this unsettling study were confirmed by another made at an Arkansas university-affiliated hospital by hospital pharmacist Kenneth Barker, in which he found medication mistakes in one out of every seven doses. Voluntary general hospitals appear equally culpable: similar surveys of 300- to 500-bed institutions reveal almost exactly the same magnitude of error—15 percent of all administered hospital medications.

The subterfuge at the Florida hospital that first revealed the enormity of drug error in American hospitals was the creation of a "hospital pharmacy interne" who was introduced to nurses as being in training. The "cover" was accepted by the nine nurses from medical, surgical and pediatric wards, who were watched for two consecutive eight-hour shifts by the *interne*. "Using disguised methods," state the researchers, "the interne was able to record the name and dose of every drug, the exact time administered, and the name of the patient to whom it was given. The nurses were never aware of this part of the interne's purpose." The "interne's" information was then compared with the physician's medication order on the original patient chart: any deviation was tabulated as a medication error. Of 572 medications given by the nine nurses during the two-day experiment, there were 93 errors! The most vigilant nurse erred once every thirteen times, but some imprudent nurses bedeviled patients almost once in every three medications.

One case history portrays the chasm between hospital self-image and the reality of medication care. A forthright twenty-four-year-old nurse, with a B.S. degree and three years of experience, indicated that she was insistent on reporting medication errors even if a physician asked her to overlook the mistake. "This is part of the nursing ethic," she volunteered. When she was asked to recall medication mistakes she had made in the last three months, she confidently answered, "None—to my knowledge I have never made one." The actual observation of this admittedly dedicated nurse underscores why the authors conclude that "self-report methods of detecting medication errors are of little value."

"During the first shift that she was observed," the report states, "this nurse gave a patient two aspirin tablets, which were not ordered. To another patient she gave at different times two doses of procaine penicillin, and, though the order on the chart was for 1.2 million units, she gave 600,000 units each time. She gave one phenobarbital tablet to another patient for whom no such order existed, and to still another patient she administered papaverine injection, though the order on the chart said 'oral papaverine.'

"During the second shift on which she was observed the same

nurse omitted a dose of 15 drops of Belladonna Tincture in water, gave one multivitamin capsule where two were ordered, and again gave a phenobarbital tablet to the same patient as the previous night though no order existed for this drug."

The piqued patient who narrated his chagrin about unclean nurses is as uncomplimentary about nurse attempts to foist unordered and wrongly dosed drugs on him. "During the first two weeks of his hospitalization, nurses looked at his identification bracelet less than a half-dozen times when medications were given in spite of a notice printed on each medicine card that it should be read each time," the knowledgeable patient wrote about himself in *Modern Hospital.* "It is estimated that during the first two weeks of his stay, the patient had approximately 40 doses of drugs. During this period, several potential medication errors were avoided only by the patient's refusal to take drugs until the order was checked." The cantankerous patient soon became an object of wonder to the nurses. "In fact," he relates, "one nurse came in one evening and said, 'Let me see your wristband. I've heard about you and medications.' *She then proceeded to offer the patient the wrong dosage of his sleeping pill.*"

The cause and cure of medication errors was weighed by the Johns Hopkins authors of the hospital study in which 176 errors were reported by the nurses themselves. One primary error stemmed from similar-sounding drug names, the constant threat of the drug world's computer-spewn nomenclature. "In many cases in which a nurse misread a label, she selected a drug with a name similar to the one ordered," the Johns Hopkins researchers explain in *Hospitals.* "When she made an error in copying the name of the drug ordered by the physician onto the nursing card and medicine tickets, she often wrote the name of a drug similar to the one ordered." The report continues: "In addition, in a few units, it was found that two drugs that were frequently confused, digoxin and digitoxin, were kept in the same section of a drawer."

The chagrined surveyors are convinced that the hospital medication system needs an overhaul. They suggest that bedside tags be made more visible and accessible for patient identification; that drugs be packaged in units in which they are dispensed, eliminating nurses' error in calculating micrograms or milligrams; that decimal systems of dosages be made clearer (perhaps with fractions) so that 2.5 mg. is not misinterpreted as 25; that writing the doctor's orders onto medication cards be double-checked; that the same be done with instructions to cut off medication; that more checks be built into medication procedures so that if the nurse should forget one step, or make an error, it will automatically be detected at some other level.

The current medication terminology system that doctors use for prescriptions, an inelegant mixture of Latin, English and medicalese that pleases prideful doctors, frustrates critics who believe it harbors a wasp's nest of confusion. "Nurses sometimes confused certain standard medical abbreviations," the Johns Hopkins surveyors state, arguing "that the medical profession should undertake research to devise a system of terminology that is less confusing." (Pharmacist Barker found incomplete or jumbled orders by M.D.'s to be a major source of error.) The symbols "q.n." (every night) were confused with "q.h." (every hour); "q.o.d." (every other day) was confused with "q.d." (every day). Eli Schlossberg, pharmacist at Arizona State Hospital, adds that this confusion is compounded by "official, common names, abbreviations and chemical formulas."

The possibilities for reform are as immense as the current deluge of mistakes. Kenneth Barker found that using a centralized unit-dose dispensing system in which the medication is pre-measured, packaged and clearly marked by name and dosage, reduced the over-all error rate by half. Such systems are more expensive, but obviously essential. Pharmacist Schlossberg suggests that informal labels on bottles—whether Scotch-taped on, marked on glass, or one label pasted over another—are a potential source of mix-up. Dr. Herman E. Feldman of the Methodist Hospital in Gary, Indiana, states that the doctor's prized illegible handwriting contributes to medication error, a caution that has prompted some hospitals, including New York's Mount Sinai, to initiate handwriting classes for physicians. Dr. L. Snedeker of Children's Hospital Medical Center in Boston calls on stern Yankee vigilance. "A rigid regimen is needed to reduce the chances of error in medication. It may be necessary," he states, "to have one nurse check another when particularly potent drugs are being used."

The offended patient is generally dismissed in such contemplations, but two observers, Miriam Safren and Dr. A. Chapanis, who conducted the Johns Hopkins survey, sagely suggest that he be made a partner in his own survival. The patient, they believe, should be provided with more information about the medication he is supposed to receive. "Being vitally concerned with his own health and safety, he would thus become an active and interested partner in eliminating certain kinds of common errors," they write. "The patient who knows, for example, that he is supposed to receive two blue pills every four hours (even though he may not know what they are supposed to do) will almost certainly object if a nurse attempts to give him an intramuscular injection, if he is offered two yellow pills, or if he is given two blue pills only fifteen minutes after having already swallowed two."

Whether it prompts a medication error or a patient falling out of bed, the hospital is an accident-prone environment, which further reduces the patient's opportunity for healing or survival. Patients *do* fall from bed; are burned by chemicals, hot liquids or warm radiators; cut by broken thermometers; injured by equipment or hospital personnel; and even crash while using wheel chairs. Some misadventures are unavoidable, others are the result of negligence. Some are minor inconveniences, others catastrophic. "The hospital has a moral obligation to provide sick and injured patients with a protected environment, one from the risk of accidental death," argues Dr. Henry M. Parrish.

The statistics and case histories show this obligation still largely unfilled. In a large voluntary New York hospital, two patients with leukemia fell from their beds, causing uncontrollable hemorrhage and death. A six-month-old baby in a Denver hospital suffered horrible, disfiguring burns as a result of negligence in using a steam vaporizer. In California a patient after undergoing surgery was returned to her room and left in an unconscious state for an hour. When she awoke, she had a second-degree burn on her body in the exact shape of a hot-water bottle.

Rather than the controlled environment it presents to the world, the hospital is "as inherently hazardous as a factory, if not more so," Dr. Eric Stone, former director of the VA Hospital, Manchester, New Hampshire, reminds us. "Actually, a hospital presents a complex of hazards that makes it a dangerous place for employees and patients alike," he states in *Hospitals*.

Accident hospital rates, like most medical computations, are understated. One count by Dr. Stone of 108,005 patients in several hospitals turned up 3747 nonmedical accidents. Nationally, such accidents total almost 1,000,000 a year. At a hospital in New York, Dr. Parrish conducted a breakdown of hospital accidents, with interesting insights.

Not surprisingly, some 70 percent of all nonmedical accidents occur within a ten-foot radius of the patient's bed. That bed, it appears, is constructed (and ill-maintained) to be his nemesis. Of the 614 patient accidents in one year, 283 were bed falls, causing damage from slight injury to "death."

The typical, ill-designed, towering hospital bed is apparently a perfect patient-launcher. At the very least, a quarter of a million patients fall out of hospital beds every year! (In the Manchester, New Hampshire, survey, it was responsible for half the total accident toll.) Bed falls—and the resulting pain, hip fractures, death and malpractice suits—are the result of three main factors: excessive bed height, guard rails down and, surprisingly, even guard rails up. The uncautious nurse may forget to put the guard rails up on the beds of the sick and the infirmed. Now it appears that even caution is insufficient, since the rails on most hospital beds are pitifully ineffective in safely containing the human body.

"Since 106 of the 283 falls from bed occurred while bedrails were in place," Dr. Parrish explains in the *New York State Journal of Medicine,* "one must conclude that currently used bedrails are ineffective in preventing falls. Indeed they may intensify the severity of an accident by causing a patient going 'over the rails' to drop an additional 2 to 3 feet to the floor. Also, most hospital beds are too high for patient safety. Twenty-seven falls from bed clearly could have been prevented by using lower beds, since patients slipped and fell on either a footstool or a chair while climbing in or out of bed." Dr. Parrish quotes the typically annoyed patient: "This hospital bed is much higher than my bed at home." The hospital administrators who buy a sensible (lower) hospital bed should be immortalized with the discoverers of cures for more esoteric, if no more serious, medical "ailments" than the hospital pratfall.

Patients also fall on slippery hallway floors, stairs, examining tables and especially in bathrooms. In a recent case in Georgia, an unattended patient died in a fall from an X-ray table. In a dazed, nauseated condition because of drugs, the forty-seven-year-old patient attempted to get off the X-ray table to go to the bathroom and was fatally injured in the subsequent fall. In the New York survey (in which the accident rate was about average) fifty-nine of the accidents were attributed to faulty equipment and/or personnel negligence, including three cases in which the side rail was defective; instances of defective heating pads or excessively waxed floors; two cases in which the X-ray machine hit the patient; three cases of broken glass thermometers being inserted into human orifices; accidents caused by broken wheel chairs; and seven cases of bedrails left down.

The deficiencies in hospital regimen—whether mislabeled blood, faulty beds, or unmopped, disease-spreading floors—are easier for the layman to assess than the deficiency in his hospital medical care. For centuries doctors have kept laymen guessing as to the extent of hospital quality, using public relations tools rather than significant proof, to impress. Today, the hospital is just beginning what might evolve as an era of quality-control study, in which it will be audited, by doctors, for both professional and lay perusal. The epochal two Trussell-Morehead reports, prepared by Columbia University School of Public Health and Administrative Medicine in 1962 and 1964, analyzing the care of patients in over a hundred hospitals, are the initial probes into this previously uncharted, neurotically guarded doctor bailiwick.

The detailed analysis of "medical" (nonsurgical) care in ninety-eight hospitals in the most recent Trussell report is a documented insight into errors of neglect, omission and commission to which the patient may fall victim. In it, 120 histories of general medicine cases—patients suffering from heart disease, diabetes, respiratory conditions, ulcers, liver and gall-bladder disease—were surveyed by two specialists, a full professor and an associate professor of medicine at two large medical colleges.

The chance of the adult nonsurgical patient receiving what they term "optimal" hospital care is apparently low: less than one in three. Of the 120 cases, the opinion of the two surveyors coincided 90 percent of the time. Their conclusions: *only 31 percent of the care was "good" or "excellent"*—the remainder being relegated to the category of "fair" or "poor," their catchalls for "less than satisfactory."

Superficial, negligent medical care dominates the report. "By far the major reason for care judged 'less than optimal,' in all cases except those with cardiac disease, was the failure to explore fully the symptoms for which the patient was hospitalized and to establish a diagnosis for which a rational treatment program could be instituted," the report states with candor. "All too frequently there was superficial therapy given to the most obvious complaint, with failure to study other signs of pathology which were contributing to the patient's illness. Anemia, evidences of renal disease, and possible concomitant cardiac involvement were frequently left unexplored and unresolved."

Medical omissions, especially the lack of diagnostic thoroughness, permeate the hospital case histories. A fifty-nine-year-old man complained of rectal bleeding for three months before his hospital admission. His case (No. 104) is a lesson in missed application of modern medicine: "Discharged on tranquilizers as psychogenic gastrointestinal reaction. X-ray demonstrated diverticulosis [sacs on intestines]. No further gastrointestinal studies, i.e., proctoscopy [deep rectal examination]. Diabetic history and sugar in urine not followed up."

This pattern is repeated continuously, as if the physicians involved were co-operatively schooled in incompleteness. A forty-nine-year-old woman was hospitalized for five days for renal colic. "Evaluation incomplete. Only one urine examination," state the surveyors. "No chest film, urine cultures, calcium, phosphorus or serum uric-acid tests."

"No. 198, 43-year-old female, hospitalized 9 days," begins another surveyed case. "Bronchial pneumonia. History of 3 prior respiratory illnesses and father dying of tuberculosis. No investigation of tuberculosis made." A fifty-seven-year-old diabetic (Case No. 205-7) was admitted for ulceration of the great toe, a complaint that can often lead to gangrene and amputation in diabetics. "Superficial evaluation," the surveyors state. "No complete urinalysis. No check of elevated urea nitrogen. No electrocardiogram. Discharged with ulceration still present."

Ignoring patients' symptoms contributed not only to the physicians' abstract "failure" in almost two thirds of the cases, but to fatal conclusions. A sixty-five-year-old man (Case No. 240-1) was initially hospitalized for ten days because of a history of edema (swelling) and hemoptysis (spitting up of blood). Commenting on this first admission, the surveyors noted: "Exploration of respiratory disease superficial. Cardiac condition improved." Nine weeks later the patient was readmitted to a hospital. States the report succinctly about his second hospitalization: "Hemoptysis, congestive failure and bronchopneumonia. Treated symptomatically, but underlying disease not investigated." Two months later the patient was admitted to a Veterans Administration Hospital, where he died of cancer of the lung.

Several cases involved the double sin of diagnostic neglect *and* faulty treatment, a category the report calls: "Medical therapeutic regimen ill-advised, inappropriate, inadequate." One such admixture plagued hospital patient No. 131. On his first admission, lasting eighteen days, he suffered fever for twelve days, and was discharged with a diagnosis of bronchopneumonia. "No blood culture despite 12-day fever," say the surveyors. "Multiple myeloma [bone marrow tumor] suggested but not investigated. Final diagnosis not substantiated."

Despite his discharge, the patient was readmitted to the hospital five days later in a worsened condition and died within a week. "Admitted for loss of consciousness," the surveyors report. "Expired. Final diagnosis: bronchopneumonia, septicemia, possible cerebral thrombosis [blood clot in brain]. Neurological examination poor. No work-up for subdural or skull fracture despite history of fall. Brain abscess not explored. Staphylococcus septicemia treated with achromycin; other drugs preferable."

Several hospital patients judged as inadequately handled were cardiacs, or those suspected of having heart conditions. "A major factor among the cardiac cases for judgments of 'less than optimal' medical care was the failure to explore, by accepted diagnostic standards and/or procedures, the degree of heart pathology," the report explains. "Of equal importance, however, in the unsatisfactory ratings was the treatment the patient received. Patients with suspected or proven heart attacks (coronary occlusions) were allowed out of bed or sent home too soon. The use of digitalis and other drugs was frequently irrational and inadequate."

The neglect of *known* heart treatment is illustrated by several cases of cardiac mismanagement. "No. 121–1, 47-year-old male hospitalized 20 days," states the report. "Critically ill coronary patient allowed out of bed on 14th day and discharged on 19th. Care insufficient and inexperienced." In one situation the attending physician was castigated for establishing a premature cardiac diagnosis in a young man, despite the possible psychological side effects of such action. "No. 102, 33-year-old male hospitalized 4 days," states the report. "Sudden pain in chest and arms. Patient signed himself out. Admission and discharge diagnosis: coronary heart disease." The surveyors studied the case record, then blasted the doctor. "This diagnosis, at this age, with little justification, can cause great harm. The patient having signed himself out makes no difference to this criticism."

A male heart patient (Case No. 338), with three separate admissions spaced one year apart, is the subject of a continuous narrative of over-casual care. "Fifty-two-year-old man hospitalized seven days. Admitted for chest pain," the report on the first admission begins. "Electrocardiogram showed fibrillation [irregular, usually rapid excitation of heart muscle], yet this was not commented upon. No evaluation for rheumatic heart disease. Patient allowed to perform heavy work despite diagnosis of coronary disease."

The following year the same patient was hospitalized for the same heart condition for six days, with this evaluation of his still skimpy care: "Again admitted for chest pain with no studies undertaken to determine etiology. Therapy symptomatic." At the age of fifty-four, he was brought to the hospital again after the "sudden onset of chest pain," this time for an eighteen-day stay. "Patient continued to fibrillate, with no attempt to diagnose or control. No cardiac consultation obtained," the report despondently records.

By contrast, the well-handled cardiac case received unarticulated but implied congratulations from the surveyors. The physician and hospital caring for a sixty-two-year-old man hospitalized for eighteen days received this simple tribute: "Admitted for congestive heart failure [inability to properly pump blood], pulmonary infarction and fibrillation. Therapy aggressive. Patient carefully followed," the report states simply. No patient could rationally ask for more—or less.

These few cases of reasonable treatment notwithstanding, the long list of mismanaged diabetics, ill-doctored respiratory cases and medically mauled intestinal ailments makes discouraging reading. Pediatric care in the hospital was not judged appreciably better, with twelve cases of unsatisfactory care as opposed to only nine "optimal" diagnoses and treatments.

An eight-year-old child was hospitalized with a laceration of the forehead, ostensibly for observation. "If hospitalization was indicated for observation of possible head injury, then this was not done insofar as monitoring of vital signs," the pediatric surveyors reported. "Tetanus antitoxin not given (reason not stated), but 300,000 units of penicillin substituted. Inadequate therapy." (In a separate interview, one of the pediatric surveyors later indicated that in the case of such head injury to a child, the pulse and respiration must be watched closely, perhaps every fifteen minutes for twenty-four hours, for signs of intracranial bleeding.)

The full hospital audit, the probing of every hospital case in this manner, is a greatly needed if disregarded undertaking. The emergence of the tissue committee after World War II, however, initiated a closer study of surgical operations in the hospital. Under the prodding of the American College of Surgeons and other professional groups, these committees were set up to examine material removed from the hospitalized patient's body and to determine whether it was diseased, malignant or normal. They have successfully incriminated segments of the medical community in the sophisticated layman's oldest suspicion—unnecessary operations.

The damning proof of widespread unnecessary surgery in certain procedures has been more than annoying. Tonsil removal (more than nine in ten of which are probably unnecessary) is but one of the common operations that have been implicated, along with many hospitals. In Baltimore, Dr. J. Frederick Sparling of the Johns Hopkins Hospital surveyed 1002 appendectomies in five hospitals, three accredited community institutions and two university hospitals. In the community hospitals *less than half (49.2 percent) of the appendectomies were found to have been necessary.* Twenty-one percent were patently unnecessary and the balance were "doubtful." The university institutions did better (67.3 percent), but even one in three of their operations could not be labeled as necessary.

It is impossible for a hospital to have a 100 percent record in justified appendectomies. Occasionally the best diagnostic appraisal indicates acute appendicitis, with the discovery after surgery that the signs were deceiving, and the appendix normal. But the low incidence of correctness in some hospitals and by some doctors is a clue to either slovenly medicine or chicanery. "We are convinced that removal of an occasional normal appendix may be justifiable," say the tissue committee members of the Memorial Hospital of Charleston, West Virginia, "but we cannot condone the removal of as high as 50 percent normal appendices, as practiced by some surgeons."

The problem is unquestionably nationwide in scope. In Michigan nineteen hospitals participated in a survey of appendectomies that showed a wide disparity between institutions. One hospital had an amazing record of 93.6 percent correctness, as close as one should come without belaboring medical overconservativism. On the other hand, the *majority* (52.1 percent) of appendectomies performed in another institution involved tissue having "no disease." A physician in one hospital was apparently running an appendectomy "mill." Seventy-three percent of his patients under the knife were later found to have had normal appendices!

If we realistically estimate that 15 to 25 percent of appendectomy operations performed are unnecessary, the toll of pain and death is considerable. Of 410,000 appendectomies performed each year, almost 100,000 are probably unneeded, involving a mass of patients in anesthesia risk, infection, surgical complication and even death. Of this group, we would expect at least 500 fatalities.

The uterus is another seemingly dispensable organ that is a favorite of the impetuous, perhaps unthinking, or greedy surgeon. The organ's removal is almost as popular as the appendix excision and accounts for 359,000 hysterectomies each year. "There is no avoiding the thought that some surgeons are too ready to remove the uterus," states *GP* magazine editorially. "Sometimes this may be because, in all sincerity but without real justification, they expect too much of this operation. It has never sufficed as a method for relieving vague female ills. Other times, surgeons may do a hysterectomy purely for reasons of expediency. Then there is the woman-patient's part in the problem—her strange passivity or even willingness to sacrifice this part of her body. If the record for this operation is to be improved, hospital discipline and surgeons' and patients' education need reorientation."

Patient willingness to participate in such a defiling procedure is partly based on ignorance of the seriousness of the operation: losing a uterus is not like losing a tonsil. Hysterectomy may be advised (often correctly) when a female patient presents irregular bleeding from the vagina, pain, the presence of a fibroid tumor, cancer of the uterus or a dozen other indications. The uterus, or womb, is the repository for the unborn child, a pear-shaped organ about three inches by two inches in the nonpregnant woman. Its removal *is a major operation* with the attendant problems of all surgery, plus hazards peculiar to the hysterectomy. The misadventurous result may be hemorrhage; a dangerous scalpel cut of the bladder or the ureters (long narrow tubes that carry the urine from the kidney to the bladder); peritonitis; tears of adjacent tissue; and potentially fatal shock.

In Los Angeles, gynecologist Dr. James C. Doyle conducted an extensive survey of 6248 hysterectomy operations from thirty-five hospitals in the area, with evidence of substantial surgical abuse. Almost 40 percent (39.3) were judged as operations "that may be criticized." In 12.5 percent of the cases, *nothing* was found to indicate the need for an operation. In an additional 24 percent of the cases, the surveyors felt that "more conservative treatment" was indicated.

The report noted incredulously that 86 percent of the women with menstrual aberrations were not given curettage (scraping to clean out the uterus cavity) prior to deciding on a hysterectomy. "One might speculate," says Dr. Doyle, "as to how many of these hysterectomies would have been obviated had this diagnostic procedure been em-

ployed." In several hundred cases the operation was needlessly done
for the most unscientific criteria. "Pain was the only complaint of
185 patients and backache the single symptom of 86 others subjected
to hysterectomy, *in none of whom did a pathological lesion* [italics
mine] actually exist," he states. This major procedure was unwisely
done for minor female abnormalities, including the retroposed, or
backward-tilted, uterus. "A uterus in 'retroposition' as a lone observation does not justify its removal," Dr. Doyle reminds his colleagues in *JAMA*. "In 130 cases this was the only diagnosis preopera-
tively and/or postoperatively, and in none of the 130 did the pathologist record any lesion whatsoever."

The most tragic aspect of unneeded hysterectomies is that it permanently destroys the childbearing ability of young women. Despite
this sobering censure, women in their twenties were the most victimized by surgeons. "An appalling number of the patients aged twenty
to twenty-nine who were subjected to hysterectomy had no disease
whatsoever (30 percent)," reports Dr. Doyle. Many other young
women who had their uteri removed impetuously had suffered from
infections of the uterine tubes or ovaries, or had small fibroid tumors.
The growths, he says, might have been handled by simpler procedures, including myomectomy, for the uterine tumor removal.

For conservative physicians, surgery is not necessarily justified
simply because the pathologist can find some diseased tissue on his
laboratory workbench postoperatively. Controversy, for example,
rages over the use of hysterectomy to remove fibroid tumors—even
though it is considered surgically "justified" in such audits. Dr.
Doyle believes surgery should be discouraged when the fibroid
tumor is small, and the patient without symptoms. Another critic,
Dr. R. W. Telinde of Baltimore, believes that the possibility of
malignancy in fibroid tumors is so small that the risk of the operation is as great as, or greater than, the possibility of cancer mortality.
Even large tumors are not sufficient reason for hysterectomy unless
they cause trouble, he told his colleagues at a recent International
College of Surgeons meeting.

The quality of surgical judgment varied from hospital to hospital in
the Doyle report. In the best Los Angeles institution, Hospital X,
only 5 percent of the hysterectomies were criticized. The worst
institution, Hospital W, seemed to have no intelligent criteria, and
the necessity of almost 84 percent of their hysterectomies was challenged! The damage and death from such sloppy (or deceitful)
surgical decisions are not difficult to calculate.

The Doyle survey, published in 1953, covered hysterectomies
performed in 1948. Have conditions changed or improved drastically since? A subsequent study (1954–59) of five hospitals, reported in the *Bulletin of the American College of Surgeons,* shows
approximately the same number of normal uteri removed from

female patients. The hospitals varied from a score of 41 to 88 percent justified operations on the uterus, with the two middle institutions—scoring 60 and 65 percent—most typical of the hospitals. A later survey, the first Trussell report, released in 1962, shows the needless surgical waste: 33 percent of the hysterectomies performed in 105 hospitals were judged unjustified by the surveyor, Dr. Alan Guttmacher, then director of obstetrics and gynecology at Mount Sinai Hospital in New York.

Those who believe there is currently less opportunity for such excess because fewer hysterectomies are being performed, are badly misinformed. The CPHA survey of 115 hospitals throughout the nation shows that both the number and rate of hysterectomies have *risen* in the last few years, from 3.7 of all female non-maternity patients in 1960, to 3.9 percent in 1964.

Extensive damage, even death, is the harvest of unnecessary hysterectomies. The Trussell survey describes one case which could have been resolved by a simple D&C (dilation and curettage), which instead culminated in two trying hospitalizations. A forty-two-year-old woman who was hospitalized for postmenstrual staining and vaginal pruritis (itching and irritation) was examined by a gynecological consultant called in on the case. He recommended a Pap smear to diagnose possible cancer, and a dilation and curettage. Neither were done. The attending doctor instead diagnosed the condition as an ovarian cyst and decided to perform a hysterectomy.

No cyst, but only two small polyps were found postoperatively. "There was no excuse to do a hysterectomy," the surveyor noted. "A dilation and curettage would have removed the small polyps and almost certainly cured her postmenstrual staining. This was bad medicine." Six days after her hospital discharge the patient was struck with "thrombophlebitis, of the broad ligament," an inflammation of the area which encloses the blood vessels to the uterus, and readmitted to the hospital. "The surveyor noted," states the report, "that if an unnecessary hysterectomy had not been done in the first place, the second admission would not have been required."

Gynecological surgery, the unfortunate conversational forte of some middle-aged women, can be a much overused therapy by gynecologists, general surgeons and scalpel-wielding GP's. The gynecological surgery performed in five nonteaching hospitals in Virginia, Kentucky and Tennessee over a four-year period, are statistical affirmations of old suspicions. Fifty-six percent of all gynecological procedures were judged to be either unnecessary or doubtful, with "resection of ovaries" the prime culpable operation. This ovarian surgery was considered justified in *only one in every hundred operations,* and patently unjustified in 83 percent of the cases. Unilateral oopherectomy (ovary removal) was also incriminated as being justified in only one in every five operations. A gynecological standard often performed on complying matrons for less than sage reason is the "uterine suspension" operation. The procedure, in which the uterus is made more secure in relation to the abdominal wall, was found to be unjustified in a "majority" of cases.

Continued surgical abuse is possible because some patients, especially those past the childbearing period, seem casual about parting with their reproductive organs, either because they are misled or ignorant about potential body repercussions. The late Dr. Max Thorek, founder of the International College of Surgeons, pointed out that loss of the ovaries can alter the patient's hormonal interchange and have many deleterious effects on the body, including the cardiovascular system.

The plethora of surgery of every type is synonymous with modern medicine. A more conservative standard might make much currently "justified" surgery seem unwise. But even by current standards, where every diseased tissue is sufficient reason for excision, *two million operations* performed each year are probably unnecessary. A five-hospital surgical survey reported by Dr. Virgil Slee in the *Bulletin of the American College of Surgeons* covered seven popular procedures: simple mastectomy, gastrectomy, appendectomy, operations on the uterus, cholecystectomy (gall bladder removal), operations on tubes and/or ovaries, and operations on the thyroid.

The percentage "justified" by diseased tissue varied from a shockingly low 40.7 percent on uterus operation at Hospital D to 100 percent for gall bladder removal at Hospital A. The perennially over-popular gastrectomy (partial or full stomach removal, generally for ulcers) and uterus operations were the least justifiable of the procedures, averaging between 60 and 70 percent justified, while thyroid and gall bladder surgery generally ranged in the more assuring 80 to 90 percentiles of justified procedures. The rate on "all operations" varied greatly from 86 percent justified at Hospital B to a perturbing 63 percent justified at Hospital D. Twenty-six percent of the surgical procedures—one in every four operations—involved "normal" or only "slightly" diseased tissue whose removal is usually justified in only a small percentage of cases.

The most vital element in surviving a hospital stay may well be avoiding unnecessary surgery, and therefore hospitalization itself. This might be better accomplished were patients to seek double medical consultation on every major ailment or recommendation for surgery.

Once ensconced in the hospital and involved in surgery, the quality of that hospital and the skill of the surgeon are the pertinent factors in life and death. Surgical skills have been increasing, but with the volume of surgery, human fallibility and less-than-stringent methodology in many hospitals, the patient is still subject even to the grossest of surgical blunders. Dr. Max Thorek, in his *Surgical Errors and Safeguards,* a classic text, stresses the extent of the problem.

"In addition to needless and clumsy operations, there are also those performed in too much of a hurry," he states. "Haste is not limited to decisions as to when and how to operate. It can also take its toll at any and every step of the operation itself. Again, perusal of the literature will yield appalling evidence of the results of incomplete inspection of the parts being dealt with and of insecure or inadequate closure of operative wounds. How often have ureters been mistaken for tubes and tied off during removal of an ovarian cyst or some other pelvic operation? How often has a solitary kidney been removed without the surgeon apprising himself of the fact that there was no other? How often has the omission of an extra row of sutures resulted in the breakdown of an anastomosis [a joining of organs, or parts] and subsequent fatal peritonitis? The number of reported cases gives us only a hint of the true situation."

In proper surgical procedure nothing should be taken for granted, not even that the person under the surgical drapes is the right patient, or that the operation scheduled is the one ordered! Although not an everyday occurrence, the wrong operations are performed on the wrong patients in many a hospital. A boy scheduled for a hernia operation was given a tonsillectomy; a mix-up in charts caused a Tennessee patient in need of a hemorrhoidectomy to have a testicle removed instead.

A woman who caught her hand in a punch press was scheduled for minor surgery in a Midwestern hospital. She was placed on the operating table, but instead of hand repair, her gall bladder was removed! Dr. Kenneth B. Babcock, long-time director of the Joint Commission on Accreditation of Hospitals, related this mishap in a medical publication, and detailed the amazing series of *assumptions* that can lead to this type of surgical farce. The orderly was told the gall bladder patient was in "Bed No. 2," but picked the wrong bed out of a line of four. Without asking if she was the gall bladder patient, he wheeled her into the operating room, where the O.R. supervisor (who should ask whether she is Dr. Y's gall bladder patient) merely told her to get up on the table. The surgeon should identify the patient personally, but in this tragedy of errors the surgeon, who was not yet in the O.R., told the anesthetist to put her to sleep and said he would follow shortly. The anesthetist, the last possible bastion against such tragic nonsense, merely continued the chain of circumstance. Instead of asking if she was the scheduled gall bladder patient, he muttered professionally: "Just take a few whiffs of this and you'll be asleep in a minute."

The incredible mix-ups scattered throughout modern surgical

history include operations not only on the wrong patient but on the wrong limb, digit or side of the body. The situation is sufficiently serious for the Canadian Hospital Association to have instituted recently new regulations of identification controls designed to prevent such mayhem.

To the layman, the most familiar surgical mishap is the misplaced "sponge" (gauze pads used to soak up blood) evidently lost by surgical assistants during the operation, until it menacingly turns up inside the patient's body. Women are somewhat more prone to be sponge victims than men, especially because of the apparent ease with which surgeons lose sponges during gynecological operations. These innocent-looking sponges can cause serious disease and death. In the fortunate patient the sponge will be encapsulated aseptically by a body mass and cause no trouble. In other cases it can become part of a sinus (pocket) in which it will fester with a deep pus infection. This postoperative inflammation may require a second, possibly dangerous operation for its removal—if the sponge can be found.

Sponges have been left in patient's abdomen during appendectomy, in the arm during orthopedic surgery, in the uterine area during hysterectomy, even in the breast. Often the foreign object is not discovered for years, when its internal disruption begins to cause pain or dysfunction. In a West Virginia case a sponge left in a woman's abdomen was not discovered until a second operation ten years later.

Surgeons may be suspicious that a sponge has been misplaced but are sometimes fearful of passing on their fears to the patient. In one recent case, in Virginia, the surgeon's failure to let the patient know he suspected a sponge had been left in a breast was partially instrumental in a $6,000 verdict for the woman patient. The sponge ostensibly had increased the infection, fever and pain of the wound.

The common error can be reduced if physicians could be taught to use only "radiopaque" sponges, which can be seen on X-ray, and to do a rigorous surgical count after each operation. "Our big worry," an operating-room worker writes to a *Modern Hospital* columnist, "is that during all types of surgery, surgeons insist upon using the homemade [non-radiopaque] sponges which they have designed. Don't you think this is a dangerous practice?" (Frances Ginsberg agreed that it is rather "hazardous" and "precarious.") Other authorities warn that the sponge count must be compulsive, as must a watch for such errors as a sponge that was picked up and not reported, a sponge that was torn in two, or one dropped on the floor that starts a fierce, futile search inside the patient. A place should be set aside for soiled sponges and used small instruments. One surgeon cautiously places a metal ring on each laparotomy (abdominal incision) sponge, to make it more conspicuous and to insure that it will be seen on X-ray if lost.

The surgically opened body appears to be a veritable magnet for foreign objects in a badly ordered operation room. It attracts parts of retractors (device used to hold incision open), suture needles, hemostats (instrument to stop the flow of blood), even surgical towels. A woman who had been operated on for a total hysterectomy, complained afterward about pain in her back. She was given heat treatment and medication but the pain persisted, and she was finally advised to have her back X-rayed. "You have something that looks like a wing nut in your abdomen," the radiologist told her. When the surgeon who had done the operation saw the X-ray, he reportedly identified it as "that wing nut that was missing" from part of a retractor.

Besides elusive sponges, instruments are the most common foreign bodies left behind in the patient during surgery, killing about 40 percent of their victims. Artery forceps (hemostats) are common offenders, as are curved suture needles that break or are lost during operation. A tonsillectomy knife was broken and left behind in the throat of one patient; a hypodermic needle was left in the abdomen after a Caesarean operation; needles for procaine injections have been lost in the throat wall, as have needles in the lower area after injection of the sciatic nerve. A drainage tube was lost in the chest during an operation for empyema, and not found for three years; needles have been lost in the spine, as have sponges and drains; a blade of turbinectomy (nasal cavity operation) scissors broke off in one operation, causing fatal meningitis.

Dr. Max Thorek has offered several suggestions for physicians on how to avoid dispensing unwanted surgical souvenirs. Drainage tubes should be red for easy spotting and better X-ray visualization; every suspicious case should be X-rayed before hospital discharge, especially for elusive hemostats; small instruments should be eliminated wherever possible; the operative field should be examined closely before the wound is closed; the surgeon should make pre-operative record of all instruments to be used; he should count all instruments again before the wound is closed; and a double check on sponges should be routine in the operating room. Nurse Frances Ginsberg asks for *three* sponge counts to prevent accidents: one prior to surgery, another after the first closure stitch, and a third when the operation is completed.

Another error that gnaws at the hope of surgical perfection is the wound that opens postoperatively because it has been sutured badly. Wound disruption, as it is called, is not sufficiently uncommon, occurring *once in every two hundred operations* according to one study, and *in one out of fifty-five gynecological operations!* The incidence of disruption, which can be brought on by such added strain as coughing, vomiting, constipation, urinary straining, is even higher in patients from forty to sixty-nine years of age. There are many surgical oversights contributing to this tragedy, one of which, says Dr. Robert M. Miles, assistant professor of surgery at the University of Tennessee College of Medicine, is the failure to use tension sutures.

In a study of 151 patients with disruption of wounds at Baptist Memorial Hospital in Memphis, Dr. Miles found that 121 of the accidents occurred when tension sutures were not used. Dr. Miles admonishes the surgeon to be scrupulously careful about the closing of wounds, a point reiterated by Dr. Thorek. "In my opinion, many surgeons take the closing of operative wounds much too lightly. All too often they complete it hastily, or, worse yet, leave it entirely to an assistant." The combined result of this carelessness and an unavoidable attack of coughing or vomiting, Dr. Thorek warns, can be a "burst abdomen." (The patient is reminded of the confident surgical star in the movies or on television, lifting his hands upward with finality as the operation is completed, barking at a green assistant: "It's done. Close it up!" The drama, unfortunately, is a too accurate enactment of certain surgical irresponsibility.)

The quality of surgery can be measured with many gauges: the training of the surgeon; the postsurgical infection rate; the number of anesthesia deaths; the volume of gross blunders such as foreign bodies left in the patient; the mortality rate of particular operations; and the amount of unnecessary surgery. The Trussell report provides another standard—the examination of case records by surgical experts who review and grade every case in a particular surgical sample.

The first Trussell report examined several types of operations: hysterectomies; other female genital surgery; Caesarean sections; gastrectomies; and other major abdominal surgery. In general surgery, 123 cases were studied, fifty-six of which were judged below standard, either "fair" or "poor." This incidence of nearly half (46 percent) relative failure involves a myriad of neglect, oversight and ineptitude, with resulting complications, pain and suffering.

In one case, a sixty-year-old man had a stomach removed (total gastrectomy) because of a duodenal ulcer. The report compliments the initial work-up, but comments that three days following surgery, "a bile stain fluid" appeared which was interpreted as a "duodenal leak." The patient was disharged with drainage continuing, and the surgeon optimistically predicting that "it should close in seven days or so." Instead, the patient was readmitted two weeks later because of the unstopped drainage, fever and chills. The patient was watched for sixteen days: blood tests were taken, but no chest X-ray made until the fifteenth day. "On the sixteenth day, the surgeon made 2 notes; the first stated that the patient seemed critical, and the second said that the patient was in shock," the report reveals. "An operation was scheduled for the following day, but during the induction of the anesthesia, the patient went deeper into shock, and died on the operating table before the incision."

The surgical case was rated "poor" because of the failure to realize that an abscess was involved, for failure to take a chest X-ray earlier, for waiting so long before doing a second exploratory operation. "There is," added the report, "an element of self-deception in the optimism on the first admission, when the surgeon said the duodenal fistula opening would close in seven days. It seems that his wish became father to his thoughts."

The surgical score in the second Columbia Report (chaired by Dr. Trussell's wife, Dr. M. A. Morehead) in 1964, showed no appreciable gain in surgical proficiency. Of 136 cases under study, fifty-nine cases—43 percent—were rated as "less than optimal," the euphemism for "fair" or "poor" ratings. The case-by-case description of inadequate, ill-considered, mismanaged and unnecessary surgery is illuminating. A fifty-two-year-old woman was given a cholecystectomy even though "studies did not indicate presence of gall bladder disease." A seventy-one-year-old woman was given surgical repair of an umbilical hernia, even though it had been present for ten years and was "very small."

A fifty-two-year-old man was operated on for hemorrhoids only two weeks after having pneumonia. A thirty-five-year-old patient, who had already had a gastric resection not justified by pathology reports, was subjected to a laparotomy (opening of the abdomen), and given a type of ulcer surgery, vagotomy and jejunostomy. "Indications for surgery not present; procedure not justified," sadly state the surgical surveyors. A fifty-nine-year-old man given an operation for duodenal ulcer died fifteen days later. The surveyors' comments indicate doubts as to the necessity of surgery, and that "a longer period of ambulatory treatment was indicated." The surgical method itself was criticized: "Technique of removal of impacted ulcer questioned," the report comments.

Surgical technique was often placed in the glare of medical doubt. In one case two rectal polyps, twelve and fifteen centimeters above the anus, were located and a laparotomy done to remove them. Other tissue was removed too, but *not* including the area at the base of the polyps. The most consistent attack on surgical technique and decision involved a dozen-odd hernia operations, a sampling of the 499,000 hernia operations performed each year.

After tonsillectomy, hernia repair is the second most common surgical operation performed in America. It is mainly a male operation but, surprisingly, 120,000 females also receive surgical repair of hernias each year. Hernia is a general medical term that means "abnormal protrusion of an organ or part of an organ through the containing wall of its cavity." The term may refer to any one of a dozen hernias, from the umbilical to the esophageal (hiatal), but usually refers to hernias of the abdominal cavity, where the peritoneal lining balloons out and organs slip into the hernia sac that is formed. The "inguinal" hernia, in which abdominal material slips down into the groin through weakened spots, accounts for four of every five cases of hernias in men, and are popularly known as "ruptures." Hernias may be congenital (inborn), the result of a strain or lifting, a complication of an operation, or the result of muscle weakness.

"Repair of draining incisional hernia [a hernia through the incision scar of an operation] resulting from laparotomy one year earlier," the Trussell surgical surveyors state about one hernia case. "Surgery should have been delayed until sinus [pocket] cleared. Technique of repair inadequate." The same patient was readmitted for a two-week hospital stay because of the same hernia. "Repair of incisional hernia four months after above admission. The wound eviscerated [burst open] and also became infected. Technique inadequate."

That last comment became a veritable fugue throughout the hernia commentary. In the repair of an incisional hernia on a forty-three-year-old woman, a space was packed with gauze instead of being sutured. A six-week-old baby was subjected to surgery to repair an umbilical (intestines pushing into the navel opening) hernia, although the report felt surgical "repair not indicated for this age patient."

The apparent multitude of badly done hernia operations is explained by Dr. Amos R. Koontz, emeritus assistant professor of surgery at Johns Hopkins, who speaks of the "colossal ignorance" of many surgeons about hernia problems and their cure—a legacy of poor teaching on the subject in medical school and surgical residency training.

Dr. Koontz attacks current complacency about hernia surgery, pointing out that under present surgical proficiency, hernias recur postoperatively as often as 25 percent of the time instead of a more reasonable 1 percent. "Many young doctors leave medical school with little or no knowledge of the anatomical or surgical importance of hernia," he charged at a Washington medical meeting. Despite this ignorance, he states, some surgeons falsely feel anybody can operate on hernia. But "examinations given by the American Board of Surgery every year reveal the colossal ignorance of board-qualified candidates in this highly important field of surgery."

In *Hospital Medicine* Dr. Koontz elaborates, charging "Poor Teaching" and "Poor Operations" for the current failure. "Hernia is so prevalent (involving approximately 1.5 percent of our popu-

lation) that medical schools should give the subject a prominent
place in surgical teaching. This is not done, because many professors of surgery think the subject is relatively unimportant," he
writes. The "poor surgery," he believes, is a legacy of the fact that
the supposedly "minor" procedure is shunted off to junior residents,
and many surgeons-in-training never properly learn how to do it.

Dr. Koontz has sage suggestions for the surgeon and patient on
the proper cure of hernia, including the use of silk sutures instead
of catgut and immediate operation instead of a truss, once the
condition is discovered. But he fails to mention the crucial concern:
how the patient can distinguish the knowledgeable surgeon from
those specialists who are *colossally ignorant* about hernia repair.

Another common operation with hidden pitfalls that prick the
sensitivity of more critical doctors is the cholecystectomy, the gall
bladder removal made famous by President Johnson's abdominal
scar. Despite assuring headlines of "low risk," the operation is
among the highest risk of all common procedures. The removal
of the gall bladder "carries a significant operative risk," say Drs.
Robert M. Zollinger and Roger D. Williams of Ohio State University Hospitals, who add that the risk is increased in patients with
"obesity, chronic bronchitis, cardiac disorders, the presence of
jaundice or pancreatitis." The operation is performed on three
hundred thousand patients every year, and increasing in volume.

The surgical mortality rate for gall bladder surgery depends on
patient selection and type of procedure. At the Hermann Hospital
in Houston, a series of 2285 operations on gall bladder and bile
ducts had an overall 2.4 mortality rate. The mortality was 1 percent
on gall bladder removal, but the figures zoomed to 14.2 percent
for the cholecystostomy—opening the gall bladder to drain its
contents—and 8.5 percent in surgery on the bile ducts. The seriousness of gall bladder surgery led Drs. Zollinger and Williams to warn
recently in *JAMA:* "The time for more uniformly good results from
cholecystectomy is long overdue."

The gall bladder is a small, 2½ inch organ which rests close to
the liver, for which it stores the excess bile produced by the liver
until a person needs it for heavy-duty digestion. When called upon
by food-stimulated intestines, the gall bladder releases about an ounce
of bile into the small intestine where it breaks down the fat mole-
cules and does other digestive work. If the gall bladder becomes
inflamed and contains "stones" that endanger the gall bladder and
the bile ducts—or the organ is in danger of perforation—it is generally removed and the patient then placed on a low-fat diet.

The operations on this area (biliary tract) carry a high complication rate, which is compounded if the surgeon does not avoid "stumbling blocks," as Drs. Gerald S. Dowdy Jr. and George W. Waldron

explain. "The history of gall bladder surgery has been marred by frequent complications. Although the rate of complications has declined in the last two decades, it continues to be high," they state in *GP*. "Most problems in gall bladder surgery are caused by a failure to recognize the many manifestations of gall bladder disease, the high incidence of coexistent diseases, the improper timing of surgery, and a faulty surgical technique."

Some stumbling blocks are complex, but others are vital knowledge for the sophisticated patient. Preoperative diagnosis should be thorough and include a cholecystogram (X-ray of gall bladder) that should definitely show evidence of gallstones before surgery is decided on. Gall bladder surgery is hazardous for patients with severe cardiac, cerebral, pulmonary, or hepatic disease; patients, they state, should not be rushed into surgery until conditions such as severe anemia are corrected; taking of a prothrombin test for blood coagulation is essential. (This last point is occasionally overlooked and the result may be increased bleeding during or after surgery.) Other critics warn that the obese patient should first be made to lose weight; that chronic coughs be controlled before gall bladder surgery is performed; that the "cystic" duct from the gall bladder and the "common duct," which is the joining of that and the liver duct, be thoroughly searched for stones during the operation. "A common cause of persistent symptoms following biliary tract surgery," warn Drs. Zollinger and Williams, "is the presence of an overlooked stone in the cystic [gall bladder] duct or common duct."

Operations on the colon, that part of the five-foot-long large intestine that ends at the rectum, are also quite common (210,000 on all of the intestines), and capable of producing pitfalls. "In studying this group of patients it was obvious that colon surgery carries with it certain hazards that are not yet fully conquered and that further research and study are needed," a group of San Antonio physicians write in the *American Journal of Surgery*. "Research in fields of organ transplants is most glamorous and rather easily supported. However, as the purpose of the medical profession is to do the most good for the most people, more research is indicated in the more mundane fields." An example of the problems involved is the revelation that of the colon surgery of the forty patients covered in their report, twenty had postoperative complications.

In an aptly titled paper "Pitfalls in Colon Surgery," Drs. Dinsmore, et al., of Charleston, West Virginia, give the first pitfall as hemorrhoid surgery done when a more serious colon condition is responsible for the bleeding. "Rectal bleeding should not be ascribed to hemorrhoids alone," they state. "We continue to see patients who have undergone anorectal surgery for a benign condition in the presence of an unsuspected neoplasm of the colon. No patient past the age of thirty-five years should undergo anorectal surgery until after proctosigmoidoscopic and barium studies of the colon have been carried out."

Surgical shortcomings may be pertinent to a particular operation such as hernia repair or gall bladder, or they may affect a whole genre of patients. "An appalling lag" is the way Dr. Robert E. Gross, professor of children's surgery at Harvard, describes the failure of the profession to provide proper pediatric surgery for children. Speaking at Johns Hopkins Hospital, he stated that "while across the country there are spotty parts which are outstandingly good, by and large the small patient is getting a rather poor deal . . .

"All too often," charges Dr. Gross, "a general surgeon in the community (admittedly having a high order of skill in managing the daily problems confronted in adults) suddenly had placed before him on the table, a baby of 10 pounds with an intestinal obstruction. He probably has poor anesthesia assistance, has instruments which are grotesquely large, but worst of all, he stumbles onto something in the abdomen of which he has previously heard little and for which he certainly lacks a clear idea of the best mode of treatment." Unfortunately, says the noted pediatric surgeon, too many surgeons are sublimely but falsely confident that they are qualified to handle any patient, whatever the size. "Postoperative results too often show that they have badly overestimated their capabilities," he bemoans for medicine.

An editorial in the *American Journal of Surgery* addresses a similar problem: the lost opportunities for pediatric surgery on the first day of a child's life. Dr. H. William Clatworthy, Jr., suggests "that we are doing too little, too late, for too few infants with surgically correctable maladies." His scheme for improvement: to set up central institutions in various parts of the country which will attract pediatric surgeons to devote their full energies to the problem.

The pitfalls, errors, hazards and complications that affect the hospitalized surgical patient, whether child or eighty-year-old, are less elusive than they are encyclopedic. Some are rare, others more common, but they can never be fully described, nor fully anticipated. The patient undergoing a subtotal thyroidectomy (removal of part of the thyroid gland) may find his vocal cords and speech partially destroyed by a wandering scalpel; pulmonary embolism (clot fragments in pulmonary arteries) can strike any surgical patient; appendectomy patients under general anesthesia may suffer atelectasis, a collapsed lung; patients being operated on for varicose veins have had their leg arteries dangerously damaged by mistake; death and injury are caused by pneumothorax, letting air into the chest cavity during surgery; bladders are accidentally cut during hysterectomy.

Error, even extravagant error, appears to be part of the natural order of surgery in the modern hospital. Dr. Leroy H. Stahlgren of the Philadelphia General Hospital has—as we have seen—reported that of seventeen geriatric patients who died, "errors were committed in the surgical care of 7 of the 17." Of 551 hip fracture cases studied by University of California doctors, 133 patients died, a figure they consider "high" and probably avoidable by more individual anesthesia, less opiates and unrushed surgery.

Even when error and complication seem to pass a patient by, it may only be temporary *bonne chance* that may take its toll a generation later. One young surgeon, Dr. M. Shein Win, chief surgical resident of Quincy City Hospital, Massachusetts, writes his unsettling observation in a letter to the *New England Journal of Medicine:* "I find myself in the care of geriatric patients, confronted with the complications of surgery done many decades ago for diseases that seem to have been regarded as comparatively simple and minor surgical problems even today; the occurrence of an anal stricture after hemorrhoidectomy . . . ; and the occurrence of the chronic venous-insufficiency syndrome in the lower extremities, associated with thickened, shiny skin, pigmentation, recurrent ulcerations and infections, which are notoriously resistant to treatment, after ligations for deep thrombophlebitis in the legs and occasionally after ligations and stripping of the long saphenous veins for varicosities." He concludes with a request that is thought-provoking for the patient: "I should like to hear comments from various surgeons."

With such potential for surgical mayhem, who should the patient seek out for more substantial odds and for a better chance of survival? The Trussell reports attempt to answer this query in several directions: one method is by analyzing the cases to see which were done by surgical specialists, and which by GP's. Another is to scrutinize the setting of the surgery—whether performed in a proprietary, voluntary or university-affiliated hospital. In the first report, 43 percent of the surgery in "voluntary or government hospitals" was judged below standard, while more than half (54 percent) of operations done in proprietary hospitals were equally criticized.

The second Trussell report (1964) went deeper into the surgical-quality differences. Of 125 patients who underwent "major" surgery, those operated on in hospitals affiliated with medical schools were judged eminently successful (92 percent optimal), while the voluntary, municipal and proprietary hospitals dragged suspiciously behind, all performing at approximately the same inadequate level— 55 percent satisfactory surgery.

In terms of training, the board-certified surgeons and/or members of the American College of Surgeons performed somewhat better than their colleagues. The surgical specialists dispensed good or excellent treatment in major surgery in forty-eight of seventy-three cases, or 66 percent of the time; the surgeons who were not specialists but who had appointments at voluntary or municipal hospitals gave proper care in only eighteen of thirty-five major surgeries, or 51 percent; the surgeons with neither specialist background or voluntary hospital appointment—generally GP's working in proprietary hospitals—were acidly judged as performing acceptable surgery in only one in five cases, or 20 percent.

"It is reliably estimated that one half of the surgical operations in the United States are performed by doctors who are untrained or inadequately trained to undertake surgery." This comment by the late Dr. Paul R. Hawley, when he was director of the American College of Surgeons, refers to the vast extent of surgery performed by general practitioners, whose activity is a knifing insult to the surgical specialist. The ACS must be complimented for its effort during more than fifty years to improve surgical standards—from the creation of surgical residencies to their pox on fee-splitting between surgeons, and between surgeon and GP.

Surgery can be learned without specialty residency, and some outstanding older men have absorbed the skill by other means, from preceptor training to just "doing." But by and large, formal surgical training is essential to competence, and the surgical residency training lengthens perennially as more complex operations are devised in hope of readapting the injured human body by excision or repair. After graduation from medical schools, tyro surgeons take an internship plus four, sometimes five, even *six* years of surgical residency training. After this arduous novitiate, plus additional experience, the candidate is eligible for election to the American Board of Surgery and the American College of Surgeons. Those who specialize beyond general surgery—in the subspecialties of neurological, thoracic (chest), urological, proctological, orthopedic, plastic, gynecological surgery—require specific training in their chosen area during the residency.

The "untrained" general practitioner should be awed by the flexing of such academic biceps. He is apparently nonplused, for he continues to compete effectively in the securing of surgical customers. In 1961, several years after Dr. Hawley's dire pronouncement, the ACS completed a survey which showed half the nation's surgery still being done by what they considered nonsurgeons.

The smaller and medium hospital is the pulse center of GP surgery, while the specialist gravitates toward the complex modern institution. A survey conducted by the Health Information Foundation showed that over 80 percent of surgery was performed by nonspecialists in hospitals of under fifty beds, and mainly by GP's (65 percent) in hospitals of under 100 beds, but that the ratio reversed to 59 percent specialist surgery in the 100–249 bed hospitals. In mammoth institutions of over five hundred beds, the situation was exactly converse to the small hospital: 80 percent of the surgery was specialist-performed.

The internecine GP-surgeon clash is generally not a personal one, but is apparently emotional enough to raise organizational, and even some individual doctor's, ire. When Dr. Robert S. Myers of the ACS emphasized his organization's revulsion at GP-conducted surgery, it brought a denunciation from the delegates of the AMA, to whom a doctor is a doctor—is *unrestrictedly* a doctor. Dr. Edward R. Annis, former AMA president, chided the ACS for exposing these medical squabbles to public view. "All I suggest is that they have the good sense to keep family quarrels in the family," he asked of the sometimes-crusading ACS. The patient might suppose that the use of his body had made him privy to such family secrets.

In an exchange of letters in a medical forum, the occasional rancor of the argument between GP and surgeon burst forth. "As a surgeon, the GP is as dead as the dodo," a Georgia surgeon wrote. "These days he shouldn't even be let loose on tonsils. What does he know about the relation of adenoid symptoms and hypertrophy to middle-ear disease? Not much. He's Jack-of-all-trades and master of none. Out of the last dozen T&A's I've done, half had already been performed by the little men with the home medicine kits. All they'd done was leave half the tonsils and most of the adenoids. Turn in your first-aid merit badges, GP's, before your hapless patients start getting wise to that 'Doctor of Magic' degree!"

The cacophony of GP outrage that followed was deafening. One commentator in the same publication, while criticizing the "greed" of some GP-surgeons, wisely equated this failing with the science-defiling "arrogance" of some surgical specialists. This failing can cause as much flesh-and-blood harm to the blindly specialist-worshiping patient as that created by the undertrained GP.

The GP-surgeon may operate on laymen, but when doctors need surgery for themselves or families, only specialists will do. The Columbia University School of Public Health and Administrative Medicine personally interviewed 468 New Jersey doctors about their medical care over the past three years and found that *none* of the physicians had patronized a GP-surgeon. Of 244 operations, 82 percent were performed by board diplomates or fellows of the American College of Surgeons; 5 percent were unidentified; and the remainder were full-time surgeons, although not certified or College members.

One surgical infamy of which few patients are aware has attracted the attention of the American College of Surgeons by its insidiousness. This is "ghost surgery," an incredible medical playlet in which the doctor hired by the patient steps silently aside while an anonymous "ghost" dons the gloves and performs the operation on the unknowing, anesthetized patient. Why should this subterfuge be perpetrated by physicians on their paying patients?

To explain such unethical practices in surgery, the outspoken Truman Report of the AMA—which studied the ethics of medicine —showed that some young surgeons often seek any possible arrangement to create a respectable operating schedule and income during their first five years in practice. Before referrals from other physicians become frequent and surgical incomes become more than substantial, many exist on general-practice work, while others submit to unethical practices, including fee-splitting and ghost surgery.

"A young doctor [surgeon] becomes a victim when he tries to establish himself in practice," says a GP interviewed by the AMA committee. "The young surgeon who tries to set himself up in an area very soon finds himself without a referral reservoir unless he is willing to split the fees with the referring practitioner." One surgeon deplored ghost surgery but told the AMA interviewers he understood the background for it: "There was a ghost surgeon in town . . . He would split the fee down the middle and . . . he did ghost surgery for many men. He was a darn good surgeon, too! I don't know what happened to him."

A gynecologist confirmed the existence of this surgical plague. "A man of good training who can't get hospital privileges . . . he may not desire to do it [ghost surgery] or be proud of it, but it may be the only way he can use his skills . . ." the surgeon explained to the Truman Committee. "It is simply a question that when a practice is so widespread as it is at the present time, and there are so many young surgeons who have a tough time getting surgical cases, the economic factor overcomes the ethical factors . . ."

The young ghost surgeon may work for a GP-surgeon, who steps aside after anesthesia as the young specialist wields the more expert scalpel. Or conversely, the experienced and successful surgeon may have a group of young "ghosts" who do the work—under his name— which he is too busy, too tired or too rich to bother with. "I know some chiefs of staff—top men and very competent surgeons—who have their little coterie of 'boys,' as they call them, with fee-splitting arrangements between them," one physician straightforwardly told the committee.

The patient who hires a prominent private surgeon, then gets operated on by one of his "boys" instead, may more frequently be a victim than is currently believed in the profession. "There is one increasing unethical surgical practice that you ought to put in your book," the chief of surgery of a large hospital told the author. "While surveying a hospital for approval of surgical residency I had lunch with the residents, and asked them about the kind of teaching at the hospital and how many surgical beds they had charge of. They told me 'None.' So that they could get surgical experience, the director had bludgeoned the attending surgeons into secretly giving them private cases to operate on. Once the patient was under anesthesia, the private doctor would switch with the resident, who would do the operation. It's immoral, and legal dynamite. If the patient is paying for an experienced surgeon he should get him, not a resident-in-training."

"Surgery" is a general term that government statisticians use to include the delivery of children, the 3,700,000 "operations" that are performed each year in America's hospitals on mothers-to-be. The reasonably low rate of maternity deaths (three per ten thousand)— once the scourge of womanhood—has made mothers relatively unafraid to give birth in the once deadly maternity wards. Our infant survival is still not comparable to many other civilized nations (eleventh place in the world); however, the mother-to-be can at least feel that her child will live to complete the first year of life in nineteen of twenty cases. During 1964, for a pleasant statistical change, the infant mortality rate decreased 3 percent, although it rose again in 1965. The less attractive side of the infant-survival coin shows that the figure of 30.3 children per one thousand births, who will die stillborn or within the first twenty-seven days of life, is excessive. The death rate has dropped only five per one thousand since 1950, and virtually leveled off during the last decade. In addition, still others will perish in the remaining eleven months of the first year of life.

Within this framework there are numerous obstetrical problems that should deeply disturb the modern hospital, and the obstetrician and GP, each of whom delivers almost two million children each year in its maternity wards. They range from abysmal, therefore killing, anesthesia facilities for mothers, to abuse of induced labor and excessive drugging of the susceptible fetus through the placenta of the mother.

Poor obstetrics have been blamed for much of the fetal (unborn child) death and damage, which make up a large part of these statistics. "Even though most labors terminate normally, there are *many* labors which are handled so poorly that fetal loss or damage results," an outspoken New Jersey doctor writes in *Medical Tribune*. "We realize that small premature babies and those with severe congenital malformations cannot be salvaged. However, a certain number of mature term babies entering labor with normal fetal heart in a normal mother are stillborn, or die within four weeks or are damaged. Many of these result from less than perfect obstetrical management. There are no published figures as to how large this group is, but from estimates it would appear to approach 30,000 babies yearly."

The obstetrician—once considered a midwife masquerading as

a specialist—has become a prominent third wheel after doctors who practice either "medicine" or "surgery." The modern obstetrician often does gynecological surgery, administers prenatal care, does preventive medicine such as the Pap test and breast cancer checks, advises the young marrieds, and delivers the child at the appropriate moment in the local hospital.

That delivery, by obstetrician or GP, can become troubled if anesthesia care is not proper. "Obstetrics is the stepchild when it comes to anesthesia," says Dr. Alan F. Guttmacher, former chief of obstetrics and gynecology at Mount Sinai and now president of Planned Parenthood. "Most of the elective surgery is done in the daytime, but there are about as many deliveries in the night as day. As a result, the anesthesia for delivery is often given by the house staff or by the youngest guy on the anesthesia staff. It's also a matter of economics. The hospital charges less for a delivery than for regular surgery, and it's reflected in the anesthesia coverage." This deliberate shortchanging of the young mother can mean death, as we have seen, by aspiration of vomitus while "under" or even permanent damage to the fetus from excess anesthesia that pollutes its oxygen supply.

Obstetrical anesthesia, state Drs. Otto C. Phillips and Harold A. Ott, "by and large, is improperly given and consequently has become a major contributor to maternal and neonatal mortality." Anesthesia, they point out, is one of the four leading causes of maternal death, and has been reduced less in the past decade than any of the others. "Unfortunately, two lives are lost; seldom does the infant survive the mother," they state in *Modern Hospital.* "Particularly tragic is the fact that nearly all of these deaths are preventable and could have been avoided by judicious adherence to the fundamental tenets of safe anesthetic practice."

Safe practice is made infinitely more difficult not only by the shortage of anesthesiologists but by the seeming professional boycott of mothers-to-be by properly trained personnel, who appreciate neither the smaller-than-usual recompense or uneven hours involved in killing the pain of childbirth. Dr. Willis G. Watrous of Saratoga, California, reveals that only one in thirty maternity hospitals surveyed could boast an anesthesia residency program, and that only one fifth of obstetric anesthesia is administered by the most qualified men—anesthesiologists and anesthesia residents. At Columbus Hospital in New York recently, nurses still taking a course in anesthesia administration were found administering anesthesia to mothers-to-be without any medical supervision.

The modern obstetrician—whether specialist or GP—is an overbusy fellow. The obstetrician delivers an average of 176 children a year (some handle over three hundred childbirths a year) in addition to his other duties, and he often decides to have little

Johnny arrive at his rather than nature's convenience. He is in and out of the hospital like a medical kangaroo, and increasingly uses the process of "induced labor" to regularize these visits, especially when they tend to fall in the wee morning hours, as nature often wonts. (A tally of 601,222 births in America and Europe show that the stork tends to arrive at ungodly hours: the peak period for births is 2 to 5 A.M., with 14 percent of spontaneous births; the low three-hour period is the more conventional 4 to 7 P.M. with less than 11 percent of deliveries.)

The powerful hormones that bring on labor and birth artificially are much like the use of forceps. When indicated, and wielded by the right medical hands, they are lifesaving; when used indiscriminately, they are of grave potential danger to the child. These drugs, including the much-used oxytocin, bring on birth by stimulating uterine contractions and may be medically indicated in one or two out of every hundred births, particularly when the mother has diabetes, toxemia, rheumatic heart disease, and other ailments.

The growing trend toward the artificial induction of birth in *normal, healthy* women may, however, be an unworthy trifling with nature's calendar, for which she may extract a tribute. In two studied hospitals in the East, the technique was responsible for 10 and 20 percent of all births, respectively, and has reportedly been used on over *half* the patients in the private service of some hospitals. "Physicians should realize that induction of labor is potentially dangerous," states Dr. J. Robert Willson of the Temple University School of Medicine. "You cannot always tell when the patient is ready, and you cannot always induce labor safely." An oxytocin-stimulated labor "cannot be prescribed by telephone," he warns his colleagues, whom he counsels to be on the scene for such procedures.

Two Buffalo specialists have studied 2862 labor inductions brought on by doctors, 90 percent of which included artificial rupture of the membranes. Their conclusion is that the technique increases hazard to the fetus, including otherwise preventable death from prolapsed umbilical cord (cord precedes fetus and is squeezed shut by the baby's head), respiratory ailments, prematurity and resulting hyaline membrane disease (the ailment that killed John F. Kennedy's son Patrick). Discussing twenty cases of supposedly preventable fetal death occurring after induced labor, the obstetricians Drs. Kenneth Niswander and Robert J. Patterson of Buffalo General and Children's Hospital, comment: "There can be no doubt that an increased incidence of prematurity and the frequency of labors complicated by the prolapse of the umbilical cord can be related to the election of induction . . . Even in the hands of an experienced obstetrician, even when rigid criteria have to be met before labor can be induced, there is an increased risk of infant mortality and neonatal dysfunction."

The contemporary nature of induced labor, of trifling with the biologic wishes of a well-regulated uterus timed to contract 280 days after conception, makes it less than admirable. In order to maintain more convenient hours, the obstetrician has increasingly been making what may be a poor bargain. A report to the American College of Obstetricians shows that of 137,582 births studied in fourteen hospitals, there have been twice the accepted number of uterine ruptures, a traumatic condition attributed greatly to the use of oxytocic drugs.

One induction drug, sparteine sulfate, known as the "obstetrician's friend," is no friend of the fetus, says Dr. William J. McGanity of the University of Texas (Galveston). The drug, he says, can slow the about-to-be-born baby's heart rate radically and reduce oxygen supply to the fetus. "But whatever is used to induce labor," says the professor of obstetrics, "the obstetrician should *remain* [italics mine] with the patient, keeping a careful check on the pattern of uterine contraction to avoid compromising the fetus."

In both induced and natural labor, the prematurity of the child is the major cause of mortality and morbidity (including mental retardation), and deserves increased research attention and increased hospital dedication. Dr. McGanity has two intelligent thoughts for obstetricians and mothers-to-be: since kidney infections may prove to be a major cause of prematurity, urinalysis should be done on all pregnant women to check for the disease. By doing this and treating the positive cases (50 percent of whom had no symptoms), he was able to lower the pre-maturity rate in twenty-five hundred births from 10 to 7 percent. Ascorbic-acid deficiency in the mother is another creator of premature children, he says, and should be checked whenever necessary.

Medical debate rages as to the ultimate method of obstetrical hospital coverage that will ensure mother and child safety. The present failure of doctor coverage in some obstetrical cases prompted Eleanor Lambertsen, R.N., chairman of nursing education at Columbia Teachers College, to complain recently that the obstetric nurse is too often called upon to do the job of the obstetrician. "The educated nurse knows that she is not a midwife trained to deliver the mother, not an anesthetist qualified to administer either analgesics or anesthesia, and not an obstetrician qualified to diagnose adverse symptoms," she writes in her medical-publication nursing column. "But in practice, nurses are being called upon too often to do not only these things but also to prescribe, by loose interpretation, 'standing orders.' " Too often, doctors "wait at home to be called a half-hour (or less) before the delivery," she states with annoyance.

Attracting more physicians to obstetrics is one obvious solution, as is the partnership plan in which weary obstetricians alternate night and weekend coverage of their unpredictable pregnant clients. A few hospitals are experimenting with the European midwife system, the use of R.N.'s who have taken additional training in obstetrics. Dr. Guttmacher believes that a system based on the use of board-certified obstetricians *assisted* by scientifically trained midwives, who can stay with the mother, is the best future for obstetrical care.

Conditioned by the medical profession to consider erroneously medical care as a homogeneous entity, the public often believes that "a hospital is a hospital." The distinctions in care available from one institution to another are actually enormous. Possibly in no other field is performance as unstandardized, and therapeutic results as varied as in the American hospital. "Good" hospitals often tolerate a sizable minority of bad care, and "bad" hospitals invariably produce a minority of excellent results. But the distinction between hospitals must be made, examined and re-examined.

The existence of significant differences in hospital infection rates has already been demonstrated. A survey of the medical and surgical practices of fifteen general hospitals by the Southwestern Michigan Hospital Council shows the grave disparity in care possible among hospitals in the same area. Tissue reports on 738 appendectomy cases illustrated that while two hospitals had a 68 percent rate of necessary appendectomies, two other hospitals were removing normal tissues 80 percent of the time! In medical (nonsurgical) care, the differentiation in hospital quality was as pronounced. Seven institutions performed essential blood-sugar tests on at least 90 percent of diabetes patients (100 percent is the *reasonable* figure). At the nadir of performance, one hospital omitted the basic test in *55 percent* of the cases!

Treatment of pneumonia patients in the same fifteen hospitals was no less uneven. One hospital X-rayed 95 percent of pneumonia patients, while another unpardonably omitted X-rays in the *majority* of pneumonia victims. (Six poorly performing hospitals failed to X-ray at least 30 percent of pneumonia patients.)

This audit of fifteen hospitals has since been expanded into a national effort, the Commission on Professional and Hospital Activities, centered in Ann Arbor, Michigan. The CPHA statistically coordinates the hospital treatment activities of 314 hospitals in thirty-nine states, Puerto Rico, six provinces of Canada, and even one hospital in Australia. Its member institutions handle 2,800,000 patients a year, and 362,000 births, almost 10 percent of the American total. The CPHA sample includes the full gamut of the types of American hospitals: medical school-university institutions; nonprofit voluntary; church-sponsored hospitals; privately owned "proprietary" hospitals; city-owned; county; state; and federal hospitals.

Their joint involvement in the CPHA does not eliminate their quality differences. A report on the intelligent use of hospital "antibiograms" (tests to determine which antibiotic is best for a patient's infection) shows a wide divergence of use. It varied from 2 to 18 percent in "large hospitals," while some "medium small hospitals" almost never made use of the valuable technique.

Hospital "quality" seldom enters into the family decision of where to give birth, but obstetrical method of delivery has an unduly wide variance among American hospitals. A CPHA survey of 152 hospitals showed that while, in sixty-seven institutions, children were almost never delivered by artificial rupture of the mother's membranes, induced labor was virtually *routine* in several others. Twenty surveyed hospitals reported "artificial rupture" in 30 percent or more of childbirths! Caesarean section, which typically runs 3 to 4 percent of births, accounted for at least 9 percent of deliveries in six of the hospitals.

The variance from hospital to hospital in blood use, lab tests, X-ray, various surgical operations, even infant mortality, has been made obvious by the CPHA. Among a sample of thirty-five Michigan hospitals, infant mortality per one thousand births and stillbirths varied from 28.7 in city hospitals; 27.6 in church hospitals; and 25.8 in other nonprofit institutions. Within the hospital groups, the variance was even greater. The ten city hospitals had a spread of infant death from 19.5 to 36.7; the church hospitals varied from 27.6 to 35.8 and the voluntaries from 21.8 to 36.3.

Considering the chaotic nonstandardization of hospitals, what index can the patient use to equate hospitals? How can he differentiate the *good* from the *inadequate?* The two Trussell reports attempted a general *class* differentiation, avoiding the grading of particular hospitals. The first Trussell survey of 402 admissions at 105 hospitals in the Greater New York area divides hospital care into two distinct groups: "Voluntary and Government" and "Proprietary." The privately owned hospital, with the least compulsion for standards, had the most unsatisfactory record—61 percent inadequate care. All other hospitals had 36 percent unsatisfactory treatment.

The hospital itself—rather than just the skill of the doctor—as a major determinant of quality care, was indicated by a breakdown of how board-certified men performed in various hospital settings. Board-certified physicians at the university hospital performed unsatisfactorily only 21 percent of the time; at voluntary hospitals with interne and resident programs not affiliated with a university, their efficiency dropped to a 33 percent failure rate. At hospitals without a training program, specialist performance soared downward to 59 percent "unsatisfactory" case ratings.

The performance of *classes* of hospitals is further delineated in the second Trussell report. The 430 cases were broken down into "optimal" and "less than optimal" care by hospital group, with only one strong emerging opinion: the percentage of satisfactory care was by far the highest at university hospitals, where fifty-seven of the sixty-nine medical and surgical cases, or almost 83 percent, were judged as receiving satisfactory care.

The remainder of the institutions were "quality" bunched, separated by only a few probably insignificant percentage points. The university-affiliated hospitals were followed by voluntary hospitals with training programs which dispensed satisfactory care 52 percent of the time. They, in turn, were followed by both voluntary hospitals without training programs and proprietary hospitals, which were judged as approximately 45 percent satisfactory. If the judgment of these *university surveyors* is accurate, the *university-affiliated* hospital can provide the best opportunity for satisfactory medical treatment. Care in other hospitals appears to be a rank gamble—50 percent either way.

The existence of a house staff of internes and residents is essential to a modern institution, where the resident often has as much or more informal control of a case as the admitting doctor. What quality of care does the house staff itself provide when in charge of a case, as is typical in indigent and some emergency admissions? The first Trussell report showed the house staff in operation in two different types of institutions: the hospital affiliated with a medical school, and those without affiliation. Apparently the house staff's excellence depends on their supervision. At the university-affiliated institutions the surveyors graded them as providing "good or excellent" care in 80 percent of the cases; in other hospitals, the internes and residents were judged much less the doctor, with only 41 percent satisfactory performance.

The proprietary hospital scored resoundingly low in the first Trussell report, but regained some ground in the second, perhaps a reflection of then New York Hospital Commissioner Trussell's vigorous vendetta against private-hospital laxity and his regulation that unaccredited private institutions would be closed by 1965. (Several did close during his tenure at New York's Municipal Building.) The entire phenomenon of a healing institution seeking a profit from the sick seems like a modern paradox, but the existence of a thousand such hospitals in America makes it a force to consider.

The proprietary hospital is never university-affiliated and it rarely has the comforting presence of young internes and residents in white. Basically it is a receptacle for the private doctor, a service-surrounded hospital bed where he can care for his patients by himself. Whatever medical care he does not personally provide is generally not given. No special cardiology teams await the serious cardiac, few blood-exchange groups are available for the Rh baby, special radiation for the cancer victim is unusual. Studies of un-necessary surgery and hospitalization often show the "proprietary" as a leading offender. Its doctor-less halls seem to invite medical emergencies in which hand-wringing nurses will watch life ebb away while the switchboard frantically seeks out the physician—at office or on the golf links. Its vital auxiliary facilities, such as pathology and pharmacy, are often part-time-staffed. Its full-time medical staff is most typically one young foreign physician—some licensed to practice medicine, some awaiting licensing exams, and others hav-ing just failed them.

Why, then, would a sensible patient patronize such an institution? The fact that he does is indisputable. Proprietary hospitals care for almost two million patients a year (approximately 6 percent of the patient population) including a disproportionately higher percentage of the middle and upper-middle class in modern suburbia. In Cali-fornia the proprietary hospital rivals the voluntary institution in number of hospitals; the Long Island suburban boom has tripled the number of proprietary hospitals in that area, a burgeoning that has been duplicated in the new Texas suburbs, especially around Dallas and Houston.

This paradox of the most financially able seeking out what many professional critics often consider inadequate hospital care stems from a simple sociological fact: the community general practitioner has increasingly been frozen out of the prideful voluntary hospital, and the suburban exodus has left financially able patients a grating geographic distance from the voluntary institutions their families traditionally used. Rather than stimulate the community into spon-soring a voluntary hospital in which the laity might be prominent, local physicians use their own and borrowed capital to build a proprietary hospital under their control, and with no opportunity for them to be staff-excluded. The local doctor's desperate need for hospital beds to maintain his practice is satisfied, as is the pro-moters' desire for sound investment.

The patient—often grateful for the construction of a local hos-pital, especially one bearing his new community's name—is typically quite satisfied with the institution. Many proprietary hospitals are modern brick-and-mortar, with attractively furnished rooms and friendly, attentive nursing care. Typically smaller in size than other institutions, it maintains more the feeling of home than the modern medical center—a comforting medical *Gemütlichkeit* that could be a lesson for oft emotionally sterile larger hospitals.

Its basic problems arise from lack of proper medical-staff or-ganization and rigorous standards. At one Long Island proprietary hospital, the chief of medicine is a brilliant board-certified internist whose flourishing private practice often keeps him busy until mid-night. Pressured by his own medical affairs, he can hardly supervise the work of less well trained practitioners who provide the bulk of unaudited care in the hospital.

New York's Dr. Ray Trussell, perhaps proprietaries' most aggressive critic, worries about their overconfident aggressiveness in handling complex ailments, including general-practitioner-performed surgery. "There is considerable evidence that major surgery and complicated obstetrics are performed in some private hospitals by doctors without adequate training," he states. "We do not feel that putting a floor on the level of surgery is unjustified." Their clinical laboratories came under equal fire, being insulted as the "worst of any group in New York City."

The galling intrusion of profit into the health picture further complicates the proprietary hospital's ability to operate as a community healing center. Few have real emergency-room facilities, and patients are turned away from their doors. To the sick a "red cross" on the building façade means "hospital" and willing medical care. Proprietary hospitals do not advertise their free-enterprise concepts, and the sick do not hurriedly distinguish when seeking aid. But no matter how sick the patient may be, admission to private hospitals generally requires *advance proof* of hospital insurance (Blue Cross or commercial) or sizable cash deposit before a bed is proffered.

Critiques of the commercialism and inadequate standards of proprietary hospitals are legitimate and urgent. In fact, such hospitals should *eventually* be closed and replaced by voluntary institutions. The sophisticated patient should not, however, permit the proprietary to become *the sole scapegoat* for inadequate hospital care, the same unfair role the general practitioner has reluctantly played for other doctor frailties. The proprietary should no longer be permitted to escape community supervision, but on the other hand, its failings are not so much different from those of other hospitals that it should bear the enormous burden of reform alone. The second Trussell report, in fact, showed that the proprietary hospital's shocking performance of only 45 percent satisfactory care was shared by *voluntary* hospitals without interne programs, and only 7 percent lower than non-university hospitals with internes or residents.

In the current medical chaos, in which the profession undertrains, then discriminates against the general practitioner, the proprietary hospital performs a vital function by absorbing the medical proletarian, the family doctor. In cities and many suburban areas the proprietary is often the only hospital that will offer him an appointment, without which he cannot fully practice medicine. When New York City adopted a code of medical control for private hospitals, it shivered the family doctors into protest. "The adoption of the newly proposed Proprietary Hospital Code in the city of New York could force the closure of every proprietary hospital," a concerned

Dr. George Liberman, president of the Kings County Chapter of the American Academy of General Practice, wrote to the *Medical Tribune*. "This code also aims at pushing the general practitioner out of the proprietary-hospital practice of medicine and relegating him to the status of a second-class medical citizen." He added that the American Academy of General Practice is dedicated to preservation of the general practitioner and "his workshop," the proprietary hospital.

The American hospital—whether voluntary, university, proprietary or governmental—is much like the American doctor, a relatively free agent; in this case required to conform to little except building and fire codes. (The unique New York City law gives their health commissioner unusual power over "proprietaries," but typically no ability to police the more numerous voluntary hospitals.) Their record of life, infant mortality, death, infection, anesthesia death, accidents, and medical and surgical culpability is their own affair, externally dictated only by the vagaries of public relations pressures. In the one public arena where compulsion should be *sine qua non*, untrammeled license reigns serene.

In such an unfettered environment it is not surprising that the only external quality control—hospital accreditation—is voluntary. The Joint Commission on Accreditation of Hospitals, a Chicago-based organization founded by the American College of Surgeons in 1918 and now sponsored by the American College of Physicians, the American College of Surgeons, the American Hospital Association and the AMA, has established minimum standards for all institutions of over twenty-five beds. Every three years one member of a staff of sixteen full-time doctor-surveyors visits every hospital that *requests* him, investigating the facilities and staff organizations. "All of our investigators are M.D.'s. They work for us full time. Some are GP's and some are specialists," says a JCAH spokesman, "but all of them have been in medical practice before they came to work for us. They are trained for a short while here in the office, and then spend a week or two with a field supervisor before going out to visit hospitals on their own."

Each investigator inspects over a hundred hospitals a year, generally spending one to three days at an institution, depending on its size. The hospital is given several weeks' notice before he arrives, an imperfect system of non-surprise. (One former patient is reminded of the order magically wrought in a frenetically administered hospital ward by the impending arrival of the chief of service on grand rounds.) Hospitals that pass muster are given three years' accreditation, along with a certificate that is mailed to them; those in doubt are warned to repair their deficiencies and are placed on "probation," actually a one-year accreditation. The failures are invited to try again.

There are 7127 hospitals registered with the American Hospital Association. Of these, 4204 are "accredited." Accreditation is not that harsh a scrutiny; only seventy-four hospitals that were examined were turned down in one recent year. The missing three thousand hospitals include almost a thousand of twenty-five beds or under which are not eligible ("They usually can't afford the facilities we require," says the JCAH), and two thousand hospitals which blithely ignore the existence of the organization, or fail to gain approval. This includes some seven hundred unaccredited proprietary hospitals ("Most of them never request to be inspected," says the JCAH), and about twelve hundred voluntary general and mental hospitals. In total, some 80 percent of the eligible voluntary general hospitals in the nation are accredited, along with 30 percent of the proprietary hospitals and an equally low percentage of mental institutions. No noticeable effect in patronage has been observed in the unaccredited institutions.

Accreditation is a valuable status pressure point and a *beginning* for a future potent program in hospital standards and control. At the present time it separates those hospitals with at least minimal standards from those below minimal, or from those unwilling to participate in external surveillance. Whatever the core of nonaccreditation, patients who patronize an over-twenty-five bed institution that is not accredited are, to be charitable, foolhardy. However, confusing the JCAH minimal standards with hospital quality or proper regulation would be equal folly. Accreditation is absolutely no guarantee of patient safety.

The first Trussell report stresses the minimal nature of JCAH standards: "The standards for hospital accreditation state that 'members of the staff must be qualified legally, professionally, and ethically for the positions to which they are appointed.' However, the determination of specific criteria of eligibility for physicians is left entirely to the discretion of the individual hospital medical staff. *It has generally been recognized that the standards for accreditation are minimal, and that they do not, in themselves, guarantee a high level of medical care* [italics mine]."

With commendable frankness, the JCAH makes the same admission. "Because of this determination not to grade hospitals and because the standards are prepared as 'minimal' standards," states Dr. James Z. Appel, former chairman of the Joint Commission, "the public should not be led to believe that accredited hospitals are 'superior.'" He also fears that hospitals themselves will feel confident merely because they are accredited. "These standards are not and should not be used as signpoints to excellence. This idea must be gotten across to hospitals somehow. Perhaps review surveys should be more strict than the original one which accompanied accreditation. Perhaps some credit should be given to the hospital which, in such review, shows evidence of having the initiative to go beyond the mere meeting of standards."

The Joint Commission should be praised for "persuading" three out of every four voluntary hospitals to meet even their minimal standards. Without this *only* broadly sponsored medical quality control, the posture of the American hospital would be even less upright than it currently is. It is no longer overly difficult for most medium and large hospitals to satisfy JCAH requirements for a fire-resistant structure; for proper kitchen, laundry and garbage facilities; pathology and radiology departments; proper garbage disposal; registered nurses to supervise nursing; special facilities for newborn children; control of abortions and sterilizations; medical records; staff meetings; and a tissue committee to review the excised tissue.

The JCAH's ubiquitous surveyors have bagged surgical racketeers, filthy kitchens, firetraps, a hospital abortion mill, and on occasion an especially high infant mortality rate. The type of offense that usually meets with JCAH rebuke is nonclinical. A review by Dr. Kenneth Babcock of one year's activities showed that 144 institutions were either failed or placed on probation because of twenty serious deficiencies. Incomplete written material such as medical records were the major offenders, followed by various lapses, from "fire hazards" to "autopsy rate below 20 percent." Only four indirectly clinical items were mentioned, including "no postanesthesia follow-up" (seventy-nine hospitals) and inadequate newborn nursery (forty-five hospitals).

This is all *basic* hospital criteria. In the less tangible areas, where quality of hospital care *beyond a bare minimum* is determined, the Joint Commission operates within the medical tradition. It has a gentleman's code, agreeable rather than chafing, persuasive rather than regulatory. This is one of accreditation's primary limitations. The Trussell report has indicated the wispy generalities employed in listing the qualifications of a hospital medical staff. The same evasive niceties are employed in Joint Commission "requirements" for hospital consultations.

The "consultation" is medicine's venerable tradition of one doctor seeking out another to discuss a sick patient, either for advice, succor and stimulation or to please the worried family. Dr. James H. Means, professor emeritus of Harvard Medical School, speaks nostalgically about "the consensus of opinion" that was once garnered from face-to-face confrontations of several doctors, usually at the patient's bedside. "This manner of procedure is probably nearly extinct," he writes regretfully. "There is no longer time for such formalities." He describes the present consultative method, in which the physician sends the patient to another doctor, then personally digests the information received. "This type of procedure is, I think, inferior to the older one. There is no direct meeting of minds."

The typical American patient is less insistent. When sick in the hospital, he would be pleased with any second opinion on the state of his health. His contemporary physician greets this honored tradition coolly, often with an immature posture of infallibility. "It has seemed to me that in recent years," says Dr. Means, "doctors have become increasingly reluctant to call for consultations . . ."

The need for a second or third opinion before instituting radical therapy should not be debated. "It is a foolish physician, indeed, who does not welcome the opportunity of having another share his responsibility, and a prudent one who emphasizes the practical value of the consultant," states Dr. H. S. Zfass in the *Virginia Medical Monthly*.

The value of the hospital consultation is recognized by the Joint Commission, but in gentlemanly manner it is left to the discretion of the reluctant physician, even in cases of critical illness! (It is only specifically required in cases of first Caesarean, sterilization or interruption of pregnancy.) While the JCAH can be quite definitive about the temperature of kitchen water, they leave consultations to the doctor's judgment. Consultations are needed, says the JCAH, on *"cases on all services in which according to the judgment of the physician:* (a) the patient is not a good medical or surgical risk; (b) the diagnosis is obscure; (c) there is doubt as to the best therapeutic measures to be utilized [italics mine]."

The American physician has chosen not to exercise that judgment. Surveys of consultations show an average of only 10 to 20 percent of hospitalized cases at major institutions (less at others) in which a second formal opinion was sought. The JCAH—perhaps cognizant of the American physician's hesitancy to admit the need for counsel —considers a 15 percent consultation rate reasonable. This is *unreasonably* low. Perhaps no single step in hospital medicine would improve patient survival more than requiring a medical consultation (hopefully held at the bedside) with a formal, written opinion for *every patient in an American hospital*. This probably awaits the development of a quality control group anxious to go beyond current "requirements" that have apparently made 50 percent unsatisfactory hospital care "standard."

The current accreditation program is equally lax on hospital staff meetings. In 1862 Dr. James Gregory of Edinburgh wrote about the subtle, controlling pressure such meetings can exert on the doctor: "I do not know, nor can I conceive, any human contrivance that can more effectually and irresistibly oblige the physician to study carefully the case of his patients; to attend to every symptom or change of sympton; to exert himself to the utmost for his patient's relief; and at the same time to be as cautious as possible in the remedies that he employs; than to find himself under the necessity of giving a minute account of everything he has done, in a very public manner, and before a number of competent judges."

Dr. Gregory's thought may be an exaggeration of the moral pressure exerted today by peers at a hospital staff meeting, but it is undoubtedly *one* of the many checks required for quality hospital care. Despite this necessity, the JCAH has been *lowering* rather than raising its hospital-staff-meeting requirements. In December, 1953, its published standards included the following ironbound attendance requirement for doctors: "Each active staff member shall attend 75 percent of the staff meetings unless excused by the Executive Committee for exceptional conditions such as sickness or absence from the community."

The regulation exasperated the freewheeling-doctor community. The result was a watered-down requirement in the new accreditation standards issued in 1960. Today attendance is not compulsory, a victory of the laissez-faire medical attitude. "Attendance requirements for all medical staff meetings shall be determined by the Active Staff," says the new code.

Dr. Anthony J. J. Rourke of New Rochelle, New York, a prominent hospital consultant, has only half facetiously asked that a "Scarlet A" be placed over the entrance of every hospital that is not accredited. One might well go further in disciplining errant hospitals, but it would be immature to consider that a hospital with accreditation is always deserving of it. "Many hospitals go to sleep between the accreditation surveys," writes Dr. Robert Myers. "Surveying a hospital once every three years may not be frequent enough."

Many large institutions, especially city and county hospitals in many parts of the country, are accredited despite *known inferior care*. The accreditation may be granted because of technical fulfillment of JCAH standards, or as an accommodation to maintain the interne and resident program for the care of charity patients.

America has a tradition of inferior municipal and county hospitals. There are several exceptions, but the unsatisfactory care provided by many city hospitals has been grist for constant newspaper exposés. Despite this, almost all have consistently been approved by the AMA for interne and resident training, and accredited by the Joint Commission. (The giant Cook County Hospital in Chicago, with more than twenty-seven hundred beds, had failed to pass two annual accreditation inspections but won "provisional" one-year accreditation nevertheless, and is now fully accredited.)

In New York City the accredited giant chain of municipal hospitals had been criticized by several prominent physicians. The tenure of civil-service-employed nurses has apparently been a deterrent to good medical care, as has the failure to inspire *esprit* among physicians in the welfare medical environment. Increasingly, community physicians have been volunteering less time for city hospital work, preferring to devote their efforts to prestige institutions or to their lucrative private practices.

The conditions in many municipal and county hospitals spark periodic reform campaigns. Former Marine Corps Major General Thomas J. Hartford was brought in to give new life to the Newark City Hospital. The most ambitious plan of improvement has been underway for several years in New York under the tutelage of Dr. Ray E. Trussell of the Columbia University School of Public Health and Administrative Medicine who spent a four-year leave of absence as New York City Commissioner of Hospitals. Dr. Trussell recognized the basic inadequacy of many city-run institutions, and decided to affiliate them with stronger voluntary hospitals.

The weak condition of many of that city's hospitals had been revealed by the Mayor's Commission on Health Services report on grave medical problems resulting from shortage of trained doctors. ("Some patients waited for more than a week to have a broken bone set at this hospital," a former official commented when interviewed.) For several years *not a single* American-trained interne was brought into the house staff of fifteen of the city's twenty-two hospitals. The coverage provided by the volunteer community doctors was spotty at best, and often considerably worse.

"The state of medicine was very, very poor here," reports the physician then in charge of one city hospital's affiliation with a strong voluntary institution, brought in to improve the medical and surgical care of the city hospitals. "Fifty percent of the residencies were vacant, and the rest were almost all foreign graduates. The internships were 75 percent unfilled. The attending staff was a mixed bag, but the number of good people were small. The hospital couldn't get local doctors to volunteer to run the outpatient department. There were so few attending doctors that some patients waited five to six days for treatment."

The excellent reforms initiated throughout the New York City municipal system are a *beginning*. Full-time chiefs of staff have been hired, generally over the complaint of local physicians, at respectable $25,000 to $40,000 salaries, as well as other full-time and part-time doctors. In the outpatient clinics, the missing charitable physicians have been replaced by specialty-trained physicians at $10 an hour. American-trained internes and residents rotate part of their time from their regular hospital to the city institution.

Medical improvement is apparent, but it should not be supposed that city hospitals are a viable form of medicine. The red tape, the absence of *esprit*, the civil service status of the nurses, the current medical indifference to the indigent patient make this very form of hospital untenable as a place of excellence. ("The nurses here don't care. If they feel like it they just take a half-hour off and go for a walk," says the surgical chief at one city hospital.) The brilliant moves of Dr. Ray Trussell might best be exploited in the future by making the affiliation even stronger, and having all city and county hospitals totally absorbed by the best voluntary and university hospitals, with only financial but not bureaucratic control by the cities. If the American city-run hospital is a preview of socialized medicine, we are best off being spared it. (Certain well-run army and navy hospitals are, of course, an argument in the opposite direction.)

City, county or state bureaucracy cannot be blamed for lack of proper care at most hospitals, but one critical factor which is typically overlooked is that many American hospitals are virtually *doctorless*. Under the system perpetuated by organized medicine, hospitals are discouraged from "hiring" physicians. The American hospital is designed primarily as a workshop for the private, practicing physician who becomes an "attending" or "staff" doctor at a hospital, whether a voluntary or a proprietary institution. His primary interest in that hospital is his own patients, whom he admits, then cares for during hospital visits. While the attending is away practicing in his office, internes and residents are ostensibly filling in—carrying out his orders in the care of the hospitalized patient.

The theory was once reasonable but has two drastic drawbacks today that make it an impractical method of staffing the nation's hospitals. The voluntary attending doctor is too occupied by his heavy office practice to provide personally the necessary complex observation and care. Most destructive of this idealized concept is the absence of internes and residents to backstop the attendings medically. Of the nation's 7127 hospitals, only 765 have internes on its premises, and a bare 650 more have residency programs. Among this minority of hospitals who support their physicians with young men in white, a sizable percentage have unfilled places. There are almost 6000 unfilled interne positions and 8000 residency vacancies, in addition to the 7000 positions occupied by foreign-trained doctors.

The current inability or unwillingness of the community doctor to provide full hospital care is underscored by critics such as Dr. Stephen Manheimer, director of Chicago's Mount Sinai Hospital. "In a large number of hospitals due to the demands of private practice the voluntary staff is a staff in name only," he writes to a medical publication. "The doctors' visits to the hospital are irregular and inadequate, and the time spent at the bedside, with very few exceptions, is practically nil." The medical care of the patient he points out, is left to the house staff, which very often is unsupervised.

"Medical records are slipshod, orders are given verbally and not written, required consultations are delayed, and general discipline is loose."

The situation is deteriorated even more seriously in the almost six thousand hospitals without doctors-in-training. These hospitals must make do, improvising with stopgap measures that are deleterious to good medical practice. One more-than-stopgap measure is the hiring of outstanding, full-time men as chiefs-of-service, whose whole practice is centered about the hospital. This medical advance is being tenaciously fought by medical vigilantism wherever possible. Opposition is strongest in the community institutions that need it most, but which are restricted from hiring full-time or part-time doctors by supposed medical "tradition," and even by medical society pressure. "The attacks on this proposal (full-time salaried hospital doctors) are a matter of public record and need not be recounted here," Dr. Ray Trussell told the New York Academy of Medicine, "except to say that some of the vested interest issues are still with us."

These vested interests have made it necessary for hospitals to improvise doctor coverage. Many hire unlicensed foreign physicians to stand by on the premises; some hire new physicians for emergency night duty; some use "moonlighting" junior and senior medical students from nearby schools; some hospitals may even have nurses perform minor physician tasks. Despite such pitiful stopgaps, some of which are illegal, many American hospitals are virtually *doctorless,* precipitating emergency crises that make survival a chore.

"Finding" or "calling" a doctor is the macabre game played out in such hospitals. In one case a teen-age girl was placed in a hospital with a physician diagnosis of acute violent rheumatic fever with beginning heart damage. "Before leaving the hospital at 7 P.M.," a report of the case describes, "the patient's physician told her mother, who was going to stay in the room with her, that she should have immediate medical attention if she should go into heart failure. The mother testified that shortly thereafter the girl developed a fever, her heart began to pound, and her body began to turn blue."

As is so often—and tragically—the case, the patient was left solely in the care of nurses, who are legally—if not medically—incapable of dispensing medicine without doctor orders. Apparently no other physician was on the premises, and the nurses saw no reason to call the patient's doctor at night. (Should the nurses decide the patient does *not* require medical aid, they are, in effect, also dispensing medical care, but the law does not look at it that way.)

"Every 10 or 15 minutes the mother went to the nurses' desk across the hall and asked that somebody come to check the girl, but nobody came," the report continues. "After the change of shifts at 11 P.M., the mother asked the nurse in charge of the new shift to call the physician and tell him she believed the girl was in heart failure. Following the call, the child was given a hypodermic shot for her cough, but the nurse did not check her condition. The mother finally contacted the Supervisor of Nurses who, after looking at the patient, immediately called the physician. He arrived 10 minutes later, at 1 A.M. He placed the girl in an oxygen tent, elevated her bed, and gave her a rapid-acting form of digitalis and a diuretic intravenously. She rallied somewhat, but died early the following morning. The physician stated that the patient had been in heart failure for a long period of time the first night, during which her mother had unsuccessfully sought help from the nurses." Had the doctor been able to leave the sick child in the care of a "hired" night doctor instead of a night nurse, the girl might well be alive today.

The doctorless hospital has taken an unreported heavy toll in death and morbidity. Case histories of tonsillectomy patients hemorrhaging because of no available physicians are not infrequent, as are other unattended emergencies. The conflict between those who would alter this antimedical situation to protect the patient and that portion of the recalcitrant profession dedicated to maintaining community-physician control has been joined, even in state legislatures and our courts. In 1959, Wisconsin passed a state law *prohibiting* hospitals from hiring doctors except as trainees. In 1964, the State Board of Medical Examiners investigated several hospitals and forced one institution to discharge three physicians who had been hired as full-time employees.

A *Medical Tribune* "Pulse of Medicine" survey of a thousand doctors elicited the answer that 70 percent were against the full-time salaried doctor in the hospital. One Iowa GP answered "No" most forcefully: "We recently had a court case to prevent this, and won." The American Medical Women's Association (apparently more social-minded than their male colleagues) have, conversely, put out a call for their members to work part time on salary in local hospitals to remedy the tragedy of the doctorless hospital.

It is obvious to anyone concerned with life rather than protocol that fifty state laws requiring all hospitals to have a licensed physician *on duty on the premises twenty-four hours a day* is the absolute minimum. Beyond that, the hospital must re-evaluate its role in society and reorganize itself for patient protection rather than doctor privilege. This will, more than likely, indicate the use of a full-time staff of chiefs of services and several full-time assistants to maintain hospital regimen in the absence of busy private doctors. (The trend has already begun in several large institutions, where approximately one in twelve physicians other than anesthetists, pathologists and radiologists are full-time or part-time salaried.)

This exquisite nonplanning of American medicine is also exhibited in the current chaos of the hospital "emergency room." This often ill-equipped one-time "accident room," which provides the dramatic setting for several television shows, was not prepared to meet the onslaught of patients attracted by its on-the-spot medicine.

"There is little doubt in my mind that the weakest link in the chain of hospital care in most hospitals in this country is the attention given to and in the emergency department," Dr. Robert H. Kennedy, the American College of Surgeons' chairman of the Committee on Trauma, states in *Hospitals*. "The first impression given should be that of quiet, efficient, personal attention in pleasant surroundings. Does the emergency department in your hospital impress you that way? Or more to the point, have you ever seen it in action? Often one is met by a brusque orderly or clerk or an overwrought nurse and turned over to a young doctor who is too often poorly equipped for the task assigned to him."

The nation's emergency rooms have quadrupled their traffic in the past fifteen years, and now treat more patients—thirty-five million a year—than are bedded down inside. Their popularity may not be a factor of quality care, but rather a compliment to their availability, and a subtle answer to the private physician's masterful retreat behind his aide, appointment book and unlisted phone number. "Something happened to medical practice after World War II," Dr. Kennedy explains. "Use of the hospital for inpatients increased rapidly, house calls became rarer, physicians disliked coming to their offices except for regular hours and they were frequently unavailable nights, weekends, holidays and the weekly golfing afternoon."

This doctor unavailability can nurture the patient habit of first seeking out the emergency room. "Most such patients first come to our emergency rooms on Thursday afternoons or weekends," says Dr. E. Shortliffe of the Presbyterian-University Hospital in Pittsburgh. "Later, when they need care again, they come here first."

The result has been an emergency-room deluge of every class of patient: wealthy, poor, medical emergencies and otherwise, seeking help for a speck in the eye or a brain concussion. The majority of the patients do represent true emergencies, but 42 percent of patients had decided to use the hospital instead of the private physician for regular illness, states a nationwide survey conducted by three Cornell Medical School professors (Drs. Skudder, McCarroll and Wade) in conjunction with the American College of Surgeons. A survey at Genesee Hospital in Buffalo shows that 70 percent were "bona fide" emergencies, but that half of these emergencies could have been treated in a doctor's office.

The Cornell report, which covered the emergency facilities of 286 hospitals, produced some startling revelations: twenty-one hospitals had no emergency facilities; only 6 percent had their own ambulances; 67 percent said their emergency rooms were physically inadequate for the job; 20 percent had no signs indicating the way to the emergency room; in thirty-seven hospitals the emergency area was not even accessible from the street; 25 percent of the hospitals permit doctors who have not seen the patient, but who have given phone advice to the emergency-room nurse, to bill emergency cases.

Dr. Kennedy, who surveyed emergency rooms in thirty-four states, adds several other failures of this now popular medical setting: "In many small hospitals the emergency department is kept locked at night. Some have a large, loud bell which rings at the telephone switchboard, in some the night nurse carries a gun when she goes to admit a patient." Patients, he believes, should be seen by a *doctor* within fifteen minutes after arrival, but "we often find that the time is 30 to 60 minutes." Dr. Kennedy states another simple proviso of good emergency-room care: that *every* patient be seen by a doctor, a requirement that is often waived to mean care by a nurse via telephoned doctor instructions, a travesty of proper attention.

With too-common medical irrationality, emergency-room help is organized on a daytime pattern, while the patient traffic is less obliging. "Peak loads are usually on the 3 to 11 P.M. shift," Dr. Kennedy reports. "The major number of personnel on duty is usually on the 7 [A.M.] to 3 [P.M.] shift." The failure to staff evenings in the American hospital properly, whether in the emergency room or on the wards, is a consistent ulcer in care, part of medicine's manic desire to conform sickness to nine-to-five hours.

The environment and procedure in emergency rooms are symptomatic of its unplanned growth as a treatment center. "Look for yourself at typical emergency quarters during busy hours," states Gordon Davis, a *Modern Hospital* columnist. "Harsh lights. Hard chairs. No place to hang coats or hats. People standing at times because there is no place to sit. Patients with injuries waiting in obvious pain in the midst of the melee, with no one paying the slightest attention to them. And the personnel of the emergency department, toughened by daily exposure and immersed in paper work sometimes gives the impression of complete indifference to the whole business."

The callousness of the emergency room is becoming a near-permanent hospital fixture, possibly a reflection of the transience of the patients, and the jerry-built, still unclarified nature of the situation. It may also be a result of professional abuse of the defenselessness, even guilt, of an unadmitted patient virtually beseeching medical care at an hour which he has been "taught" is abnormal. A portrait of the heavy indifference that ladens the atmosphere is presented by Dr. Paul Errera of Yale and Mary C. Dye, a nursing instructor at the same institution. The team conducted a study of the "emotional" content of treatment given twenty patients in the emergency room of a large (780-bed) university hospital.

"A doctor reaches beyond a patient for a telephone, hits him on the head with his elbow, and makes no comment," they report in *Modern Hospital* on one case. A bleeding woman arrives at 10:44 P.M. "The female aide is now standing near the patient's head and is watching the obstetrician prepare the intravenous. The aide sighs and shakes her head. The patient puts her hand under her head in an attempt to keep her hair out of the blood. The aide does nothing."

The staff avoid (as much as possible) direct conversation with the patient, usually to the point of rudeness, the surveyors report. "A nurse notices that a young patient is in the wrong examining room. Without a word she takes the girl by the wrist, pulls her down the hall and says to a passing aide: 'Take her to room E and get her undressed.'" Their findings are not isolated: the executive director of Henrotin Hospital in Chicago concurs that emergency care can be inhumanly remote: "Unfortunately, whether we want to admit it or not, the lack of interest in the welfare of the patient as a total human being is too often lacking in our emergency room."

The callousness can be compounded by the insistence on paper work, on unrelenting questionnaires to be completed, often before treatment is proffered. "No form, no medicine" is the unsubtle intimidation that permeates many emergency rooms. "My husband crushed his hand," a wife relates in *RISS,* a publication for residents, internes, and senior students. "By the time I got him to the hospital, he had lost so much blood he couldn't stand. They said: 'Sit down and wait your turn . . . Fill out these forms.' I'm not the violent sort, but I raised Cain. 'Stop this bleeding!' I screamed. 'You stop this bleeding!' I think it's cruel the way they treat you."

The inadequacy of many emergency rooms is a by-product of its low status in the hospital hierarchy, an ignoble position that penalizes it in both equipment and personnel. "Too often we find instruments discarded by the operating-room supervisor finding their way to the emergency department. A dull skin needle hurts just as much on the ground floor as it does higher up in the hospital," Dr. Kennedy states. "A large needle, which a plastic surgeon would not be offered in the main surgery, still makes just as large a hole in a pretty face in the emergency department and 00000 silk is rarely found here."

The sometimes-crusading American College of Surgeons (an anomaly in the present medical world) has uncovered scores of deficiencies in emergency care, several of them during unscheduled visits. For over two years a committee of three Denver surgeons visited seventy-three of Colorado's hospitals, almost all of which treat victims of car accidents. They found "serious defects," including lack of lifesaving equipment to perform a tracheostomy (to make an air opening in the windpipe); nurse ignorance of lifesaving techniques; improperly constructed ambulances in some areas; unclean conditions; radio contact with emergency vehicles only in one out of six cases; unmarked emergency doors. Surgical technique also came under attack; wounds were not properly closed in several of the hospitals visited.

Radiology is an important part of accident care, and the American College of Surgeons stresses the necessity of having X-ray equipment, a developing lab and a technician directly on the premises at all times. Caution is often expressed not to overhandle injured patients in order to take X-rays, but some institutions shuttle patients within the hospital and even on ambulance trips to other institutions for X-ray purposes. Because of the medical orphanism of emergency rooms they seldom boast a radiologist, and X-ray plates involving fractures and concussions are read by general doctors, even inexperienced internes. As we have already seen, X-ray diagnosis is a complex art, at which radiologists themselves can be wrong 20 to 30 percent of the time. The typical doctor may have a considerably higher percentage of error.

In a recent case a sixty-five-year-old man struck by a car in New York was brought to the emergency room of the nearest hospital, where he was X-rayed. The doctor on duty read the plate, saw nothing, and several hours later sent the man home in an ambulance. The next morning the hospital radiologist studied the plate and saw an irregular line near the left hipbone. An urgent telegram was dispatched to the patient: "Please come to the emergency room to see physician." By the time the telegram arrived the patient was dead. He had suffered a fractured pelvis, with massive internal hemorrhage and shock.

To the auto victim, the nearest emergency room is the one of his "choice," where he may, or may not, receive adequate care. Some crash victims with acute head injuries will die, a Loyola University neurosurgeon told an International College of Surgeons meeting, because of "relative neglect and dangerous delays" found in emergency rooms. One cause is the lack of proper medical personnel, a reflection of poor planning and lack of concern on the part of doctors. "Our Enemy: The Emergency Room," a physician writes in a medical publication, a reflection of the attitude that many community doctors consider it unfair business competition, ignoring the fact that they have virtually driven the patient there by their unavailability. In the Colorado survey it was found that some doctors were reluctant to answer emergency-room calls for several reasons, including the factor of competition.

The alert emergency room should not, as many do, depend on such unreliable, contingent help as community doctors on call. One of the simplest solutions for a small or medium hospital is to "contract" with a team of local doctors who *give up* their regular practice in order to run the local emergency room. This is being done successfully in Alexandria, Virginia, with the fees going to the doctors, plus a retainer for welfare cases. In Detroit, Harbor Hospital hired six local doctors to tend the emergency room on a rotating basis, attending to their regular practice the rest of the time.

The growth of the emergency room as a treatment center makes a standardized system essential, if nonexistent. The American College of Surgeons has recently set emergency-room standards, including the establishment of an "emergency department" (rather than just a "room"), headed by a full-time director. Sufficient medical personnel should be on hand to provide care within fifteen minutes of arrival, backstopped by additional doctors for contingencies. A mechanism should be established to have specialized doctors when needed. The department should be open twenty-four hours a day; a physician should see every patient. It should have a separate, well-marked ground floor entrance; waiting-room space for relatives and friends; X-ray and laboratory facilities; instruments of the same quality as the rest of the hospital.

The New York Hospital-Cornell Medical Center in 1962 opened a model emergency establishment that could, in most ways, be a model for the "weak links" throughout the nation. Open to all, twenty-four hours a day, it is a miniature hospital with operating suites, a dental room and a plaster room for fracture work. No internes serve here. All care is rendered by residents in specialty-training, including surgery and internal medicine. A difficult piece of "dirt" in the eye is removed by a tyro ophthalmologist. The immaculate and efficient establishment even "enrolls" its callers during the first visit, presenting them with an identification card that will make the next "emergency" simpler to process. Fees approximate those charged by private doctors.

The din of an ambulance bell seldom disturbs the New York Hospital emergency room, for despite protests, the hospital has no ambulance service. If the emergency rooms of our hospitals symbolize a "weak link" in the chain of care, our ambulance system may be the stress needed to tear it asunder. An accident victim struck one block from the elegant New York Hospital, for example, would be picked up by a city ambulance and driven several miles, probably to a municipal hospital, given both an unneeded ride and the probability of inferior care. (The same absence of an ambulance service is true of prestigious Columbia-Presbyterian Hospital.)

The operation of ambulances throughout the country makes as little, possibly less, sense. The American College of Surgeons, now conducting a nationwide ambulance survey, has found that *undertakers furnish ambulance services for the more than half the nation's communities.* Dr. Robert Kennedy criticizes this ridiculous reliance on morticians, illustrating that their fierce competition often brings three of their "ambulances" (often hearses) on the run for the same accident. "They are," he adds, "sometimes more interested in the fatalities than the injured."

The absence of a national ambulance system has resulted in scores of groups, from undertakers to police, sponsoring ambulance care, often inadequately. The best, says Dr. Kennedy, are the volunteer rescue squads (operating in New Jersey, Maryland, New York suburbs, Virginia, Ohio), and the police or fire departments. Occasionally a private, franchised service, such as one in Charlotte, North Carolina, has worked well. Charlotte previously had an undertaker-ambulance system, but, states Major J. C. Goodman of the Police Department, "they were not particularly concerned with caring for the injured." Reverend John Stevens of Houston's St. Timothy's Church, who has campaigned for better ambulance service, also castigates a wealthy nation's reliance on undertakers for hospital emergency transportation. He, too, charges that they have on occasion "left live accident victims on the street and run off with the dead ones."

The future of ambulance systems will either require that *all* hospitals run their own, or that communities adopt a modern centralized, voluntary system operated with modern communications, dispatcher and callboard. Attendants require considerably more training than they have at the present time, and better-equipped ambulances are an urgent need. Undertakers, symbolically (and commercially) less interested in the living, have no place in proper emergency care.

The hospital's failings are becoming increasingly obvious to medical critics. The typical patient's judgment of a hospital is a simpler affair. "How do they treat you here?" he is more apt to ask a veteran patient. The food, the attention, the courtesy are essential items to his well-being. To the sick, nothing can be as meaningful as the *human* and *humane* dimensions of the bustling institution.

As in medical quality, hospitals vary in the degree of compassion and interest they are willing to invest in their transient visitors—the patient. No exact index of public dissatisfaction is possible. But available evidence, including surveys and subjective comments of articulate patients, indicates that the callousness found in the emergency room is merely an after-hour expression of a deeper indifference to patients that permeates too many American hospitals.

Columnist Inez Robb entered a hospital recently for surgery, and rapidly concluded that her presence was highly unwanted. "I had not been in the hospital an hour when I realized that I was a nuisance to everyone connected with the place," she wrote. The nurses, the medical staff, the housekeepers were unanimous, she felt, in their attitude that the patients are annoyingly disruptive of what is truly sacred—the hospital routine. "They [the nurses] slammed in and out of the room, taking my pulse and temperature as if I were Typhoid

Mary," she comments, adding that the doctor who had to take her blood pressure every hour after the operation considered the job loathsome. She quotes him in a masterpiece of medical detachment: " 'She's going to live,' " the doctor said to the nurse, " 'and by tomorrow she'll be sitting on that bell.' "

When she did ring the bell at 3 A.M. one morning for a sleeping pill, the nurse looked at her as if she were "poor Thomas de Quincey trying to kick the opium habit." Miss Robb found herself, like many intimidated patients, "babbling an apology for disturbing her and giving way to base appetites"—such as sleep. Miss Robb's facetious solution to the patient conspiracy of interrupting the gossip of nurses and the routine paper work of institutions: eliminate the patients and leave the hospitals to doctors and nurses, their "togetherness" and routines.

The regimen of many hospitals is an ogre of noncivilized behavior geared to the peculiar needs of the shifts of workers, nurses and doctors that ply through the building, and is often fiercely anti-patient in design. A "patient" invited to address a regional hospital assembly, reminded administrators of the lack of space in his room, the noise, the anachronistic five o'clock dinners. "What I really think is that you plan the hospital, as you run it, not for my comfort and convenience at all, but for the comfort and convenience and efficiency of the doctors and nurses."

Although sleep is often more curative than all man's medicaments, the routine of many hospitals is to wake patients at 6 A.M. or before, despite their physical condition, and bombard them with an abnormally early breakfast, the almost ceremonial changing of the sheets, and the wash basin that assures their staying awake so that the army-like discipline can be maintained. "At 5:05 every morning a low-flying airplane opens its bomb-bay doors and lets loose 10,000 freshly scoured stainless-steel bedpans," humorist Eric Hodgins wrote quite seriously about the early awakening in a hospital in which he spent many months. "The incredible sound, which would have made Lazarus twitch, announces the beginning of a new hospital day."

The new hospital environment has made the registered nurse a veritable administrator, several professional (and emotional) stages removed from the young, willing girl nursing at the patient's bedside with the traditional "TLC"—tender loving care. Nursing care in the modern hospital is often a more impersonal event, dispensed with lofty pride of position even when it can be secured, by good fortune, importuning or display of annoyance. Eric Hodgins, in the odyssey of his hospital incarceration, *Episode,* relates his frustration at not receiving proper attention. He once relied on the subterfuge of calling the nurse's desk from his room telephone, posing as his own doctor and ordering "immediate attention" for his patient. "Thoughtful American physicians have been talking for years about the importance of treating the patient as a human being, not simply as a malfunctioning organ," says the author. "Where all this talk is getting us is hard to discover, and the hardest place to discover it is in the American hospital."

The sensitive American physician is becoming concerned about the human failure in some hospitals. Dr. Alfred P. Ingegno of New York speaks of the "implacable patterns of habit and lack of concern that are all too prevalent among hospital administrators, nursing staff and lay personnel." (He exempts the doctors.) A physician in Atlanta, Georgia, answering a *Medical Tribune* query on what he would change in the American hospital, replied: "I feel that in the past few years hospital administrators have shifted emphasis from concern for the patient's welfare to concern for the welfare of the hospital." A New York radiologist felt that large institutions "lose sight of his [the patient's] human wishes and feelings."

The emotional climate of the hospital and its care is often dependent on its nurses. When they are empathetic and friendly, that atmosphere can be warm and healing; when they are brusque and dehumanized, the hospital is that much less the hospital. A survey by the Health Information Foundation reported a strange dichotomy in a survey of hospital patients. One third of the patients expressed dissatisfaction with the hospital, but 61 percent of the patients' doctors stated that their patients were somewhat dissatisfied, most often (54 percent of the time) mentioning "poor nursing service, not enough attention, lack of personal attention" as the major complaints.

The shortage of nurses—the gnawing problem of 250,000 non-existent R.N.'s—is generally credited with being the cause of these complaints. Eleanor C. Lambertsen, chairman of the department of nursing education at Columbia Teachers College, grants the shortage, but believes that "more simple courtesy would quiet critics of nursing care." The *Modern Hospital* nursing columnist is candid with her hospital personnel readers. "A frank appraisal of a significant percentage of the reactions to being a patient in our hospitals reveals that patients and families are primarily reacting to attitudes and behavior of hospital personnel—the way personnel treat them as people," she writes. "They are not complaining about the quality of therapy provided but about the manner in which their questions are answered or not answered; the impatience with which personnel respond to their requests for fresh drinking water, a bedpan, a bed raised or lowered; signal lights being ignored for long periods of time; meals that are cold and unappetizing; rooms that are not clean." The patient, she reminds us, is not asking for "deep psychological understanding," but for simple courtesy.

Much of the nursing-care problem revolves about the new image of the R.N. Her Florence Nightingale halo has been replaced by supervisory duties and awesome paper work, which can remove her from the nurse's traditional obligation of caring for the sick. "And if nurses no longer nurse but supervise, why call them nurses?" asks Dr. W. Edward French of Baptist Memorial Hospital in Memphis, Tennessee. Approximately 50 percent of nurse time is relegated to the mounting paper work and ward supervision, the operation of a veritable office at the nursing station. As her managerial duties increase, her clinical value decreases, and the "touching of flesh" may even seem beneath her, especially when she has aides to carry out the true nursing duties. When bureaucratic philosophy replaces patience and concern as the hospital's criteria, it is little wonder that nurses categorize patients as "good" or "bad," depending on how well they submit to hospital routine.

A recent survey of fifteen hundred nurses reveals that their definition of a "good" patient is one who disturbs them the least: "appreciative," "undemanding," "patient," "courageous." An author of the survey, Miriam Ritvo of Boston University, seems upset by this nurse immaturity—that they judge patients "by the same criteria applied to a pleasant neighbor, a worthy member of the community, or a socially successful guest at a cocktail party!" The "bad" patient, conversely, is "demanding" and "self-centered." "He seems to be expected by his nurses to subordinate his illness to the comfort of all concerned with his care," Miss Ritvo reveals. The mature concept that patients are neither "good" nor "bad" but only "sick" was grasped by only eighteen nurses of the fifteen hundred.

The understanding of these hospital pitfalls—of wrestling for survival against insufficient nursing care, medication error, precarious beds, blood-transfusion accidents, failure of medical and surgical thoroughness, poor surgery, doctorless halls, anesthesia error, infection, and myriad more—can help intelligent patients not only to make more intelligent decisions about their own care. Thus armed, the community itself can insist that all American hospitals become what they were intended to be—homes of healing, places of impeccable science and pervasive warmth.

Chapter VI

Iatrogenic Disease:
The Scourge of Doctor-Caused Illness

The classical admonishment to the physician, *primum non nocere*—
"first do no harm"—has been the philosophical umbrella of medicine
for centuries. When nostrums were the doctor's only remedies, the
warning was a searing reminder to temper his enthusiasm for healing
lest it cause injury to his patients or, in Hammurabic retribution,
to himself.

The modern doctor, in a philosophical malaise, has temporarily
forgotten this warning not to kill or maim. Infatuated with the
potential power of his armamentarium of complex therapies, drugs,
tests, surgery and transfusions, he appears to medical critics as indifferent to and ignorant of the near-epidemic harm that has accompanied modern medical treatment like an evil talisman. Without
fully understanding his onerous new role, the doctor has become
one of the major causes of contemporary death and illness. He
has become the unseemly carrier of doctor-caused, or "iatrogenic,"
disease.

In his Third Law of physics, Newton postulated that to every
action there must be an equal and opposite reaction. Euphoric fans
of modern medicine, including many doctors, have strained to repeal
the medical insight of this basic tenet. But critics within the profession have insisted on shocking the profession abruptly back to
reality. Dr. David M. Spain, clinical professor of pathology at Downstate Medical Center in New York, cautions that after bacteria,
the modern physician is the most "important factor" in the creation
of human illness, one that exists "almost as an equal" to the negative
potential of microorganisms.

As "iatros," the Greek word for physician, the modern doctor has complicated the patient environment with a massive array of treatments that the patient—and medicine—has yet to digest fully: antibiotics, antihistamines, oral diabetic drugs, diuretics, tranquilizers, psychic energizers, X-rays, anticancer chemicals, steroids, transfused blood and plasma, antihypertensives, radiation therapy, diagnostic catheters that painfully probe every body opening, needle biopsies for samples of living flesh, injections and blood sampling, with no apparent end.

"These tools, however, are powerful and contain not only much that is beneficial but also a considerable potential for harm. These are two-edged swords," says Dr. Spain, adding this caveat for his colleagues: "As physicians we have been entrusted with and are the guardians of the lifesaving therapeutic products of nature and the ideas derived from creative scientific achievements. It is not within our prerogative to abuse these gifts or pervert them into harm for man."

Iatrogenic disease can be crueler than nature's own distortions. It is a vast syndrome that encompasses paralysis, psychosis, skin eruptions, brain damage, tissue necrosis, blindness, hemorrhage, crippling, cardiac attack, deafness, suffocation, fatigue, ulcers, shock, fractures, blood clots, convulsions, anemia, kidney disease, diabetes, liver ailments, cancer—and death itself.

We have already witnessed the damage accomplished by the rash therapy of gastric freezing for ulcers. Much of the harm in iatrogenic disease, however, is the unwanted offspring of more conventional, if overapplied and abused, modern methodologies. The current high toll of iatrogenic disease is the dread reaping of a philosophy of medical action in which every procedure, rash or otherwise, is prefaced with the rationalization that it is "medical progress." The argument renders the dispenser, and the recipient, insensitive to any intelligent commentary that it might actually be antiprogress and a miscalculated risk.

The narrative insight into this contemporary sickness is a frightening medical script. A young woman, the wife of a physician, was undergoing a diagnostic work-up at a large eastern medical center. To test her blood-circulation rate, physicians prescribed an intravenous injection of dehydrocholic acid. Moments later she weakened, her pulse becoming feeble and rapid, and her breathing labored. In fifteen minutes she was dead from acute anaphylactic shock, the body's massive allergic reaction to foreign material.

A male patient taking a "routine" barium enema examination had just finished having his lower intestines fluoroscoped as part of a "GI Series." In the fluoroscopy suite, while evacuating the barium, he slumped dead of cardiac arrest. "The debilitating role of preparatory purges probably played a major role in this episode," reports a physician.

A young nurse-patient approached the bone-marrow aspiration with little trepidation. Physicians had chosen to take the sample from her sternum, the flat narrow bone in the center of the chest. Unfortunately, her attending physician was equally unaware of the potential danger in the procedure. The needle was inserted, and to the doctor's horror it passed through the bone, puncturing her heart sac like a dart, causing death. Unknown to her, and to her doctor, the nurse's sternum was too thin to be safely biopsied.

A male patient, in the hospital for treatment of polycythemia, an illness characterized by excessive red corpuscles, was placed on a drug therapy of anticoagulants. His physician prescribed a common one, heparin, by intravenous injection. Not long after, a massive hemorrhage in an undiagnosed abdominal tumor flooded his body. The patient bled to death, his normal clotting ability paralyzed by the therapy.

A middle-aged victim of cirrhosis, vomiting blood, was admitted to the hospital. During the work-up, an esophagoscope, a lighted diagnostic probe, was placed in her throat and down the nine-inch esophagus for a look at her innards. During the probe the doctor nicked the channel, creating a laceration. The injury triggered a quick deterioration in her condition, followed by death in a hepatic coma the following day.

A female patient in a mental hospital was being treated for more than eighteen months with a psychiatric "wonder drug," a derivative of phenothiazine. She suddenly developed unusual facial movements, writhing motions of the mouth and tongue, and uncontrollable jerking of the limbs. Psychiatrists quickly stopped the treatment, but the bizarre symptoms continued. The injury, labeled dyskinesia and suggesting organic brain damage, proved to be permanent and irreversible.

A talented young composer of songs and stories for children was one of the "fortunate" victims of penicillin reaction who had survived its powerful allergic shock. A year later she could not read or write, and required supervision to carry out simple household chores. Physicians diagnosed her condition as permanent brain damage caused by anoxia (oxygen starvation of the brain) that ravaged her during the severe penicillin shock.

The extent of this recurring daily harm is seldom recognized by the untroubled American physician or the trusting American patient, and is only now being revealed by concerned doctor-observers. Working in his isolated practice, the doctor rationalizes those untoward accidents of his treatment that he observes (most escape him) as occasional, unrelated events. The doctor typically assures the worried patient of the safety of the treatment, a prediction where belief is too often followed by grief. Doctors like to speak convincingly about the "calculated risk" of a particular therapy, when in actuality they are often totally ignorant of the statistical, calculated realities of iatrogenic harm.

Prior commentators have blithely labeled the iatrogenic toll as "the small price we must pay" for modern medicine. More recently, medical critics such as Dr. Spain and Dr. David Barr have more realistically titled them "The Complications of Modern Medical Practices" and "The Hazards of Modern Diagnosis and Therapy," even comparing iatrogenesis with the ever-present "blunders of mankind."

How widespread is iatrogenic disease? Do doctors create or worsen illness, or cause death, in one patient in a hundred, one in fifty, or one in five? The first insight that iatrogenesis was more than acne on the face of medical progress was offered by Dr. David Barr, who frightened the medical community when he surveyed admissions to New York Hospital-Cornell Medical Center, more than 5 percent of all admissions to the medical service were involved in "major" toxic reactions and accidents as a result of medical treatment, both diagnostic and therapeutic. Some of the iatrogenesis caused the sickness responsible for the original hospital admission.

The full extent of iatrogenic disease, including those created in the hospital, was argued in medical circles with no apparent resolution until the recent publication of several surveys of iatrogenic harm. The most comprehensive and upsetting review of doctor-caused illness and death is the work of a young house staff member of a prominent medical center, Dr. Elihu M. Schimmel, then chief resident at the Yale-New Haven Hospital, an institution connected with the Yale University School of Medicine. In a simple survey that belies its importance as a now-historic document, young Dr. Schimmel decided to inventory the untoward effects of medical treatment in every possible patient, private and charity, that came through the eighty-bed, three-ward Yale Medical Service.

Published in the *Annals of Internal Medicine,* the survey was the joint, semi-underground reporting effort of thirty-three members of the house staff who brought Dr. Schimmel detailed word of iatrogenic "episodes"—what he refers to as "noxious response to medical care"—as they occurred. At the conclusion of eight months of such self-critique, Dr. Schimmel and colleagues tallied the results.

They revealed a virtual epidemic of modern iatrogenic disease. Of the 1014 patients "there were 240 iatrogenic episodes," occurring in 198 of the patients. "Thus," says Dr. Schimmel in his unemotional report in the *Annals,* "20 percent of the persons at risk suffered one or more episodes of medical complication in the hospital." *One in five* of the patients was made ill by medical treatment, and it caused or contributed significantly to *more than one in ten* of all hospital deaths! "During the course of the study, 154 of the 1014 patients admitted to the medical service died in the hospital," states Dr. Schimmel. "Of these, 16 deaths were related to noxious episodes . . ."

Of the 240 iatrogenic episodes affecting the 1014 patients, 48 were graded major, 82 moderate and 110 minor. Those that persisted after discharge numbered 105. The episodes covered much of the technical gamut of modern medicine: there were 31 reactions to blood transfusions; 29 diagnostic accidents from biopsy to endoscopy; 23 acquired infections including five deaths; 119 drug reactions; 24 reactions to therapeutic techniques, and 14 episodes from miscellaneous hazards.

The national inferences of these figures are staggering, both to the imagination and collective corpus. Using Yale as a national yardstick, and Dr. Schimmel's *limited* definition of iatrogenesis, a simple extrapolation of the 1252 admissions and the 240 untoward episodes provides a national toll for quiet consideration. According to this sample, doctor-caused iatrogenic disease—compared against 28,000,-000 annual hospital admissions and 1,000,000 annual hospital deaths —is created in over 5,000,000 hospital patients annually. It kills, or contributes to the death of, 100,000 Americans in hospitals alone each year!

The Yale study *underestimates* the full cataclysm. It purposely *eliminates all errors made by doctors and nurses,* and does not include complications and death from surgical error or faulty anesthesia. Further, the vast iatrogenic toll of patients not in hospitals, whose medical-made illness—from drugs, tetanus antitoxin, antibiotic reactions, infections and badly set fractures—might result from the care of a private doctor, are not tallied. Similarly excluded from the Yale study are those cases whose original reason for admission was iatrogenic—which, as we shall see, includes many victims. With the buttressing of all these additional "episodes," it might be conservative to estimate death from doctor-caused disease in the magnitude of 200,000 a year. (Should the actual figure be *half* this reasoned estimate, the situation would be no less grave in its implications.) Physicians and modern medicine have thus become a close rival of cancer and heart disease as a major killer of man.

The careful technique of the Yale doctors cannot be discounted, but if substantiation is wanted, several studies have been made on the medically most glamorous aspect of iatrogenic disease—drug reaction. Dr. Leighton Cluff, professor of medicine at Johns Hopkins, recently startled his colleagues at the Association of American Physicians with a report of a study conducted by himself and U. S. Public Health Service epidemiologists. They traced the iatrogenic drug fate of 714 patients at Johns Hopkins' Osler Service for three months in 1964. The report not only hints at a national drug-surfeiting (polypharmacy); it shows that one in every seven patients, or 14 percent, developed drug reactions. An additional 4 percent of all patients (another Cluff report raises this to 5 percent), were initially admitted for that reason. The drug death rate, five or six in each one hundred deaths, also substantiates the Yale findings.

Whose fault is iatrogenic disease? First of all, it depends greatly on how *iatrogenic* is defined. Some would define it as the errorless, unanticipated fault of any medical activity, the *inevitable* price for medical technology. Others—more objectively, I believe—would list as iatrogenic *any* ailment precipitated by the intervention of a doctor or his agents, whether that intervention is handled competently or in error.

Only by knowing the *full,* accurate toll of the harm caused by doctors and their medical intervention can we estimate how well a medical technique—performed, in the final analysis, by fallible men —weighs in the balance as balm or bane. This, finally, is the true "calculated" risk. Iatrogenic disease, by this fuller definition, would also include nursing medication errors, surgical failure and complication, cardiac arrest during surgery, anesthesia death and brain damage, some of which we have already witnessed.

All of medicine must be held responsible for widespread iatrogenic death and disease, and must justify the general necessity of each of its current procedures. The individual doctor, likewise, must be held strictly accountable for his own use of a potentially dangerous instrument, therapy or drug. His blamelessness or culpability depends then on the skill and knowledge he brings to its use, or its judicious neglect. "The modern technology of medicine was designed for ideal use in an ideal situation," says a physician at New York's Sloan-Kettering Laboratory. "Its practical use requires on-the-spot judgment by the doctor, which too often, unfortunately, is lacking."

Dr. Elihu Schimmel is equally firm at bringing in the individual doctor as the protagonist in iatrogenic disease. "In the strategy of modern medical management it becomes increasingly difficult to justify equivocal procedures with the comment, 'It can't hurt!'" he says. "The probable benefit of each test or treatment must be weighed against its possible risk."

The modern diagnostic tool is often the vehicle for iatrogenic disease. Conventional diagnostic tests done in the doctor's office— such as the drawing of blood samples—entail only a small risk. The galaxy of complex diagnostic tools that one finds in specialty work and in the hospital provides not only unprecedented medical intelligence but unlimited opportunity to produce illness and disease. The potential becomes exponential when wielded by the doctor who considers only the device's beneficence and not its coiled evil.

The new diagnostic procedures have almost as much inherent medical glamour as open-heart surgery: mechanical probes that enter body openings from the penis to the throat; biopsies that cut out tissue and organ samples by piercing through the skin and flesh; contrast "dyes" that are injected to make sophisticated X-rays of otherwise nonvisible organs; catheters penetrating the body to sample the blood of the heart; air injections to visualize the brain.

The insertion of a mechanical probe into a resisting orifice can be like a minor operation, with all its difficulties. The bronchoscope, which permits the doctor to see the lung area with a series of mirrors and prisms, cannot be forced down a patient's throat. The patient is generally given atropine to cut down the gastric secretions, and meperidine (Demerol) and pentobarbital to reduce the pain and make him drowsy and noncombative. Dr. Schimmel reports on one such patient who went into shock following the administration of these medications, even before the bronchoscope could be inserted down his throat.

Endoscopy is the general name for these probes, and their iatrogenic reactions are both numerous and dangerous. (The proctoscope for rectal examinations, when handled by an *experienced* man, is a general exception.) Schimmel reports six in his study, including two deaths: three from esophagoscopy; two from cystoscopy; and one from bronchoscopy. The hidden danger in esophagoscopy is usually a doctor's unsure hand and a nicked esophagus, with subsequent reaction including death itself.

The cystoscope, used in urinary examination, contains an outer sheath bearing the lighting system, space for the visual system, and room for the passage of operative devices up the bladder. Urinary inspection with the cystoscope resulted in the death of an obese woman with high blood pressure who complained of having blood in her urine. When the device was inserted, the woman suddenly lapsed into cardiac arrest and died. In the second case of cystoscopic backfire in the Yale study, the bulky probe produced a case of pyelonephritis, a kidney inflammation.

Dr. David Barr, in his *JAMA* report "Hazards of Modern Diagnosis and Therapy," relates another "not infrequent" danger in cystoscopy: infection. He describes a severe blood-stream infection that followed a probe, "controlled with difficulty with antibiotics." In another cystoscopic case, which took place in a physician's office, a strong dose of a local anesthesia was used to prepare a male patient for the cystoscope. It sent him into convulsions, precipitating a slipped disc and orthopedic surgery.

Some annoyed physicians believe that these important mechanical probes are unnecessarily overused by doctors in certain hospital situations. "These diagnostic procedures can be very necessary, but I have a suspicion that they are often overused by internes and residents looking for experience," says a graduate of a residency in internal medicine. "The work is often done by an inexperienced physician without proper supervision, who may be doing it for academic 'completeness' rather than because he has weighed the necessity of endoscopy against the possible danger. Sometimes the doctor is not fully aware of the potential danger, or his own limitations. I personally wouldn't do a bronchoscopy because I don't know how to do it well enough. I don't think any general internist should do an esophagoscopy unless he has had special training."

The most sacrosanct contemporary diagnostic technique is the cardiac catheter, which can return heart pressure, oxygenation and other information to the physician from an otherwise inaccessible heart chamber. It can also, with poetic irony, trigger heart damage as lethal as the one it was designed to describe. The heart catheter is usually inserted through a large vein in the arm or a leg artery, then threaded up toward the heart chambers with the aid of a fluoroscope.

Accidental puncture of the heart is one of its hazards, especially in the young, whose undeveloped myocardium (heart muscle) is no match for the mechanical probes. A catheter puncture of one infant's heart was described by a former resident in a large midwestern hospital:

"I was working on the service when the head of cardiology and his assistant came to do catheterization on a four-month-old infant with a congenital heart ailment. The youngster was given morphine beforehand, but I noticed he was reacting badly. He was turning blue from anoxia. 'The kid is all flaked out. Why don't we bring him around and cut it out for today,' I said. I gave him some oxygen and morphine antagonist, and he came around. But the cardiologist wouldn't stop. He insisted on continuing the catheterization. It's a tricky thing slipping that catheter through the valve into a baby's little heart ventricle, and the doctor was getting impatient. Finally, he just poked it—right through the ventricle wall. When he injected the contrast dye for radiography, he saw that it went into the pericardial cavity instead of into the right heart ventricle. The infant was rushed to surgery but he died."

Catheterization in youngsters is fraught with iatrogenic problems, including the use of anesthesia. Parents of a two-year-old who died during catheterization argued in a malpractice suit that they had not known the full risk of the procedure—a common medical consumer weakness. They lost the decision because they had ostensibly been informed of its mechanics. The pediatrician had advised catheterization when he suspected that blueness around the lips and lassitude after exercise might be signs of a congenital heart ailment. The child received an anesthetic, but awoke during the catheterization and started struggling. To quiet him, more anesthesia was injected into the blood stream through the heart catheter. Within twenty seconds the boy's heartbeat slowed, his blood pressure dropped and his pulse all but disappeared. Oxygen and cardiac massage were unsuccessful. Four hours later he died.

The University of Indiana Medical Center, after seven hundred successful catheterizations, suddenly had four accidental heart punctures in approximately a year. Each of the accidents involved infants, and in three cases the catheter puncture was "the immediate or precipitating cause of death." The report authors, Drs. Paul R. Lurie and Mario Grajo, warn in *Pediatrics:* "The risk of accidental puncture of the heart is without doubt increasing with the persistence with which a thoroughgoing attempt is made to catheterize all chambers and outflow vessels of the heart." They add that the physician should always weigh the need against the risk.

The delicate task of probing a heart is surrounded with risk no matter what the subject's age or health. In an attempt to reduce the "higher morbidity and mortality" accompanying it, Dr. C. Walton Lillehei of the University of Minnesota Medical School has suggested a new, if awesome, technique to sample the heart. It is a "direct" cardiac catheterization accomplished with an eight-inch-long needle punched directly through the chest wall. The fact that this reportedly "safer" procedure, done on 122 persons, claimed one life—that of a six-year-old boy—and created a dozen complications, indicates the risk usually involved.

Dr. Arthur Selzer of San Francisco points out in the *New England Journal of Medicine* that catheterization of the right side of the heart is the safest, while catheterization of the left side carries a "higher risk." Caution against excessive use of heart catheters is expressed to family-doctor readers of *GP* by Dr. J. K. Perloff, who dismisses the idea that they are ever "routine." *Whenever possible,* he says, heart disease should preferably be diagnosed by clinical means.

The mere act of inserting a foreign device into a body orifice seems to be a major catalyst for creating disease—a mechanical disturbance of the body homeostasis, or natural balance. The common urinary catheter, a rubber-tube drain which permits urine flow in a congested person, is a potentially fatal case in point. The commonness of infections following bladder catheterization has led critical doctors to view the simple device as much an enemy of man as its friend. It is more so when handled by doctors in a slovenly manner, which is *usually* the case. The Yale study produced seven cases of such infection. The patients runs a chance of infection in each urine catheterization, but, says Dr. Jay P. Sanford of the University of Texas Southwestern Medical School, the infection rate *"increases to virtually 100 percent when an indwelling catheter is employed* [italics mine]."

When the urinary catheter is left in (indwelling) during the hospital stay, the damage is often lingering. Dr. E. H. Kass of Boston reveals that as many as 25 percent of such patients have residual urinary-tract infection "one year afterward"! There can sometimes be more danger in the badly handled postoperative rubber drain than in the scalpel and anesthesia. Dr. C. D. Creery makes the point dramatically: "More patients die by the catheter than by the prostatectomy [prostate removal]."

Such iatrogenic villains are often overlooked as the cause of complex medical riddles. In a case history reported in *Modern Medicine,* the attending physician called a consultant excitedly. "I hate to bother you this late at night, but I need some help and advice," he said. The patient, he explained, had "cyanosis [lack of oxygen], rapid pulse, and fever" and suffered from "mental changes followed by vomiting." The consultant asked; "Is the patient in shock?" "He looks like it, but the blood pressure is 100/80 mm," the doctor answered. "I suppose it's a coronary or a stroke or something, but that wouldn't explain the high fever. I certainly hate to see this happen. I've known this patient for several months."

The patient had been in the hospital for a cataract operation, and urine retention developed that night. "Everything seemed to be going along fine until early this afternoon when the ward nurse found him wandering down the hall. He was confused, argumentative and disoriented," the attending explained. When the consultant M.D. learned that the patient's white blood cell count had risen, he made a stab at what now appeared the obvious diagnosis: "Then it is something infectious. Let's have the technician come back again and do some blood cultures. I think this illness began with acute urinary retention, not with surgery." The attending agreed: "I think insertion of the indwelling catheter resulted in a bacteremia with some Gram-negative organism." The consultant added the complication of "toxic shock." When the attending physician plaintively asked, "What are his chances?" he received the dour response, "Slim."

The urinary-catheter infection is one of the recurring reminders that basic sterility as espoused by Lister is still an unreached, even unattempted, goal. Some physicians react to the indwelling catheter's virtual 100 percent infection rate as if it were an immutable truth. Critical physicians such as Dr. Robert E. Desautels of Harvard Medical School are convinced that the damage is exclusively doctor-made, rather than the product of harsh nature.

Instead of being fettered by the usual "100 percent" infection rate, Dr. Desautels kept 174 of his 200 patients using indwelling catheters *infection free!* "Meticulous care of the catheter and its drainage apparatus is an extremely effective method of reducing the incidence of infection," university urologists Drs. Hinman and Cox lecture their colleagues in *JAMA.* In *Hospital Medicine* Dr. Desautels explains the sterile principles that have worked in 85 percent of the cases, adding: "With a more rigid application, it is believed that a result approaching 100 can be obtained."

The detailed advice given by these doctors on how to clean the patient's organ and adjacent area properly, and how to disinfect the drainage bottle in order to reduce infection from *100 down to 10 percent* is somewhat upsetting to the layman, who thought his physicians were educated in basic medical techniques. "Good technique is self-evident," Dr. Jack Levin of New Haven understates in *Annals of Internal Medicine,* "but often neglected."

The catheter, in any of its forms, is a supreme iatrogenic hazard. Investigators warn that the polyethylene catheter, inserted (cut) into the arm for delivering intravenous medication, often becomes dislodged from its adapter and enters the circulatory system, where it can only be removed by surgery. An editorial in the *British Medical Journal,* which reports thirteen such cases of "lost" catheters, asks manufacturers to make them radiopaque so that they can be located. The patient, of course, would prefer not to play anatomic host to plastic catheters, X-ray sensitive or otherwise.

The biopsy—the extraction of a piece of tissue for sampling— is a perfect field exercise for the iatrogenic-prone doctor. It is a valuable tool in the diagnosis of certain conditions but functions with equal facility as a harbinger of trauma and disease. "But with all such procedures," warns Dr. Spain in his text *The Complications of Modern Medical Practices,* "there are hazards with indiscriminate use or unsupervised and improperly performed techniques, as well as from neglect in heeding the specific contraindications."

Liver biopsies kill an estimated one in every six hundred and injure many more, generally from hemorrhage or biliary (bile tract) peritonitis, which can produce a shock-like state. One physician explains the unanticipated death as it often takes place. "After the biopsy, bleeding can take place internally. The patient appears to be asleep, and is not noticed until the nurse comes around an hour or two later. When she checks the patient, she finds he is shocked out or dead."

Dr. Schimmel reports three liver biopsy accidents. Dr. Spain cautions that doing a liver biopsy can be "foolhardy, desperate or irresponsible" in certain situations: when there is a lack of patient co-operation; in almost all cases of infants or children; a suspected liver abscess or susceptibility to hemorrhaging. "You can't assume that a person won't hemorrhage after a liver biopsy," says a physician who has done over a hundred of these organ samplings. "The cautious doctor should always do blood tests beforehand. This includes a bleeding time test, done by pricking the finger; a clotting time test; a prothrombin test, which also measures a clotting factor; and a red cell count to see if he is anemic."

The punching, or suctioning out, of tissue from inside the body is always potentially dangerous. The kidney biopsy is no exception, and its complications rank with, or exceed, those of the liver sampling. The trauma ranges from the gross discharge of blood in the urine (one in every twenty cases) to renal obstruction in one out of every thirty-three cases, plus assorted difficulties, from back pain to low blood pressure. Experts believe the kidney biopsy is contraindicated in cases where the patient has only one functioning kidney, or large renal cysts, cancerous growths, the suspicion of an aneurysm (ballooning) in a renal artery, or perhaps congestive heart failure.

The intelligent physician should be involved in an intellectual skirmish between his more conservative tendencies and perhaps injudicious overaggressiveness. He will find the pleural biopsy—extracting a sampling of the lining of the lung with a blunt-end needle pierced through the chest—one trial of his mettle and judgment. The technique may aid cancer diagnosis in certain cases, but its effectiveness is still debated. Meanwhile, Dr. Spain warns doctors (and patients) of its perilous side. "Serious complications from blunt-end pleural biopsy include intrapleural hemorrhage, pneumothorax with effusion [air in the pleural cavity] and unexpanded lung. In a few cases, the pneumothorax has terminated fatally. Because the intrinsic value of this procedure is still in question, the nature of the complications must be accorded full consideration in deciding whether or not to perform pleural biopsy in any specific case."

The invention of the X-ray by Wilhelm Roentgen in 1895 is one of the milestones in medical technology, and its contribution to disease diagnosis can only be gainsaid at the risk of ridicule. Less than ridiculous, even sage, perhaps, is the contemporary criticism of the ill-considered use of hazardous radiological methods that poison the system, either with potentially toxic contrast-media "dyes" or with radiation itself. The physician who without any reservations accepts modern radiological techniques—from the arteriogram (X-ray of the arteries) to the myelogram (X-ray of the spine)—can be numbered among the iatrogenic guilty.

Unlike the bones, the internal organs of the body—the heart, liver, kidneys, intestines, arteries—do not normally show up on X-rays. To use Roentgen's genius effectively, the physician must "fill" these organs with a radiopaque "contrast medium," sometimes potentially toxic substances whose danger he must first carefully weigh.

The 1964 malpractice award of $725,000, the largest in history, involved the creation of facial cancer from a radiodye inserted into a patient's left sinus for X-ray pictures. The dye was later left in despite professional warnings of the medium's toxicity. Years afterward, the patient complained of a burning in the nose and throat, and discharges of blood and pus. When one of his teeth was extracted, a dark, viscous liquid—the dye—flowed from the socket. Shortly after, a surgeon removed the dye from the sinus, but a biopsy

showed cancer. Radical surgery, including the removal of the left eye
and much of the structure of the left side of his face, was the price
for injudicious medicine.

Many radiopaque dyes are reasonably safe, but their periodic
hazards—such as a recent "epidemic" of iatrogenic death—should
give all physicians pause. A female patient entered Johns Hopkins
Hospital with a complaint of colicky pain. To check out her gall
bladder, she was given, by mouth, 4.5 gm. of a relatively new contrast
medium, bunamiodyl sodium. Twelve hours later an X-ray picture
of the gall bladder showed that the contrast had failed to "dye"
it. The doctors tried it again a few days later, this time with a dose
of 9 grams of the bunamiodyl sodium. "Two hours later," says the
doctor's report in *JAMA,* "she was noted to have an irregular rhythm
which ECG showed to be atrial fibrillation [dangerous, rapid, irregular heartbeat] with a rate of about 150 beats per minute."

Instead of a simple gall bladder film, physicians were now faced
with a heart condition, severe low blood pressure, vomiting and
hallucinations. Kidney failure appeared imminent, and on the eighth
day the patient was placed on the artificial kidney. By the evening
of the ninth day she died. The University of Maryland also reported
eight cases of renal insufficiency following the dye's use, six of which
resulted in death.

In an unusual dispatch from a doctor to a politician, one of the
Johns Hopkins physicians wrote the then Senator Humphrey in
1964 that eleven deaths had been reported from two hospitals and
that extrapolation from these figures indicates that the incidence of
acute renal failure and death nationally is in excess of 100. The
doctor-correspondent was exercising professional restraint. Since the
contrast medium (now removed from the market) was then in heavy
use in gall bladder visualization (cholecystography), the national
death toll involving this one medium may well have exceeded that.

The case histories of such iatrogenic death are as emotionally
tearing as they are informative. A woman who had been injected
with a contrast medium, sodium acetrizoate, for an aortagram (X-
ray of the main heart artery) immediately suffered extreme pain
in her chest and abdomen. This was followed by numbness, then
paralysis in one of her legs. X-rays showed that some of the solution had escaped from the aorta, a danger that exists in up to 10
percent of aortagrams.

The awesome term "angiogram" was for years a staple dialogue
ploy on the *Ben Casey* television series, where its use by the young
neurosurgeon was seldom clouded by comments on its grave iatrogenic danger. Technically, the term is synonymous with "arterio-
graph" or "arteriogram" and refers to any X-ray of a blood vessel.
Angiogram is also used to refer to the cerebrovascular system and
to the detection of cerebral aneurysms and clots. Although often

a necessary procedure, this brain search produces, say authorities, untoward results in 2 to 6 percent of patients, including paralysis on one side of the body, and sometimes leads to death itself.

Its greatest danger is its use in noncritical situations. One young boy who suffered from "spells" of seeing things was examined by a neurologist who decided that an angiogram was necessary to decide whether the situation was basically emotional or organic. The technique proved extreme for the boy's system, and partial paralysis was the result not of the supposed disease but of the inquiry.

The cerebral blood system is visualized by injecting the contrast medium into an artery, generally the carotid artery of the neck, from where it is supposed to travel uneventfully to the brain for proper contrasting and subsequent X-rays. Unfortunately, the injection is too often eventful. The complications may be neurological or, as the Yale study shows, large painful hematomas, masses of blood and tissue at the site of the injection.

Although carotid arteriogram may be the most dangerous, the method itself can produce danger at almost *any* body site. A study of 2845 patients given arteriograms, which was reported to the National Stroke Congress, showed twenty-two deaths from the technique and forty-nine complications, a total of 2.5 percent. Another study, of 777 patients whose blood vessels were probed and X-rayed, showed a complication rate of 3.9 percent.

The major discretion for the doctor to exercise is to reserve the arteriogram for necessary diagnoses only, do it with consummate skill and have emergency medications ready in case of shock. Another vital reservation is to limit its use to suitable institutions. "Hospitals, before establishing facilities for some of these intricate procedures," Dr. David Spain points out, "should evaluate critically whether the available or potential material and personnel is adequate to meet the requisite standards of safety and results; whether there is a real need in the community for the procedure or whether it is merely a question of status."

The X-ray itself can often be the "harmless" process physicians are wont to describe it as. It may also be the patient's perilous iatrogenic trial. A Dr. Stephenson, quoted in *JAMA,* reported twenty-three cases of cardiac arrest which had occurred in X-ray departments. The non-incriminating-looking X-ray tilt table is sometimes the culpable agent. Loss of consciousness, convulsions, cardiac arrest and subsequent death have been reported in the use of the tilt table for non-X-ray techniques such as electroencephalograms and electrocardiograms. In *JAMA* a Navy neurosurgeon, Lieutenant Commander David R. Cooper, warns of the possibility of cardiac arrest being triggered by the modern motorized tilt table, which raises the patient to a near-upright position with the feet off the floor, for the taking of myelograms.

Dr. Cooper recounts the case of a near-miss from myelogram positioning which proved to be an excessive strain on the patient's heart. "A forty-three-year-old white male was taken to the X-ray department for a myelogram on September 26, 1962," he recounts. "He had episodes of low back pain and left leg pain of seven-year duration . . . He was apprehensive. The head of the table was elevated about 35 degrees to distend the lumbar sac. As the skin was cleansed with tincture of thimerosal the patient complained of not feeling well and promptly fainted. The table was quickly lowered to Trendelenburg position and he recovered consciousness immediately . . . Following a delay of ten minutes, he was repositioned and the head end of the myelography table was raised more slowly and cautiously than usual. He lost consciousness again but did not respond to the head-down posture this time. His respirations became irregular, then gasping, and ceased." Only medical heroics, including cutting open the chest and massaging the heart, saved him. Dr. Cooper advises his colleagues that such tragedies are not in the natural order, but are preventable.

The other X-ray hazard, the debilitating effects of radiation (that ability to cripple cells that paradoxically makes it a therapeutic against cancer), has been the subject of much postwar discussion. The danger that results from the peaceful use of radiation, both in diagnostic X-rays and therapeutic radiation, is no less real.

The value of radioactivity against malignancy has been documented since the first treatment of cervical cancer with radium in 1905. But over these six decades, there has also been what Dr. David Spain calls "considerable abuse" that may have nurtured an ill, gamma-ridden wind whose full ferocity may not yet have been felt. A major misuse of radiation by physicians, he says, has been the employment of powerful rays to cure benign (noncancerous) conditions including plantar warts, eczema, acne, rheumatism. One study of 165 patients with benign conditions treated with radiation confirms the penalty often gained by using extreme therapies to treat minor ills. Twenty-two of the patients developed skin cancer at the radiation site.

The most frightening abuse has been on children, who are more sensitive to radiation's ill effects. The same radiation given regionally to an adult can become almost "whole body" radiation in a child. According to University of Cincinnati College of Medicine researchers, the doctors who use radioisotopes in children seldom know that the same dosage can deliver up to twenty times the whole body radiation to infants and children that it does to adults.

From the 1920's through the late 1950's (perhaps even today) two near-mythical childhood "diseases" that generally require no therapy—enlarged thymus gland and enlarged tonsils—were "treated" with radiation doses averaging between 500 to 800 R's (roentgens). The result of this treatment, many experts believe, is doctor-caused cancer, generally in the nearby thyroid gland. One report on twenty-eight children with proven cancer of the thyroid showed that ten had received radiation in infancy for their enlarged thymus. In a surprising revelation, Dr. Spain states: "I have personal knowledge of one pediatrician who irradiated over 1000 children for 'hypertrophied [enlarged] tonsils.'" He adds that most studies of children under fifteen who have developed cancer of the thyroid show that 75 to 100 percent of them have a history of such radiation exposure.

Dr. Louis Hempelmann of the University of Rochester Medical School reported that an increased incidence of thyroid cancer and leukemia was found among 2809 children who had their thymus gland radiated in infancy between the years 1926 and 1957! Leukemia may be an increasing iatrogenic result of unwise radiation. Even the English have engaged in bizarre radiation therapies, with the penalty of increased leukemia. A sample of British adults treated with radiation for ankylosing spondylitis (arthritis of the spine) suffered five times the incidence of leukemia expected in a random group.

The typical patient is more apt to be faced with a diagnostic situation in which he is asked to "take an X-ray." The American public accepts 135,000,000 diagnostic X-rays a year, but many patients are frankly worried about the possible aftereffects. "Can such X-rays cause cancer?" the patient asks himself. "Might it be more harmful than helpful?" Concerned doctors are seeking intelligent regimens when to use and when to avoid diagnostic X-rays.

"It is common knowledge that X-rays are one of the most important of all medical procedures, saving or prolonging life of thousands of people each year," states Dr. Donald R. Chadwick of the Public Health Service. He then adds this disclaimer: "On the other hand, X-rays contribute a large proportion of the total radiation received by people in this and many other countries. Responsible authorities agree that all radiation exposure carries some risk of adverse biological effect, and therefore unnecessary exposure should be reduced or eliminated whenever possible."

How can this be translated into intelligent risk-taking for the average patient? One caution that has been openly expressed is not to expose an unborn child to X-rays, especially in the mother's first trimester of pregnancy. Studies conflict on the danger involved. One report collected the experience of 700,000 children, 569 of whom eventually got cancer. The frequency of prenatal diagnostic X-rays was 40 percent higher in the cancer group than among other children. Dr. Melvin Griem of the department of radiology of the University of Chicago, however, is not convinced. When interviewed, Dr. Griem explained that preliminary findings of his controlled study

for HEW indicate no significant cancer difference between children whose mothers were or were not X-rayed during pregnancy.

The Strang Clinic for cancer detection in New York has a common-sense approach to the question of X-ray danger. "We exhibit caution, rather than concern, in the use of certain X-ray procedures such as the barium enema and GI series," says Dr. John F. King, associate director of the Clinic. This caution over the stomach and intestinal X-ray probes is warranted because both usually involve the use of the fluoroscope. The patient receives an average of 5 to 10 R's during only thirty seconds of exposure in extremely competent hands—perhaps two hundred times the radiation he would get from a simple chest X-ray. Others estimate the typical fluoroscope dose higher, between 10 and 25 R's per examination.

"We feel that no unnecessary X-ray should be used on a routine basis, and only those patients in whom we might expect a higher than normal yield of illness receive these radiological procedures," Dr. King continued. "Of approximately a hundred patients screened each day, for example, only five to seven will get a barium enema or GI Series. We don't know the patient's other radiological experiences during the year, and we don't want to add to it unless the process is necessary. Until the advent of more knowledge in the field of radiation physics, we prefer to be cautious, and not to expose people to additional radiation without good reason."

Dr. King's concern does not extend to the routine chest X-ray. "We are not worried about the radiation from routine chest X-rays, which each of our patients receives," he states. "Studies have shown that even tuberculosis patients who used to receive weekly chest X-rays have had no radiation aftereffects."

The apprehensive patients, who are ridiculed by physicians as "neurotic" if they worry about routine X-rays, need not refuse necessary diagnostic films, nor need they accept doctor derision of their fears. (If a strong patient stand against physician supercalmness is desired, merely recount their former radiation indiscretions such as the tragic treatment of "enlarged thymus.") In fact, there is disturbing verification in one study, at least, that excessive diagnostic X-rays, on a cumulative basis, may contribute to leukemia. In this study, 2948 adults, who either had leukemia, other forms of cancer or were disease-free, were questioned about their X-ray history. Points were arbitrarily assigned to each X-ray technique (intravenous pyelogram for kidney investigation, 6 points; barium enema, 4 points, etc.) and the scores compared to the cancer incidence. Although it should be strictly noted that the results are disputed, the study authors concluded that diagnostic X-rays probably account for 8 percent of all cases of leukemia, while therapeutic radiation accounts for another 3.6 percent.

An editorial in the forthright *Canadian Medical Association Jour-*

nal warns that the value from such diagnostic X-rays should always exceed the danger of producing leukemia. They state that "one case of myeloid leukemia may be produced for every 46,000 trunk exposures, and . . . the average barium meal involves seven such exposures." Their figures substantiate the caution expressed by the Strang Clinic that it might be less harmful to do nothing than to do routine barium X-rays of patients without any possible hint of stomach cancer.

The possibility of X-ray danger is greatest when instruments are wielded by less-than-competent hands. In the *New England Journal of Medicine,* noted radiation physicist Hanson Blatz of New York chastises the indolent and sloppy medical dispensers of X-rays who might be causing iatrogenic harm through excessive patient exposure. "The greatest problem to be faced today is in keeping the dose to patients at a minimum," physicist Blatz states.

Doctors of prior generations, when the hazards of radiation were virtually unknown, were much more irresponsible than today. Many physicians, including pediatricians, made fluoroscoping of internal organs an integral part of the "routine" physical, and boasted of their thoroughness. "The old GP," says a contemporary radiologist, "had a crummy old fluoroscope, with a great big field that irradiated everything from the door to the ceiling. While the patient was under intense radiation, the doctor kept his foot on the floor control for sometimes as long as ten minutes, spreading the radiation around like it was water. Kids received whole-body irradiation as a routine matter. A lot has changed in X-ray use since then."

To accept the flattering comparison of generations would be foolish if only because the quantity of medical X-rays has increased fivefold in twenty years. Contemporary quality, too, is apparently far from ideal and quite capable of leading to iatrogenic blunder. In the *NEJM,* Mr. Blatz—whose Office of Radiation Control has inspected ten thousand medical and seven thousand dental X-ray units —is angered at doctor's X-ray incompetence. He argues that a great reduction in risk to patients could be accomplished by physicians making "corrections" in their X-ray equipment and technique. "If this were done today the average dose to patients would be reduced, in my estimation," he states, "by at least 50 percent overnight in most installations and 75 percent or more within a month or so."

"If the corrections are so simple and so effective, why haven't they already been made?" Mr. Blatz then asks. Unencumbered by medical diplomacy, he candidly offers the opinion that many physicians are both untutored and unconcerned about X-ray safety. "Registration and inspection records in New York City show that about 85 percent of the X-ray equipment in use is owned by physicians who have not had formal training in radiology," says X-ray controller Blatz. "There is evidence that most of the educational literature distributed to physicians is not read. Illustrated pamphlets giving simple recommendations have been mailed to every medical X-ray user in New York City, and yet, when inspectors arrive and offer to discuss them, few of the physicians remember having received the material."

The American patient, says Hanson Blatz, is receiving unnecessarily high doses of X-ray radiation during diagnostic X-ray for many reasons, some of which the sophisticated patient should be familiar with. Kilovoltage should be kept at optimum level, which is often impossible in older sets without a kilovoltage meter or with faulty control knobs seriously in error. The distance from the film should be as *long* as possible. Faster film for shorter exposure time should be used more often. X-ray film rather than fluoroscope (which delivers up to three hundred times the radiation) should be used for most diagnoses, except where study of "dynamics" is necessary. Perhaps the major cause of excessive exposure, Mr. Blatz believes, has been doctor failure to limit the beam to the part being X-rayed.

Indiscriminate body bombardment is apparently commonplace. "Even today many people, in taking X-ray films of the chest, expose essentially the entire body of the patient whereas only the chest need be exposed," Mr. Blatz charges. The result, he shows, is that the reproductive organs receive "hundreds of times" more radiation than necessary, as do the sensitive eye lenses. This iatrogenic stupidity can be avoided with proper technique, including the use of adjustable rectangular "collimators," which focus the rays.

(The danger to reproductive organs can be considerable in dental X-raying because of the angle of the beam. A report from Hartford, Connecticut, implicated forty-one local dental X-ray machines as exposing patients' sex glands to radiation. Most major cities are now in the midst of X-ray control programs of varying success; meanwhile, concerned patients should advise their dentists to use lead-and-rubber "lap shields" to protect the vital organs.)

Criticism also emanates from radiologists, many of whom believe other doctors are less equipped than they to maintain X-ray safety. Mr. Blatz's critique stems from New York, but criticism is equally fervent when it comes from smaller medical communities. In response to a jarring *Medical Economics* article, "Your X-rays Aren't Safe," a western radiologist writes in his complete concurrence. "Some people may think your article overstates the case. It doesn't!" he writes. "As a radiologist working in northern Arizona, an area of sparse population and small hospitals, I found unsafe procedures in every single hospital and office I visited."

Fluoroscopes are potential radiation blasters, and often the weakest link in X-ray safety. Most physicians, physicist Blatz states, are not aware that fluoroscope screens are hazardous when aged. Screens more than twenty years old should be replaced, says Blatz, for "patients examined with such fluoroscopes are receiving three to five times as much radiation as is necessary."

In fluoroscopy, as in many medical arts, unfounded doctor arrogance can be a grave danger to patient health. For minimum fluoroscope dosage, the physician must "dark-adapt" his eyes, preferably with goggles, for at least ten minutes. Otherwise, the doctor increases the dosage to get a bright picture. Overconfident physicians often short-cut this barrier, which prompted Hanson Blatz to comment acidly: "A recent survey by a medical journal resulted in comments by some physicians that they were quite capable of becoming completely dark-adapted in a few minutes. This is sheer nonsense . . ."

Critics underscore another physician failing: underestimating the time he keeps the fluoroscope focused on the patient, thus delivering too many R's. Physicist Blatz recounts a test in which an observer with a stop watch asked well-qualified radiologists to estimate the length of their fluoroscopic examination. "In all cases estimated times were substantially shorter than that shown by the stop watch," says Blatz. "In some cases the estimate was as low as one quarter of the actual time." The moral: those physicians who use fluoroscopes should have an attached automatic timing device. Or perhaps the patient is best equipped with his own kitchen alarm.

Marshaling against iatrogenic disease is a complex concept, for its medical backfire permeates every aspect of treatment, from the wandering "R" of radiation to the "innocent" injection. The hypodermic needle jabbed into the muscle may appear to be early primer for the doctor, but its complicating damage is quite sophisticated. While some physicians consider its use so simple that they teach high-school-graduate aides by having them jab an orange, critics are convinced that doctors are insufficiently aware of the danger of an improper stab. Dr. Daniel J. Hanson, a pathologist in Toledo, Ohio, used the pages of *GP* to castigate doctors and nurses for widespread injection damage.

Better training of physicians and nurses is necessary, he states, if we are to avoid the frequent abscesses, cysts, lingering pain, skin-sloughing, scarring, bone inflammation and even paralysis that can result from an incorrectly placed hypodermic needle. The sciatic nerve—which starts at the spine, continues almost to the center of the buttocks, then runs down either leg—is one offending target. If pierced by the needle, it can paralyze the patient for life. A recent malpractice judgment of $128,000 on the West Coast illustrates the danger. A repair man was bitten by a dog and drove to the hospital, where a nurse in the emergency clinic gave him an antibiotic injection in his rear. The needle struck the sciatic nerve, and four days later the patient was paralyzed from the waist down.

To find the appropriate spot for the needle, many physicians divide the buttock with imaginary vertical and horizontal lines, then make their injections in the upper, outer quadrant. This is not an adequate precaution, for patients' buttocks do not always conform. A safer method of avoiding the sciatic nerve, says Dr. Hanson, is to inject in the gluteal muscle at the upper, outer portion of the buttock, and considerable distance from the site of currently misapplied injections. The warning is especially valuable for female patients, some of whom invite a "quickie" injection by pulling up their undergarments, exposing the most paralysis-prone part of the buttock to the doctor's needle. Infants, whose gluteal muscles are not developed, are best injected in the backs of their thighs, he says.

A wandering hypodermic can also cause paralysis of the arm by striking the radial nerve. With rare exception, says Dr. Hanson, the present practice of injecting adults in the upper arm is not proper. The muscle bed is often not large enough, and a slip can bring the needle into the unguarded nerve.

Medications destined for intramuscular injections, and those specifically developed for "IV" (intravenous, or "through the veins") use, must be dispatched as planned. Most physicians and nurses are careful of this, but the medical literature includes more than one case of such mix-up. In Omaha, Nebraska, a student nurse disregarded a warning on the ampule that the product was for intravenous use only, and injected the drug into a newborn infant's buttock. Shortly after, the child's leg became crippled.

Iatrogenic ailments, like the naturally inspired ones, take the most bizarre forms, often as phenomena that baffle both patient and doctor. Electroshock treatment in psychiatric cases has been physician-promoted as especially safe—one of the reasons why it is used instead of hazardous insulin-shock therapy. But bone fracture and hearing loss have reportedly resulted from electric shock. In another area, seemingly sterile injections have produced cases of clostridial myositis, a deadly infection caused by anerobic, or non-air-using, organisms. Two hospitals in Philadelphia recently reported five cases, three of whom died.

One bizarre iatrogenic complication, the "discovery" of nonexistent disease in a patient, is increasingly common. It may be a by-product of mismanaged physician attempts at worthwhile, thorough diagnosis. These doctor-caused diseases include "cardiac neurosis," in which the injured heart exists only in the physician's, then in the patient's, mind. Dr. John W. Keyes of the Henry Ford Hospital in Detroit, in a paper entitled "Iatrogenic Heart Disease," speaks of cardiac neurosis as a condition "in which a physician has, through statements, actions or treatment," helped produce cardiac symptoms including "functional dyspnea [labored breathing], palpitation, chest pains, dizziness, fatigue, and general exhaustion."

Creating an iatrogenic heart case can be deceptively simple. The patient, feeling some chest pain and fatigue, is asked to take an electrocardiogram by his physician. Stimulated by what Dr. Keyes calls "snap judgment," benign markings on the electrocardiogram become interpreted by the physician as significant of a previous "heart attack." The patient is soon diagnosed, treated and, most significantly, then *views himself* as a cardiac case with all its physical and psychological limitations. This unnecessary new disease, which can be crippling, is partially the result of what Dr. Frank Wilson refers to as the "wretched state of electrocardiographic diagnosis and the misery attributable to it."

Dr. Keyes catalogues some of the physician errors leading to iatrogenic heart disease, including nervous-system reactions on the ST and T waves of the electrocardiogram that are "frequently misinterpreted," he states, as heart changes. "Many people with such changes on the EKG have been followed for years," Dr. Keyes reports, "without significant cardiac changes taking place." The tragedy is dramatized by thirteen cases of "cardiac" patients who had been falsely told they had heart disease, nine of whose diagnoses were based on erroneous electrocardiogram readings.

The ubiquitous chest pain of varied origin has also confused some physicians into a hasty diagnosis of heart disease. The undefined gastrointestinal distress transferred to the anterior chest region, which masquerades as a cardiac ailment, is a common trap for the unthinking doctor. The patient who prefers not to be a "cardiac neurotic" can thank his physician for his solicitude after a heart disease diagnosis, then, unknown to his doctor, *triple-check* the diagnosis with other physicians, including a cardiologist.

As the Yale, Johns Hopkins and other surveys corroborate, a national drug binge is responsible for a sizable portion of our iatrogenic epidemic. Tragic incidents such as the thalidomide scandal, however, have given a false patina to the drug problem. Many patients and physicians have been led to believe that if "bad" drugs could be eliminated from our pharmaceutical armamentarium, safety in drug therapy could be achieved.

This medical simplicity has been challenged by newer information, which explains that *drugs themselves are intrinsically toxic*. The patient can pay with doctor-induced illness if overmedicated—no matter what the drug or how bland its molecular structure appears to be. The revelation that the sheer *quantity* of drugs ingested creates iatrogenic danger comes out of the government-supported Johns Hopkins report by Dr. Cluff, and his U.S. Public Health Service epidemiology assistants. It is a noteworthy but overdue service that the profession should have performed a decade ago. Of the 714 patients surveyed at their Osler Service, 122 had drug reactions.

Five died, and four more were potential fatality victims. (The Yale report was similar: of 1014 patients, 119 had iatrogenic drug reactions, and nine died as a result.)

The figures are apparently "understated." This is admitted by the Johns Hopkins surveyors, who excluded from their statistics any physical manifestation that could not be "specifically" attributed to the drugs, even though it could not otherwise be explained. The "seemingly insignificant reactions" which doctors tend to ignore, may, they warn, be "the premonitory indication of more serious manifestations."

The gap between typical physician ignorance of the problem's severity and the grim statistics of drug disease is inadvertently made clear by Dr. Cluff. He explains that physicians at Johns Hopkins (and assuredly at less prestigious institutions) have been reporting only an infinitesimal fraction of drug accidents! Behind this undoubtedly nationwide reporting negligence is a blend of reticence, ignorance, pride (or shame) or simple covering up of iatrogenic disease that might detract from the doctor's concept of his brilliance or his belief in the infallibility of modern medicine.

"We have used a hospital-wide card reporting system to detect untoward drug reaction," writes Dr. Cluff. "A 'report of drug reaction' card is attached to every hospitalized patient's record, filled out by the physician at the patient's discharge, and returned for analysis. For over 2½ years this system has proved unsatisfactory for detecting drug reactions, although a similar system previously had been shown to be reasonably satisfactory for detection of hospital-acquired infections. *During the recent daily intensive surveillance of one service, four times as many reactions were detected than had been reported on the cards from the entire hospital* [italics mine]."

The quantity of drugs administered to the sick is immense and expanding with the force of a malignancy. More than twelve thousand pharmaceutical preparations are now in use, two thirds of which have been introduced since 1950. Dr. Walter Modell of Cornell University Medical College, editor of *Clinical Pharmacology and Therapeutics,* asks: "Will they realize that there are too many drugs for the patient, for the physician, and surprisingly enough, for the pharmaceutical industry?"

The meaning to the typical patient of this drug explosion was clarified when the records of those taking a new antibiotic, methicillin, were tallied at Johns Hopkins. Physicians learned that the same patients were being dosed with an average of thirteen other drugs. One patient was ingesting thirty-two different medicaments!

The deleterious effect of this sheer quantity of drug therapy is a noteworthy observation of the Cluff report. Of 138 semiprivate patients, the 111 who did not develop drug reactions received an average of less than six drugs. The twenty-seven patients who were made ill by drug therapy were taking an average of almost twice as many medications—11.2 each. "The risk of developing an adverse reaction to drugs is apparently directly related to the number of drugs administered to the patient," states Dr. Cluff. "In some instances, this may be attributable to drug interaction, but for the most part this is probably an additive risk."

This overmedication of the American patient was inevitable. From the structure of medicine and current medical education, the doctor gains the shallow impression that *science* consists of fighting one symptom of a disease at a time, and that the cumulative effect of these individual drug therapies produces health. Such a misinterpretation of science is the result of insufficient awe for the complexity of the body and its resistance to constant intrusion, whether it be thirty-two drugs or a gamut of diagnostic probes. Science cannot yet anticipate every bodily reaction to external chemistry, and the modern doctor might well learn the ancient lesson of grave respect for the human body and less awe of his own often meager erudition.

"It is a pseudoscientific approach that requires the physician to use immediately every new drug and every new procedure," writes Dr. Sigmund L. Wilens. "The same attitude also requires that the patient be routinely subjected to innumerable diagnostic tests, but it has been observed that 'change and newness does not necessarily imply betterness' and that the degree of benefit to the patient is not by any means directly proportional to the number of procedures, tests, and drugs used."

Dr. Cluff's correlation between "polypharmacy" and drug reactions could prove a lifesaving truism if taught to practicing physicians. He asks for "a critical evaluation of present-day drug therapy," while prescribing a common-sense remedy that most ingenuous patients thought was now standard medical procedure. "Perhaps," Dr. Cluff suggests, "reduction in the number of drugs given to patients, eliminating all but essential medications, would have a considerable impact on the overall problem."

It is also essential for the doctor (and patient) to understand the iatrogenic potential of particular drugs, for they do vary in their propensities for both good and harm, and in their allergic and toxic properties. Reactions in the Hopkins report range from 27 percent in one drug to less than 1 percent in another. The truly "safe" drug of the doctor's (and our) comfortable imagination will probably always elude him, despite drug company protestations. The authoritative and candid *Medical Letter*—a nonprofit newsletter on drug safety, read by 30,000 doctors—cynically summed up this unkind reality: "Relative freedom from side effects is often reported in early trials of a drug, but not later."

The most onerous cases of drug toxicity, like thalidomide, are heavily publicized. This creates the unfortunate impression that "standard" drugs are not capable of such iatrogenic horror. The classic digitalis, the dried leaf of the foxglove plant, prescribed for heart patients for generations, is an illustration of sometimes unappreciated danger inherent in many currently used drugs. Digitalis aids the weakened heart, but as the *Medical Letter* states, "maximum therapeutic effect often requires a dose close to the toxic level."

Its overaggressive use by some physicians—the Lorelei of seeking "maximum" effectiveness—has created a severe iatrogenic complex that can culminate in death. "Serious disturbances of cardiac function in patients with heart disease are being produced in increasing numbers by the more aggressive use of digitalis," writes Dr. Samuel J. Kowal of the Boston University School of Medicine. "Although this single drug has contributed so much to the management of congestive failure and certain arrhythmias, it has been responsible for the development of such derangements of cardiac function that death is not an infrequent result of its use."

The effect of digitalis is on the heart's muscle; by increasing the force of heart contraction, it dramatically improves cardiac output in a failing heart. In toxic doses, however, the plant miracle destroys the natural rhythm of the myocardium muscle (arrhythmia) and forces the heart to "fire" in a rapid, fit-like motion that can cause death. There is apparently no standard dosage for digitalis, whose proper amount depends on the individual's weight and other idiosyncratic factors. Dosage that is lifesaving in one cardiac case may be fatal in another.

The extent of digitalis poisoning can be determined by several surveys. Dr. Schimmel at Yale reports seven digitalis episodes, including three in which it contributed to death. Dr. Cluff at Johns Hopkins reports twenty-three digitalis poisoning cases out of two hundred treated heart cases, and eleven illnesses from quinidine, a similar-acting drug, in the treatment of forty-three heart cases. Dr. Barr of New York reports "no less than 10 instances of digitalis poisoning," with one death. Other surveys show toxicity in up to 15 percent of users.

Modern medicine has actually intensified digitalis poisoning by prescribing it for cardiac cases in combination with diuretics. This seems to increase digitalis toxicity because of the body loss of essential potassium. "I would not prescribe the two altogether unless it were essential," says one New York internist. "If it were absolutely necessary, I would take the patient on and off the diuretics to reduce the risk."

New preparations which deliver the digitalis quickly to the myocardium (effective for emergencies) have also increased digitalis poisoning. They have made it possible, says Dr. Kowal, for "anxious" physicians to deliver doses that are "too large" to the heart, "too quickly."

The modern insistence on "maximum" results—thus maximum danger—in the use of digitalis has been attributed to medico-philosophical failure. There has been an unfortunate rejection of sage conservative management attitudes which sometimes stress life regimen and caution over injudicious therapy. "It is unfortunately common practice to instruct the young physician to 'push digitalis to the point of toxicity,'" Dr. Alfred Soffer of Chicago confirms in *JAMA*. "Pursuance of such a regimen invites disaster because approximately half of the lethal dose has been administered when toxicity appears." This unfortunate tendency, he believes, explains why hospital house officers "all too frequently adjust the daily maintenance dosage of digitalis upwards when instead a decrease" might be in order.

He relates the story of an experienced doctor who must keep himself fleet-footed to outmaneuver his digitalis-happy young residents. "An attending physician in a leading academic center recently informed me," Dr. Soffer recounts, "that he must race the patient to the hospital to write drug orders if he is to avoid an encounter with digitalis intoxication eight hours later!"

Dr. Kowal of Boston is one of the critics who believe that neglect of tested conservative regimen for heart patients—of bed rest and limited activity—has created our present "ludicrous and dangerous situation." To maintain the cardiac patient almost as if he were a fit individual, some doctors place excessive "reliance on digitalis manipulation," he warns. The result: the "inevitable consequences of toxicity."

Several heart medications are apparently iatrogenic stimuli. The great cholesterol fad, when for a time each pat of butter was viewed as a sign of cardiac sinfulness, also produced its share of bizarre iatrogenics. Many physicians participated by prescribing drugs to lower the ostensibly vile cholesterol level. The drug many chose was MER-29 (tripanarol), a medication that was eventually removed from the market, but not before reportedly creating a series of cruel reactions, ranging from cataracts to loss of hair.

That particular hazard is over, but patients and doctors faced with the anticoagulant problem are in the midst of an iatrogenic dilemma that will require more astute thought and less dogma. In the event of heart attacks, anticoagulants such as heparin may stave off fatal clots. The iatrogenic problem in anticoagulants involves the possibility of a hemorrhage during long-term use. It can create a swift, unanticipated drug backfire that overweakens the blood's clotting ability and stimulates bleeding from a hidden source.

The commonness of this bleeding accident is verified by many investigators. The Yale study reported nine bleeding reactions to anticoagulants with one death; Johns Hopkins reported six hemorrhages, plus sixty-six patients whose "prothrombin" clotting factor test was lower than desired.

Anticoagulant-triggered bleeding may spurt from any part of the body. In *JAMA* two University of Miami School of Medicine physicians, Drs. Donald M. Dooley and Irwin Perlmutter, describe three case histories of one type of anticoagulant misadventure—intracranial bleeding. A forty-three-year-old man was admitted to the hospital in a sleep-like state, a condition that had persisted for twenty-four hours. Five days before, he had complained of a generalized headache. Medical history revealed that he had suffered an acute myocardial infarction a year before and was on a daily dose of anticoagulant, one tablet of warfarin per day. The doctors suspected intracranial bleeding, which was confirmed by an arteriogram, showing blood in the left subdural region. When surgery was performed, doctors noted "profuse bleeding from all open surfaces." The next day he was returned to the operating room again and another accumulation of blood and clot was removed. Fortunately, the patient made a recovery.

The tragic versatility of hemorrhage sites is shown by the iatrogenic drug survey of Mary Fletcher Hospital of the University of Vermont. The anticoagulant used, sodium warfarin, was responsible for hemorrhages in ten patients, causing the death of three. The fatal cases included unanticipated bleeding from the kidneys, the head and the lungs, and in one near-fatal case, the abdomen.

In the *American Journal of Surgery,* Drs. William Klingensmith and Patrick Oles of Texas catalogue, from patient case histories, the site of hemorrhaging during anticoagulant therapy. They list bleeding from nose and gums; gastrointestinal hemorrhage ("often from an unknown or quiescent peptic ulcer"); intraspinal hemorrhage with paraplegia (paralysis); hemorrhage into the brain with stroke; hemorrhage within the abdomen. Some of the iatrogenic incidents, they explain, were the result of poor laboratory control of the prothrombin clotting test. Others involved patients who should not have been put on anticoagulant therapy; contraindications to their use of anticoagulants "were ignored" by their doctors. Others hemorrhaged despite careful selection and supervision.

A fifty-five-year-old patient was placed on anticoagulants because of a suspected myocardial infarction, the classic heart muscle damage. Six weeks later he showed signs of pulmonary embolism, a large clot in a chest artery. Anticoagulant therapy was continued, and anemia and a large heart shadow developed. Repeated thoracenteses (chest taps) were performed, removing bloody fluid. The patient eventually died, and autopsy showed a massive pericardial hemorrhage, uncontrolled bleeding into the membranous sac enclosing the heart. There was no evidence that the patient had ever had the suspected myocardial infarction for which he was taking the drug.

Quite untragic, but irritating, are several minor anticoagulant accidents: warfarin can cause "purple toes," painful to the touch three to eight weeks after the beginning of therapy; heparin can cause intense itching and burning of the feet; the same anticoagulant, in 10 to 70 percent of cases, says one authority, causes alopecia, a type of baldness. The hair falls out in patches of an inch or two in diameter, but thus far, the damage has been reversible.

Estimates of the hemorrhage risk vary anywhere from 5 to 40 percent. The argument whether this iatrogenic bleeding cancels out its value in preventing blood clots is still unsettled. Contrary to some doctors' sureness, the profession is involved in a heated battle over whether it is therapeutic or dangerous, a lifesaver or killer. Dr. Benjamin Rosenberg of Brooklyn reports the same 47 percent hospital mortality in treated and untreated groups of heart attack victims, and forty-eight-hour postattack mortality rates separated by only 1 percent (38.5 and 39.5).

The *Medical Letter* has reviewed the question, and featured studies on both sides. A Swedish report shows substantial benefit for anticoagulant therapy for the first year following an attack, but no benefit in lifelong treatment. A contrary survey, conducted at the Glastrup Hospital in Copenhagen, found that among eight hundred patients who survived the first twenty-four hours after the attack, the mortality rate—28.9 percent—was exactly the same in the anticoagulant and nontreated groups.

The *Letter's* conclusion: anticoagulant therapy might be beneficial during the first six to eight weeks following a heart attack in controlling clots within the heart chambers and "embolisms" to the lungs and other organs. With less assurance, they state the *possibility* of advantage for men under fifty-five during the first year after an attack. Considering the grave dangers of bleeding from the drug, their advice for its use is dependent on the existence of close "medical supervision," the "facilities for careful control of clotting factors" and an ulcer-free, co-operative patient with no tendency to hemorrhage.

The very word "drug reaction" conjures up images of antibiotics. No medical therapy has produced so much nonintended action, both minor and serious—whether an "itch" from penicillin, a fatal blood disease from chloramphenicol or permanent deafness from eighth-cranial-nerve injury by streptomycin. The *grande dame* of antibiotics is unquestionably penicillin, whose growing propensity for creating allergic reactions has reached epidemic proportions. Almost 10 percent of the population can expect some sort of iatrogenic disease from the drug, according to the Johns Hopkins survey.

Death from penicillin itself is harsh and often unanticipated, merciful only in its swiftness. Sometimes—within seconds if the drug has been inserted into the veins—the patient succumbs to extreme allergic anaphylactic shock. His blood pressure falls; his pulse becomes imperceptible; he finds it almost impossible to breathe and may go into a convulsive state, followed by death. (Dr. Francis C. Lowell of the Allergy Unit of Massachusetts General Hospital suggests that penicillin shock be treated immediately with an intravenous injection of an antihistamine drug, injection into the skin of epinephrine, and if "asthma" is part of the reaction, intravenous administration of aminophylline.)

Penicillin sensitivity has become so universal that serious reactions have been triggered without the person actually "taking" the penicillin. It can be absorbed from such occult sources as minute traces in milk, Roquefort and bleu cheese, and penicillin-dust contamination of other drugs. A concerned English physician, Dr. E. A. Hildreth, describes the case of a woman patient who had recurrent bouts of penicillin and collapse caused by traces in the milk she drank. Physicians, even pathologists, he states, often overlook penicillin reaction as a cause of death, confusing it with heart attack or stroke.

Death from penicillin anaphylaxis had been estimated at a hundred per year, but others now fix it closer to a thousand. "The number of anaphylactic fatalities from penicillin is, most likely, grossly underestimated because, from personal experience, it is clear that many clinicians and medical examiners never officially report them," says Dr. Spain. The danger of death appears to increase in the second penicillin reaction, indicating the importance of strict doctor questioning of patient. Prior penicillin sensitivity, even if only a slight rash, is significant. Sensitivity tests have been developed but are not yet fully accurate. The greatest caution, say some physicians, can be exercised by using the crystalline commercial penicillin rather than the amorphous form, and taking it orally rather than by injection, if possible.

The patient who recovers from anaphylactic shock may find that the aftereffects can last up to six months or may cause permanent brain damage due to momentary lack of oxygen. Dr. Sheldon Cohen of Atlanta illustrates this previously undocumented phenomenon in a *JAMA* report. He relates the case of a forty-three-year-old meat-cutter who went into shock after receiving 600,000 units of penicillin-G by injection from a private physician. Three months later, he was given another penicillin injection on his admission to a hospital. Shock again followed, and his temperature soared to 104° F.

"Upon emergence from coma, the patient was very grossly confused and disoriented," reports Dr. Cohen. "He did not know the date, year, or where he was . . . He spoke in a slow, slurred manner. It appeared difficult for him to communicate and supply desired information. He appeared apathetic and had a vacant look on his face." He improved gradually over a year, but never made a full recovery. He was dogged by fatigue, gave up his spare-time hunting and farming, and his memory was impaired.

Those who escape conventional brain damage may be pushed into a psychotic episode which can last for months, says Dr. Cohen. To limit the brain damage, he suggests that in case of penicillin shock, physicians administer vasopressors (to increase blood pressure) and supplemental oxygen "as soon as possible." Careful history-taking is equally important: penicillin was reportedly administered despite the fact that the patient had shown a previous allergy to it.

Antibiotics have developed a relatively newer, perhaps more widespread iatrogenic bedevilment. This is the "superinfection," whose virulence generally exceeds the original infection under treatment. The superinfection is the result of a cataclysmic shift in body ecology, a misbalance of our bacterial environment created by the onslaught of the antibiotics.

In their almost indiscriminate destruction of microbes, the antibiotics attack both the target germs and other, useful body organisms. They permit such pathogens as drug-resistant staphylococcus—previously held in check—to multiply and spring into infectious control, often on the fourth or fifth day of antibiotic treatment. In other superinfections, fungus diseases only rarely seen in humans—candidiasis and aspergillosis—are created. Antibiotics destroy intestinal and other body flora that normally prevent the ever-present fungus from wild overgrowth.

A typical superinfection victim, described by the Johns Hopkins survey, was admitted for pneumococcal pneumonia. The patient was given penicillin, tetracycline and chloramphenicol. The microbe killers (by interfering with the germ's metabolism) destroyed much of the pneumococcus but left a fertile field for Staphylococcus aureus. The patient then contracted "staph" pneumonia, which killed him.

Such medical-caused superinfections struck eleven patients in the Yale sample, and "contributed" to the death of five. In the Johns Hopkins survey there was one death from superinfection. Extrapolating from these two divergent samples (six superinfection deaths of a total of 260 patient deaths), we can estimate that antibiotic superinfection alone claims almost *23,000 lives a year!* Even half, or a fourth, that toll makes it a significant menace.

(Antibiotic reactions in general can be estimated as simply. There were 35 antibiotic accidents among the 1014 Yale-New Haven patients, and 31 among the 714 patients at Johns Hopkins. Judging from this, antibiotics create adverse effects in over one million hospitalized patients a year, plus perhaps a million more under private doctor care. Although women inexplicably appear to suffer 50 percent more drug reactions than men, men have three times as many antibiotic reactions.)

"Staph" is not the only agent of superinfection, but its remarkable ability to adapt to antibiotics makes it a feared antagonist. The widespread, often careless doctor use of antibiotics has made many people carriers of drug-resistant staphylococcus. The relatively new semi-synthetic "penicillins," oxacillin and methicillin, have some fighting power against resistant staphylococcus, but the basic problem of virulent superinfection remains, with a death rate as high as 50 percent of those stricken.

The now common antibiotic superinfection of the colon—the lower intestine—was examined in a report by Dr. William Altemeier and associates in the *Annals of Surgery*. He studied 155 surgical patients who had developed staphylococcal enterocolitis after antibiotic therapy, forty-eight of whom died. After diagnosing the superinfection, he instituted not only specific antibiotic therapy but an unusual anti-iatrogenic therapy. The physician *gave bacteria* (Lactobacillus acidophilus) to the patient, in an allegedly successful attempt to restore the body's benign intestinal bacteria, whose demise had set off the accidents.

The experienced physician should never underestimate his (or at least, his colleagues') ability to create disease in our scientific medical milieu. Much controversy, for example, surrounds the routine "prophylactic" advance use of antibiotics in surgery to prevent infection. The subject creates academic sparks but many critics, including Dr. Frederick R. C. Johnstone of Vancouver General Hospital, believe it is a prime cause of iatrogenic antibiotic disease. He kept detailed records of antibiotic dosages given prophylactically by every surgeon in a test ward. Surgeons making free choice administered antibiotics to 401 surgical patients, while 619 were untreated. The result verified the worst suspicions: those who received antibiotics developed three times as many infections, especially staphylococcal. Only in special cases, such as bowel surgery, says Dr. Johnstone, should antibiotics be given prophylactically.

Dr. Donald B. Louria, head of the Infectious Disease Laboratory of the Cornell unit at Bellevue Hospital, believes iatrogenic superinfection can be cut by the *simplest* use of antibiotics. Treating a patient with the *smallest effective dose of a single antibiotic,* rather than the current ill-advised regimen of using massive doses of a series of antibiotics, would cut the superinfection toll, he states.

A prime difficulty in iatrogenic control is educating physicians, well and swiftly, to apparent danger. The case of chloramphenicol is historical evidence of physician insistence on using an antibiotic which is *known* to be potentially dangerous for minor ailments. Almost since its introduction, chloramphenicol has been linked to several deaths from aplastic anemia, a bone-marrow disease resulting in a deficiency of red cells.

A nineteen-year-old girl in Fullerton, California, received chloramphenicol from three physicians for various complaints, including a throat-and-urinary infection. Nine months later she died of aplastic anemia. A similar fatal reaction affected a four-year-old who received the drug for an ear infection. In a celebrated case a forty-two-year-old California woman was given eight prescriptions of chloramphenicol, counting renewals. The resultant aplastic anemia required hormone treatment to save her life, leaving her face hirsute and scarred with acne.

The drug appears to affect the blood adversely in many ways. The Mary Fletcher Hospital (University of Vermont) iatrogenic drug report lists two cases of chloramphenicol blood toxicity: one fatal case of aplastic anemia, and another "serious" case of agranulocytosis (a marked reduction in the granular white cells). In the seven-year period since the AMA established its Study Group in Blood Dyscrasias (blood abnormalities), they have received 1195 reports of drug-induced blood ailments, undoubtedly only a fraction of the total involvement. Chloramphenicol is incriminated as among the leading causes of leukopenia, a lack of white blood cells.

Chloramphenicol has had a stormy official career almost since its introduction, in 1949, including two FDA warnings against its use in minor infections which can be handled by other antibiotics. The last caveat, in 1961, stressed the necessity of a blood count during repeated therapy. Its particular antibiotic function is against typhus, typhoid and spotted fever, and other serious infections which baffle the penicillin molecule. Despite this, untutored physicians insist on the indiscriminate use of the drug in minor infections.

Several malpractice cases now in litigation against physicians and the drug manufacturers involve prescribing of chloramphenicol that took place long after the initial warnings of its bone-marrow-dampening ability. The common plaintive physician attitude of "we didn't know" infuriates those critical doctors who wince at the unnecessary damage. Dr. George X. Trimble, director of medical education at Memorial Hospital, Long Beach, California, is a critic who reminds such doctors that "a fatal case of aplastic anemia following chloramphenicol therapy was reported as long ago as 1950" in the *Annals of Internal Medicine.* Using the letters column of *Medical Tribune,* he adds: "Subsequently, during the period May–August 1952, eight papers on blood dyscrasias and fatal aplastic anemia due to chloramphenicol appeared in the *Journal of the AMA.*"

The authoritative *Medical Letter* adds this further caution: "Because of the risk of damage to the bone marrow, chloramphenicol should not be used routinely in difficult urinary tract infections. The danger of blood dyscrasias is especially great in patients who receive repeated courses of chloramphenicol, as in recurrent or chronic urinary tract infection." The *Medical Letter* adds the fear that "there is the risk that another physician may give the drug without realizing that the patient had it previously." The medical psyche is inexplicably intractable, for these many warnings have yet to register permanently. Johns Hopkins Hospital only *recently* discovered that one of their services was still using chloramphenicol as a widespread prophylactic antibiotic—a technique they quickly curtailed!

Of all human organs, the liver and kidneys are especially susceptible to iatrogenic harm. "Renal metabolism and nephron structures are extremely complex, and therefore vulnerable in a variety of ways," states Dr. George E. Schreiner of Georgetown University Hospital. "Since many drugs and other substances are capable of causing serious kidney damage, and the list of potentially hazardous compounds grows yearly, it is important that the physician have a good working knowledge of the subject of toxic nephropathy." His list of kidney punishers is impressive: heavy metals, solvents such as carbon tetrachloride, radiation, electroshock, diagnostic media, diuretics and a compendium of antibiotics. Implicated in iatrogenic kidney damage have been sulfonamides, streptomycin, kanamycin, vancomycin, bacitracin and neomycin.

The liver under attack from iatrogenic disease receives equal concern from other knowledgeable sources. As an editorial in the *New England Journal of Medicine* explains, the liver is the first organ to receive blood from the intestines, and thus an early target for any toxic agent—especially since one of its most important functions is "detoxification." Dr. David Barr explains that liver injury and dysfunction has been encountered with the tranquilizer chlorpromazine, the anti-inflammatory agent phenylbutazone and several antibiotics, including streptomycin, chlortetracycline, oxytetracycline, and other drugs of varying description. One antibiotic, triacetyloleandomycin, was recently reported to impair liver function in some *50 percent* of all patients.

Tetracycline, a popular member of a family of potent antibiotics, has now been implicated in at least six deaths involving liver toxicity. All six were young women, four of whom were pregnant and two of whom had already delivered their babies. They were given sizable intravenous doses of tetracycline for urinary infections common in pregnancy. Dr. J. C. Schultz reported on the fatalities in the *New England Journal of Medicine,* indicating that the autopsies showed grave liver damage. Intravenous dosage of the drug, he explains, should be cautiously low.

The tetracyclines have other iatrogenic propensities, especially in children: they may inhibit the growth of premature children, and permanently discolor children's teeth in shades of yellow to yellow-brown. The Eastman Dental Dispensary in Rochester, New York, found thirty-five discoloration cases while examining 1724 school-children. In every history obtainable, the youngsters had received one or more doses of the tetracyclines.

Although less important since the advent of antibiotics, the "sulfa" drugs are still commonly prescribed. These sulfonamides can be quite toxic, producing fever, eruptions, blood abnormalities and hepatitis. Sulfisoxazole, a newer sulfa drug, was reported as the cause of one death in the Drs. Murdo and McKay study of Mary Fletcher Hospital. In the fatal reaction, the patient suffered exfoliative dermatitis, a shedding or peeling of the skin. The same drug has been implicated by the AMA as one of the leading causes of leukopenia.

Dr. David Barr of Cornell describes an acute hemolytic—red blood cell destruction—accident during the use of another sulfa drug, sulfadiazine. The Johns Hopkins survey reports on a middle-aged woman who developed a blood abnormality after taking a sulfonamide for a urinary infection. When it recurred, she was given sulfisoxazole, tragically followed by the discharge of blood in her urine, kidney failure and death. The autopsy revealed sulfonamide crystals in her kidneys.

One of the newer therapies available to the doctor, and therefore the likely precursor of a series of iatrogenic accidents, are the oral diuretics—the thiazides—which force the body to eliminate fluids. They have proved of value in a variety of illnesses, including congestive heart failure, hypertension and edema, and are sometimes even prescribed for weight loss in patients with large fluid retention. One physician, commenting on the new drug's popularity, estimated that "millions of Americans" have taken diuretics.

Its iatrogenic traits are apparently equally versatile. These amazing fluid removers have caused hepatic coma (liver insufficiency), nephritis, pancreatitis, photosensitivity, blood irregularities, hypokalemia (lack of potassium), ulcers, alkalosis (high bicarbonate blood content causing slow pulse and jerky muscular action) and even reversible diabetes.

Some of the reactions were uncommon, but the Registry of Blood Dyscrasias recently showed two diuretics among the top five drug agents producing thrombocytopenia, a dangerous ailment in which there is a shortage of platelets, the small colorless discs which are important in blood clotting. When diuretics damage their concentration, spontaneous bleeding takes place in certain individuals. Another ailment, hyperuricemia (a rise of uric-acid level in the plasma), which can lead to gout, is apparently common in diuretic users, according to one survey reported by Dr. Spain. Checking high blood pressure victims taking chlorothiazide, researchers found hyperuricemia in 15 of 62 cases, and in 16 of 103, an exceedingly high incidence of iatrogenic disease.

Another warning, possibly implicating diuretics with stroke, comes from Dr. Stanley H. Schuman of the University of Michigan, who notes the possibility that the recent increase in the use of diuretics—without adjusting the dosage for the season—may "predispose elderly persons to strokes during sudden or prolonged heat waves."

A new iatrogenic scare might affect a vast proportion of the millions of diuretic-potassium users. In a much-discussed paper in the November 16, 1964 issue of *JAMA,* three physicians from Hennepin County General Hospital in Minneapolis found that twelve of their patients over a period of about a year had contracted small-bowel ulcerations, a disease that, as a recent *JAMA* editorial stresses, "is infrequently seen in practice." Seeking a common etiology, the doctors realized that eleven of the twelve patients were taking thiazide diuretics. The pill included potassium chloride to replace potassium lost in fluid expulsion.

One patient died before surgery, and one other in a surgical attempt to correct the lesion. Examination, in autopsy or surgery, revealed that all twelve had acute perforation of the small bowel. In one patient, at the site of the perforation, was an undigested potassium chloride pill given in conjunction with the diuretic therapy. Almost unanimous corroboration has come in the form of over a hundred small-bowel ulcer cases in only eleven hospitals. Even Sweden has reacted, with a report of thirty-three cases of ulcerative stenosis (narrowing) of the small bowel in diuretic-potassium users.

The agent implicated now appears to be the potassium in the pill. The iatrogenic role of popular diuretics requires sober thought by its dispensing physician, too many of whom prescribe diuretics in large quantities, then ignore the necessary vigil of checking its effect on the patient's health.

The self-confident physician uses the term "side effect" to describe the multitude of iatrogenic drug reactions that plague his patients. This common misnomer presupposes that the drug's "chief effect" is the physician's intended therapy, a coincidence of purpose that nature may not endorse. It is equally possible that the unwelcome reaction of a drug represents the *main effect* of the drug, while the doctor's therapy is the *side effect*—a concept that may put certain potent therapies in clearer perspective.

Another popular fallacy shared by many physicians is that drugs generally work by righting an abnormal situation. This is pierced by a pharmacology authority, Dr. George Perera, associate dean and professor of medicine at Columbia's College of Physicians and Surgeons. Many drugs, he told physicians at a recent AMA convention, "act on tissues and organs more through interference with normal physiological functions than through the alleviation of abnormality." Antihypertensive (high blood pressure) drugs, he gives as an example, are aimed at the nervous system to produce dilation (widening) of the arteries. The beneficial effect of the drug is to lower the body's blood pressure and prevent the ravages of hypertension on organs, a fact of statistical significance in life expectancy. Its iatrogenic effect is that it simultaneously reduces the output of the heart working under stress or against coronary atherosclerosis (hardening of the arteries). When the blood flow is limited by atherosclerosis, the reduced blood pressure, especially in the sick and aged, can injure the brain, the kidneys and other organs. Which, the affected patient may ask, is the "side" and which the "main" effect?

Dr. Perera uses this basic lesson in physiology to alert physicians to the importance of pharmaceutical knowledge. "He [the doctor] must first learn when it is better to do nothing, hence he must know as much as he can regarding the disease under therapeutic scrutiny," he states, adding the always appropriate note of caution: "And finally, whenever he uses a drug he must be a concerned and conscientious watchdog, familiar with the signs, symptoms, and patterns which will alert him—preferably beforehand—to the complications and even dangers produced by his good intentions."

As each new drug therapy becomes available, it often passes through several stages of initial doctor and public enthusiasm, then drug reactions, changed acceptance, then perhaps secondary reactions, followed by medical re-evaluation. The steroid therapies have passed through these—and still other—stages in their hectic, cyclical career as healing and iatrogenic agents. Readers with agile memories will recall the early days of cortisone introduction and its reception by the enthralled medical and lay public; then tales of horrifying reactions, including the production of psychosis, which has even been enshrined in history by a Hollywood film. Cortisone and its chemical cousins have trod impressive distances since, as have the list of iatrogenic offspring of the steroids.

The seeming insistence of nature for a "trade-off" of one ailment for another—an iatrogenic response for a curative effect—is perhaps nowhere more pronounced than with the steroids. Because of their strong biologic effect on the body, cortisone and other steroids have been used therapeutically for scores of ailments. Some have been used wisely, others with iatrogenic rashness in which the cure is more fearsome than the illness.

The *Medical Letter* attacks the increasingly common use of powerful corticosteroids for minor allergies, such as allergic rhinitis (the hay-fever-like running nose). They admit its power but warn of the ferocity of long-term adaptation to steroids. "Though oral cortico-steroids do relieve allergic rhinitis, they should be used only when desensitization injections or control of the environment is either in-effective or not feasible, and when oral antihistamine drugs do not provide adequate relief," says the *Letter*. "*Long-term corticosteroid therapy of allergic rhinitis involves risks which are excessive; in ad-dition to Cushing's syndrome, these include peptic ulcer, hyper-tension, and psychoses, as well as the risk of reducing resistance to infection.*" ("Long-term," as used in steroid therapy, can mean as "short-term" as two or three weeks.)

The action of the steroids on the human body is an apt example of the faulty use of the term "side effect." Evidence can also be mustered to indicate that the steroids' *main* effect is deleterious to the body, and the therapy is a mere by-product. Prolonged use of corticosteroids, such as cortisone, has a dual major action: it sup-presses the adrenal function by supplying the body's steroid needs artificially; and it hinders the body's healing ability and power to fight infections and stress. One might say that the *side effect* of such ravages is its anti-inflammatory power, which makes it such a potent conqueror of skin conditions (poison ivy, etc.) and certain allergies. Initially, it appeared to be the "magic bullet" against crippling arthritis.

A medical-journal case history of a fifty-eight-year-old woman with rheumatoid arthritis illustrates the potential ravages of its treatment. Prednisone therapy gave her pain relief and seeming improvement, but it required a constantly increased daily dosage to maintain the favorable results. The patient was finally hospitalized for general deterioration of her condition, after which she died of bronchial pneumonia triggered by the treatment. At autopsy, pathologists found a sick body further insulted by excess steroids: swollen adrenals; thyroid gland involvement; fatty degeneration of the liver; artery damage involving the kidneys, lungs and spleen; atrophied heart muscle; and degeneration of the aortic vessel.

The susceptibility to infection of patients taking steroids is well known. Even mild bacteria can cause severe infections in the weak-ened steroid patient, a fact which prompted *JAMA,* in an editorial, to suggest isolation of these patients in the hospital to keep them away from pathogenic sources. Staphylococcal abscesses terminating in fatal septicemia have been encouraged by steroid treatment, as have cruel internal growths of fungus. Pneumonia and tuberculosis are quick to take advantage of corticosteroid treatment, which prompts careful physicians to take a chest X-ray and a tuberculin skin test before initiating steroid therapy.

In 1949, when investigators announced the dramatic disappearance of symptoms of rheumatoid arthritis with cortisone acetate, the "miracle" cure quickly captured national fancy. Later it became evident that the drug did not reverse the crippling or impede the deformity of the disease, but merely alleviated the symptoms—if used in sufficient dosages. Today the heavy iatrogenic toll of corticosteroids is known, and treatment of arthritis with aspirin, when possible, is considered more prudent.

The roster of iatrogenic ailments produced by steroids is impressive. Gastric ulcers have stricken almost one in five cases on prolonged therapy; Cushing's syndrome, which includes the body deformities of "moon face" and "buffalo hump" (on the upper back); hypertension; mild insulin-resistant diabetes; electrolyte imbalance; serious bone weakening; myopathy (muscle weakness); infection; psychoses; and cataracts of the eyes.

The widespread creation of gastric ulcers from long-term steroid therapy has been rigorously documented by many physicians. One English physician computed that the expected rate of new ulcer development in the general male population aged thirty-five to sixty-five was less than 0.4 percent per year. The new ulcer rate for men in the same age group who received corticosteroids, was *39 percent per year*—a hundred times as much!

Quiescent ulcers have flared actively during steroid therapy. Patients given steroids can develop multiple gastric ulcers, with resultant perforation, hemorrhage and death. Although ulcerogenic activity is greatest in adult males, no one is immune to steroid ravages, as illustrated by an infant who was given corticosteroid drugs and developed multiple bleeding ulcers of the stomach and duodenum, and bled to death.

Drs. Howard Holley and Robert Hogan of the Medical College of Alabama, in an arthritis primer for doctors in *GP,* warn that another iatrogenic hazard awaits improperly managed patients. Steroids have an insidious narcotic-like effect that makes their *withdrawal* as dangerous as excessive therapy. "Patients receiving long-term therapy should be informed that these drugs must never be terminated suddenly," they point out. "Such action almost always causes a severe exacerbation of symptoms and may precipitate overt adrenocortical failure." Since the adrenals have been weakened by the steroid therapy, treatment must be tapered gradually to permit the body to readjust, if possible, and restart the mechanism to make its own steroids.

Stress is a general enemy of the steroid-treated patient. It can trigger an iatrogenic accident called "adrenal exhaustion" in such traumatic situations as surgery. Even patients who have discontinued therapy for a year are reportedly still susceptible. In perhaps the first recorded case of this doctor-made illness, Dr. C. G. Fraser reported in 1952 that irreversible shock and death *followed* surgery of a patient who had been taking cortisone for several months. In-

ternist Dr. Luis Fernandez-Herlihy of the Lahey Clinic in Boston
warns of this now common danger in the pages of *Hospital Medicine.* "Since then," he states, "several reports of fatalities following
surgery in steroid-treated patients have appeared, and doubtless
there have been many more that have not been recognized or
reported."

The tragedy of this iatrogenic ailment is that the surgery triggering death is usually successful, uncomplicated and uneventful
until shock sets in within twenty-four hours after surgery. The patient
goes into sudden collapse, and presents low blood pressure and high
fever. Medical authors have documented that steroid-treated patients
are generally poor surgical risks. A study of ulcerative-colitis surgery, reported in the *NEJM,* showed that patients who had been
steroid-treated were involved in fierce postoperative complications,
including massive hemorrhages, peritonitis, psychoses and peptic
ulcers.

Proper caution, states Dr. Fernandez-Herlihy, can be exercised
by a painstaking inquiry into whether the patient has taken any of
the cortisone derivatives that have been manufactured in the past
sixteen years, reading out each one of them to the patient by name.
If the patient has been steroid-treated within a year, he advises a
dose of cortisone as a "prep" before surgery to help the patient
through the stress.

Steroid therapy predisposes the patient to infection from many
common pathogens, with such possible serious complications as
herpes simplex paratitis, staphylococcal furunculosis and pulmonary
tuberculosis. "To protect patients who are receiving this therapy,"
warns *JAMA,* "isolation precautions [in hospitals] should be instituted."

The high percentage of iatrogenic victims in steroid therapy is a
most disconsolate fact. The commonness of steroid-produced cataracts was verified by a recent study by Dr. Robert Irby of the
department of ophthalmology of the Medical College of Virginia.
Depending on duration of steroid treatment, up to one in four patients developed cataracts, while in a control group of other eye
patients the incidence was only one in fifty.

Topical steroids, those applied to the body surface, have had
a more innocent iatrogenic record, until recent evidence showed that
they can create increased intraocular pressure, a precursor of glaucoma, when applied to the eyes. (Chloroquine, a popular non-
steroid used in the treatment of rheumatoid diseases, has also been
incriminated in eye damage. Its long-term, high-dosage use in the
treatment of arthritis—as opposed to its low-dosage use against
malaria—has been found to injure the retina of the eye, sometimes
leading to a progressive form of blindness.)

The bizarre iatrogenic effect is always the most unnerving. Steroids have been known to *worsen an arthritic condition* by alleviating the pain and discomfort, and permitting the patient to move a diseased joint freely which he would otherwise treat cautiously. Dr. Spain describes a case of "steroid destruction of a hip joint" that was caused by such ill-advised movement. "In one case where the X-ray picture revealed moderate osteoarthritic changes in the hip joint, six months later the X-ray picture showed extensive changes with a loss of the joint space, sclerosis and flattening of the femoral head [tip of the long leg bone]. Twelve months following this, there was complete destruction of the femoral head . . ."

With such organic hazard inherent in the steroid molecule, what can the doctor and patient do if faced with its use? The sanest rule is to avoid steroids when possible. If they are deemed essential, the patient on long-term therapy should be considered vulnerable to a plethora of woes, and be checked accordingly. "I'd thoroughly check out the possibility of an active or latent case of TB, which would flare up immediately in the presence of steroids," says one internist. "If I went ahead, I would use antacid prophylaxis against ulcers, and check both the blood and stools for signs of bleeding. I'd watch for the 'moon face' of Cushing's syndrome, check his blood sugar for what we call *diabetes de novo,* and regularly examine the urine for signs of steroid excess. Since steroids can cause many other ailments, a full check-up of the patient during treatment is warranted."

Commonly used local anesthetics—which make "minor" surgery possible in the doctor's office—have been implicated in several iatrogenic accidents reported by physicians. Procaine, lidocaine and other localized pain killers are versatile tools that are valuable to patient and physician alike in plastic surgery, the insertion of painful diagnostic probes, and in many situations where the use of general anesthesia may be contraindicated. One report of the death of two young women that took place during the administration of lidocaine and mepivacaine prior to cosmetic surgery, however, "emphasize[s] the extreme potency of the drugs," according to Dr. Irving Sunshine and Winston W. Fike, Ph.D., of the Cuyahoga County (Ohio) Coroner's Office.

One of the female patients had a 2 percent lidocaine solution injected into the right side of her face, head and neck. "After the injections were completed the patient requested some orange juice," states a report by the Cleveland researchers. "Upon his return to the surgery room the surgeon found her on the table unconscious, with no detectable pulse rate. He injected 1 ml. of epinephrine to no avail." The second tragedy involved a young woman having both breasts enlarged. She successfully survived the first operation, then rested during a sixty-minute interval, after which preparation of the operation on her left breast was begun. "After 2 or 3 injections she began to have violent convulsions," states the report. "The surgeon held her on the table while the nurse ran to get the epinephrine . . . A rescue squad was called, and, despite the use of a respirator and oxygen, was unable to revive the patient."

Dr. John Steinhaus, chairman of the department of anesthesiology at Emory University School of Medicine in Atlanta, warns physicians that the unexpected accident from administration of local anesthetics is related to the doctor's "failure to anticipate the episode and prepare for the treatment." The serious reactions from these anesthetics is due to their depressive effect on the respiratory system and other vital centers of the brain stem. When given in *large* doses, or to patients with diseased hearts, says Dr. Steinhaus in *Hospital Medicine*, "local anesthetics may cause serious or fatal depression of the myocardium and cardiac output." His general precautions to physicians for the safer administration of local anesthetics include the following: avoid overdoses; administer the injection over a period of at least two minutes to aid body absorption; consider the patient's general condition and body size in determining dose and usage; plan emergency treatment, including administration of oxygen, in advance. Perhaps most important, he offers this local anesthetic caveat: "extensive use" of such agents "should be limited to areas which have facilities for the administration of oxygen."

Iatrogenic recounting is negligently incomplete without insight into the harm caused by the "miracle" mood drugs. The story of the amazing therapy of the psychochemicals, from the crudest tranquilizers to the antidepressants, has been told recurrently with appropriate kudos to men such as Dr. Nathan Kline of Rockland State Hospital in New York. Virtually untold is the story of the iatrogenic ailments precipitated by physicians—whether general practitioner or psychiatrist—who have been prescribing these new drugs for literally millions of Americans with a ferocity bordering on abandon. With the use of psychochemicals measured in tonnage, what was once known as the Age of Anxiety might more appropriately be termed the Age of Tranquilization. Sometimes the use is indicated and vital. Frequently it is a biochemical crutch that some physicians believe will provide easy answers for "nervous" patients. Some immature patients hope they will be a prescription for happiness—the more pills, the more bliss. Knowledge of the increasing iatrogenic harm from these "miracle" pills can help patient and doctor make more sensible decisions as to their use.

The simplest form of psychochemicals—the mild tranquilizers, more correctly known as "nonbarbiturate sedatives" or "sedative-hypnotic drugs"—are, paradoxically, the most addictive. Although patients are seldom warned of this by their doctors (many of whom appear ignorant of the fact), the ingestion of an excess amount of meprobamate (eighteen trade names), chlordiazepoxide, diazepam and four other of these commonly prescribed items, can reportedly cause both a type of "intoxication" and actual physical addiction similar to that of the narcotics.

This warning comes from an authoritative source, Dr. Carl F. Essig of the Addiction Research Center of the National Institute of Mental Health, who points out that the drugs are similar to alcohol and narcotics in some of their properties. The "happy pills" can reportedly cause confused thinking, in-co-ordination of movement, and even violent and assaultive behavior. Dr. Essig comments on a study of fifty-eight users whose driving-accident rate was ten times normal.

The drugs can trap the innocent into narcotic-like addiction with all its symptoms, including withdrawal sickness and death. Dr. T. C. McCormick, Jr., of Austin, Texas, describes in *GP* the meprobamate addicts seen in emergency rooms, whose life can depend on their addiction being immediately recognized by physicians. The first sign of withdrawal syndrome, he states, is the grand-mal epileptic seizure or sudden hallucinations. A thirty-eight-year-old married woman is a descriptive case in point. She had been under intermittent psychiatric care, and was readmitted to a closed psychiatric unit in an agitated and stuporous condition. "About twenty-four hours after admission, the patient had a grand mal seizure while she was standing and talking with a nurse," relates Dr. McCormick. "She fell and dislocated her shoulder. There was no previous history of a convulsive disorder. The patient's husband later brought four of her prescriptions from home. Each contained meprobamate of a different kind. It was estimated that the patient was taking from 6 to 10 gm. of meprobamate daily for many weeks."

The more potent tranquilizers, the phenothiazines, were the drugs that made medical history more than ten years ago when the first of their group, chlorpromazine, was introduced into the treatment of the mentally ill. Today there are fifteen such compounds which cannot "cure" any mental illness, but have remarkable ability to eliminate "schizophrenic" symptoms in some patients. The noteworthy advance typically subverted clinical attention to the drug's undesirable reactions, only now being tallied with increasing trepidation.

"Sudden Death During Treatment with Phenothiazine Derivatives" is the headline of a recent *JAMA* article clinically detailing the sudden, inexplicable death of six "tranquilized" patients in a Veterans Administration Hospital in Palo Alto, California. These "otherwise healthy patients" were receiving phenothiazines in "the fairly large doses customarily given to psychiatric patients," and died in sudden seizures followed by cardiac arrest. Some of the deaths were attributed to the fatal aspiration of food during the seizures.

One of the iatrogenic victims, a forty-five-year-old man, ostensibly became psychotic following head injuries in a car accident fifteen years before. Since 1956 he had been on antipsychotic drugs, and for fourteen months prior to his death he had received thioridazine hydrochloride and chlorpromazine therapy daily. Shortly before his death, 2 mg. of trihexyphenidyl hydrochloride was added three times daily. Aside from his psychosis, the patient had been in good health and had no record of seizures. One day while having dinner, he suddenly slumped dead to the floor, his mouth full of half-chewed food.

Before an iatrogenic accusation can be made, it is essential to rule out (as well as possible) a natural cause for the disaster. Although a post-mortem does not always fully explain the cause of death, Drs. Leo Hollister and John C. Kosek, the authors of the *JAMA* article, concluded: "Compared with past experience with deaths in hospitalized psychiatric patients, this mode of death appears to be definitely associated with drug therapy." Case records of several other similar phenothiazine-seizure deaths are substantiation, as is clinical evidence that phenothiazines are known to evoke or aggravate seizures. Suspicious pigmentation has also been found in the victims' heart muscles.

The relaxed doctor mind, which has been prescribing these "miracle drugs" without awareness of possible disaster, will find such reports a jolting reminder that nothing should be assumed. The adverse iatrogenic effects from these tranquilizers continue to mount in volume and intensity, including disturbances of the central and autonomic nervous system, jaundice, agranulocytosis (a serious blood disease), aggravation rather than improvement of the schizophrenic condition, disturbed body temperature, dermatitis, deposits on the eye lens and cornea, bladder paralysis, and low blood pressure crises which can cripple rather than lift one's concept of well-being.

The possibility of damage to the liver by fatty deposits created by long-term chlorpromazine therapy has been raised by several men, including Drs. Leo Waitzkin and H. Edward MacMahon in the *Annals of Internal Medicine*. Less speculative is the increasing occurrence of skin discoloration, especially in women. Now that long-term use of the drugs is common, the unanticipated is becoming commonplace. Seventy-eight patients at Provincial Mental Hospital in British Columbia, Canada, developed "a bizarre blue-black pigmentation of the exposed areas of the skin" after receiving high doses of chlorpromazine for prolonged periods.

The discoloration is somewhat like an extraterrestrial sun tan, changing the color of the skin exposed to light to varying shades of purple, blue and slate-gray. The damage is most prominent on the bulbous tip of the nose. The pigmentation increases in summertime but fades only somewhat in winter, since the melanin particles involved are deposited in both the upper and lower portions of the skin. *JAMA,* in editorial comment, raises the possibility of "permanent" damage.

The iatrogenic case against the psychochemicals has been building like an intricate legal brief. So-called extrapyramidal effects of the drugs—facial grimacing, writhing motions of the mouth and tongue, and jerking motions of the limbs—have been known for some time but thought to be quickly reversible on discontinuance of the tranquilizers. Recent evidence, however, showed that thirteen of 250 female patients had an *irreversible* syndrome, with the possibility of permanent brain damage. "The symptoms and signs remained unchanged after medication had been discontinued for 8 to 36 months," states the troubled *JAMA* editorial. "Irreversible dyskinesias and the presence of dementia in all 13 patients suggests the existence of organic brain damage."

One of the most punishing tithes that the phenothiazine tranquilizers have extracted for their controlling beneficence has been their indiscreet stimulation of the female libido and a corresponding decrease in male potency. (Tranquilizers are thus a cruel "family" medicine.) This unbroadcast "feminizing" ability to make women, especially in the post-thirty susceptible age, aroused and sexually hungry, may have caused thousands of women transient pleasure and permanent misery. Too often female patients are not told by their doctors (who may not know) to expect this increased sexual libido, and they are unprepared for the whirlwind that follows. Given to suppress a gnawing, uncodified anxiety, the drug thus succeeds only in creating a larger, specific one. This unfortunate endocrine-like effect, which can conversely render male patients impotent or disinterested, can also trigger lactation in the female, and even the metabolic setting for a false pregnancy test.

The psychochemicals have achieved popularity in the treatment of minor emotional upsets without patient knowledge that some of them are capable of triggering *negative* psychological reactions—which may be more disturbing than the original "neuroses." In sedating "anxiety," for example, the nation's most popular psychochemical, Librium, has been known on occasion to create what has been called "depression." (This tendency has prompted the manufacturer to advise precautions "in the presence of depression or suicidal tendencies.") At the Women's Medical College of Pennsylvania, two thirds of sampled clinic outpatients who had been receiving Librium had resulting "depression," which investigators defined as "a psychomotor retardation with some slowing of thought processes."

Phenothiazine tranquilizers are also capable of behavioral *upset* —distorted psychological reactions known as "paradoxical." The nervous patient taking the phenothiazines, explain psychochemical researchers, may become *more nervous,* the result of a restless, excited feeling during the day, and insomnia, even bizarre dreams, at night.

The second revolution in psychochemistry began in 1957, when two antidepressants (some of which are referred to as "psychic energizers"), iproniazid and imipramine were introduced. Since then, several new antidepressants have been used in private and psychiatric hospital practice. The iatrogenic effects of the antidepressants have been numerous, but were originally thought to be mild, such as drowsiness, slight tremor of the extremities, anxiety and some mental confusion. As the drugs receive wider use, the inevitable, serious ailments have made their macabre appearance. Underlying schizophrenia has been triggered; jaundice and fatal liver disease developed; lethal cases of agranulocytosis have been reported; researchers see an increased tendency toward first-degree heart block; overdoses have reportedly caused death; seizures have been observed during treatment.

Several antidepressants have been withdrawn from the market for serious blood and liver disorders. One monoamine oxidase inhibitor (inhibits the enzyme which destroys the chemical essential to normal brain function), Parnate, has had a checkered career. When hundreds of cases of high blood pressure, several dozen cerebrovascular "strokes," and fifteen deaths were linked to the use of Parnate, the manufacturers withdrew the effective antidepressant from the market, at the FDA's "suggestion," only to have it remarketed six months later with sharply altered labeling. In addition to warning against its use in older people, and those with high blood pressure, caution extends to its joint therapy with other antidepressants. In a strange iatrogenic reaction, eating cheese and pickled herring also makes the Parnate user more vulnerable to strokes.

The FDA now *advises* that Parnate be used only in hospitals or, if in private practice, only when other antidepressant drugs do not succeed. (Canada has restricted its use to clinics and hospitals.) Skeptics, with good reason, are convinced that the widespread use of Parnate for mild depression will continue almost unabated by physicians. A New Haven physician offered such a pessimistic opinion in a letter to the *Medical Tribune:* "If the revised prescribing information is heeded, little Parnate will be used. Previous experience with chloramphenicol, however, fails to give assurance in this respect."

The painkillers that fill the physician's therapeutic arsenal provide excellent opportunities for misadventure. A thirty-six-year-old salesman who found little relief from severe headaches with several drugs was placed on a therapy of methysergide with apparently excellent results. After four months the patient was placed on a placebo, in the hope that the condition would control itself. When the headaches returned with "severe exacerbation," methysergide was prescribed again. Eighteen months later the patient complained of aches in his groin, legs and testicles. He underwent surgery at the Mayo Clinic, where a condition known as retroperitoneal fibrosis, scar tissue that had injured his kidney function, was found and repaired.

Three such cases have been recorded at the Mayo Clinic. Staff urologists admit that the connection is not proven, but advise caution. "Furthermore, it seems judicious to advise any patient who has taken methysergide continuously for a year to discontinue medication for at least three months and to have a urinalysis, a test of renal function, and excretory urography performed," state the Mayo staff men.

Old iatrogenic menaces are often forgotten by the medical community, who are then abruptly reminded by the problem's reoccurrence. Two pain and fever killers frequently dispensed by physicians, aminopyrine and dipyrone (in some thirty to fifty preparations), have once again appeared on the lists of blood-destructive agents. Warnings were placed on the use of aminopyrine thirty years ago, but physicians have increasingly been prescribing dipyrone, many without knowing that it is a closely related drug. In late 1964 the AMA and the FDA issued a warning to physicians that there have been forty cases of granular white blood cell damage (agranulocytosis), and thirteen deaths, associated with the use of dipyrone. The drug is still available, and its future as a pain-rather-than-man-killer depends entirely on the judiciousness of the American physician, a virtue for which he is seldom eulogized.

Americans need little urging from doctors to ingest painkillers, for we have traditionally medicated ourselves with aspirin and assorted mixtures of APC: aspirin, Phenacetin, caffeine—the all-purpose panacea. It now appears that at least one of the headache ingredients, Phenacetin, may have unleashed a fierce iatrogenic toll. Much of the overingestion of the pills is not on doctor order, but APC has been a standard, advised for every condition from the common cold to muscular aches. "Take two headache pills" has been the physician's age-old rejoinder. Some of these headache pills have now been tied to kidney damage and death, iatrogenic information that doctors have failed to alert patients to.

Minor use of aspirin appears reasonably safe for most people, but the aspirin binge, which amounts to 20,000,000 lbs. a year, is medically contraindicated mainly because of its gastrointestinal-irritating powers that make it suspect as an ulcer producer. Dr. James L. A. Roth, a gastroenterologist at the University of Pennsylvania, reports that with or without buffering it causes slight, "occult" stomach bleeding in the majority of users. Some investigators, including Dr. Rene B. Menguy of the University of Kentucky, are convinced that aspirin decreases the ability of the stomach to secrete the protective barriers that guards it against bleeding and ulceration. The blood loss may be small, but may also be significant, he believes, if the person has anemic tendencies. In those with possible gastrointestinal disease, the habitual use of aspirin might act as a trigger of hemorrhage.

The "P" of the APC, Phenacetin (acetophenetidin)—which was a standard part of Anacin and several other popular headache remedies for generations—may represent the more significant iatrogenic problem. Dr. Telfer B. Reynolds of the University of Southern California has seen ten cases of what he says is "probably" acetophenetidin-induced kidney disease. Each of the patients was a heavy user of pain remedies, taking from eight to twenty tablets daily for long periods of time, often for chronic headaches. Three of the patients died of uremia poisoning resulting from kidney failure.

Reports from around the world implicate acetophenetidin in kidney disease. Physicians at the Sydney Hospital in Australia believe that powders and pills containing it were suspect in fifty deaths from kidney failure at their institution alone. The circumstantial evidence is based on the high proportion of renal disease in patients taking large amounts of acetophenetidin. In the small Swedish town of Huskvarna, where it was the custom for industrial workers to take pills containing the drug in order to keep up the pace, twenty-two men died of uremia.

Dr. A. H. Rubenstein of Johannesburg, South Africa, reports six cases of "papillary necrosis" from acetophenetidin overdose (generally defined as five or more pills a day), including a thirty-nine-year-old patient who was taking twenty-four tablets a day for three and a half years to relieve the pain following an ulcer operation. On examination, the tubular system of his kidneys was found to be "grossly disorganized." A Swiss researcher found fifty-five cases of overuse of the drug in twenty-four hundred hospital admissions during a two-year period. Of the fifty-five, eight had severe uremia, and four died of it. There have been a few implicating reports from the United States, including one involving a forty-seven-year-old man with nephritis who had been consuming excessive amounts of acetophenetidin for years. When taken off the drug, he gradually improved.

The medical community is split over the evidence, which prompted the FDA to appoint an *ad hoc* committee. The committee reported back a scientific indictment of the headache remedy—that "a high index of suspicion exists, concerning a cause-and-effect relationship" between overuse of the drug and renal damage. What action has been taken to protect the public? Rather than remove the acetophenetidin from its present *over-the-counter* position, a warning has been placed on certain painkilling remedies. The makers of Anacin, among others, acted prior to this, eliminating the acetophenetidin and converting their famed "combination of ingredients" to only aspirin and caffeine. The manufacturers of some of the other pain and cold remedies have decided to keep the Phenacetin in, apparently until kidney death has been proved.

The human most susceptible to iatrogenic-drug damage is the unsuspecting fetus, who has often been liberally dosed under the doctor's illogical assumption that he was treating the mother, not the unborn child. The non-science of such thought became obvious in the thalidomide incident, which was the teratogenic (causing of fetal abnormalities) effect of the mother's own tranquilizer therapy.

The congenital malformations of children are a gnawing medical problem; they affect as many as 308,000 infants in a year. The tragedy may well be aggravated by the mother's ingestion of prescription drugs during pregnancy, drugs that affect not only the fetus during its first trimester of development, but can reach the child up to the moment of birth through the mother's placenta.

Dr. Helen Taussig of Johns Hopkins University has stressed that pregnant women should take no new drugs unless absolutely necessary. Dr. W. Lenz, the Hamburg geneticist who discovered the thalidomide link with malformation, restates her admonition even more strongly, if possible: no woman who is or may be pregnant should take *any drugs* unless it is necessary to save her life. "Everything should be done to discontinue our involuntary and blind experimenting with human embryos," he told a New York scientific meeting.

The toll of drugs on developing embryos has been grave. Streptomycin given to pregnant women suffering from tuberculosis "probably caused" deafness in their unborn children, according to a report in the *New England Journal of Medicine*. Pregnant patients given hormone treatment have seen their female children born with male genitalia. Such permanent masculinization of the female infant has followed use of progestins, testosterone and stilbestrol. In Denmark, health authorities have stated that one fifth of all girls born to mothers who had taken one hormonal drug for menstrual problems had produced children with unmistakable signs of masculinization. In America, such synthetic hormone preparations as norethindrone have been used to ward off miscarriage and spontaneous abortion, but have taken their toll in the production of girl children who have been heavily masculinized, including at least two girls who required surgery of the genitals to restore the proper sexual appearance.

Other implicated drugs given in early pregnancy that resulted in still other abnormalities in the newborn include tolbutamide (oral diabetic drug), cortisone, and aspirin in toxic doses, according to an editorial in the *Annals of Internal Medicine*. Even simple iodides such as those found in cough syrup may be harmful to the fetus.

Two Lincolnshire physicians have notified the *British Medical Journal* of the birth of two children with fatal internal deformities whose then pregnant mothers had taken an appetite depressant common in America, phenmetrazine. In the same journal, two cases of hemolytic anemia (destruction of red blood cells) in the newborn have been reported associated with diuretic therapy given during pregnancy. Also in Great Britain, the College of General Practitioners have reported that twenty-nine congenital malformations in newborn were associated with the use of antiemetics (one of them containing meclizine) taken by their mothers during pregnancy to stave off nausea.

Dr. A. F. Hardyment, writing in the *Canadian Medical Association Journal,* warned against these and other pregnancy drug dangers: thiouracil, used to control an overactive thyroid, can cause goiter in the child; reserpine can create a nasal discharge in the youngster and a potentially fatal danger to its breathing function; long-acting sulfonamides given before delivery may harm the susceptible fetus.

Not only is the fetus involved; the bearer-mother also appears to overreact to certain drugs. A twenty-eight-year-old pregnant woman began vomiting in her eighth week of pregnancy. She was given quinine sulfate tablets in an attempt to stop the vomiting, but on the third day a bloody vaginal discharge appeared, and her urine became red and scanty. She was admitted to a hospital in Galveston, Texas, where she had a miscarriage. The diagnosis was acute renal failure—kidney shutdown—reportedly brought on by the quinine sulfate. Dialysis, the internal washing out of the blocked fluids, proved successful. Authors quoted in *JAMA* have reported up to a dozen similar cases, most of which ended in death for the mother. As we have seen, six pregnant women receiving large intravenous doses of tetracycline antibiotics for pyelonephritis (kidney infection) died with the typical "fatty liver" syndrome; four cases more have since been reported.

The encyclopedic nature of iatrogenic disease defies any full accounting. Blood transfusions and anesthetics are a natural part of medical-caused death and illness, as are medication error and surgical complication. As we take anywhere from a half to one and a half steps backward and medicine moves one step forward, the frustration—of the patient and doctor—becomes the central focus of iatrogenic ills. How can they utilize modern medicine without becoming its flaccid, overwilling victims?

The admonition to "go slow" is not often appreciated, but it is one that thoughtful physicians insist on making, despite the accolades constantly accorded medical pseudo-progress. In the area of drug therapy, the physician has proved his inadequacy of knowledge, and his inability or unwillingness to understand intimately what he is prescribing. "Now because of adverse reactions to these drugs," Dr. G. E. Cartwright, professor of medicine at the University of Utah College of Medicine, told an AMA convention, "we are moving from the period of wonder drugs to the period of wondering about drugs."

Lurking behind the grim statistics of iatrogenic disease is a favorite doctor phrase—meaningless, yet used to the point of cliché. It is "calculated risk," and he wields it in explanation of any procedure he favors, whether it be excess radiation, ill-advised catheterization or the prescribing of overpotent drugs. In truth, of course, he knows very little about the particular risk of any of his favorite therapies, and less about their danger in consort with one another. He may, in his ignorance, have become professionally enamored of techniques which, if truly "calculated," would prove to be more harmful than beneficial. As several surveys have shown, the possibility of this calculation has been weakened by the doctor predilection not to report the many misadventures of his therapies.

Calculating the true risk of every medical procedure, and its incidence of iatrogenic disease, is undoubtedly among *the most vital research that medicine can do today,* yet only a handful of physicians have occupied themselves with the task. Concentrating on a part of the problem—drugs—Dr. Leighton Cluff hammers at the necessity of such information. "Before sound judgments can be made concerning drug therapy," he writes, "the physician should have information on the incidence of adverse reactions, patients who are peculiarly predisposed to reactions, the types of reactions which might occur, the therapeutic effectiveness of a drug, and alternative drugs which might be used." His Johns Hopkins survey aided that cause. Dr. Elihu Schimmel's Yale iatrogenic survey broadened it to include injury from diagnostic techniques, blood transfusions, and hospital-acquired infections and superinfections—what Dr. Schimmel refers to as "the cumulative risk to the patient who accepts the whole of our medical care."

These are excellent beginnings, the nuclei for fuller surveys which should include the extent of doctor and nurse error, surgical and anesthetic mishaps, hospital medication errors. The full hospital iatrogenic survey will be a constructive step. The reluctant private physician too must start to examine his practice objectively and record his mistakes for publication. Such intensive reckonings of the true "calculated risk" of modern medical care can only improve doctor comprehension of what he is now doing, and what aspects of it should be done differently, with less fervor, or not at all. When this suggestion was made to a prominent physician interested in iatrogenic disease it elicited interest, followed by pessimism that it would cost "at least a half million dollars" and was therefore an impractical survey-in-the-sky. When balanced against the millions of dollars spent for esoteric research, this accounting of lives lost to inadvertence, and worse, seems eminently practical.

The key therapy for iatrogenic disease is the most difficult to apply—doctor (and patient) common sense. A patient being given thirty-two, or even ten, drugs simultaneously, and put through a diagnostic hoop of a score of tests, is obviously being exposed to grave risk whose danger must carefully be balanced against the potential gain. The proof of the danger inherent in the mere *number* of drugs given the patient is an objective confirmation of what good common sense should mean to every practitioner.

Dr. David Barr of New York speaks of the tendency toward overaggressiveness in modern medicine "in which each symptom receives some remedy" from the compulsive doctor. "For patients in a diagnostic clinic or in the ward of a modern hospital, the application of twenty or thirty diagnostic tests is not uncommon," he states. "Many of these tests may be repeated on several occasions. A seriously ill patient or one who has been subjected to a major operation may receive twenty to forty different drugs in addition to numerous mechanical procedures . . . Since such combination of measures and medicines is frequent, it is not surprising that iatrogenic disturbances are frequent."

Deciding the extent of modern medical technology to be applied to a patient requires not only wisdom but restraint by internes, residents and their supervisors in not considering the helpless patient merely a mass of orifices and vessels to be probed and sampled. The private physician in his office practice has less opportunity for such massive patient activity, but his proclivity for prescribing potentially dangerous agents for trivial complaints is now well established.

A plea for doctor caution is obviously in order, a watchful conservative attitude which does not "give up" and accept therapeutic nihilism. Nor does it chauvinistically trumpet modern medical grandeur and insist on confirming it by using the "newest," unproven or most dangerous therapies on every patient. "The concepts of caution and medical aggressiveness are not diametrically opposed," says one New York internist. "A doctor can be both careful in the therapies and techniques he uses, and wield them actively when they are needed—the most potent ones for the most serious illnesses, and vice versa. To risk danger to the patient when the illness is not grave is folly."

The opportunities to block iatrogenic disease with caution are infinite, including the checking of susceptible organs, such as the liver and kidneys during potentially harmful therapy. Similarly, urine checks for steroid excess and other complications, blood tests for possible blood cell abnormalities, and study of electrolyte balance (sodium and potassium) can sometimes be sage precautions. Others have been enumerated here, and the astute physician is aware of many intelligent cautions he can bring to his work, from leaving dangerous diagnostic probes to experts to using digitalis and antibiotics judiciously.

The more subtle manifestations of fighting iatrogenic disease include the development of a well-tuned medical radar, seeking out the earliest clues of impending danger to the patient. Dr. Cluff, in his most recent report, laments two iatrogenic deaths where warning was given—by a reaction to prebronchoscopy medication, and by blood damage from a sulfonamide for a urinary infection. The warnings were ignored and the same medications given again, with death as the result.

The iatrogenic-disease-prone doctor may find his re-education not as difficult as it might first seem. Much of the failing is philosophical as well as scientific, for he must first humble himself inwardly if he is to understand truly his potency to do harm as well as good. He is now driven to seek a speedy answer to all of his own and his patient's problems through the unstudied manipulation of the medical environment. In his supreme confidence he appears willing, almost eager, to take great risks with his patient's safety in order to pay homage to his exaggerated concept of his own skill. The extent of iatrogenic disease indicates that this confidence is unwarranted and that the warning "first do no harm"—*primum non nocere*—must somehow be re-emblazoned on the doctor's psyche.

Chapter VII

Human Experimentation
and the American Patient:

Failure at Nuremberg

Was it the air currents wafting through the newborn nursery ward or was it the hands of hospital personnel that carried the staphylococcal contamination from infant to infant? The question was clear, and the team of physicians had carefully designed the experiment. All that was needed were the "laboratory animals," and the most conclusive of all, *animus nobile*—human beings in the form of scores of newborn babies in their cribs—were available. Their mothers in the maternity ward had no suspicion that their youngsters had been "selected" as potential martyrs for science.

Since the experiment was to deal with the spreading of disease by hand contamination, the experimenters sought out an infant already "contaminated"—a child who was shown to be a carrier of Staphylococcus aureus. The child was given no antibiotics and placed in a key "index" position in the nursery, where he was picked up by the nurses before each of their contacts with other babies, in an attempt to see how many of the other children would be contaminated with the staphylococcus.

To create a "control" group for comparison, the nursery was divided into two parts. Nurses caring for the children on the "A" side washed their hands routinely: three minutes of scrubbing by brush with hexachlorophene on arrival for duty, one minute on return from meals, and ten seconds between each child contact. The "B" nurses, however, *were instructed not to wash their hands at all between contact with the children,* and only to scrub up in the morning and after lunch. They bathed and fed the children, and changed their soiled diapers with their hands scrupulously filthy, spreading the staphylococcus efficiently from child to child. The experiment proved to be a signal success: forty-five of the forty-nine innocent youngsters in Group B acquired the staphylococcus bacteria, almost twice as many as in the control group.

The locale of this incredible experiment? It was not, as colorful imagination might place it, in a Nazi experimental laboratory. This human experiment was carried out recently in a major hospital in Cleveland, Ohio, in the nation's heartland. Rather than a secret experiment administered furtively, the results of this violation of the newborn were proudly published in the *American Journal of Diseases of Children*.

Where could zealous doctor-scientists find even one mother, with full knowledge of the facts, to knowingly volunteer her newborn offspring for such an experiment? Possibly nowhere, for in answer to a query, one of the doctors involved frankly admitted that there was "no consent" obtained from the parents. They did not believe consent necessary, he stated, but the experimenters had nevertheless kept their scientific "fingers crossed."

One such isolated divergence from the Hippocratic oath, the Nuremberg code and medical tradition—all of which compel the physician's single-minded devotion to *his patient* rather than to abstract science—is not significant. What is of gnawing import is that the staphylococcus-contaminated children in Cleveland are not isolated subjects, but only one group of compulsory or deluded participants in an incredible orgy of human experimentation that has engulfed the American medical community. It threatens the integrity of the physician, and the sanctity and safety of the patient.

The injection of live cancer cells by Sloan-Kettering experimenters into chronically ill patients at the Jewish Chronic Disease Hospital in Brooklyn occupied newspaper headlines because of its supposed uniqueness. Even the cursory reader of current medical literature and the receptive listener to the fears of medical critics can see that such callous human experiments have become commonplace. The onerous threat of a dehumanized medical science that implacably considers humans—infants, pregnant women, the retarded, the dying, the well, the sick—as "laboratory animals" is apparently a contemporary medical reality.

A vocal group of physicians are appalled by the reality of unethical human experimentation. Dr. Henry K. Beecher of the Massachusetts General Hospital is shocked by the involvement of his colleagues, many of whom, he says, assume "a god-like prerogative of choosing martyrs for science." Speaking to a recent symposium, he stated that such incidents are "by no means rare." He has found, he explained when interviewed, evidence of unethical experimentation in "university hospitals, voluntary hospitals, private hospitals, the Air Force, Veterans Administration, public health service and industry."

Dr. Herrman L. Blumgart, special consultant to the dean of the Harvard Medical School, charges that certain physicians are conducting an "increasing number of investigations that confer little or no conceivable benefit to the subject undergoing hazardous investigation." In a Harvard address he blamed much of it on doctor complacency, even acceptance of what he calls "the general sanction of such studies reflected in articles in leading medical periodicals."

"Specifically," he told his shocked audience, "I refer to the catheterization of the urinary tract of babies in a foundling home to establish the identity of normal bacterial flora, cardiac catheterization and coronary angiography of normal subject with the inadvertent production of myocardial infarction, and the production of unconsciousness and convulsions by a combination of Valsalva maneuver and forced hyperventilation in normal volunteers to study the carbon dioxide tension and electroencephalogram!"

The extent of human experimentation in America appears to reach, in both damage and implication, far beyond any physician's voiced outrage. Dr. Blumgart has mentioned three random cases of human experimentation, some involving innocent infants, and Dr. Beecher has spoken of eighteen cases. This author has personally isolated many shocking examples after a search through the medical literature and has interviewed several of the doctors involved. A British physician, Dr. M. H. Pappworth, has assiduously compiled five hundred cases—half from America—which he believes are unethical tampering with the human being in medical experiments. "It's so bad, it's unbelievable," he stated recently when interviewed via phone in London.

The well-fictionalized portrait of the typical human "guinea pig" —the idealistic youth or the prisoner seeking repentance or hope of parole—is easily recognizable. What we have yet to contemplate is the new laboratory animal—the patient—from birth to terminal illness. He presents himself to the physician for medical aid, only to be used for abstract science without possible benefit to himself and often without his knowledge or informed permission. Sometimes the damage is mere theory of risk or inconvenience; other times it may be serious injury or death.

It is too often a violation of the sanctity of the patient, which it has taken 5000 years of ethical doctor-patient relationship to establish. Independent of society and the law, the physician has assumed the dual role of doctor and experimental scientist, applying either or both of his talents to the patient on his terms. The unsuspecting patient is not aware of the dual nature of this new doctor (what one physician in a Boston hospital working on endocrine experiments calls his "Jekyll and Hyde" nature) and thus freely offers himself, his children, and his dying parents as patients, then unwitting subjects. Having seen science without ethical control dominate other aspects of his life, the newly sophisticated patient may now have to reckon with this same specter in his medical care.

On August 19, 1947, the tribunal at Nuremberg delivered its verdict of death and imprisonment against the Nazi physicians who had abused their medical code, placing into unofficial international law ten points of experimental ethics. The first tenet makes "voluntary consent" of the human subject essential. "This means," stated the Nuremberg tribunal, "that the person involved should have legal capacity to give consent; should be so situated as to be able to exercise free power of choice, without the intervention of any element of force, fraud, deceit, duress, overreaching, or other ulterior form of constraint or coercion."

To many observers, this makes all experimentation on children that does not center about therapy for their own sickness unethical; the person involved—the child—cannot possibly give his informed consent. The manipulation of him as a laboratory animal, either by the doctor acting alone or with the unknowledgeable assent of a parent, is a tragic misuse of confidence placed in the physician. "No child must ever be the subject of such an experiment," Dr. Duncan Leys of Kent, England, reminds his colleagues in a letter to *Lancet,* the prominent British medical journal. He describes an experiment in which potentially harmful doses of a drug, agene, "were given to children in an orphanage in order to see whether such doses were toxic."

The popularity of children as laboratory subjects is based upon their inability to complain effectively and their availability. Almost four million newborn American children are in the hospital for the first five days of their lives; captive mentally retarded children are available in homes, as are orphans, as well as juvenile delinquents, many of whose bodies have been freely offered to doctors for their experiments.

An antibacterial drug, triacetyloleandomycin (TriA) has been implicated in creating jaundice in children in isolated cases. Investigators from George Washington University and the Chicago Medical School, supported by a grant from a drug manufacturer, decided to test the drug's long-term toxicity on the human liver. They chose fifty mental defectives and juvenile delinquents as young as thirteen years of age at the Laurel Children's Center in Maryland. The unknowing subjects, none of whom had an illness more serious than acne, took 1 gm. of TriA a day for a period of three or four weeks.

The suspicion that the drug could be toxic was confirmed. Eight of the subjects developed liver trouble and were transferred to the hospital "for more intensive study," which included the piercing of their livers by a needle to obtain a biopsy sample of the flesh. Six of the subjects had symptoms of liver dysfunction, including abdominal pains, and two came down with jaundice.

The remaining forty-two subjects had not escaped the experiment totally unmarred: more than half had other-than-normal laboratory test results. By the end of three weeks the experimenters were so concerned about the results that they intervened, reporting that "the high incidence of significant hepatic dysfunction and the development of jaundice in two patients led to the discontinuation of administration to the remainder of the group at three weeks."

The captive children are seldom involved because they are sick to begin with and require medical aid. The reason for their frequent use as subjects is that they are biologically *normal,* and serve the same purpose as a rat or guinea pig, except that the disturbances or changes created in them are more interesting and significant to the experimenter. They are used at any age, from newborn to near-maturity, and for any type of experiment including those involving *radioactivity.*

Radioactive isotopes, when injected into the human, trace out many body functions for the scientist. Their radioactive danger is not fully known, and physicians have been implored to be very cautious, especially since cancer may be a result. "The isotope most commonly used in children is Iodine 131," states an editorial entitled "Due Caution" in the *American Journal of Diseases of Children.* "Recent information relating thyroid carcinoma to radiation in children has made clinicians cautious in the diagnostic as well as therapeutic application of radioiodine." Similar warnings have been issued regarding radioactive calcium, because of its potential danger to the bone marrow. Radioisotope dosage, measured in microcuries, also depends upon the size of the subject; the same dosage is more dangerous in children.

A captive group of seventeen youngsters three to five years of age received their dosage of Iodine 131 without being either sick or in need of diagnostic iodine. As residents of the D. C. Training School in Maryland, the mentally retarded tots were used as laboratory animals to study thyroid hormone metabolism in children. Thyroxine tagged with radioactive iodine was injected into their veins, and blood samples taken every day for a month.

The injection of I-131 seems a popular experiment on humans. Several studies have been published, including one in which the radioactive isotope was injected into babies—including premature infants—at the University of Arkansas School of Medicine. The potentially dangerous radiation was measured about their thyroid gland, which is the cancer-prone area. The I-131 was injected into full-term babies through an umbilical catheter, and into the premature through a vein in the scalp.

Nine boys of an average age of twelve, living at the Walter E. Fernald State School in Waverly, Massachusetts, have also been used as radioactive laboratory subjects to study what would happen to radioactive calcium, Ca-45, injected into the body. (The survey was conducted by Harvard and M.I.T. scientists and supported by a breakfast-food company, the National Institute of Health and the Atomic Energy Commission.) The experimenters found that their young laboratory subjects would retain the potentially dangerous radioisotope in their bodies for some time after the experiment. "The quantity of injected Ca-45 excreted in the feces during several days was small," they state. "This suggests that only a minor fraction of the calcium absorbed on any one day is re-excreted promptly and that the major portion is retained for some time."

The number of mentally retarded orphans and incarcerated youngsters available for experimenters is sizable, but as we have seen in the Cleveland staphylococcus experiment, the supply of newborn children is virtually unlimited, especially for experiments that have absolutely nothing to do with improving their health. Scientists in Los Angeles are among those who have made use of this by performing experiments on infants as young as *one hour old!* With a grant supplied by a large Los Angeles general hospital and the U. S. Public Health Service, three University of California pediatricians conducted a series of experiments on 113 newborn infants to learn their intra-artery blood pressure and to study the "effects of crying, of exposure to cold, and of postural tilting."

The description of the manipulations performed on these innocent youngsters, although supposedly "not dangerous," is as chilling as the ice bath in which they inserted part of the youngsters' bodies. The infants, including twenty-six premature babies weighing as little as three pounds, had a catheter tube put into an umbilical artery and up to the aorta of the heart. The blood pressure of the child, with the tube in his artery, was measured "at rest" and "while crying."

The next test on the little laboratory subjects, the "cold pressor" test, is best described by the pediatrician-experimenters themselves: "This procedure was conducted as follows: 1 foot was immersed to the ankle in ice water at 4 degrees C to 5 degrees C for a period of 1 minute. The aortic pressure was recorded continuously during the immersion and at 30 second intervals thereafter for 2 to 5 minutes. Since the youngster invariably cried when exposed to the cold, one to three pre-test immersions at one-minute intervals were made until all signs of discomfort disappeared."

The infants were next subjected to an experimental travail that placed them on a tilt board, with the catheter still in their aorta, in order to study the effects of unusual posturing on their blood pressure. If the unnerved babies showed "discomfort" during the test, it was *done over again* until the infants' discomfort did not interfere with the scientists' calculations. "The subjects were secured to a circumcision board with the upper extremities restrained in flexion and the lower extremities in extension," the scientists reported. "The board was tilted over the edge of the table with the catheter tip at the estimated level of the right atrium. Great care was taken to fix the fulcrum at this level. Tilting was accomplished within a second and usually did not cause any signs of discomfort. *When it did, the test was repeated until a satisfactory pressure recording was obtained* [italics mine]."

Not only the normal child but the desperately sick child has been used as a laboratory subject in potentially hazardous experimental studies *not intended to diagnose or heal the child.* Such action is an outrageous abuse of current medical freedom—or anarchy. One frightening study conducted at two prominent Boston children's hospitals used both well and sick newborn youngsters from two to thirty-four hours old. Catheters were inserted directly into their hearts, a dangerous technique used sparingly even on cardiac children who may require it. *None* of these youngsters required heart catheterization, for the sick ones were suffering from respiratory diseases. The study was developed to learn the difference in circulation between normal and respiratory-ill children. Unquestionably, the youngsters were being used as laboratory "animals" in the classic sense of the word.

In fifteen of the children the catheter was inserted in the umbilical vein by the experimenters, then manipulated up and into the heart. In five cases, maneuvering difficulty caused doctors to abandon the experiment. In twenty-eight more children a cut was made below their groin, and the catheter was inserted into the saphenous vein and threaded up toward the heart. In sixteen children the attempts to enter the pulmonary artery with the catheter had to be abandoned: the electrocardioscope showed that the experiment had produced ectopic (abnormal) heartbeats!

The children were also subjected to fluoroscopic radiation as the catheter was followed. Sensible radiation studies at Duke University, conducted with wooden replacement boards instead of human laboratory animals, show that the fluoroscope and cineangiocardiograms (motion pictures) produce a radiation of almost 10 R's in a child four years of age, some eight hundred times as much as a chest X-ray! Such radiation bombardment, which is much more severe in the newborn and tragically unnecessary in these Boston babies, is a danger "not only to the child alone but to future generations" as well, says the Duke study.

The sequel to the Boston experiment is not happy. Eight of the ten critically ill children died "with increasing respiratory symptoms" three to fifty-eight hours following the catheter study. "There was also no evidence to indicate that the catheterization procedure had contributed to the fatal outcome of these infants," the experimenters state gratuitously, with no real evidence for their statement either. It would have seemed more humane for the doctors to spend the effort and precious time attempting heroic medical salvage of the children instead of tampering with their frail bodies in human experiments.

As startling as are these experiments on infants is the fact that in the Los Angeles and Boston cases, at least one parent of each infant gave permission for the experimentation. Although doubt exists as to whether parents have the right to offer up their children freely as experimental subjects—are the experimenters absolved from blame because they appear to have parental permission?

An interview with one of the Los Angeles pediatricians involved reveals how meaningless such "permission" can sometimes be—how the adroit use of semantics in explaining the experiment can elicit less-than-informed consent. The parents in Los Angeles were told, he states, that the tests "might be of value to the child," a piece of unworthy subterfuge that is standard-inducement armament for many experimenters on humans. Although the parents were also told that the tests did not have to be done for the baby's health, the concept of human experimentation is remote to the often uneducated parent in a Los Angeles charity ward, where some of the mothers were as young as fifteen. The image of the doctor-healer is close at hand, however, and the doctor's subtlest false hint is sufficient to compel co-operation from most.

The Nuremberg code prohibits the use of deceit or even the simplest "overreaching" to obtain consent. Most patients can barely conceive of a physician risking unnecessary harm, and some doctors skillfully trade on this historic trust, using deceitful medical catch phrases to wheedle patient consent.

The technique of this insincere art was inadvertently explained by a Veterans Administration physician who used adult hospital patients *without* cardiac conditions to learn the effect of digitalis on the normal heart. The tests were involved and uncomfortable, with the patient pedaling a bike-like affair while a tube in him measured his cardiac output and his expired air was collected. The men were given a digitalis drug—whose effect on the normal heart is in debate—in between tests.

In answer to the question whether the men were "volunteers," the physician answered candidly, "You might say 'volunteers' in quote marks. It was not legal, informed consent as I understand it. I have a standard spiel. I tell them that they don't have to take it but that it is a test of their heart and respiratory function." Under the influence of such persuasion, the trusting patient would feel he was not co-operating with the doctor in his "medical care."

• • •

Just as an orphan or a mentally retarded child provides an accessible "captive" for the experimenter, so does the sick person who presents himself for medical care. As a hospitalized laboratory subject, the patient may find himself involved in experiments not involving his illness in any way, as part of a controlled study weighted against him, as a statistic in a surgical series. He may even be a participant in radical, perhaps fatal, medical and surgical procedures that smack of callous experimentation rather than medicine.

The patient generally gives the surgeon permission to do whatever additional procedures may be indicated after the incision, but surgery should not be an opportunity to use the exposed organs for experimental purposes. A classic experimental case took place in a government hospital in the Washington area when eleven patients undergoing heart surgery, including children, had *strain gauges sewn onto their hearts* to test an abstract principle, Starling's law.

Experimental tampering with the body during surgery—with procedures not intended for the patient's benefit—precipitated a major professional debate in the Boston area recently. Doctors at the Children's Hospital Medical Center, during heart surgery on eighteen children, performed an unrelated experiment on skin transplantation in which *the thymus gland, which may be essential to body immunization, was cut out of the eleven children.*

"Eleven of these patients were randomly selected to have a total thymectomy, where the remaining seven had only a biopsy of the thymus and served as controls," the doctors' report states. "At the conclusion of each heart operation a full-thickness skin homograft, approximately 1 cm. in diameter and obtained from an unrelated adult donor, was sutured in place on the chest wall."

In a subsequent issue of the *New England Journal of Medicine,* an outraged Connecticut physician, Dr. Byron H. Waksman—fearing both for the children who had lost the organ and for medical propriety—reminded doctors that a "series of papers over the last two years has shown that the thymus has a key role in the development and maintenance of several types of immune function." He questioned the "value and propriety" of human experiments such as this, in which "total thymectomy was carried out as a purely experimental measure in subjects not having a disease to which this procedure is relevant."

Dr. Waksman added his concern about possible transmission of serum hepatitis from graft donors, and other ethical and physical dangers. "One may also ask if the long-term hazards, unknown at present, were duly noted and called to the subjects' attention. It seems pertinent to raise these questions at a time when the literature, especially in the field of transplantation, is being flooded with reports of human experimentation based in many cases on inadequate laboratory data and with insufficient attention to the long-term hazards."

The experimenters answered Dr. Waksman by claiming that their own "article unfortunately implied the creation of thymectomized patients," whereas the procedure in the eleven children was a "necessary part" of the surgery. This doctor-experimenter claim is interesting, but their original article on the experiment more than "implied." It stated: *"Eleven of these patients were randomly selected to have a total thymectomy . . .* [italics mine]."

Experimental tampering can be dangerous for any patient, but is especially disturbing and inexcusable in the sensitive pregnant woman. Despite this, the literature is well stocked with experiments conducted on pregnant women *which are not in any way intended for their, or their unborn child's, benefit.* The extent and danger of such experiments may be sizable: one New York physician recalls an experiment in which especially dangerous *biopsies* were taken from the kidney of pregnant women!

One frightening experimental study involving pregnant women was conducted at a Cincinnati hospital. "The material consisted of five normotensive (normal blood pressure) subjects whose ages varied from twenty to thirty years and who were in the last trimester of pregnancy," the doctors' journal report states. "The patients were admitted to the hospital and kept at bed rest for a few days before the experiment." The experiment itself involved the injection of an anesthetic into the spine, and the use of a Foley catheter left in the bladder to collect urine for study. The danger to the mother and unborn child from the unnecessary anesthesia, and the possibility of urinary infection in infection-prone pregnant women from the Foley catheter, should make such an experiment unthinkable.

In another case, X-ray experiments were conducted on pregnant women at a city hospital in New York. Twenty pregnant women admitted to the hospital for complications were subjected to a potentially dangerous experimental "angiography" technique, to make the arteries in the pelvic area visible. The technique includes puncturing an artery in the leg, giving the patient a popular narcotic for the pain, inserting a contrast dye and radiating the area for X-ray pictures. The dangers to the fetus from such intrusions—dye, radiation and drug—can be considerable. That the work was an "experimental" search for knowledge rather than needed diagnosis is freely admitted by the doctors. "In this preliminary study no particular effort was made to select patients either for diagnosis or because they showed abnormalities," the physicians state, "but rather to survey the possibilities of the technique as a diagnostic tool and as a research instrument for study of placental circulation."

In medical folklore—promulgated in book to television—the human experiment always involves the hopeful, last-minute therapy or surgical technique whose lifesaving ability dominates the dramatic scene. In today's climate of the overpopular "controlled experiment," the physician's use of patients as experimental animals often has less fabled motives in mind.

The so-called controlled study, in which two groups receive different therapies, is used by the experimenter to determine the efficiency of a method of treatment. In an ethical controlled experiment, the physician should not know which of the two therapies is superior. He is thus providing each half of the sick patients with alternate routes to recovery. In this category, for example, are physicians who may be totally confused at our present level of knowledge about the value of anticoagulants used long-term after a heart attack. *This* physician may, ethically, provide half his patients with the drug and deny it to the other half.

If, however, he holds a firm opinion on a therapy he must—as a man sworn to heal—use the best possible therapy in his medical judgment for all his patients. In such a case, a "controlled" experiment is unethical, for he would then honestly have to divulge to half his patients that he believes they are receiving inferior care. Such candor would make it difficult, if not impossible, to obtain "informed consent" from the sick, and thus—as it should be—rule out the experiment.

The controlled experiment has become an almost deified medical entity, receiving more dedication from some experimenter-doctors than the healing of the sick. The zenith of its callousness is reached when it is performed by doctors who *know* or who are *effectively sure* that one half of the control group will suffer from inferior treatment or be exposed to hazard. Most heinous of all is consciously denying patients accepted proper treatment. Such experiments contribute to abstract science—but are outside the ethical boundaries as they should be defined by an intelligent civilization.

Many experiments which cause grievous harm to those patients in a control group involve scientific information previously demonstrated or computed and available in the medical literature. Despite this, many experimenters demand a "definitive" controlled experiment. At present they appear to have the power to exercise that desire, despite potential catastrophe. A classic case involves the blindness produced by the high-oxygen treatment formerly given to premature babies, on the theory that it would increase survival. How its study was handled differently by the Americans and by the British illustrates the damage possible in unbridled experimentation.

Soon after World War II, several reports were published in the medical literature which indicated a link between the high percentage of blindness in premature youngsters and the high-oxygen environment they had been placed in. The disease, retrolental fibroplasia (or RLF), had become the leading cause of blindness in children. One report showing the suspicious correlation was published in *JAMA* in 1949; another, detailing the problem in Birmingham, England, was published in a British ophthalmological publication; still another in an Australian journal in 1951; another in the *American Journal of Ophthalmology* in 1952; and a statistically impressive report in the *Archives of Disease in Childhood* in 1952.

In England, doctors took early notice. In October, 1951, the leading hospitals of Manchester—Duchess of York Hospital and St. Mary's Hospital—discontinued high-oxygen therapy and reverted back to low oxygen for premature babies. In the preceding five years they had had eighty-three cases of retrolental fibroplasia, including thirty-six with permanent eye damage, and twenty-one children who were totally blinded. From November on, *not a single case of blindness to a premature baby developed!* A report on the success by Dr. E. Jefferson was published in a prominent medical journal. A follow-up during 1953 showed the same result: the disappearance of retrolental fibroplasia and no change in general survival, a result achieved by common-sense science and merciful judgment.

While the disappearance of the disease was sufficient for the British, many American doctor-experimenters apparently sought a "definitive" controlled study. It was achieved, but at the expense of babies blinded for life. A considerable time *after* the Manchester hospitals had discontinued high-oxygen therapy, physicians at a university-connected hospital in New York decided on the now medically famed "controlled" experiment. "Several physicians have noted an association of RLF with intensive oxygen therapy," the American authors reported in *JAMA,* in the spring of 1954. "Adequate controls are needed, however, to establish such a relationship beyond question. The present study was designed to test this relationship under controlled studies. We found a high incidence of blindness among infants given liberal oxygen treatment and none among those receiving little or none."

Their study, written up dryly, deprives the human experiment of its proper impact. Twenty-eight youngsters received a mixture containing 38 percent average oxygen, while thirty-six of the babies were kept in a 69 percent high-oxygen concentration for a period of two weeks. The results: none of the youngsters who had been given low-oxygen therapy had their vision damaged, but eight of the high-oxygen babies were stricken, at least six with total blindness. Today six adolescents in New York are without sight for having served as "controls" in this study—a study to "prove" what had apparently been known. With "informed" consent, would the parents of these children have permitted the blinding high-oxygen therapy?

The hospitalized patient *always* deserves the best, safest therapy known to the physician. Using this definition, the experimenter on humans has often shown himself, in the case of many controlled studies, not to be a *doctor* in the traditional healing sense at all, but a researcher working in the same environment as the true doctor, and deceptively garbed and addressed as one, confusing both the medical community and the trusting patient. His mission, as he distortedly views it, is "knowledge," not the healing of patients. If the controlled study he has designed is a destructive one, his patients can *only* be harmed in the process. Under some physicians' current concepts of human experimentation, the doctor-scientist himself makes the determination of whether the experiment is to be done and who is to suffer in his "academic" quest.

The antibiotic chloramphenicol has been implicated several times in the literature, as far back as 1955, as causing bone-marrow depression when used in large doses of anywhere from 4 to 12 gm. a day, instead of the standard 1 to 2 gm. Bone-marrow depression can be debilitating and worse in a well patient, but may be especially dangerous for the sick. Despite this, physicians at a Veterans Administration hospital in Los Angeles conducted a "double-blind controlled study" *in 1965,* in which middle-aged and elderly war veterans suffering from serious infections—from postoperative wounds to pneumonia—were given chloramphenicol *in excess* so that the toxicity it would create in their blood could be studied!

Half the group were given the standard therapy of 2 gm. a day, while the other half were given 6 gm. a day for as long as six weeks. The experiment was a "success": eighteen of the twenty-one severely ill men receiving the 6 gm. of chloramphenicol developed "toxic bone-marrow depression," while only two of the twenty receiving the smaller dose were similarly affected. The doctor-experimenter's advice was considerably at variance with his practice. "To reduce the risk of aplastic anemia," he states, "we believe that even mild toxicity should be avoided by limitation of the dosage and duration of therapy . . . It may also be worth re-emphasizing that, in the individual case, there should be a good clinical indication for the use of chloramphenicol in preference to other antibiotics."

One of the most shocking "controlled studies" was discussed by Dr. Henry K. Beecher of Harvard. This experiment also involved chloramphenicol; in this case in a disease—typhoid fever—for which it is perhaps the best lifesaving drug available. Despite its proven efficacy, the drug *was denied* to 157 typhoid-fever patients in a charity ward by doctor-experimenters, who—says Dr. Beecher—acknowledged chloramphenicol as the definitive treatment! In the experiment, 408 individuals with typhoid fever were divided into two groups: one received the standard therapy, while the other did not. The doctor-experimenters reported twenty-three deaths more than anticipated with normal therapy!

The controlled study is most easily accomplished in those groups of the population which are the most captive: the informed citizen might learn and object to bestial deprivation of proper medicine. For example, servicemen are prime captives, as was illustrated by a controlled experiment done at an Air Force base in Wyoming. A number of servicemen with "strep throats" were divided into two groups; 291 severely ill and 294 controls. *None* of the men in either group received penicillin therapy, although *standard, proven, incontrovertible* evidence shows that penicillin is the prime treatment for "strep throat." If this antibiotic is not applied vigorously, the patient risks danger of rheumatic fever, then rheumatic heart disease with serious damage to the heart valves. The first group was treated with relatively ineffective sulfa drugs, while the second group received no antibacterial therapy at all. The result was that twenty-five of the servicemen deprived of penicillin therapy developed preventable rheumatic fever and may be crippled for life. The experiment has unspeakable ramifications for doctors everywhere.

The tendency to play God (or anti-God) with patients in the experimenter's quest for "knowledge" (or fame) leads uncontrolled physicians astray. One doctor even took diabetic patients off insulin to make several tests.

The unsettling aspect of the controlled study is the infinite variety of such experiments which can be done by physicians who are eager to have their names attached to *definitive* studies published in leading medical journals, few (if any) of whom screen their articles for violations of ethics in experimentation. Any standard therapy—from insulin to antibiotics, from drainage of boils to setting of fractures—can be definitively "proved" by withholding treatment from a control group as in the "strep throat" case involving the servicemen. Likewise, any therapy currently considered ineffective or harmful can be scientifically "nailed" by a negative controlled experiment in which half the patients are purposely sacrificed to the debilitating treatment. What appears to honor the scientist may prove to dishonor the profession.

The surgical "series" is another experimental method that can either be used for patient benefit or overaggressively abused by experimenters. Basically, a "series" is an operation performed on a number of people, often with a control of patients who do not undergo any surgery or those who receive a substitute operation. When a surgeon is not convinced about the preferability of one operation over another—as in gastrectomy vs. vagotomy in ulcer surgery—a surgical series using both procedures on patients absolutely in need of ulcer surgery is ethical.

It may also be ethical when surgeons are not sure whether surgery or nonsurgery is the preferential treatment for an ailment. In a *JAMA* editorial on "Ethics and Experimental Therapy," the author mentions three such still-inconclusive surgical procedures: "The few examples to be cited are ones in which the distinguished experts in the fields are divided, proponent versus skeptic, and in which the evidence is not clear-cut: presacral neurotomy for menstrual pain, sympathectomy for hypertension, and thymectomy for myasthenia gravis."

Often, the editorial implies, such surgical series are extravagantly large and risky. It reveals that a "move is on foot" to do a surgical series at six medical centers on a thousand patients with myasthenia gravis, a disease of weakened voluntary muscles. One theory holds that removal of the thymus gland is beneficial. This thymectomy operation carries a death rate of approximately 7.5 percent, says the article, pointing out that a surgical series involving a thousand patients would precipitate seventy-five deaths. "Is there no less costly and surer way of settling the matter?" asks the editorial, answering that it could probably be done as well, or better, with 50 instead of 1000 patients—25 to receive thymectomy and 25 to receive a sham operation, with skin incision only. The lives saved? Four deaths as against the 75. In either case, surgery should only be done after full informed approval, *JAMA* states, "when all patients had the situation fully explained to them . . ."

Of all the restrictions on the experimental doctor, perhaps the most stringent should be required of the physician who uses the severely ill, the incurable or the dying as his subjects. As the injection of live cancer cells into the "incurable" patients in New York indicates, these helpless laboratory subjects are the single greatest temptation (aside from newborn infants) for the ethically hazy physician. Making value judgments on the extent of life remaining in the patient to decide his expendability in a medical experiment is a vice of both ignorance and immorality. The healer must be concerned only with maintaining the reasonable life left, and in dignity and comfort.

In the cold execution of human experimentation the physician's weapon for healing, his "therapeutic intent," can be blunted, even destroyed. Dr. Roald N. Grant, writing in the magazine *Ca,* examines the loss of this intent in overexperimentation on the mortally ill, whose decreased life expectancy seems to make them fair game for the callous study-maker. "For example," he states, "cancer patients who are most in need of medical care of the 'act of love' type are too often those least likely to receive it. Because so many of them are mortally ill, they are especially vulnerable to therapeutic experimentation in which their lives are, in effect, offered up on the altar of research or medical education."

Dr. Grant makes the judicious point that physicians can no longer be individually empowered to make these experimental decisions— that "tumor boards" to screen a doctor's treatment of the mortally sick cancer patient are essential. "This 'expendability' of cancer patients to further our knowledge has long been of concern to thoughtful physicians and others who wish to protect cancer patients from needless suffering and death," he states. The tumor board can, he believes, expose treatment of cancer patients which is not in the patient's best interest. It is thereby possible, he states, to "screen out much medical nonsense, incompetency and even brutality from the proposed therapeutic regime, thus assuring the patient of 'therapeutic intent' which is best for him."

Dr. Duncan Leys describes a case in which patients suffering from incurable cerebral tumors were used as laboratory subjects so that it might be learned whether aureomycin was injurious if given through the lower back area. For this experiment—which could not help them—the severely ill patients received multiple lumbar punctures. At the University of Pennsylvania School of Medicine, in a government-supported project, experimenters wanted to know if the intravenous administration of glycerol solution was harmful. Animal experiments had shown that non-oral (parenteral) administration of glycerol produced low blood pressure, weight loss and central nervous system disturbances. The human subjects chosen for the test were hospitalized cancer patients who in the opinion of the researchers were apparently on the verge of death and therefore ostensibly expendable. "Nearly all the human subjects had malignant disease and were considered to have limited life expectancies," state the presumptuous researchers.

In this case the glycerol proved to be harmless (which was not *known* in advance), but experimenters dealing with patients *in extremis* have also made decisions that may actually have precipitated death considerably.

The attempt to transplant a lung is an interesting case in point. No lung has been transplanted successfully into a human because of the immunological barrier, which eventually rejects its foreign tissue. One of the first attempts, in 1963, involved a fifty-eight-year-old patient who was admitted to a southern university hospital with a diagnosis of repeated attacks of pneumonia. The patient was then quite unaware that he would be dead eighteen days after a decidedly unproven lung transplant operation.

Further examination of the patient also revealed kidney disease. The left lung showed both infection and signs of cancer, and a decision was made for its surgical removal. According to the medical report of the fatal experiment a thoracotomy (chest opening) and lung excision were indicated, which would still leave the patient his right lung. That lung was noncancerous. It was labeled "emphysematous" but it "expanded well and the breath sounds were within normal limits," according to the doctors themselves. As thousands of people have learned, most human beings can live with only one lung, a margin for survival that nature has built into man.

To experimenters, he was a perfect laboratory subject: he was a prisoner serving a life sentence, and—as they imperiously guessed—he had a "limited prospective life span." He was considered a candidate for a never-successful lung transplant because of this and because of his "limited exercise tolerance." He would be less "dyspneic" —*short of breath*—if it succeeded! The transplant was explained to him, along with diagrams, and he was told that should the transplant lung become gangrenous it could be removed by a second operation. He gave his permission. The transplant was performed, and no second operation was ever necessary, for the patient died eighteen days later.

The fervor for human experimentation in transplantation of organs may catastrophically injure physician dedication to save life. It may make an apparently "dying" patient look more like potential transplant material—donor or recipient—than a human to be heroically salvaged.

The many excesses of human transplant experimentation need to be curtailed by a clear understanding of what is permissible. The strongest critical fire has been drawn by the premature attempts to graft animal organs into human bodies. Patients have had baboon kidneys implanted in their thighs; chimpanzee kidneys have been grafted into several patients, many with temporary success up to several months, followed by death.

A premature attempt has even been made to transplant a chimpanzee heart into a human, a procedure that was attempted by University of Mississippi surgeons. A sixty-eight-year-old man dying of a heart condition, whose life expectancy doctors measured in "hours," was chosen as the recipient of a heart transplant. The donor this time was a ninety-six-pound chimpanzee, but the smaller primate heart worked insufficiently in the human body for only one hour before the man died.

The obvious unsoundness of the situation, medically, ethically and experimentally, drew searing fire from medical quarters. "As of today, a primate heart must be rejected by a human recipient despite immunosuppressive therapy," *Medical Tribune* editorialized about the experiment. "Should the primate heart be transplanted into human beings for the prolongation of life by—at the best—a few weeks? Should further refinements in physiology and drug therapy be pursued in the experimental laboratory before heterotransplants [from other species] are attempted in man?"

The *New England Journal of Medicine* has cast a dour Yankee eye at such experiments. "Even if the immunologic problems are mastered," they editorialized, "the anatomy of most primate organs will remain permanently impractical for transplantation to man." The ethical distortion of certain transplant experiments was perhaps best examined by Dr. Eugene D. Robin of the University of Pittsburgh School of Medicine, who fears the new role of the doctor.

He criticizes the impetuosity of the surgeons engaged in dangerous heart transplant attempts in human beings. Before experimenting with a transplant, there must be "a reasonable possibility of clinical success," he reminds us. "For example, it has been well established experimentally in the animal that cardiac homotransplant cannot maintain life on a long-term basis. Therefore, there is no moral justification for attempting this procedure in human patients," states Dr. Robin. "Nor should the physician rationalize such attempts by the consideration that the patient was 'going to die anyhow.' The fundamental role of the doctor must be that of the healer and not that of the executioner."

In a similar vein, Dr. Robin also criticizes the lung transplant as a supposed therapy for lung cancer; the use of adrenal transplants in humans "despite the availability of highly acceptable substitution therapy"; and such kidney transplant "travesties" as the recent transplant of an eighty-year-old mother's kidney to her sixty-year-old son. "Needless to say, the son died post transplant," he reports, "and the mother recovered after a painful and complicated post-operative course." Asking for a new moral code to guide medicine through such new ethical dilemmas, he calls for "a conference under the auspices of some nationally recognized group to consider the general nature of ethical practices in this area."

The birth of detached attitudes toward patients (known as "materials" in experimental reports) is ingrained in the personality of many modern doctors. It is also implicit in the supposed scientific orientation of his work, where his subject matter is "biology" rather than "humanity." The detachment he brings to his experimental work thus makes truly ethical concern a remote, even strained concept.

In prior eras, the medical experimenter was typically a person of heroic proportions who considered a study suitable for others only if the doctor were first willing to make himself or his family risk the danger. The famed yellow fever experiments involved heroic young army doctors who died proving that yellow fever was spread by the bite of the Aedes aegypti mosquito. Thirty-five years ago heart catheterization became possible after Dr. Werner Frossmann threaded a tube up to his own heart through a vein in his arm.

In 1830 a French experimenter, Tanery, swallowed strychnine poison along with charcoal to show that the charcoal would absorb the alkaloid, which it did. In 1849, an experimenter named Oliver injected extracts of the endocrine glands into his own son. In 1767, John Hunter inoculated himself with gonorrhea pus to show that it was transmitted through the genitals.

Perhaps the courage of Dr. Joseph Goldberger of the U. S. Public

Health Service should be retold for the spiritual edification of the contemporary experimenter. Studying pellagra, the scourge of the South, Dr. Goldberger lived among the Negroes and poor whites of the area, and observed that the disease appeared to be related to their diet. He fed an improved diet of meat, eggs, milk and vegetables to a group of children and adults, and not only prevented pellagra but cured it in those who had already contracted it. His next step was to prove that pellagra was not communicable. He solved the ethical dilemma the only possible way: he, his wife and fifteen ex- perimenter associates inoculated *themselves* with the blood, urine, feces and peeling skin of pellagra victims. Their survival was proof enough. There is no greater assurance of the doctor's confidence in the safety of the experiment than *first* involving his own flesh and blood.

Considerably more self-endangerment is called for in the con- temporary physician-experimenter. As Dr. Henry Beecher has pointed out, "whenever doubts exists as to safety, it is advisable for the investigator first to subject himself to the possible hazards in- volved."

Who are to be the laboratory subjects when it is not feasible to use only the doctor himself? What legal safeguards and ethically strength- ened codes are needed to ensure doctor decency?

It is apparent that medical experimentation on humans has been excessive, that much of it has been trivial, redundant and scientifically worthless. Proper legal controls on impetuous doctors would reduce the volume of experimentation and boost its quality. A single study in each case, well sponsored and publicized medically, would replace the overlapping and nonsensical compulsion for human experimenta- tion and journal-publishing that exist today.

When experimentation is intelligently called for, only *informed adult volunteers* are ethically possible. Who are to be these volun- teers, and how can we define "informed consent" as required by the Nuremberg regulations? Firstly, sick patients—now the sustenance of the ambitious experimenter—must be totally, legally, irrevocably ruled out as subjects in *medical experiments not primarily intended for their cure*. Consent from a sick patient is meaningless. He is hospitalized and almost totally dependent upon his physician, in whom he has "faith" and whose ire or displeasure he has no in- tention of stimulating by non-co-operation. "To obtain the consent of the patient to a proposed investigation is not enough," states the British Medical Research Council. "Owing to the special relationship that exists between a patient and a doctor, most patients will con- sent to *any proposal* [italics mine] that is made."

Children too, as Dr. Leys, Dr. Beecher and other aroused critics have stressed, are not suitable candidates for experimentation not involving therapy for their own health. In such cases, parental consent is undoubtedly meaningless. The subject himself must give informed consent, and involving a child in medical hazard without hope of specific gain for the child is not within the ethical purview of the parent. It is unlikely that under common law the parent can volunteer the normal, well child's services as a laboratory "animal" for abstract science.

Permissible experimentation on children varies from cases in which parents give permission for a child to take a new measles vaccine to a recent experiment in which a dwarf child received a newly developed growth hormone whose hazards are not fully known. In experimental medicine intended *only* for the child's benefit, the parent must be fully informed and gauge between the benefit and hazard.

Some experiments have been conducted with full consent, some without any consent at all, and others with a truncated concept of what "informed" means. Consent clouded by doctor subterfuge, off-handedness or ignorance is not consent at all. "This might possibly help you" or "it is a study of your . . . function" is a deceptive ploy that violates the Nuremberg concept against using deceit to obtain experimental permission. An experiment presented in such technical language that it is not fully understood by barely educated participants is equally unethical. Most important for informed consent is the physician's full, total, even compulsive disclosure of hazard, either danger suspected by the researcher or reported in the literature— *whether or not the physician agrees with those suspicions.*

The typical consent form (when one is used) is the height of glib assurance, hinting darkly at little. The proper form for human volunteers to sign should be frank, bleak and uncompromising. One form used by an experimenter working on a skin-grafting project might provide a model for the ethical physician more interested in medicine than in experimental skulduggery. The middle portion of the stark document reads:

I sign this authorization with full knowledge that this attempt to graft tissue may not be successful. The risks and uncertainties involved, as well as the possibility that I MAY BE PERMANENTLY INJURED, SCARRED, OR DISFIGURED AS A CONSEQUENCE OF THIS OPERATION, have been fully explained to me. Nevertheless, I make this request and grant the authority set forth above, voluntarily and upon my own initiative, and with no assurances from anyone as to the results that may be obtained, either in respect to myself or the recipient. IT IS CLEAR TO ME THAT THE ABOVE OPERATION MAY BE OF NO SPECIFIC BENEFIT TO ME, BUT IS TO BE PERFORMED FOR THE PURPOSE OF EXPANDING MEDICAL INFORMATION PERTAINING TO THE PROBLEMS OF TISSUE AND ORGAN TRANSPLANTATION.

The experiment involves the removal of a piece of skin, about the size of a postage stamp and one quarter of an inch thick, from a fore-arm of a man or the armpit of a woman, and its replacement with someone else's skin. The purpose is to learn more about the body's immunological rejection of foreign tissue to enable us someday to defeat the rejection of transplanted kidneys and others organs.

"The experiment is not that dangerous, but I purposely made the form as bleak as it is mainly because I have to sleep at night," says the physician-experimenter at Downstate Medical Center in New York, its author. "There can never be fully enlightened consent, because no patient can understand all the remote eventualities that lurk in the recesses of the doctor's mind, no matter how well I explain it. But I try to get as close as humanly possible to informed consent. Firstly, and very important, we choose only intelligent volunteers so that we know that they fully understand. We don't pay any money because we want sincerely interested adults. Generally they are relatives of victims of kidney disease who want to do something to help out. I have made the form as frightening as it is in order to make people realize that experimentation is not a lark, and that they are doing something serious that could hurt them. Actually, though, we have done one hundred and fifty thus far and have had no serious complications."

The necessity for informed consent is stressed by Dr. Henry K. Beecher in an editorial in *Clinical Pharmacology and Therapeutics,* in which he points out the impossibility of communicating the risk to the incompetent—including infants and children, the mentally deficient and uneducated laymen. "Can the guardians of the first two rightly consent to something they themselves will not experience?" asks Dr. Beecher.

Aside from these "incompetents," who cannot give informed consent, we must also face the issue of consent elicited falsely because of patients' belief in doctors. The hospitalized patient, as we have seen, is not really a free agent. Nor, says Dr. Beecher, is the medical student, whom he considers one of the captive experimental groups. "Granted that the use of medical students has been sanctified by long practice, no instructor should permit his students to be used in his investigations," he states. "The reason is obvious."

Similar controversy has surrounded the use of prisoners, who at first glance seem ideal volunteers for human experimentation. The "duress" and "coercion" prohibited by the Nuremberg regulations, however, could be interpreted as implied promise of parole or pardon, making the consent of the prisoner less than voluntary. The establishment of drug company experimental laboratories right *on the grounds* of a Michigan state prison should be examined for the implied coercion involved. It requires little knowledge of recent history to know the price society pays for considering incarcerated men and women as being any less than other humans. The federal government has recognized the ethical dangers involved by prohibiting the use of prisoners of war for human experimentation.

The current debacle of physician morality makes a reconsideration of the tenets of human experimentation imperative. Rather than drawing on a clear-cut code of medical behavior, the physician has been improvising from a less than finely developed or educated medical conscience. This excessive power must be curtailed not only for society but for the sake of physicians themselves, for whom the eventual loss in dignity would be severely punishing.

Although they must be strongly reinforced, there are some historic guides to morality and legality in human experimentation. The first restriction against purposeful, destructive tampering with the human body is contained in the Hippocratic oath: *"I will use that method of treatment which, according to my ability and judgment, I consider for the benefit of my patient, and abstain from whatever is deleterious and mischievous."* In 1949 the World Medical Association added its contemporary concurrence to Hippocratic wisdom. "Under no circumstances," states their code of behavior, "is a doctor permitted to do anything which would weaken the physical and mental resistance of a human being except from strictly therapeutic or prophylactic indications imposed in the interests of the patients."

The conviction at Nuremberg of twenty-three Nazi scientists, twenty of whom were the M.D. "doctors of infamy," and the subsequent execution of some of them, was punishment for human experimentation on Russian officers, Poles and Jews. The experimental horror included "exploding" human brains at sustained high-altitude environment; freezing victims to death in cold water to observe their reactions; radiating male genitals from a powerful, hidden X-ray machine to produce sterility; infecting Polish women with deadly tetanus, gas bacilli and staphylococci to test the effects of new drugs on these diseases; contaminating patients with typhus for the same reason.

The "controlled experiment" was a common Nazi method, and in one nefarious case, five groups of subjects were used in a salt-water drinking experiment. Two groups drank pure salt water, two drank salt water to which a preparation had been added and one group drank distilled salt water. "In individual patients weakness and especially thirst took such extreme forms that after only a few days they could no longer leave their beds. In one case I remember the patient broke out into paroxysms of screaming," a witness at Nuremberg testified.

In another "controlled experiment" Catholic priests and monks were infected with disease, and divided into three groups. One was treated with medical drugs and technique, another with a "homeopathic" method and the third was given no treatment at all. Twelve of the clergymen died.

During the trial it became apparent that *two hundred* German doctors were involved in the medical-experiment crimes and several hundred more were aware of what was going on, but the medical profession itself had made no complaints. The revulsion against these German doctors resulted in the so-called Geneva Code of the World Medical Association and the Nuremberg regulations on "permissible human experiments." The Geneva Code is an updated adaptation of the Hippocratic oath, which they recommended be affirmed by every new doctor on graduation. In part, it reads:

> I will practice medicine with conscience and dignity. The health and life of my patient will be my first consideration . . . I will maintain the utmost respect for human life from the time of its conception. Even under threat I will not use my knowledge contrary to the laws of humanity.

The Nuremberg rules, which were the first explicit code on human experimentation, are now urgently in need of revision to meet the current experimental orgy. The ten rules basically state that the subject must give his consent without duress and without the use of deceit or subterfuge; he shall be fully informed of the risk and method so that his consent will be "enlightened"; the experiment shall yield fruitful results unprocurable by other methods; the experiment shall be based on preliminary knowledge and prior animal experimentation; no experiment shall be conducted where death or disabling disease is expected, unless the doctor himself serves as a subject; the degree of risk should not exceed the possible gain; the scientist should discontinue the experiment if it appears that the subject may be harmed.

These codes were precipitated by Nazi beasts imbued with racism. The new adversary is paradoxically the scientist who is convinced that his detached efficiency inevitably operates for mankind's good. This new *Übermensch* feels qualified to trifle with life and destiny as long as *he* ascertains that it is for mankind's overall benefit.

This calculating arrogance of science is a contemporary threat, one in which certain forces are seeking an ideological change to make individuals expendable for mankind's supposed good. They are also seeking to by-pass informed consent as an unnecessary obstacle to supposedly efficient medical study. "This tendency of science to consider its mission solely to increase knowledge regardless of the use to which it is put has been implicit in many scientific articles," Dr. Herrman L. Blumgart stated in a clarion address to Harvard Medical School. "The fact, however, that social and ethical considerations must ever be kept in mind has rightfully aroused the public conscience and protests against human vivisection."

This perverted zeal for "science" is the onerous threat than can make any patient—infant, mature or aged—a vulnerable subject for the experimenter who sees himself as a crusader for the future, if not for the present, of humanity. Dr. Henry Beecher quotes a "distinguished scientist" who believes that "the individual is not infinitely valuable," and that the scientist has the *right* to choose martyrs "because more lives will be saved." Such a scientist is obviously insensitive to western life values, and may also be highly exaggerative about his ability to save life. This anticivilized argument was actually used by one of the Nazi doctors in defending himself at Nuremberg. When asked by the defendant if he would not purposely sacrifice a handful of humans for the future benefit of many, Dr. Andrew C. Ivy, the AMA's official observer, answered that he would not, in order "to maintain intact the method of doing good."

The detachment of many contemporary experimenter-doctors is one of the culpable evils, says Dr. William B. Bean. "The most praiseworthy zeal for knowledge may lead the man whose technical background overshadows his caring for the patient into a disregard for the subject of his researches," states Dr. Bean. "Thus, potentially dangerous experiments may be done without the subjects' knowledge or express permission. Whether it be thoughtlessness or heartlessness, such practice is a measure of the moral obliquity which exists in some places of research today."

The patient who has such an experimenter-researcher-scientist for a doctor may have no physician at all. Dr. O. E. Guttentag suggests that such a patient requires two doctors, one a physician-friend to act in his defense against the encroachment of the physician-experimenter. This unsettling imbalance in patient protection is an unfortunate part of the inevitable decline of the clinician-healer in the status ranks of medicine.

The adversary is virile and insistent, and in his "scientific" arrogance, convinced of his rightness. In an exchange in *Lancet,* a physician who had been attacked for using normal children as controls in a possibly hazardous experiment, answered that his "own working policy" was not to involve children in risk *unless* it could help "other children," the comment of the overdetached scientist. He was answered by an outraged Dr. Leys in a subsequent issue of *Lancet* to the effect that there is no justification for risking an injury to an individual for the possible benefit of other people. "Such a rule," he wrote, "would open the door wide to pervasions of practice, even such as were inflicted by Nazi doctors on concentration camp prisoners. The magnitude and crudity of their 'experiments' must not be allowed to blunt sensitivity to breaches of the medical ethic made on a smaller scale and with greater plausibility."

The entreaties of the emotionally detached are becoming louder and louder. The new FDA regulations which appear to prohibit experimentation with new drugs without consent, actually contain a facile evasion of the doctor's moral responsibility. After an edict that seems to require consent of the person before dosing him with an unproved drug, the watered legislation adds: ". . . except where they [the doctors] deem it not feasible or, in their professional judgment, contrary to the best interests of such human beings."

At a symposium on human experimentation, a University of California scientist included "the subject with fatal disease," in a list of potential experimental subjects. As *Ca* has already pointed out, this hapless group of the sick is currently being abused by scientists who believe such life is expendable. (The Nazis listed the senile and the incurably ill as candidates for mass euthanasia-murder.)

Dr. Beecher eloquently addresses himself to this foe. Stating that "responsible investigators are weary of such glib phrases as 'for the good of society,'" Dr. Beecher condemns the use of the incurable in human experiments except in therapeutic ones designed to benefit them. "Second, the use of the 'hopelessly incurable' as experimental subjects had developed recently," he says in *JAMA*. "I have already stated the reasons for my deep-seated conviction that those who are in imminent danger of death should not be subjected to experimentation, except as part of the therapeutic effort for the benefit of the subject himself. Occasionally, reports are found wherein use of the 'hopelessly incurable' seems to justify dangerous experimentation. The error in this appears evident. *It is not the physician's prerogative to make or to profit from such dubious judgments* [italics mine]." Dr. Guttentag adds his insight into the current callousness toward the "incurable": "As a matter of fact it creates the paradox that the healthier the patient, the more he should be the concern of his physician; the sicker, the less."

Admonition to the physician that he is not extralegal or extramoral has apparently been insufficient. Pope Pius, years ago, reminded physicians: "The doctor has no other rights or powers over the patient than those which the patient gives him, explicitly or implicitly and tacitly." The history of German doctors at Nuremberg and that of some contemporary American physicians involved in an unethical orgy of experimentation, has proved that relying on the conscience and professional ethics of supposedly specially conditioned individuals is *not* an effective deterrent to moral catastrophe.

The folly of society relying solely on such negated trust is the core of Dr. William B. Bean's argument. "At a time when ethical standards are high, or religion elevates moral tone, this situation would have other correctives. They are not effective today," he states in the *Journal of Laboratory and Clinical Medicine*. "The recent degradations of physicians in Nazi Germany exemplifies the decline and fall of a group whose moral obligations went by default in a single generation. The house would not have fallen had not many timbers been rotten. Descent into the gas chamber by doctors of infamy had its beginning in disregard for the patient. Never forget that the difference between an experiment on human beings without clear understanding and freely granted permission, and the determination of the M.L.D. [median lethal dose] in man is one of degree, not of kind. The patient, however humble and however ill, in whatever degree derelict and forlorn, has sacred rights which the physician must always put ahead of his burning curiosity."

We have already probed some of the areas of possible regulations, and others are being presented by deeply concerned groups. The *British Medical Journal* comments that "resistance to any kind of control has been obvious for sometime and has been growing." The authoritative journal recommends specific restrictions on human experiments. "Persons retained in prisons, penitentiaries or reformatories—being 'captive groups'—should not be used as subjects of experiments," the *BMJ* states. Likewise, they add, "persons retained in mental hospitals or hospitals for mental defectiveness should not be used for human experiments."

The Central Ethical Committee of the British Medical Association, apparently more interested in these issues than is their politically oriented American counterpart, have instructed British researchers to ask themselves, in essence, the following questions: "Does the patient know what it is I propose to do? Have I explained fully and honestly the risks I am asking him to run? Am I satisfied that his consent has been given freely and is legally valid? Is this procedure one I would not hesitate to advise or agree to if it were to be used on my wife and children? The *BMA*'s provisional code further states that *the patient must never take second place to a research project, and that no new technique be undertaken unless strictly necessary for the patient's treatment!*

The World Medical Association Draft Code prohibits the use of children in institutions (a favorite of American experimenters), but permits parents to give permission for the use of their children as subjects. The *New England Journal of Medicine* pricks at this easy assumption of parental privilege: "One may even question the moral legitimacy of such freedom, and in the light of present knowledge on the way in which parental responsibility is sometimes discharged, this could sometimes be of little value in protecting the rights of the individual."

Having examined evidence and sifted attitudes and counter-arguments, this author would be remiss unless he suggested a new comprehensive protective code for human experimentation that could be enacted into law and medical principle. Such a "Code of

Human Experimentation" (to be *added* to the Nuremberg rules) is offered as a basis for consideration, for all concerned, whether the American Medical Association, or state legislatures. Recourse to law, including imprisonment of the offender, is vital to the patient's protection.

1. No sick person—at home, in the doctor's office or in the hospital—may become a subject in a human experiment that is not designed *primarily and specifically for his own therapy*.

2. No sick child, sick newborn or hospitalized premature infant shall be the subject of any human experiment whatsoever that is not specifically and primarily designed for his benefit. No parent shall have the right to give such consent, nor shall any doctor have the right to request permission for such an experiment.

3. No well child, including hospitalized newborn infants, shall be the subject of any human experiment, including that of being a control in a controlled experiment, nor shall any parent have the right to give consent to a physician for this purpose. The only exception, with parental consent, shall be participation in experiments involving immunization, vaccines and other preventive measures for diseases involving children of the subject's age.

4. No child living in an institution—whether orphanage, home for the mentally defective or home for juvenile delinquents—shall ever be a subject for human experimentation not involving his therapy.

5. No known beneficial therapy shall ever be withheld from a sick patient as part of a human experiment unless a therapy considered superior is being offered in its place.

6. Subjects acting as controls in a controlled experiment shall not be penalized by receiving known inferior therapy or care.

7. No sanitary or aseptic condition shall be tampered with by the experimenter to produce a less than normal environment in the course of a human experiment involving sick, hospitalized or institutionalized patients.

8. No diagnostic technique not being used specifically for a particular patient's diagnosis shall be part of the human experiment involving a sick person.

9. No institutionalized mentally ill person shall be the subject of any human experimentation not involving his own therapy. If the experiment is primarily for his therapy, written permission must be granted by the subject himself and/or by his living relatives, and approved by the mental institution in writing.

10. Medical experiments done for the extension of knowledge rather than for a particular patient's therapy, must first be done, whenever possible, by the experimenter on himself before he shall be legally able to solicit other volunteers.

11. No member of the Armed Forces shall be permitted to participate in a human experiment of any kind not involving his own therapy or a preventive vaccine. Similarly, no prisoner of war shall be used for human experimentation.

12. Medical students who participate in human experiments must

be assured by the dean of that institution, in writing, that there is no coercion, nor any official gratitude or punishment involved in that participation.

13. To ensure informed consent of all adult volunteers in human experimentation, consent forms must contain extracts from medical articles summarizing the possible hazards involved in such experiments. Attached to the consent form must be descriptive material summarizing, in detail, what has been explained to the subject, with a signed statement by the physician that in his opinion the patient sufficiently understands the procedure and its implications to constitute "informed consent." All known and potential hazards must be listed in capital letters in such consent forms. In experiments involving more than two volunteers, such forms shall be countersigned by a higher medical authority (chief of medicine, hospital director) attesting that the experiment and the consent form have been approved by him. The American Bar Association should be invited by medical authorities to participate in the drawing up of a model consent form.

14. No experimental drug shall ever be given to a person without full disclosure of its potential hazards, in writing. In addition, there must be signed, informed consent of the subject.

15. No pregnant woman shall be used for any experimentation of any kind not specifically designed for her own therapy. Experimentation involving her therapy shall be approved by the head of the responsible medical institution.

16. Incurable patients and mortally ill patients shall in no way be considered different from other sick patients, and the full protection of ethics and law shall apply to them.

17. There shall be no extenuating circumstances of any kind in which the physician may experiment on a competent, conscious individual without first obtaining the subject's written consent.

The urgency of the situation in human experimentation allows little time for further erosion of medical responsibility. Until action is taken to restrain the poacher of patients' rights, the impetuous physician might do well to recall Hippocrates' prophetic aphorism:

> Life is short
> The Art long
> The occasion instant
> Decision difficult
> Experiment perilous.

Part II *Who Are the Doctors?*

Chapter VIII

The Doctor
As a Person:
The Non-Renaissance Physician,
His Conspicuous Leisure
and Declining Prestige

No one, aspiring corporate executive or exurbanite matron, is more concerned about his, or her, image than the American physician. Buoyed one day by a revelation from the National Opinion Research Center that after seventeen years his place in the national pecking order is still solidly second (bested only by the nine men on the Supreme Court), he works more assuredly, secure in the thought that his place as magical shaman has not yet been toppled. On other occasions his senses may tell him otherwise: that change is omnipresent. The vocal anti-doctor layman at a social gathering, the unfriendliness of some patients, complaints about fees and service, the awesome warnings about his personality and status uttered by his colleagues at medical lecterns, profoundly disturb his spirit.

All around him, he hears concern for his traditional high place among men. "I have seen the image of the doctor decline steadily to the point where the revered, respected and beloved family doctor has become in the eyes of the public merely a scientific technician, no different from any other skilled practitioner or trade." This chilling (to the physician) statement, made recently by Dr. Elmer Milch to the graduating house staff of Buffalo General Hospital, is symptomatic of a new medical self-consciousness. Dr. Milch is one of the probers who speaks of "mutual alienation" between patient and physician, in which "the patients called us machines, money grabbers; and we called them ingrates."

In this doctor-written argument the physician is the villain. "We have lost sight of the whole man, to whom we as physicians were obligated, and allowed ourselves to become impersonal practitioners of what had become an impersonal art," he charges. "And when the patient, the whole man, senses our lack of involvement, when his inarticulate spiritual needs demanded attention and we did not give it, he rebelled against us. He could not forgive in us that lack of involvement which had become the distinguishing characteristic of our society, for he came to us in time of need . . . But we, to whom the practice of medicine has become just such an everyday affair, could not comprehend this need and so could not answer it."

The most definitive statement on the physician's repute among his fellow men was made by an official AMA committee. After six months of research the Committee on Medical Practices, headed by Dr. Stanley R. Truman of California, reported back on the "public hostility to the profession," and the "public's disaffection with medicine." The medical investigators told their parent body: "For there is no question that public hostility toward the medical profession is mounting rather than diminishing."

The physician is troubled. He wants to know whether such dire diagnoses accurately reflect public opinion. Mr. Jacob J. Feldman of the National Opinion Research Center confirms this widespread professional nervousness over status. "It is feared that popular sentiments of distrust and hostility might be translated into unfriendly legislation or into some other undesirable consequences," he states. "Thus, there appears to be a great deal of anxiety among medical leaders concerning what people think of doctors."

The reality, or the mythology, of the doctor's loss of status is as fiercely debated as the involvement of cholesterol in heart disease. Literate commentator Dr. Lindsay E. Beaton, former president of the Arizona State Medical Association, is one of those who believes that the deterioration is true, if not justified. "No demonstration is needed to prove that the physician has found himself in a chillier climate of national opinion in recent years," Dr. Beaton states. "Traditionally he was not only respected for his professional skills but beloved for his personal relationships with those for whom he cared. He was the accepted symbol of selfless devotion to duty. Today, he has undergone what often seems to him like systematic and studied deprecation. Beneath the rapturous platitudes about medicine with which we regularly beguile ourselves, let us note a hard fact: many people now think of us as men concerned first with personal gain and only secondly with the welfare of the sick."

The din of professional self-reproach is almost as shrill as the complaints of annoyed patients. Dr. James A. Halstead of Detroit, Michigan adds his anxiety in the *New England Journal of Medicine:* "The diminishing prestige of the medical profession in the public eye is a matter that must concern the practicing physicians, medical educators and administrators, as well as the leaders of organized medicine." Dr. John S. DeTar, former president of the American Academy of General Practice, speaks of "untarnishing" the medical image. Dr. Charles H. Bradford, in addressing the Massachusetts Medical Society, did not spare his colleagues' pride of profession. "How have the doctors lost their prestige," he asks, speaking of the physicians' "former status" as a nostalgic memory of a simpler, better day for doctors.

Not every physician is willing to accept this diminution of doctor godhood. The renowned Dr. Edward D. Churchill, professor emeritus of surgery, Harvard Medical School, is one doctor who decries such defeatism. "On all sides I sense an apologetic self-derogatory mood in the profession and a lack of the conviction that should uphold the dignity and importance of the position of medicine in the contemporary culture," he told the Harvard Club in Boston. "So far as the 'tarnished image of the doctor' is concerned, this can be taken in its literal meaning. An image is an imitation or representation, not a directly perceived object. It is subject to distortion by the mind that forms it. Tarnish on the image of the doctor is as likely to be the product of the mind in which it is represented as a flaw in the doctor himself."

Are there "facts" to substantiate either view? Does the doctor still command the unquestioning respect and affection of America?

Even in the grand old days of medicine, from the turn of the century to World War II, the doctor's prestige was challenged. George Bernard Shaw, in the preface to his 1906 play, *The Doctor's Dilemma*, observed *"that hostility to the doctor as a man which exists and is growing as a result of the present condition of medical practice* [italics mine] *. . ."*

The American doctor's public stature was low until the early 1900's, when scientific medicine flourishing in Europe made its first conquests here. This advent of science, and the reported humanism of the early American physician instituted—despite Shaw—the doctor-patient *affaire d'amour* which has already become a legend in our curt, nervous culture with its dreams in the unhurried past.

The physician's repute has obviously fluctuated through history, but the man assigned to heal has always held a special place. Primitive medicine was a ritual in which the "doctor" was often part of the priestly or shaman class, and the incantation was as vital to the cure as the medicine.

In the crescent of civilization, Near Eastern medicine was intimately related to religious practice, and the region's philosophical bent produced the first set of medical ethics, the Hammurabic code. Although stern in its admonitions, it indicates the region's respect for the *successful* healer. Medical prestige was not based solely on "priestly" status, for this era of pre-Greek medicine had its share of scientific proficiency. Surgery, including plastic surgery, was practiced in Egypt and India, and the Chinese reportedly developed a form of smallpox immunization as well as therapeutic drugs, including heart stimulants from the skin of toads.

Hippocrates' teaching that illness was natural, not supernatural, changed the course of history, and put doctor prestige on a more rational basis. After Hippocrates, the physicians were taught the "Hippocratic Corpus," which stressed not only the importance of clinical observation but the vital human relationship between healer and patient.

Greek physicians, under the sign of the still-symbolic snaked staff, had banded together in the "Sons of Aesculapius." Their strength of organization was passed down as the medical guilds of medieval times. Three "doctor" guilds eventually developed in Europe, with the university-trained "physicians" at the status top, followed by the apothecaries and then the barber-surgeons, who learned their trade as apprentices. The spectacular prestige rise of surgeons in the twentieth century is evidence of the changing fashions of medical status.

Unlike the teacher and clergyman, whose services were customarily paid collectively through contributions or taxation, the doctor evolved in the commercial fee-for-service mold. He was paid by the sick patient or his family, as he dispensed his services. This payment method of "fee for service" has had a powerful, continuing effect on the doctor's status. The wealth it often developed placed him high in the standing of men. But simultaneously it created the constant nagging complaint that he was money-craving and capitalizing on sickness, a charge that has continually dogged his prestige.

Few doubt the contemporary doctor's excessive money involvement, but it is edifying to learn that the same status threat was leveled at him in ancient times. Plato said of the "Ideal Physician" of his day: "No physician, insofar as he is a physician, considers his own good in what he prescribes, but the good of the patient; for the true physician is also a ruler having the human body as a subject, and is not a mere moneymaker."

Does the contemporary American doctor still carry the magical mantle of high public repute? Our culture attempts to answer such questions statistically. In 1955 the ever-anxious American Medical Association employed Ben Gaffin and Associates, Inc., of Chicago to survey what patients thought about doctors. They polled three thousand people and established one uncontested fact: people think better of their own doctors than they do of doctors in general. The AMA-sponsored survey found satisfied patients, who felt that their own physicians ("my doctor") were "capable" (99 percent); "intelligent" (98 percent); "personally interested" (87 percent); "gives enough time" (81 percent); "frank with me" (80 percent). The typical patient was quite complimentary about his own physician, with a telltale minority protesting about his doctor's arrogance and unavailability during emergencies.

When asked the same questions about "most doctors," the startling contrast explained the recent dire pronouncements on the doctor's declining prestige. The collective physician was drawn in a less sanguine, even an ugly profile. A majority of patients felt slighted by "most doctors" for their lack of frankness (58 percent); their short-cutting of patients' time (70 percent); their absence during emergencies (51 percent).

The meager minority who had criticized their own physician now swelled in size when asked about *most doctors*. Comments on "snobbery" grew from 5 to 25 percent; the ranks of those who complained of doctor arrogance grew from 23 to 43 percent; criticism of doctors for being "too quick to recommend an operation" went up *sixfold*, from 5 to 31 percent; critiques on lack of dedication rose from 6 to 27 percent. While patients had little distrust for their own doctor's money policies, opinion that doctors are "get-rich-quick" artists tripled. The indictment by those who thought doctors charged "too much" grew to 43 per cent of all patients.

The AMA-sponsored survey has constructed a not-too-clever rationale to explain away the negative opinion. "People's attitudes toward their own doctors are based upon their own personal experiences, while their attitudes toward doctors in general must necessarily be based upon secondary information and hearsay," the report argues. Their conclusion is face-saving, but highly illogical. Aside from his present physician, the typical adult has had a plethora of personal experiences with other doctors—from the GP to the pediatrician to the subspecialist—involving both himself and his family. This, rather than hearsay, is undoubtedly the base for his attitudes toward "most doctors." His complimentary attitude toward his chosen physician is equally logical: if he weren't satisfied, he would have changed doctors!

Sophistry can twist negative figures, but the AMA could as easily have exploited other surveys which appear to confirm the physician's high repute. The National Opinion Research Center, under sponsorship of the Health Information Foundation, sampled twenty-four hundred adults. Their conclusion, from the anxious doctor's viewpoint, was uplifting: although "doctors are obviously not blindly worshipped," most people do believe that "the good qualities of doctors seem to outweigh their faults by a rather substantial margin."

The dissenters in the NORC study comprise a robust minority: 37 percent felt doctors did not take a personal interest in them; 34 percent thought doctors liked to dispense medicines, even if they weren't needed: *half* of those polled felt doctors did not sufficiently explain things to patients.

Those wedded most closely to the American physician—the sick—like him the least, the NORC study reveals. "We also find that those who consider themselves to be in poor health are more critical of doctors than those who consider themselves in better health," Mr. Feldman of the NORC states. "Familiarity actually seems to breed contempt. The frequent users of medical care have had a far greater exposure to the risk of occurrence of exasperating experiences with the medical establishment." Apparently, to use and to know the doctor is to respect him less.

The aged, too, tend to respect doctors less, according to the NORC. This gap is attributed to the lower income and education of the aged, and their sicknesses, which are generally chronic. Living out life's last chapter with incurable ailments that require expensive and constant medical management, they would inevitably be more cynical toward doctors than the young and healthy, who may still naïvely view the physician as a "miracle worker."

For those who can assimilate public-opinion polls without statistical indigestion, there are two more of significance. One partially compliments the patient's own doctor but castigates doctors in general. The other deplores the contemporary doctor's lack of warmth. In 1962 the Opinion Research Corporation, under the aegis of the American Academy of General Practice, found that 75 percent of a sample thought their own medical care was "good."

Surprisingly, queries about their doctor's specific traits triggered more introspective and less sanguine answers. Only 53 percent thought he was "competent"; less than half (45 percent) thought he "explains everything thoroughly"; almost half (44 percent) thought he was not generally glad "to help in an emergency"; and more than half (55 percent) could not honestly state that their physician's doctoring was a soothing force—that it "makes you feel better just talking to him."

In this same ORC study—significantly, the latest one available—the much-discussed declining prestige of the "average" doctor is finally revealed in broad statistical strokes. The numbers represent patients ulcerously angered by the doctor's motives and manners. Most patients in this doctor-sponsored poll saw the "average" medical healer as *an insincere, undedicated and somewhat unethical professional*. A small minority (24 percent) agreed with the amicable comment that the "average physician" was "sincerely devoted to his work." Even fewer (18 percent) would substantiate that he was "completely ethical in his dealings"!

Dr. Earl Koos (Ph.D.) polled a thousand random-sampled families in "Metropolis," the fictional euphemism for a city with a 350,-000 population in the industrial Northeast. The cost of medical care was not attacked, nor was the quality of care. The chief complaint of most of the patients (64 percent) was that the physicians of Metropolis lacked "human warmth," a precious commodity they related to old-time practitioners.

This hunger for the compassionate doctor is apparently not restricted to oldsters who might remember a slower, more human age. "Those who are defensive regarding criticisms of modern medical care," states Dr. Koos in the *American Journal of Public Health,* "have been known to charge that this attitude exists only among the older age groups who view the passing of the family doctor with nostalgia. Our data do not bear this out, for the respondents in the families with husbands under forty years of age were even more definite in this criticism than were those in the older age group." A young matron is quoted as typical of the disaffected. "We are new at this [raising a family]," she told the surveyors. "If we could feel that we mean something to Dr. _____, I'd be happy with him. But I'm sure he has to look at baby's history, or have his nurse tell him who we are, so he'll know what to call me."

Sadly but affirmatively, doctors concur with these pessimistic insights into their fading aura. When polled about *what they thought others think of them,* the physicians felt compelled to nod agreement. The *Medical Tribune* polled eleven hundred physicians, headlining the results: "Many MD's Not Happy About Their Public Image." Ninety percent had checked "Yes" on the query whether their image needed improving.

Some doctors have avoided responsibility for their lowered prestige, lashing out at scapegoats: the press, the labor unions, and government, or faulty public relations techniques. Others maturely placed the fault directly at their own feet. "Too many physicians 'show off' their wealth and too few have compassion for the fellow men," complained one Indiana GP. A Michigan surgeon felt the decline in group prestige was the result of competitive physician-sniping. "Most people still have confidence in 'their' doctor," he says. "However, too many of their doctors encourage them to believe that no other doctor in town is worth a damn." An Illinois obstetrician charged the prestige decline to doctor's lack of community interest. "They have time for sports cars and pilot training and golf but never an hour for the Red Cross, Boy Scouts, or other agencies," he berated his colleagues.

Their remedies for a better prestige prognosis were encyclopedic, ranging from more liberal socio-political values and more democracy in their medical association to whirlwind public relations maneuvers in which doctors should "take advantage" of the intimate doctor-patient relationship to discuss the physicians' viewpoints directly with the patient. An Indiana ophthalmologist countered these massive PR proposals with an unsophisticated, but warmly radiating and internally acting therapy for early-diagnosed declining prestige. "Just take good care of patients, day by day," says the sage eye doc, "and no other 'public relations' is needed."

If physician prestige is really threatened, the skeptic could ask, "How does the M.D. manage to score so brilliantly on the occupational status scale, nudging close to the select nine of the Supreme Court?" One explanation is that the profession of healing is too honored, too filled with the magic and awe of creation and oblivion for it to be denigrated *in spite* of its present practitioners. To this school of thought, the decline in doctor prestige is not an inevitable sociological fact, but a product of the doctor as a person. Rather than a complex status change triggered by technology, the declining prestige of the American physician is thus an obvious result of a shift in the doctor himself. From a societal leader, intellectually and humanly, he has changed to what he may well be today, a man of mediocre intellect, trade school mentality, limited interests and incomplete personality—the contemporary Non-Renaissance Man.

The history of the doctor teaches us that the Greeks stressed the importance of human relationship and nature in healing. The mechanistic viewpoint of man and medicine has its philosophical origin in Descartes, whose *Méthode* is unknowingly the model of today's confident young physician. "We should busy ourselves with no object about which we cannot attain a certitude equal to that demonstrated by arithmetic and geometry," said the brilliant seventeenth-century thinker.

The twentieth-century success of medicine, following Cartesian logic, is obvious. However, death and disease still have not yielded to science, and man is and will always be vulnerable. From his training and his goals the modern physician is dominated by Cartesian mechanism, and the humane Hippocratic ideal is submerged. While the modern doctor may pretend to be *certain,* the art of medicine, which translates the science to the patient through a fallible human—the doctor—is not.

The importance of the doctor *as a man* is probed by Dr. Edmund D. Pellegrino, chairman of the department of medicine at the University of Kentucky, who sees a philosophical failing in today's doctor that impedes healing. For medicine "to fulfill its potentials," he states, "it requires an idea of man which will more satisfactorily equal the requirements of both the scientific mode of thought and the needs of the person." The humanities, especially philosophy, are the obvious bridges. Dr. Pellegrino asks for a "new and closer relationship between medicine and philosophy in the formal sense," the "happy confluence" which contributed to the greatness of Hippocratic medicine.

To fulfill his critical function in medicine, the doctor must change radically as a person, he believes. "To participate in this reconciliation between medicine as a science and the dominant ideas in our culture would require a fundamental reorientation in medical education and practice," Dr. Pellegrino writes in the *Annals of the American Academy of Political and Social Science*. "But more important would be the growth of the physician himself as a person. His own idea about the nature of man can seriously impede his contact with the person behind the symptom complex he encounters in the examining room."

Dr. Frank Pignataro, former president of the New Jersey Neuropsychiatric Association, sees the failure in the personality of the doctor as an extreme one. As we have seen, he fears that the "personality of today's physicians has been deteriorating in an alarming fashion." While conceding the scientific triumph of this century, he adds: "Humanly speaking, we have, if anything, fallen back."

What are the human traits which make for the true healer? "Ahead of all others," says Dr. Pignataro in *Journal of the Student American Medical Association,* "I postulate equanimity, devotion, warmth, and empathy. To the development of those qualities, the long years of scientific training, after the premedical course, contributes, as of today, nothing! Yet, I estimate the personality of the physician as being at least as important to the making of a true healer as his scientific education."

These healing traits can be restated as "sensitivity" and "idealism," the blossoms of a civilized society. In a sense these motivations are spiritual, which would bring the ideal physician closer to the clergyman than to the scientist. The analogy is apt, since the family physician eventually ministers to the death of his patients—who he may naïvely think have been failed by science. "If medicine is to regain its former status, it must resume its service of friendship," says Dr. Charles H. Bradford of Boston, adding his formula for regeneration: "It must renew its personal interest in the patient, and it must reaffirm its faith in the mission to give life and give it more abundantly. Though medicine is scientific, life is spiritual."

To contemplate the spiritual facet of his job, the physician must have an affinity for idealism, a quality that is not extolled in much of modern medicine. Some physicians insist that they can be no better than the society in which they live, which is a facile excuse for failure of needed dedication to the patient. "The physician's prime moral obligation is to his patient," Dr. Zale Yanof states in *JAMA,* "which includes nothing less than complete devotion, conscientious attention, and sustained diligence to the task of healing, together with rendering and procuring of the best available medical care. Anything less would be as immoral as an act of theft, and in some situations even worse." Those physicians who have rationalized their failure of idealism because of "justifiable" self-interest have been anticipated by Dr. Yanof: "His moral obligation to society must transcend his own personal interest and vested or selfish group interest."

"Many doctors just don't give a damn," says Dr. Samuel Standard of New York. "Because of their training, they see the person as merely the patient in Bed #4. The doctor has never taken the time to sit and talk with people. This type of physician is a 'Sears, Roebuck' doctor, a one-dimensional man. I'm afraid that too many doctors hate people, or are indifferent to them. It is a failing of human feeling, and of the medical art."

This growing failing is undoubtedly related to what Dr. Homer L. Pearson, past chairman of the AMA Judicial Council, calls the "commercialism" and "callousness" of the younger physician. "In my job with the Florida Board of Medical Examiners, I've seen hundreds of young doctors enter medicine," he states in a recent medical-publication essay. "And the thing that has disturbed me most about them in recent years is this: Too many are in the medical business rather than in medical practice." Dr. Pearson cautiously ponders whether he is alone in his misgivings about the emotional trend in medicine: "If I were the only one observing this callousness in young doctors, I'd be inclined to temper my observation. But other doctors notice it too . . ." The timely confirmation is provided by the medical publication itself, which queried thirty-three other members of state boards of medical examiners, unearthing *only one* physician who disagreed with Dr. Pearson.

Hippocrates authored a timeless aphorism: "Wherever the art of medicine is loved, there also is the love of humanity." If his comment is accurate, the contemporary physician may not only be indifferent to mankind, but to medicine as well. A prominent urological surgeon who has earned solid professional repute before the age of forty, finds too many doctors unenamored with medicine. "My hobby is urology, and I do a good job as a doctor as a by-product of my hobby. Most doctors, as far as I can see, have a hobby of golf. It is a personal insult to me to have any of my patients die, and I will get up in the middle of the night to save them. Another of my hobbies is to be right, and my eight residents know it. If they did not have medicine as their hobby, and were not good enough, I'd fire them."

When the love of medicine and the love of mankind mate they conceive the perfect, if rare, doctor. Such a physician knows that the display of warmth is vital to healing, even if it is a neglected medical truism. Dr. Nathan K. Rickles of Beverly Hills, California, reminded his colleagues at an AMA convention that "a display of warmth and reassurance to the human being whom we treat is as essential to his ultimate welfare as the 2,500-odd laboratory tests and drugs used so widely and not always so wisely." With the dehumanized medical attitude of today, he laments, hope has become a "stepchild."

The doctor's considerate, tender loving *care* has always been the symbol of empathetic sustenance of the sick. Unfortunately, the methods of medical selection and education have helped to produce, says Professor Sol Bloom of the Downstate Medical Center, a physician whose "good attitudes" have been destroyed and replaced by the "bad" ones of cynicism and loss of humanity. The doctor thus passes the "thin line" that separates his cherished "objective" scientific attitude from crass detachment.

Emotionally unarmed, the doctor may be unable to dispense proper medical care. The term "crock," a satanic description of someone about to die, is, say medical critics, evidence of such attitudes. Dr. John V. Fopeano, in a guest editorial in *Michigan Medicine*, says it is cruel to use the word "crock" to describe a complaining hospital patient "for whom the speaker feels little can be done, and with whom he doesn't feel comfortable." He adds: "More often than not it refers to someone who is not well understood, for whom there is no sympathy . . . He is a person who is thought to be beyond the reach of medicine in its present state of knowledge and development."

Dr. Richard C. Miller of Dayton, Ohio, who has been in practice for over twenty-eight years, attacks what he believes is a shocking lack of compassion in the typical younger doctor. "Humility and Compassion—Why Hast Thou Forsaken Us?" is the title of his impressive diatribe against the coldness of his younger colleagues— what he calls the "sham" and "shame" of the modern practitioner.

"Young doctors of today have no humility. They set themselves up as medical gods who can do no wrong," the experienced practitioner complains in the journal *GP*. "The globes in the orbits are satellites with dollar signs and dreams of foreign cars, fattened money clips, ranch homes and estates which they hope to own by simply preying on Homo sapiens . . ." The new doctor, the outspoken veteran charges, does "not know the meaning of compassion."

In his spirited annoyance, Dr. Miller draws a psychological thumbnail profile of the doctor's inadequacy: "He is a laboratory fanatic with no inner feeling for humans. He finds it easy to criticize, is unshakable in his opinions and lives on an inflated ego believing he is the master of medical knowledge and he has all the answers. Instead he is a downright fool but he won't believe it because the dollar signs have beclouded his vision as well as his thinking. Why are so many young men like this?"

Dr. Miller supplies his own succinct answers: 1. Many doctors enter the noble profession because they can make money. 2. The young doctor is lazy and self-centered. 3. The medical schools do not teach the human side of medicine. In a plea atypical for a physician, he calls out: "Members of the Hippocratic legion must rally to our tottering cause before it is too late."

The absence of compassion, or even empathy, in many modern doctors is becoming increasingly obvious to observers, although some physicians fight fiercely to retain the noble characteristics. Unfortunately, the recognition that they have lost compassion comes belatedly to many doctors, often only after an illness of their own breaks through the velvet cord of affluence, status and "science" with which they have isolated themselves from the realities of normal society and human emotion.

"About a year ago I had a hemorrhoidectomy," one now-sympathetic doctor, a Norwich (Connecticut) physician, writes in a medical publication. "You can't realize the experience of the first bowel movement after such surgery unless you have gone through it yourself. Now I'm in full sympathy with my hemorrhoidectomy cases," he confesses.

To the untutored, admonitions against emotional "detachment" are meaningless, and the modern physician may well be untutored in the things of the spirit. A nonreligious society such as ours can hardly expect religious devotion of its physicians. But modern society hopes that absorption of the humane arts and letters will bring each man—and doctor—into greater contact with the more eternal, and less with confining, pursuits.

How immersed is today's doctor in the enriching arts and letters that might stretch his idealism? Galen, the Roman physician whose repute is second only to Hippocrates, was the author of an address: "That The Good Physician is a Philosopher." How much the philosopher is the contemporary doctor?

The answer to both questions is: "Hopelessly little." Although once our most learned professional, the modern doctor-technician may well be the least intellectually articulate, the least creative, the least philosophically developed of all professionals of all time. Law, science and the clergy continue to contribute philosophers and humanists of note (whether Einstein, Tillich, Oppenheimer or Learned Hand), while the medical profession moves ever closer to non-Renaissance concepts of narrow interests.

At the New York Public Library, an exhibit called "Physicians As Men of Letters" leaned heavily on the golden past of physician-artists such as Arthur Conan Doyle. It spanned five centuries of physician-humanists, back before Dr. Richard Blackmore, Fellow of the College of Physicians in London, who in 1697 published his work *King Arthur, an Heroick Poem in Twelve Books*. An exhibit of contemporary American physicians deeply involved in the arts would be a barren display virtually restricted to Frank G. Slaughter, especially since the passing of the product of another age, seventy-nine-year-old pediatrician-poet Dr. William Carlos Williams.

Only a small minority in the profession seek to broaden the young doctor. A prominent New York physician of the older humanist school, Dr. Samuel Standard, then chief of surgery at Morrisania Hospital, insisted that trainees did not talk about medicine during the regular Friday afternoon *Kaffeeklatsch* he held in his office. "Everything else—from literature to politics—was permitted, but no medical business," says Dr. Standard.

The doctor's dearth of intellectuality has been noticed, and deplored. Speaking to a West Virginia state medical convention, Perry Gresham, president of Bethany College, asked the physician to set a personal example to lift the intellectual level of the Mountain State. "There is as much relaxation in reading such classics as *The Republic, The Prince, The Wealth of Nations,* and *The Essay on Liberty* as there is in reading Ellery Queen," he told the doctors. "The Pirates and the Redlegs, the Mountaineers and The Steelers are very important, but no more important than the Shakespeare Festivals and university convocations. The discipline of writing material fit to publish and conversation worthy to be remembered are part of the essential role for today's man in white."

This suspicion that most doctors are intellectually undernourished is continually being verified by professional observers. Physicians are seldom noted for their broad intellect or nonmedical academic brilliance. (While IQ's have almost no individual predictive value, group IQ's are somewhat descriptive of classes of people. The modern medical student has a median IQ of 126, which, although quite high for a group, is lower than several other postgraduates', including those studying English, chemistry, mathematics and physics.) Dr. Myron Prinzmetal, director of the Institute for Medical Research, Cedars of Lebanon Hospital, sees greater intellectual nourishment as the cure for the doctor's prestige woes. "A half-hour's good reading before bed each night is not only relaxing but can be inspiring to us all and make us better men," he writes in a *Medical Trib-une* editorial. "This habit, once established, will give us great pleasure. Our patients will grow to respect us more, and the wise will learn to love us. Even the ignorant will notice a change." He concludes hopefully: "With such a program, possibly in a few years the present unpleasant attitude toward our profession will gradually disappear."

For those physicians bent on self-improvement this is his sugges-tion for a half-hour-a-day reading program: first Sir William Osler, the medical prophet; then the Holy Writ; Shakespeare; Montaigne; Epictetus; Marcus Aurelius; Sir Thomas Browne's *Religio Medici, Christian Morals* and *Letter to a Friend; The Wonderful Life of Pasteur* with an introduction by Osler; and Cushing's *Life of Osler.*

A few physicians, aware of the cultural impoverishment of their closed medical world, are making attempts, albeit feeble, to remedy it. In Ohio one county medical society had created a series of twelve Thursday evening lectures, a "Cultural Seminar for Physicians," in collaboration with Youngstown University. It would be insensi-tive to ridicule such well-meaning attempts, but loftier horizons than the lecture-and-coffee circuit should be contemplated. William Carlos Williams, who published a volume of his poetry while still an interne at the French Hospital in New York in 1907, might be a model for the doctor who fears the affluent morass of medical commercialism. "As a writer, I have been a physician, and as a physician, a writer," Dr. Williams said.

In a *JAMA* editorial, "The Educated Doctor," Dr. Douglas Knight, president of Lawrence College, speaks of the physician's necessity to "know something in depth about the patterns of his world and the inner nature of his patients." The doctor, he says, "has, in short, an obligation to wisdom, for . . . these are the things which a liberal education at its best can give him and must give him, and they are more needed in the relentless profession of medi-cine than almost anywhere else in our society."

The physician's typical answer has been "we are too busy for such things." This caterwaul of pardon has been so successful that many educated patients believe it, and thus expect little wisdom or humanity from their busy "scientist" doctor. The truth is less awe-some, as we have seen. The average physician's working day is less than ten hours on a six-day basis, and a little over ten hours on a five-and-a-half-day week *including* spare time spent on con-tinuing education, journals, reports, conventions, etc. Several of the specialties, such as dermatology, are approaching banker's habits. Wednesday and weekends off are no longer unusual in the profes-sion at large, and evening work hours continue to atrophy. Many executives and other professionals, especially those who commute, are as busily—or more—occupied than doctors. Yet the doctor's camouflage of busyness has accomplished a most effective propaganda victory that has smoothly excused his abysmal failure of intellect.

The true portrait of many a private-practice doctor's non-work life is one of passionate leisure, exercised with great care and at great cost. It is a conspicuously affluent personal life, most of which avoids the intellectual and feeds the pretentious, the escapist and the mundane. The modern physician is too often a leader of upper-middle-class tastes, of non-intellectualism, of showy habits, of country club and supersuburban mentality.

A conformist by training (and perhaps nature), this physician is an ardent member of a golden clique, following his medical colleagues from country club to yacht basin, to top-ticket Broadway hits, to overpriced developments, to sports car salesrooms, to private airports, to every possible costly and conspicuous outlet for his energies. Doctors, more than any other occupational class, wallow in living *big*. His life image, rather than being one of constantly occupied healer or even one of preoccupied scientist, is that of a man confident of his social class and exercising its prosaic, monied privileges—as if this were not only his prerogative as a successful physician and social leader, but his actual destiny.

The doctor's income, and his desire to present a *class* image, is warmly welcomed by everyone in the nation with high-ticket items to sell. He is the customer of preference, whether the item be mutual funds or $75,000 houses. Whatever the sylvan titles of superpriced acreage and home developments—whether Country Estates or Rolling Hills, whether erected in Sands Point, Scarsdale or Beverly Hills—the American physician is a prime buyer of the conspicuous household. Real estate salesmen confirm doctor home-buying habits, and some are ecstatic about his desire for a more-than-comfortable hearth. "Of all the fifty- to eighty-thousand-dollar homes that I sell," says a broker in Great Neck and Sands Point, the elegant North Shore area on Long Island, "forty percent of them are sold to doctors."

Once the professional with the lowest leisure bent (or opportunity), physicians are now a mainstay of the new leisure class, patronizing each of its sleekest manifestations, from country clubs to private yachts and planes. The yacht clubs and marinas of the nation are choked with physicians' boats: power yachts of every size and description, and sailboats, generally with auxiliary engines to provide less work and more rest. "Physicians seldom use sailboats, but they are big buyers of powerboats, mostly for family cruising," says a partner in one of the nation's largest yacht sales firms. "In fact, doctors and dentists account for twenty-five percent of all our power-boat sales."

A check of yacht clubs reveals that anywhere from 10 to 20 percent of their memberships are made up of physicians, including a surgeon who serves as the "commodore" ("president" to landlubbers) of one of the nation's most exclusive sailing clubs. One yacht club official states that "many of the biggest boats are owned by doctors," including giant seventy-footers which require sailing crews of eleven to fourteen. (The typical physician is more likely to own a twenty-five- to forty-five-foot inboard cabin cruiser.)

The other end of the doctor's leisure axis is his second home, the country club. At the "club" the physician has friendship at the upper-social-class level to which he and his wife aspire, fine dining, swimming and tennis for his family, and most vital—golf. The origins of physician golf-o-mania are shrouded in history, but no one can deny his contemporary addiction to the status sport. The typical American country club has a sizable minority of doctor members, from 5 up to 35 percent of its total membership, most of whom actively use their green privileges.

When the AMA visited New York for its 1965 convention, three hundred of its doctor-members were simultaneously having their own convention—the 49th Annual Tournament of the American Medical Golf Association on the links of Winged Foot Golf Club in Mamaroneck, New York.

The "image" activities attract physicians the most readily. Many a young post-resident has purchased a foreign sports car as ready evidence for himself and society that he is no longer a deprived and monastic trainee. (According to one dealer, doctor habits in foreign car purchases change with fashion. Currently the Saab, Porsche and Mercedes-Benz lead over the British and French entries.) The more expensive and zenith-status leisure activity of private-plane ownership occupies some two thousand doctor-pilots, all members of the Flying Physicians Association. Although an occasional doctor uses the plane to reach remote outposts, as in Alaska or the West, it is purely a leisure activity with most doctors, including many who fly in princely fashion to the AMA convention every year in their own planes.

Doctor-fliers are somewhat outside the common mold of the physician. More typically, the doctor is an unadventurous soul seeking leisure and rest with little original content. (Generalizations demand exceptions. The medical one is possibly the surgeon, often a more daring athletic type who may enjoy the physically—if not intellectually—unique activity. A Florida plastic surgeon, for example, recently bagged the rare Ethiopian ibex.) "We deal with a lot of doctors," says a spokesman for Fugazy, the prominent travel agency.

"They enjoy traveling, and do a lot of it, but not to out-of-the-way places. They are not big adventurers or explorers. Safaris to Africa, trips to India, or behind the Iron Curtain, are not their speed. The typical doctor goes to Europe or the Caribbean by jet plane. An increasing number of doctors are making the European grand tour. The trips are sometimes expensive, but they are not splurgers. They spend, but they are very picky about it. They watch every dollar carefully."

(Many of those who do business with doctors, including management consultants, attorneys, travel agents and car salesmen, openly state their opinion that although the typical physician spends considerable sums, he does it extremely carefully. Some service people interviewed went so far as to call doctors "cheap." Others more generously attribute their strange money habits to their training of methodology, their years of penury, and the fear of a poor retirement.)

Physicians have become an increasingly important segment of the burgeoning travel market. When a physician's wife had difficulty renting a home in Europe, she opened a European home-rental agency for vacationing Americans. "At Home Abroad," headquartered in New York, now rents anything from a *palazzo* on the Grand Canal for $5000 for the summer, to a small villa in Nice for $250 a month. Its overwhelming success is to a large extent due to doctor-customers, who take 25 percent of all their European rentals. "The typical doctor rents a house in Europe with servants for one full month for between eight and fifteen hundred dollars," a spokesman explained. "They seem to like the idea of a house in Europe, for a recent notice in an AMA newspaper drew inquiries from a thousand doctors. In fact, an item about our service in a Sunday supplement recently drew four thousand answers, twenty percent of which were from physicians."

The month in Europe, once a vain, impossible wish for the busy doctor, is now virtually typical as doctor vacation periods keep stretching beyond the layman's two weeks. A recent *Medical Tribune* survey revealed that the largest percentage of doctors took three week's vacation, not including weekends, and that 15 percent took off more than one month. A pharmaceutical-house survey of physicians shows 24 percent with a month or more vacation.

As buyers of higher-priced leisure, the physicians also indulge in local interests, such as Broadway musicals in the New York area, a status-enjoyment visiting physicians find equally irresistible. "Many physicians have charge accounts with us," says a spokesman for Mackey's, a leading ticket broker. "Doctors enjoy the theater, and I think that second to golf, it's their favorite relaxation. They can go and forget themselves for a couple of hours. They buy only the best orchestra seats, from eight twenty-eight to eleven thirty-eight including our commission. When the AMA convention was here last summer, we did a land-office business with doctors."

Some physicians are content with conspicuous affluence that impresses their upper-middle-class acquaintances and neighbors. Others are intent on social striving, hoping to convert their professional repute and incomes into class climbing among the wealthy. One critic, Dr. Gerald M. Feigen, once named San Francisco's "Citizen of the Year," inveighs against the too-frequent hobnobbing by doctors with the rich. This habit, which he calls "too rich for a physician," can, he says, "often get the physician in trouble." Writing in a medical column, Dr. Feigen warns the doctor-striver: "The problem is one of identification. When a physician identifies with the very rich and very social, he's apt to be trapped in a way of life he cannot afford. He winds up in a world that's too rich for his blood. And medicine is poorer for it."

He relates the story of a doctor and his wife who are invited out to the yacht of a wealthy industrialist, and "learn to like the feel of the big jobs sailing out the harbor while they lounge on deck." The results, he fears, can be to treat too many patients and charge too much, just to "keep up."

Much of this golden cliquishness may stem from doctor failure to find continuous challenge in his own work, pushing him to seek escape in conspicuous leisure. One California physician speaks of the challenge lagging "when you reach your late thirties or early forties," at which time, he states in a medical publication, "another ten patients—another five hundred dollars—it begins to have less and less meaning." His lagging spirit took him through the doctor's leisure loop—golf, bridge, dahlias, stocks and bonds. After that he found the answer: community service, a remedy he offers to other physicians. (Naïve patients might have thought that medical practice was a "community service.")

Non-community activities of physicians continue to prosper, including the leisure business of trading in stocks and bonds. The average doctor's investment in stocks is high, but several brokers believe doctor activity in the market is understated.

"I have handled the account of about twenty-five doctors," says a customers' man in New York's Pan American Building. "By and large I find them to be heavy investors. The great preponderance of their accounts is over two hundred thousand dollars." Another stockbroker has dealt with "a half dozen physicians," each of whom was an investor of $100,000 or more. "They are heavy investors," he says, "mainly because doctors generate an awful lot of money. However, they are babes in the woods when it comes to investing, and they'll buy any 'cat and dog' if someone has a convincing story.

Their perspective is narrow and unsophisticated. In a classic case where an investor is sold a bill of goods, the customer is likely to be a doctor. I know of one physician who was sold ten thousand dollars' worth of 'toilet paper'—stock in an invention of some kind. I was horrified. I would say that if someone has something to sell, doctors are 'preferred' as investors. They have new money all the time, and some of them are greedy."

Some physicians' tendency to try to turn a quick investment dollar is verified by a midtown customers' man. "Doctors will listen to any financial pitch," he says. This is further corroborated by a stock management service, which handles investors' accounts with power of attorney. "We have many doctor-customers. They make up about 15 percent of all our accounts," he points out. "The average portfolio we handle is between twenty-five to thirty-five thousand dollars, but doctors' portfolios generally run higher, about a fifty-thousand dollar average. I have found that many doctors are speculators. I think that's because they have available money and get it so fast. Some feel insecure about the future, and want to get rich quick. Some doctors even invest for three to six months to make enough money to pay their tax bill with the profit. During the big new issue phase in 1961, the doctors were the most gullible buyers. They bought almost anything, even if it was sold by phone or door-to-door. Once they enroll with us, however, their speculation days are over."

One pathologist who boasts that he "has never owned a share of stock" considers the physicians' stock fever anti-medicine. "For every piece of stock a doctor owns, that much less is he a doctor," he states. "When I go past the hospital cafeteria at breakfast time, I see all the doctors with their papers open to the stock page. Perhaps they should be busily reading medical journals." He describes a physician who intimately knew the price-earning ratio of hundreds of stocks, but was ignorant of the pressure intricacies of a respirator for infants he was using. "The wrong pressure would blow the child's lungs out," the pathologist adds sorrowfully.

The doctor's compulsion to exploit his majestic cash flow, has taken several of them into what one management consultant calls "side-line fever." Allison E. Skaggs, the prominent management consultant of Battle Creek, Michigan, is not complimentary about doctors' business acumen outside their own bailiwick. He has seen doctors get involved in orange groves, trampolines, bowling alleys, farms, air taxis, auto agencies, motels and hamburger stands, and adds that "nearly all" lost their money.

Doctors tend to be more successful in side lines connected with medicine, such as interest in medical buildings, nursing homes, proprietary hospitals and drugstores. Doctor ownership of, or investment in, several thousand drugstores has been a lucrative source of extra money. One doctor-owned pharmacy in Los Angeles netted $90,000 in one year on a $10,000 inventory. Such doctor holdings have been declared illegal in California as of June, 1967, but the AMA and physician-investors are fighting a holding battle elsewhere to continue to make profit on both sides of the prescription. Nursing homes have always been an active site of doctor investment, and may now become more attractive with Medicare coverage. "We turned twenty-thousand dollars into a four-hundred-thousand-dollar nursing home" boast two internists who built a beautiful 125-bed facility in West Virginia.

Is there a significant break in the doctor's non-Renaissance image, which has cast him as the technician-businessman with matching tastes and aspirations? Is there any field in which the doctor is the dedicated, magnificent amateur, the humanist and individualized participant that marks one as a Renaissance product?

At first glance, one might choose politics. A California surgeon, up at 6 A.M., rushed quickly to the local hospital, completed a sub-total gastrectomy on an ailing ulcer patient, saw sixteen other patients, then turned his attention to another broad interest of life. He opened a slew of mail relating to political campaigns, then made ardent phone calls to aid candidates of his choice. In other areas, a handful of physicians have been running for public office, their state legislatures, even the Congress of the United States. Former Congressman Walter H. Judd of Minnesota, who keynoted the Republican Convention in 1960, is a physician, as are three present members of Congress.

Some of this activity is highly individual and commendable, but a glaring preponderance of doctor involvement in politics is a reflection of membership in the golden clique—of vested medical interests being inserted into the market place of political democracy. There is nothing unethical or improper about a physician so participating, but it has been basically a group manifestation rather than distinguished individuality.

The busy surgeon, for example, is an officer of AMPAC, the American Medical Political Action Committee—organized medicine's political arm. AMPAC works for and makes sizable contributions (up to $5000–$10,000) to the congressional and senatorial campaigns of candidates with outspoken conservative stance and strong objections to medical programs such as Medicare, or any other which organized medicine might interpret as "socialized." During the 1962 campaign AMPAC backed about eighty congressmen, putting special emphasis on helping the members of the House Ways and Means Committee who had opposed Medicare.

Unlike other professionals in public life who reflect the political spectrum, the typical doctor-candidate, like the typical physician, is a Republican. A successful state senatorial doctor-candidate in the Southwest, for example, was elected on the Republican ticket after having been a successful medical society politician. His campaign was reportedly aided by "most" of the doctors in his county, plus a hard core of nurse campaign workers.

In his political allegiance the doctor is a product of his class environment, with a conservative fervor that possibly exceeds that of his affluent neighbors. During the 1964 primary campaign physicians polled by *Medical Tribune* showed a 71 percent allegiance to Republican candidates, with Goldwater their first choice, to a 29 percent allegiance to Democrats—quite the reverse of final national selection. Radiologists (89.3 percent) and surgeons (77.4 percent) had the highest Republican allegiance. Only psychiatrists evidenced a Democratic preference, with two thirds of them favoring Johnson or other Democrats.

Most doctors express their conservative impulses by mere grumblings about "creeping socialism." A fervent minority of physicians, however, have flirted with extreme right-wing groups, including the John Birch Society. One physician states that a religious denominational hospital in Boston "is a hotbed of Birchism." In Attleboro, Massachusetts, a physician is a leader of the local Birch group. "In our community the Birch Society has been uniquely associated with the medical profession," disappointedly stated the editors of the *Bulletin of the Columbus (Ohio) Academy of Medicine.* In Central Ohio, a local obstetrician has reportedly been co-ordinator for the John Birch chapters. "Well, in Ohio so many physicians are members of the John Birch Society—and they've been so vocal about their allegiance—the public might understandably assume that the whole profession has gone John Birch," one doctor has stated. A California physician who applauds the rank-and-file doctor participation in the "rightist revival," speaks of doctors displaying far-right material, including the Dan Smoot Report, in their waiting rooms.

Medical philosopher Dr. Lindsay Beaton of Arizona attempts to explain the rightist affinity of physicians. He theorizes that most American doctors are the naïve victims of excessive conservative propaganda, much of it served up by their own organizations. Doctors receive their political information, says Dr. Beaton in *Arizona Medicine,* "from sources that regularly represent only one side of the debate," especially AMA handouts and conservative newspapers, and from "pamphlets circulated by reactionary paranoids." His antidote: The Sunday *New York Times,* or a "liberal" weekly like *The New Republic* or *The Nation.* Dr. Gerald Feigen expresses similar resentment. "I'm tired of getting letters from doctor committees telling me how to vote," he says, referring to campaigns backing what he calls some "consummate ass" who "once voted against something that smelled of socialized medicine."

Doctor participation in liberal politics is predictably less, but there are noteworthy exceptions. In Attleboro, Massachusetts, two young physicians, Drs. Joseph F. Kerrin and L. Lynton Goulder, have organized a campaign to "expose" the Birch Society in their town and have expended $750 of their own funds in the attempt. "I'm afraid most doctors are fearful of standing up and being counted," says one of the anti-Birch doctors. "If they think it affects their pocketbook, like Medicare, then they will send letters to Congress and complain. But otherwise they prefer not to get involved. I think doctors, like everyone else, have an obligation to participate in public issues as individuals and not leave it to the other guy. They need not be afraid. Our medical practice hasn't been hurt in any way since we began this campaign against the Birch Society."

"Trade school mentality" is the name given by critical doctors to the physician's constrictedly narrow attitudes. "Doctors are duller persons than they used to be," says one New York internist, adding "that so many years of a trade school would dull anybody." The dullness is undoubtedly heightened by the doctor's restricted social life, which often revolves about other physicians and their wives. The golden clique sticks together, feeding each other's egos, salving their respective wounds inflicted by annoyed laymen or by any suspected loss of community status.

The public may share some of this blame. When the physician does venture out into lay society, he is often accosted—whether in movie lobbies or at cocktail parties—either for a quick medical diagnosis (with symptoms smilingly proffered as if in jest) or subjected to a violent tongue-lashing on the socio-economic evils of his profession, from Medicare to house calls. Assimilating the physician into normal society requires the same courtesy by the layman as he would expect of his doctor when seeking medical care.

Many physicians retreat solidly into the social sanctuary of professional *Gemütlichkeit*. Others do venture forward, all the while developing ploys to disarm their lay adversaries. One perhaps apocryphal story describes the doctor who listens carefully to females at parties tell of their physical woes. He then looks them sharply in the eye and orders: "Please strip to the waist!" A California physician wrote his cocktail party woe in couplet form and submitted it to the *New England Journal of Medicine*. The physician-poet cleverly reveals his feeling of encirclement in "The Cocktail Party (With Apologies to Rudyard Kipling)," which reads, in part:

> I tried to gently switch the talk: the Dodgers, boats,
> bikinis

But Medicine the guests pursued (with gibsons and martinis).

Once more, I thought, I have been trapped—it was not
  my intention
To make this pleasant afternoon a medical convention . . .

To evaluate the "doctor as a person," we should examine his medical health as well as his social well-being for any pertinent abnormality. Contrary to folklore, the young physician grasping his chest from a fierce heart attack brought on by overwork is atypical. "Doctors don't take care of themselves" is another common myth. Actually, the typical doctor *lives longer, much longer,* than the average American male. His age at death (median) is 71.1 years, several years *more* than men in general! A survey of 1077 doctors and 755,000 other males (white) showed a similar life expectancy up to age fifty-five, after which the doctors surged ahead.

In physical profile, he is quite average: five-foot-ten, 175 lbs. A survey of 5168 doctors conducted by Parke, Davis indicates good general health. Almost half (49 percent) of doctors lost no time from work due to illness in an entire year, and another 21 percent only from one to four days. He has a checkup approximately once in sixteen months, and usually by an internist rather than a general practitioner.

The one flaw in the doctor's above-average biology is his possibly disproportionate disposition to mental illness and narcotics addiction. These traumas affect only a small minority of doctors, but reports indicate that there is a problem. Mayo Clinic psychiatric records for 1956 through 1963 show that ninety-three doctor-patients were hospitalized for psychiatric reasons. "This represents one physician for each sixty-four admissions, a highly disproportionate ratio when one considers their representation in the population." Far more were treated in their outpatient settings, say reporting doctors Duffy and Litin.

The narcotics problem is a rarity in the doctor's socio-economic group, but has long been recognized as a special problem among physicians. Their easy access to narcotics makes addiction "practical." Of the Mayo doctor-patients, thirty-seven had "some form of drug addition," and several were also alcoholic. The Menninger Foundation in Topeka, which has treated doctor-addicts, recently summarized their work on twenty-five such hospitalized physicians. They found that these physicians, all of whom were in private practice, typically became addicted at age thirty-eight, and entered the hospital three years later after two prior hospitalizations. Twenty-four had used the common meperidine (Demerol) as the main addicting drug.

The cause? Generally, disillusionment in their practice, say Menninger psychiatrists, a discouragement of reality that clashes with the exuberant anticipation of medicine. In answer to why the addiction first appears in the mid-thirties, after several years of busy practice, the psychiatrists offer an explanation. "Our data seem to answer that these men are sustained in earlier life by great expectations of future satisfactions. Once the final practice terminus is reached, the naïve expectation of gaining a future paradise ends too; then disillusionment and reactive regression sets in." In simpler terms, the young physician was not trained or prepared for the exigencies of modern medical practice.

There was a time when the physician's wife was inextricably involved in these frustrations, in exercising a lonely family vigil for a seldom-present husband. In addition, she once offered her home as a place of medical practice. A portrait of this past home life of the American GP is provided by the wife of an English practitioner, whose husband's practice has not yet been revamped by such Americanisms as separate offices, aides and phone answering services. "The telephone and the front door bell assume Kafka-esque proportions when one is inhibited from going to throw rubbish in the dust bin, visiting the lavatory, going upstairs to make the beds . . . when either the telephone shrieks or the front door bell screams," a practitioner's wife writes to the *London Observer*. "It is indeed a Pavlovian dog's life.

"Wives had had enough; they take messages at all times of the day and night (when their husbands are out on calls or at meetings) and only recently has the Inland Revenue reluctantly agreed that it is no part of a wife's duty to be on call twenty-four hours a day because she happens to be married to a general practitioner . . . It is no exaggeration to say that a general practitioner's wife has no home."

This frenetic portrait of another country, and a bygone era, bears no relation to the life of the typical American doctor's wife of today. Her home is insulated from his practice and from demanding patients by a phone answering service, by unlisted home phone numbers, often by miles of distance, and by a fiercely protective doctor's aide. She can afford and usually has maid help at home, and enjoys an enviable social position in the community. As we have seen, her husband has more leisure time than any physician in recent history. Is she pleased with her position then, as empress of a formidable and affluent household?

Some physicians—especially those pediatricians and general practitioners who make house calls, and obstetricians—still have demanding hours. They are the bane of the doctor's wife, who has no intention of suffering silently like the legendary "Mrs. Doctor" of years ago. One survey of pediatricians' wives indicates annoyance at going to church "with two cars" in case the doctor was called away for an emergency. One wife complained of the constant demand for "emergency" house calls and living in a "goldfish bowl." Wives of obstetricians can remember more than one dinner spoiled or theater tickets wasted because a patient's labor pains started unexpectedly.

The tension of "not seeing my husband" is decreasingly a legitimate reason for wifely anger, especially among the growing ranks of specialists' wives. One doctor skeptic, in fact, called his colleagues "phony" if they claim they are too busy for a proper home life. Sagely using a pen name in a medical publication, the physician states acidly: "As far as I can tell, ninety percent of the men who claim to be so busy that they can't be fathers and husbands as well as doctors are using their profession as an excuse for avoiding obligations they have no appetite for anyway."

The "empress" of the medical establishment has a better, firmer position than she has ever possessed. Most are pleased and secure in it, smilingly acknowledging the status acceptance from other women. Others find being a doctor's wife burdensome, disliking the social obligations and "goldfish" aspect of prying patients. Some spoiled doctors' wives resent *any* intrusion into their leisure time from their husband's practice, and through wifely pressure are greatly responsible for our truncated nine-to-five medicine.

What do other women think of doctors' wives? To the unsophisticated woman, the doctor's wife represents the acme of potential feminine prestige. In some urban and "better" suburban areas, however, one notices a growing disenchantment with doctors' wives, whose cliquish habits have aggravated a growing segment of educated women. "Their supercilious manner, their holding themselves aloof, and their demanding the same respect—or more—given to their husbands, annoys me greatly," says one perturbed female urbanite. "They are not doctors and I don't think they should be treated as such."

No one can help but appreciate the physician's personal pressures —from his wife, himself, his patients—and the painful gap between the anticipation of medicine and its demanding realities. Contemporary medicine and life have unfortunately shaped him into a limited personality pattern that he naïvely believes best fits the necessity. That it is a ragged pattern, one that "makes do" rather than ennobles, is obvious. If pragmatism tells us anything, it is that short cuts created without grounded philosophy eventually require revolutionary change. The contemporary doctor, as a person, is just such a stopgap, an artificial creation of technical necessity who will somehow have to contemplate the Renaissance concept of man or be drastically altered without his consent.

The modern doctor may be satisfied with himself as a person, but his concern will inevitably grow as he learns that his personal foibles and inadequacies are related to his status, a commodity for which he apparently has an insatiable appetite. Public opinion polls may temporarily reinforce or challenge that prestige, but the doctor will eventually have to consider the unglossed situation.

"The physicians who don't see that their prestige is slipping," states Dr. Henry A. Davidson of New Jersey, "are just fooling themselves."

Chapter IX

The Doctor
As a Businessman:
The Golden Cult of Medical Economics

The suburban practioner had a broad smile, and a practice to complement and explain it. His waiting room in the converted ranch house-office was full, partially because he maintained evening hours several days a week to accommodate his middle- and lower-income patients. Seated facing a female patient, the doctor spoke confidently, dispensing assurance and prescriptions with aplomb. The subject of money never arose during the eight-minute visit, and the only allusion to it was a shopworn $5 bill casually placed on the desk blotter.

In answer to the patient's query, "How much will that be, Doctor?" he appeared to give it only perfunctory consideration. "Why, that's five dollars for the office visit, and ten for the X-ray." The patient thanked him, then almost inaudibly muttered, "I'll send it in." The doctor seemingly dismissed the tainted subject with the cordial farewell. "That's fine. Please give this folder to the nurse on your way out." Within a moment he was swiftly at work examining another patient.

To the onlooker, the entire performance was countermercenary, the professional manifestation of a man whose money regimen was unplanned, even subject to neglect. "Don't you make notes about the cost of the visit? How do you remember how much to bill her?" were two logical questions.

Despite its veneer of insouciance, we had actually been witness to the magnificent portrayal of an adroit, facile businessman whose economic concern, like the magician's occult rabbit, was hidden only slightly beneath the working surface. "If you noticed, while

I was talking to the patient," the doctor finally explained, "I slipped paper clips, both plain silver and brass ones, on her case folder. That's a code to the nurse to tell her how much the visit cost and whether I collected. If the clip is at the left end of the folder it represents five dollars. If it is the middle it means ten dollars, and fifteen if it is at the right end. I like to get paid rather than bill a patient, so when I told the patient the cost of the visit, I moved my hand slightly forward, if you recall, to indicate I'm ready to accept the money. The five dollars on the desk is a prop to remind the patient that medical care costs money. It also gives the impression that someone who has just left has paid me."

The physician had stunned his interviewer but had not concluded his manual of medical economics. "Remember, gold is better than silver, so the brass clips represent cash—that I was paid—while the plain ones show the nurse that I wasn't," the doctor continued. "The nurse will ask the patient for the fifteen dollars again just before she leaves, and you'd be surprised how many will give her part or all of it. If not, she makes a note to bill her. I like to collect cash because most of my bills are small. Rather than take out my wallet, which might offend the patient, I put the money in a cash box I keep in my lower desk drawer. At night when I go through the box, and get the nurse's billing statement, I can tell at a glance how much I took in that day."

This doctor's candor and method may be atypical, but his practice, like that of many physicians today, is an incomparably lucrative business. Never, in fact, has Western civilization produced as astute a small businessman as the American physician. He cannot advertise, but he has more customers than he can accommodate. He rarely checks the credit of his clientele, yet he collects over ninety-one cents on every dollar billed. He utilizes the latest innovations in billing, photocopying, computers, dictation and transcription, real estate transactions, taxation, collection, management consulting, personal corporations, factoring, foundation trusts and retirement funds, and finds time to practice medicine sufficiently to place him in the top 2 percent of the national income earners. Incontrovertibly, the American doctor has made medical economics the most highly developed of the medical arts. What he lacks in the disciplines of healing and science, he more than compensates for here.

The paper-clip ploy is only one of the intriguing techniques of modern medical economics. It does, however, illustrate the avid doctor interest in money, and money methodology, which must be understood if one is to truly comprehend the contemporary private-practice American physician. He is so financially astute that there are lessons in his smooth administration of money—from computer-billing to near-personal "foundations" that ease the pinch of retirement—which could restimulate the atrophied American small-business men into profitable imitations of the doctor.

Skeptics might ask if it is not mere devotion with little manna. Does the doctor make sufficient cash to qualify him as an expert small-business man? Could he earn all that his patients imagine in their covetous reckonings of his bank account? The probability is "yes" and "considerably more," but it will require statistical leg work to reconstruct what are apparently sacrosanct, and possibly embarrassing, figures. The latest government statistics on private-doctor income are a decade and a half old. In 1951, states the Department of Commerce, private-practicing physicians had a net income of $13,432. This was at a time when the typical American family made $3709 and a dollar was a more meaningful piece of paper than it is today.

Great attention has naturally been paid to the subject of medical munificence by *Medical Economics,* the doctors' excellent practice-management bible. Their latest information, covering the year 1964, was secured from a sampling of 8264 self-employed doctors under sixty-five on the AMA list, and followed up with three mailings. The doctors responding—41 percent of the sample—showed a median gross income of $44,060, and a net of $28,380 after all expenses, an increase of over $4000 gross and $3000 net from the year before. Almost 22 percent of doctors showed a *net* exceeding $40,000.

This net is not inconsiderable, but it stretches considerably when used in conjunction with other surveys and factors. Firstly, it would be prudent to bring this up to date. Adding 5 percent, the average yearly growth in doctors' income since 1959, brings the estimate to $29,800 net at the end of 1965. The doctor's regal median is more than fourfold the national family-income median of approximately $6800 for the same period.

Fifty-nine percent of the physicians chose not to answer the *Medical Economics* survey, a fact which can be interpreted benignly or otherwise. Like many physicians who can afford a Cadillac but choose a Buick Riviera instead lest they seem "ostentatious," the wealthier doctor may have felt uncomfortable about answering. This suspicion seems to be confirmed. The *Medical Economics* survey relates the doctor's income to the number of patient visits he handles per week: a median of 124. However, the National Disease and Therapeutic Index, constructed from the diaries of fifteen hundred physicians sampled at random, produces a busier typical physician with more patient traffic, and inevitably more income.

The NDTI report shows that their statistical "universe" of 165,000 doctors in private practice handled 1,200,000,000 patient visits in 1964. Excluding the small number of "telephone" visits, simple reckoning shows that their typical doctor sees 137 patients a week.

With almost 11 percent more patient visits, and ostensibly that much more gross, the typical doctor now looks even rosier in economic tintype: the possessor of a $33,000 annual net income, and well over $50,000 gross.

(It seems that anyone who displays a medical shingle can attract $50,000 a year in traffic. Thomas M. Novak, a successful twenty-nine-year-old Detroit "physician" had grossed $35,000 in general practice the first eight months of 1964. His only liability was lack of a medical degree; the ambitious but ersatz practitioner had only a high school diploma.)

The doctor's income mounts with increasing statistical introspection. To ensure that his success is not underestimated, we should also examine what the "median" or "typical" doctor means. The term "median" simply means that half the physicians make less and half make more. In common-sense terms, however, the median is an inadequate measure of the "typical" active person in our society. The "median" American family made $6569 in 1964. Is this the typical recognizable American middle-class family? Hardly, since the figure includes the racially deprived, immigrants, migrants, the aged, the just-beginning couple.

In the same manner, the "median" doctor is an atypical paste-up that includes the green physician fresh out of hospital training; the semiretired doctor maintaining only the barest of practice; the dedicated and poorer physician chained to an old ideal. The more recognizable, "typical" doctor is the specialist or busy GP in his mid-thirties to mid-fifties. He will not uncommonly be found in the $60,000 to $70,000 gross and $40,000 to $50,000 net class.

A physician with a $100,000 net income confirms at least the potential for this state of financial grace. "Yet my experience tells me," he writes, "that *any* capable physician in *any* specialty [italics mine], if he is in good health, can net at least $50,000 a year before taxes in any of the fifty states without charging a penny over going rates."

Even these sizable net incomes may be deceptively small. The spread between doctor "gross" and "net" is, of course, not all impersonal business expenses or money spent at all. As self-employed businessmen, doctors have considerable usable income that appears on tax returns as expenses. Rent for their "den" at home, partial car expenses, convention and business-pleasure trip costs, entertainment for themselves, wife and doctor "associates," entertaining colleagues at home, depreciation on office real estate (which adds to their net worth) and many other deductible but personally valuable items are legitimate "expenses." In addition, there is hundreds of dollars of free medical care for them and their families, the modern guild carry-over of "professional courtesy."

The obstinate search for the doctor's income could hardly end here.

People tend not to be bashful about the income of a business when offering it for sale. This led to a simple, uncontrolled, unscientific but stimulating experiment in learning how much doctors *really* make. A dozen copies of *JAMA* were chosen at random from a closet file, and the classified section at the back of each issue, "Practices for Sale," circled. A surprising proportion of these ads gives the gross or net income of the practice as a legitimate, if brash, lure to the potential buyer. Many of the doctors are GP's leaving to begin specialist training.

Recording the experiment in full is the simplest explanation. Following are the figures as they appear in the unique advertisements: $28,000 gross part-time [the equivalent of $70,000 for a five-day week]; general practice, $55,000 gross; general practice, $50,000 gross; general practice, $55,000 *net;* general practice, $70,000 gross; general practice, over $25,000 gross; pediatrics, $60,000 gross; internal medicine, $100,000 gross; orthopedic, $45,000 gross; radiology, $55,000 gross; general practice, over $50,000 gross; general practice, $35,000 gross; general practice, $56,000 gross; general practice, $70,-000 gross; general practice, $50,000; general practice, over $45,000 gross; internal medicine, over $40,000 gross; general practice, over $60,000 gross; internal medicine, $40,000 gross; general practice, $150,000 gross; general practice, $70,000 gross; general practice, $25,000 gross; general practice, $60,000 gross; orthopedic, $55,000 gross; general practice, $50,000; pediatrics, $50,000; surgical, over $50,000 gross; general practice, $60,000; general practice, $50,000 *net,* only 3½ days a week; gynecology, over $50,000 gross; pediatrics, $60,000 gross; general practice, $55,000 *net*; general practice, $30,-000 gross, for 2½ days; general practice, over $50,000 gross; general practice, $45,000 gross; general practice, $40,000 gross; and general practice, $48,000 gross. Several other doctors rely on such phrases as "lucrative," "busy," "well-established," which, although untranslatable into dollar figures, are not suggestive of penury.

The results of this impromptu want-ad survey? The practices for sale average a *gross income of $58,000.* By using the ⅝th gross-net formula common for self-employed doctors, we get an average *net income of $36,250,* or $8000 a year higher than that of doctors willing to answer money surveys. The future appears even brighter. Consultants estimate that the physicians' *net* income will increase another $10,000 a year by 1970.

Are these figures—which put other surveys in the economic shade —finally, then, how much doctors *really* make? Possibly, but we should consider one further, if tantalizing, thought: what about those well-established lucrative practices that are strictly *not for sale?*

The high average or median figures are not the complete reckoning of doctor affluence, for doctors' incomes vary depending on age, specialty and location. Physician earnings reach a peak between the ages of forty and forty-nine, dropping back about $3000 during his fifties. However, the ancient aphorism that young doctors starve is now nostalgic nonsense. The fledgling private physician can, in his first year, count on $15,000 net income, either as a young member of a group, a salaried physician or in private "solo" (one doctor) practice. One survey of 140 new doctors revealed a *net* income of $16,229 in their second year of practice. Manhattan urbanites would swear otherwise, but physicians in smaller communities earn somewhat *more*. The spread in income between general practitioners and specialists is narrowing. General practitioners now gross only $3000 less than medical specialists.

Partnership or group doctors have the economic edge on the staunch solo doctor, who apparently pays for his independence. They not only gross over $7000 more, but by sharing expenses, cut their cost ratios down. The most surprising income revelation is that the eastern physician earns *less* than his colleagues elsewhere—$8000 less, gross, than doctors on the West Coast.

Less revealing is the well-known fact that surgeons are the stars on the fiscal firmament, with earnings known to exceed a quarter of a million dollars a year. The ad "Surgical Practice for Sale" is a rarity, for despite a reported *excess* of surgeons, high surgical fees and frequent surgery keep surgical incomes rising. Surgeons reportedly gross $5000 more than the median doctor, but this is only a biopsy of the situation. In 1959 the imperial neurosurgeon netted *$12,400 more* than the median doctor, the orthopedic surgeon *$10,400 more,* and even the gynecologist was $5700 ahead.

Available survey figures show the median surgeon netting $33,-000 and grossing just under $50,000 a year. The neurosurgeon, by this estimate, would be grossing $65,000, with the orthopedic surgeon closer to $60,000. How does this jibe with the estimates of surgeons and those who refer cases to them? Barely. "The typical *established* surgeon in this area grosses anywhere from $60,000 to $150,000 a year," says a university hospital internist who regularly refers cases to surgeons. "The top earners are the neurosurgeons, followed by the urologists, the chest surgeons, the orthopedic men, the pediatric surgical specialists, and ophthalmologists, the nose and throat men, although not necessarily in that order. The abdominal surgeons can do quite well, but on the average do not do as well as some of the more narrow surgical specialties."

A young surgeon who recently completed eleven years of training draws approximately the same portrait of the *established* surgeon. The man practicing for ten years grosses approximately $75,000, he estimates, with several doing not as well, and a small handful doing "fantastically well," above the $150,000 mark. He stresses the great difficulty of getting established, and the poor rewards of the first few years of surgical practice—unless one participates in fee splitting and other subterfuges. "Perhaps in a small town where the medical ethics are looser, it is easier to make more money sooner," he explains.

The reasons for doctor affluence are clear. The drain of doctors into research, minor specialties, industry, government and administration has left fewer family physicians—general practitioners, obstetricians, internists, pediatricians—to care for the public, creating the "doctor shortage" and the so-called seller's market. To this must be added a boundless patient desire for doctoring, a reflex stimulated by consumer affluence and propagandization of the supposed "miracle" cures waiting in the physician's office. Volume is the key to family-doctor affluence, while the specialist has commanded what were once considered exorbitant fees with little consumer resistance.

Patient traffic "earns" the doctor's fortunes, but his incredibly high collection rate makes the cash a reality. One of the hallowed medical images is the empathetic physician trusting the whole town, saddled with a desk full of unpaid bills which he has never tried to collect. It is, of course, contemporary nonsense. The medical practitioner is expert in securing the last dollar due him, a compulsion which is tainting him with an increasing aura of commercialism. Dr. Daniel F. Crowley, Jr., former president of the Des Moines Medical Society, has opined that "too many doctors have fallen into the habit of thinking of themselves as businessmen," an admonishment that covers the doctors' collection procedures.

Physicians occasionally try to parry resentment against their incomes by nurturing the folk concepts that much of their work is "charity" and that paying patients are slow to honor their doctor bills. The charity ploy is an unworthy one, a false harkening back to a faded medical era of unstinting service and uninsured surgical patients. The myth of noncollection is also laid concretely to rest. "The old adage that the doctor is the last man to get paid is simply not true," says Donald F. Gearing of D. F. Gearing Associates (now in Boston), one of the nation's leading management consultants to doctors. "In fact, he's often the first one to get paid. Many doctors have business problems that need fixing, but collection of his bills isn't usually one of them. He's an expert at collections. Perhaps I can lift his collection rate a few points, from ninety-two percent to an exceptional ninety-six percent, but that's all."

The prewar doctor lost more than a quarter of his billing, but his modern counterpart has had a median collection rate of ninety-one to ninety-three cents on the dollar, and some practitioners boast a near 100 percent record. Part of the doctor's success is implicit in the economy: more patients can afford to pay their bills. For those patients who are reluctant or temporarily short of money, however, the physician has developed expert techniques to keep the cash flowing. At any given time, his accounts receivable represent $12,200 (only $5370 in the fast-paying East, but $14,560 in the West), a fiscal fact that commands his rapt attention.

Collection "management" varies, but has five basic strategies: the persuasion of a forceful female office aide; the insistent phone call; the myriad of collection letters and forms; the threat to "collect"; finally, the collection-agency pressure campaign and possible law-suit. Some physicians, such as one New York ophthalmologist, just call up their patients and personally ask for their money. More typically, the doctor hides behind the aggressive skirts of his female aide, who has been described by one management consultant as "a soft-spoken young woman who mollifies his patients, keeps his books, and guards his financial interests like a tigress."

Some tigresses are adept at disguising their fangs; others brutalize the doctor's image. One suburban pediatrician's aide publicly embarrassed mothers by discussing their overdue accounts in purposeful earshot of thirty mothers in the waiting room. "One mother with a four-month-old infant in her arms was mercilessly embarrassed by the aide in front of all of us by calling out the details of the money she owed," an ex-patient recounts. "The poor girl almost went into tears and mumbled that she would ask her husband about it."

One zealous aide accosted a regular patient whose entire family had been cared for by the physician for two years. She threatened the patient in the doctor's presence unless he immediately paid a $15 overdue balance! "We'll have to have the money right now," she advised the surprised patient, "or we'll turn the account over to a collection agency." Many physicians blushingly plead ignorance about patients' bills, but this is generally rehearsed innocence. The economic muscle is typically a co-conspiracy between aide and doctor, who usually knows intimately which patient owes money outstanding for several months.

More formal bill collections are conducted through the mail, with the help of a galaxy of gimmicks: variously colored forms for first and second notices; threatening stickers that advise patients to "protect their credit ratings"; inch-high rubber-stamp notices screeching "PAST DUE!!" Many physicians use a "set" series of collection letters calculated to throw the delinquent patient off balance. In fact, some physicians have enrolled their aides in collection courses, such as a full-day seminar set up by the American Collectors Association.

One letter-series method is explained by a prominent Dallas management consultant in a near-classic article, "Collection Letters That Really Collect, appearing in a medical self-help publication." One in a series of six letters is mailed each month to delinquent accounts. The first letter is a typical reminder; the second letter is a masterpiece of subtle pressure, which arrives by "certified mail" with "return receipt requested." This, states the author, is the best puller of delinquent funds.

The third letter reattacks, warning that the account may be turned over for collection, while the fourth one retreats gracefully. "Once you've shown that you mean business," states the expert, "it's a good idea to let the patient know you're still sensitive to his problems." The next two resume an aggressive tone: the fifth warns that the account is ready for collection. The sixth one is the chef d'oeuvre of the medico-collection universe, a touch of genius bordering on the comically inspired. Entitled "Application for Medical Charitable Benefits," it straight-facedly advises: "You may want to ask your minister or a county welfare office to join with you in completing the enclosed form." This includes a *poverty confession* and an appropriate place for the signatures of the minister and welfare office attesting to the patient's "hardship"!

It is enlightening just to contemplate the audacious ingenuity of doctor-collectors—if only to consider the talent that might be channeled into better medical care. Several physicians are now using local retail credit bureaus—members of Associated Credit Bureaus of America—to threaten delinquent patients with injury to their credit ratings. Non-member physicians buy Credit Bureau forms, which they send to patients with the truth-stretching statement: "The credit bureau has just asked us for the latest information on your account." At the bottom of the notice is another doctor hyperbole—a statement saying that the patient's credit record is now being "reviewed."

This doctor fervor for bill collection has led galled critics to warn that too good a record can injure the doctor's repute. Consultant Clayton L. Scroggins cautions the overzealous physician who uses commercial "gimmicks," such as high-pressure phone calls, "that in the eyes of patients they should remain altruistic, compassionate men of science."

Whether the doctor's patient prod is a letter or a door-to-door canvass of money owed (as one aide seriously suggested to her physician-boss), doctor failure to collect by six months after the first bill is usually followed by a curt note. "Since all attempts to have you pay this small bill have failed," it usually states, "we are turning this unpaid account over to a collection agency ten days from today. You can still protect your credit rating by paying the bill." Attorneys have warned physicians that this resolute step can trigger malpractice suits that would otherwise be passed up by dissatisfied patients. There is no evidence that doctors eager for delinquent dollars have been frightened.

William F. Martin, legal counsel to the New York State Medical Society, advises physicians to be fully cognizant of the patient's

recent medical history before suing to collect. He cites the case of a
doctor who sued a female patient for the money due on a tubal ligation (a gynecological procedure to prevent conception) only to
find that the patient was eight months' pregnant when the summons
was served!

The collection agency that applies the final "convincer" is part of
a high-commission, often high-pressure field, which receives from
thirty-three to fifty cents of each patient dollar they collect. The
agency is often out-of-state, and conducts its legal musculature by
mail. Some of the less-reputable medical-bill "dunners" have used
notorious tactics on behalf of physicians, helping to intensify the
doctor's commercial image. Two medical collection agencies in
Memphis, for example, were ordered by the Federal Trade Commission to stop sending out subterfuge forms to patients which read:
"Your papers are ready. Call . . ."

The more critical physician believes that doctors who aggressively
chase the "last" dollar are not only injuring the medical image,
but are not helping themselves either. Some believe medical collection is less a matter of law and agencies than proper doctor-
patient relationship. They are supported by facts that show that the
best credit risks, and most financially able, can be the slowest payers
because of doctor attitude. One doctor who has adopted a "soft
policy" toward collections, believes his to be the most effective
delinquent-snatcher, one able to bring in people five years later to pay
their bills. "That soft policy has paid off in personal satisfaction,
good will, and dollars and cents," he writes in a medical-letters
column. "My collection percentage is the highest in town." In the
same columns a management consultant, David L. Wall of Richmond, Virginia, has reminded his physician-readers that doctors
"don't extend credit" but that they "practice a profession." Adds
this astute counselor: "If some of your patients don't pay you, you
either didn't educate them properly or were dispensing charity."

Dehumanization of medicine is not entirely a scientific phenomenon; the patient is increasingly faced with the brutalizing mechaniza-
tion of medical economics. Many patients no longer receive bills
from their doctors, but from a hired third party which centrally bills
for many physicians. Servatron of Waban, Massachusetts, advertises
in the *New England Journal of Medicine* seeking new clients for its
"electronic data processing" monthly-billing services.

The patient has become a "serial number" in a new system of
computerized, remote billing now offered to doctors in thirty-five
cities coast to coast. Headquartered in Kansas City, it has access
to an IBM computer center. A three-part voucher is made out for
each visit by the doctor's receptionist, who writes in the serial

number assigned to the patient. Every medical service the doctor performs is listed and the charge written in, along with any payments. The patient receives his IBM receipt as he leaves, and another copy is sent to the computer center for electronic action. The computer service provides the doctor regularly with printed summaries of his economic health: a *daily* summary of his fees and patients visits; a periodic accounts-receivable report with a special list of delinquent accounts. The doctor also receives a monthly Collection Action report on monies being chased, and a monthly statement of his gross billings and receipts, including the total for the year to date.

The National Cash Register Company also maintains a doctor-billing network with ever-clicking computers in New York, Los Angeles and Dayton. Computer-printed bills are usually mailed direct to the patient out of these central offices, but some physicians prefer to be covert about the dehumanization of their practice. The physician who prefers the homey touch of a local postmark can have his batch of bills mailed to him, then deposit them in his corner mailbox!

Their economic thoroughness is disturbing, if only because it hints at how technology might aid the doctor with *medical* information and calculations—if he could develop as overwhelming an interest in medicine as he has shown for medical economics.

Despite occasional critical outbursts, the doctor's exotic money-service world continues to expand. It now even offers him a quick-cash service, Professions Accounting Services, Inc. of Philadelphia, which will pay the impatient doctor 95 percent on his receivables *in advance*.

The credit-card empire, too, has brashly intruded into the strained doctor-patient relationship. It has increased the potential for patient tension, while producing a neo-Santa Claus for cash-conscious physicians. Uni-card, a New York Metropolitan Area credit card, which states that it has "some" doctors under contract, operates an attractive plan from the physician's viewpoint. The patient signs a slip at the end of each visit. The slip is then forwarded to the doctor's local bank, which *immediately credits the doctor's bank account with 95 percent of the bill*. The plan then takes over the billing and collecting from the patient, charging him *18 percent a year interest* after twenty-four interest-free days. Since the physician keeps the money even if the patient defaults, collection of the funds is, to express it charitably, more commercial than "professional."

It should be noted that *JAMA* has thus far refused credit-card advertising, and two medical societies have counseled their members against joining. But several plans, especially Bank of America's Bank Americard in California, have solid footholds in the doctor community. The major professional concern is that the plan requires credit checks of all patients, which would subvert the concept of care on the "basis of need" rather than "on a credit rating," as one Arizona medical society has commented. Several management consultants are confident that such plans—ethical or otherwise—will eventually prove irresistible to today's money-oriented doctor, especially those of the younger generation.

Credit checks of patients may ultimately force the public and the doctor into a collision, in which the physician may be the victor, but medicine the victim. Most doctors (except certain surgeons) will treat without assurance of payment, but some physicians are openly checking patients' "credit" before treating them on a sustained basis. A California group clinic boasts of their modern system of paying forty cents a head for patients' credit files. They number each new patient with a descriptive 1 to 5, rating their economic rather than their biologic health, from the quick payer to the "dead beat." Other physicians who use credit checks insist that patients who score badly pay cash on the line for Hippocratic balm. If this supracommercial adventure accelerates, we might see the day when a patient-doctor "payment session" will precede any attempts at medical diagnosis and treatment.

The medical-scientific consultant who can survey a troubled practice and augment the doctor's healing art is unknown. The management-business consultant to doctors, however, is a thriving entity. The industry of management consulting for doctors began modestly in Battle Creek, Michigan, in 1932, when two future consultants helped local doctors to collect delinquent accounts. The firm, Black and Skaggs Associates, is now the acknowledged leader in the field. In addition to their headquarters firm, they franchise several other affiliates known as PM (Florida PM, Virginia PM, etc.), the initials for "Professional Management."

The medical consultant industry has grown phenomenally in the past decade. There are currently more than a hundred consulting firms throughout the country ministering to doctors' business problems, many of them members of the Society of Professional Business Consultants. What does a doctor's business consultant do, and how much does he charge? The questions were put to Donald F. Gearing of Gearing Associates, who spoke candidly. "First, I should tell you who it is that calls me in for help," he began. "A typical case involves a doctor in his late thirties or early forties. He's a board-certified or board-eligible specialist with a busy practice. He's working so hard that his wife is nagging him. He's tired, and somewhat frustrated by it all. He's handling more money than he once thought there was in the entire world, but it seems to go through him. He's supporting two cars, a big house, maybe a pool or a boat, and a family with high tastes. He's pouring money into his home and his office—a bigger office, better EKG and X-ray machines, and other equipment. His teen-age daughter will soon be ready to go to college, and he probably hasn't the cash ready. He's scared, but actually he's in pretty good shape with a very good income and a high standard of living. He just needs some straightening out, and that's what I do for him. When we finish our management work with him, he's making more gross, much more net, and working more intelligent hours. We make him lift his sights for himself.

"The physician takes a lot of organic chemistry, but he might be better off if he learned something about handling a private medical practice," the consultant continued his analysis. "He's totally unprepared, emotionally, intellectually and otherwise for the job he's doing. More than one and a half million dollars flow through his hands during his career, and everybody tries to take him to the cleaner's. When he gets tired of that he comes to me. Physicians aren't used to being talked to—they prefer to do the talking—but when they see that I have no axe to grind, and they have swallowed a few insulting questions, they listen. Actually, of course, they pay to listen. And, bless their hearts, they are wonderful business students once you get them to listen."

What is the management consultant's magic? "Before I can do anything for a doctor, I make a survey of his practice," says Gearing. "I spend a full day in his office. I make notes on everything. I go over every one of his records, day book, taxes and collections. I sit in his waiting room and make believe I'm a patient. I listen to the girls on the phone making appointments for the doctor, and then I spend two uninterrupted hours interviewing the doctor. A few days later I deliver a report describing his practice, his problems, and what I can do for him."

This initial survey generally costs about $600, and may be the beginning of a permanent doctor-management consultant relationship that would cost about $1000 a year. One consultant handles a group of four internists in New England for a $3600 annual fee. (The typical consultant charges anywhere from $100 to $400 a day, averaging about $200, or $25 an hour.)

Physicians are much like other small-business men, says one consultant. They balk at what they consider high consultant's fees, hoping to get as much valuable advice as they can for nothing. "When I first began, I used to go over and see the doctor and try to sell my services by showing him how much I knew," he recalls. "I even answered detailed questions on his practice problems. I soon learned that the doctors would thank me, but would not hire me. I had already told them what they wanted to know, for nothing.

Now I just make an appointment—on the phone—to do a paid survey for them.

"Doctors do have a reputation for being 'cheap,' " this consultant adds. "I suppose it is because of the financial struggle in medical school and internship. I think this is changing, though. I notice that the young doctors are willing to spend a few dollars for sound business advice."

One New York organization, Management Counselling for Medical Practices, Inc., publishes a descriptive brochure which explains why some doctor-businessmen are titillated by *nonmedical* help. It offers such tempting inducements as "seek for ways to increase leisure time of the doctor," "study of patient traffic patterns," "evaluate ways by which volume can be increased and practice expanded" (management consultants are not known to advise reducing patient volume, which might be a *medical* necessity), "tax survey," etc.

The consultant usually restricts his advice to what are business enigmas to the doctor, but he sometimes finds that the physician aches to unbend to someone about his many professional frustrations. "Judging from my experience with a wide variety of doctors, I find the greatest problem with the private practitioner is his lack of insight—his inability to cope with the human situation," says consultant George W. Condit of Management Counselling for Medical Practices. "As a man who is not well rounded in languages, social and political outlook, and the humanities, it is hard for him to function outside of the area of the technician. Unfortunately, he sees himself as a technician, and he's awkward when he attempts any other role."

Advice from the management consultant can involve changing the doctor's mode of operation from a solo practitioner to a member of a partnership or group, both burgeoning forms of contemporary private-practice medicine. Only 52 percent of physicians still practice by themselves, and the number decreases daily. Joint practice assumes many forms, some purely business-joined, others with a group medical orientation, with potential benefit to the patient. According to the Public Health Service, there are 1150 "multispecialty" groups, which operate much like small clinics. This category includes many "closed panel" groups such as Kaiser and HIP which offer prepaid insurance plans.

In a typical private group the services of perhaps a pediatrician, internist, surgeon, radiologist, gynecologist, plus laboratory and X-ray facilities are all available in the same building. The four hundred single-specialty groups—combines of internists, for example—make less medical sense, but can have business value for doctors. In the partnership arrangement, which is the most common, two or more men of the same specialty (or GP's) join to share expenses and split the burden of emergency calls, weekends and vacation fill-ins.

"The physicians I advise who are in group practices are much happier, more successful and less strained than other doctors," says Donald Gearing, once the business manager of the successful Mount Kisco (New York) Medical Group. "I believe patients like them better, and when they are properly run they do not have any institutional feeling. The patients like it because there is always someone available—day, night, weekends or emergency—and because of the physical convenience of several specialties being available in one place. For the physician it provides an opportunity for almost normal hours, quick colleague consultation, proper vacation, and an investment in building and property that can add to his retirement fund. He may get death benefits and disability provision, which could pay his full salary for three months if he were sick. On weekends, he may be one of the men on call, but more probably he is just as free as the average citizen. It doesn't have the old independent lure of 'solo' practice, but it doesn't have its drawbacks either."

Others have rational arguments against group practices. Both doctors and patients have complained of the impersonality of some groups. One dollars-and-cents dilemma is often present, and succeeds in collapsing many joint practices: how to split the income. New men are traditionally "employees" in their first year, then gain an increasing share of the funds. Discontent may be bred when senior men believe that they bring in more volume than their colleagues, all of whom generally share equally of the pie.

Group practice seems to impress a high percentage of doctors. A *Medical Tribune* "Pulse" report on 1130 physicians showed that only 15 percent were negative toward groups. Six in ten thought they provided superior scientific medical care, generally because of "more frequent consultation, better diagnostic facilities," in the words of an Arkansas GP. The large minority who disagreed felt as did a Jersey surgeon, that "they can, but they do not always do it." Some were even more skeptical. "The quality of care," says a New York internist, "depends on the quality of the physician—not on groups versus solo. A man who practices poor medicine in solo practice will continue to practice poorly in groups."

The bulk of opinion (77.7 percent) felt that groups were more convenient for both patient and doctor. The negative opinion centered heavily on human factors—on the possible loss of intimacy between doctor and patient and the "intergroup friction" between physicians practicing together. Its positive values have apparently impressed federal authorities (who have considered legislation for loans to establish group practices) and residents in specialty training, many of whom intend to desert traditional solo medicine. A survey of three thousand residents showed that only 26 percent intend to "solo" in medicine, whereas 35 percent are planning on group or partnership practice.

Much of the modern doctor's fascination with business management revolves about his new compulsion to become what laymen call "rich." To him, it is merely a sufficient capital reserve for retirement, a sum generally between $125,000 and $250,000. A recent survey of retired physicians indicated a *median net worth of $175,000*, and an income of $11,930 a year. By their sixties, another net-worth survey shows, 23 percent of the doctors have passed the quarter-of-a-million-dollar mark! This is a non-tearful status for the aged, a class for whom physicians, paradoxically, have shown little official economic compassion. Retired physicians are not only affluent; they tend to retire rather early. One in six has hung up his stethoscope by the time he is fifty-nine.

How wealthy, in a liquid-asset sense, is the typical doctor? In his forties, at the height of his career (but not his asset value), what is his true net worth? A study by the National Bureau of Economic Research places the wealth of the typical doctor in his mid-forties at between $100,000 and $120,000. This can be broken down (at the higher figure) as follows: $29,200 in common stocks; $7040 in bonds; $36,960 in real estate; $6720 in life insurance cash value; $39,000 in cash and other assets.

Overanxiousness about security is symptomatic of the contemporary doctor. Despite recent Social Security coverage, the profession constantly contrives methods to ease his fears. Blue Shield plans in communities in Montana, Washington and Kansas are putting aside a portion of a doctor's fees, tax-free, to be paid out later as retirement benefits. Many medical partnerships and groups have developed retirement benefits for their members. Doctor-run mutual fund plans, such as Beacon Investing Corporation for New England practitioners, are putting physicians directly in the money retirement business. The American Academy of General Practice and the American Society of Internal Medicine are among the many medical organizations tied to a mutual fund-annuity retirement plan.

The doctor's bounteous life is the reward for practicing a historic profession. A profession is partially defined by its separateness from commerce, an intangible superiority that permits the professional to earn fee for service, but with greater moral responsibility and without the character of trade. Many doctors would like to have the best of both worlds, and have covetously been eying the American corporation, whose superior tax structure titillates them. Today in thirty-four states, including Arizona, Virginia, Connecticut, Indiana,

Utah, New Jersey, Texas and New Mexico, physicians' lobbies have succeeded in changing the law *to permit doctors to incorporate.* Yielding their traditional status, an increasing number of doctors in these states are adding the considerably less hallowed "Inc." to their "MD." Most states require two or more incorporators, thus making the privilege available only to medical partners and groups. But several states (including Florida, Ohio, Pennsylvania and Wisconsin) now permit solo doctors to incorporate themselves, enabling them to play the fanciful tax games invented by the more mercenary-appearing corporate giants.

What porridge of fiscal flimflam have these physicians been traded in return for relinquishing a piece of their heritage? Firstly, the incorporated doctor becomes an "organization man"—a corporate executive in every sense of the word. As a salaried "employee" of his own corporation, the doctor can build a tax-sheltered pension program as "profit sharing" device. There would be no tax on money he invests in this retirement fund, and no tax on the earnings of the fund. He would pay only a capital gains tax of 25 percent if he withdrew it in a lump sum, or the graduated lower tax rate if he withdrew it piecemeal in retirement years. In addition, he could receive disability and health insurance, and Social Security as a tax-deductible "corporate" expense.

Perhaps the most ingenious doctor-corporation maneuver would be to cut the physician's earnings in two pieces—one slice for him, the other for his corporation. The split would place him in a lower tax bracket, and the corporation's share (eventually his) would be taxed at only thirty cents on the dollar—far lower than the typical physician bracket.

These Machiavellian contemplations have frightened the Internal Revenue Service as much as they might an offended patient, who must pay his full taxes while supporting his overaffluent healer. It has resulted in IRS resolutions that they will not necessarily recognize the doctor (professional) corporation as deserving of normal corporate tax benefits. Alerted by this threat, the AMA has protested the IRS ruling, perhaps with some success. Dr. Forrest H. Foreman, half-owner of an incorporated practice in Miami, Florida, who had been assessed for back taxes after the IRS ruled him a partner rather than a corporate executive, has been awarded a refund by a United States District Court.

The tragicomic potential of doctor incorporation has been sensed, and lampooned by Dr. Myron Greengold, the witty California general practitioner who visualizes a medical profession gone happily berserk trading itself on the stock market. In a majestic satire, "I'm 100 Per Cent Publicly Owned," in *Medical Economics,* Dr. Greengold describes his mythical corporate launching and its accompanying windfall: "Quicker than it takes to say 'Internal Revenue Service,' I set up generous retirement, disability, sickness and accident plans for me. I put me under Social Security. I sold me my home, cars and summer cottage and then rented them back; Uncle Sam helped pick up the tab for maintenance, repairs, and depreciation. The corporation bought and leased back my appliances and office furnishings. Pretty soon, I didn't even own the shirt on my back. There I was without a cent to my name, and I was sitting pretty!"

Ingenious physicians utilize every modern gambit for tax succor, including scaled-down versions of the Ford Foundation. One prominent attorney describes a retired doctor in Europe poring over medical history at an ancient university on a grant from a generous foundation—his very own.

The doctor's access to cash enables him to play fiscal cat-and-mouse with the Internal Revenue in many ways. J. K. Lasser's "Financial Planning for the Doctor," a popular newsletter on money and stock advice published in Larchmont, New York, suggests that doctors pay for children's college education through a "short-term reversionary trust fund." "A doctor transfers securities to a trust which is to continue for at least ten years," the newsletter explains. "Income from the trust is to be accumulated for or to be paid to the child. When the trust ends, the doctor gets back his securities." The secret lies in the fact that income from the stocks or bonds is taxed in the child's minuscule tax bracket, not in the physician's typical 50 percent bracket. The newsletter adds one caution: the trustee of the fund, rather than the doctor-father, would have to register the child in college.

None of the Bacchic financial wonders could be possible without the $5 and $10 bills that flow endlessly into the physician's coffers. The doctor's fee schedule is at the core of his empire. The leverage possible in a doctor's income by the raising of his base fee for an office visit, for example, can be phenomenal. One management consultant describes the case of a Boston specialist who raised his basic fee by $5 a visit. The busy physician saw an average of seventy-five hundred patients a year, which *automatically boosted his income by $37,500 gross,* and over $20,000 net, per year.

Shouldn't such a capricious increase drive patients away, the innocent might ask? "I have found that quite the opposite is true," says consultant Donald Gearing. "A boost in fee seems to prove to patients that the doctor is a 'good' doctor, what they sometimes call a 'big man.' He may lose part of his present practice, but the raise in fee will almost invariably attract more new patients."

Many middle-class patients can handle the doctor's usual fees for medical treatment, even if strained by the bills of some expensive specialists. The fee burden is greatest in surgery, especially if the patient is uninsured, or badly insured. Surgical fees, such as the typical $400 for a diaphragmatic hernia repair, and the simple appendectomy (which ranges from a $130.83 average in Baltimore to $246.67 in San Francisco, according to federal figures) are high, but generally partially covered by health insurance payments. Obstetrical care, too, has reached a new high plateau. The *average* price of prenatal care and delivery is as high as $185 in San Francisco, a low of $89.71 in Scranton, and about $150 nationally. To ensure easy collection of this sum, a few physicians have even started to collect for the child prior to birth, asking for monthly payments to be completed during the eighth month of pregnancy!

Average fees can be reckoned and "going rates" can be established, but fixing the reasonable surgical fee for any procedure is difficult. Surgeons—more than other physicians—rely on a medical modification of the traditional Robin Hood system of economics: soak the rich, and extract what you can from the poor. "Appendectomies tend to be standard—about $250—but a prostatectomy can run anywhere between $200 and $2000 at this hospital," says one doctor. "It depends on the reputation of the doctor and the income of the patient. The room accommodations, insurance—everything goes into the final decision." One observer points out that some surgeons involved in dramatic life-or-death procedures such as cardiac and neurological surgery charge wealthy clients up to 10 percent of their annual income for the operation.

Fee abuses in the surgical area have commanded a great deal of attraction. The Continental Assurance Company has released other surgical overcharges apparently stimulated by the existence of health insurance. A simple cyst removal in the office cost one patient $100; surgery and treatment of a muscle injury, $1057; a hernia operation $1100.

The day-to-day practice of medicine does not involve this magnitude of cost. It is possible, however, for the patient to be "5-and-10'ed" (and increasingly "10-and-20'ed") to death if the doctor fee structure is not understood. The doctor's basic office fee is generally the nonportentous $5, varying from $3.42 in depressed Scranton to $6.25 in Los Angeles. However, the basic fee has infinite variations. General practitioners often charge more for their "first visit." Increasingly, as the patient uses specialists, he finds the $5 standard disappearing. Many eastern internists, for example, now charge $10 to $15 for "revisits," a fee that is rapidly becoming standard in many suburban and urban areas.

Physicians typically charge as much, and more, for hospital visits as for office visits. This is difficult to justify, since the doctor is often handling several patients at a time at the same institution. (One wag charges that poking the medical head through the door to the patient's room and waving is sometimes charged as a "hospital visit.") One physician charges a flat rate of $70 to $100 a week, depending on severity of illness, for patients ensconced just across the street in a proprietary hospital. Another physician, an internist, explains that physicians are increasingly using the weekly hospital rate, which varies between $75 and $150. The top figure is generally reserved for the wealthier private-room patient, but—he stresses—even that can go much higher if time-consuming care is necessary.

Prior to the current-fee era, which one physician has likened to the running of a taximeter, the doctor made constant "trade-offs" in the time allotted his patients. If his standard office fee was $4, he charged the same rate to the patient whom he could dismiss in three minutes as to the patient who required assiduous diagnostic effort. Today, the clock governs the doctor more. Both general practitioners and internists reserve a special-fee schedule for the patient who needs a history and "physical"—an increasing doctor or patient demand created by new awareness of diagnostic problems.

The $5 GP is an anachronism in this new fee schedule. Over 20 percent of GP's charge $25 or more for a physical and the going rate among general practitioners is $15 in the West and $10 elsewhere. The internist, who generally demands such a work-up for all new patients and those who request a checkup, is likely to charge $20 to $30 for this procedure, with almost one in four internists charging $35 and more, for their time alone.

The $5 fee has become a weak reed in many ways. One skeptic refers to it as a "come-on" for the doctor to load the patient up with "ancillary" fees. Patients who anticipated a bill for $5 or $10 have been shocked by undiscussed extra charges, for laboratory tests, X-rays, injections. The mother who brings three children to the pediatrician for preschool checkups, and needed boosters and vaccines, can find her bill varying anywhere upward of $50.

Practical examples of how these new fee concepts can produce bills of near-surgical magnitude might be in order. A male patient with a bad respiratory problem visited a local physician. Since he was a new patient, there was a $20 charge for the history and physical. The doctor asked him to have X-rays of his chest and sinuses taken and his blood and urine tested. The annoying bill: a total of $83. The X-rays were $20 for two chest views, and $26 more for for the sinuses. The lab tests were $17. In another case, a patient concerned about his blood sugar visited an internist and received an examination, plus laboratory tests. His bill was $73, broken down as follows: examination, $30; glucose tolerance tests, $15; protein-bound iodine test for metabolism rate, $15; urinalysis, $4; other blood tests, $9. This cumulative fee problem is compounded when the patient changes doctors because he moves, or is dissatisfied with his doctor or is seeking specialist aide. In each case he must pay the higher "first visit" cost, and often undergo the very same laboratory tests he has taken before.

Doctors like to hint that laboratory tests and X-rays are economic nuisances that they provide patients as a service. This myth of nobility is absorbed by the naïve but in truth, the doctors' profit from these "ancillary" services is often quite high. They require little or none of his valuable time. In effect, the more "modern" his practice methods, the richer he becomes. Injections, at $3 to $5 each, have always provided at least a 200 percent profit for doctors. Today the laboratory test and the X-ray are even more significant profit builders. Some internists, especially those who hire technicians to run their own labs, gross between 25 and 50 percent of their total income from these laboratory fees, states one knowledgeable management consultant.

The consultant estimates that his clients add a sizable markup to laboratory test costs. Doctors typically pay a wholesale cost of 55 percent of the amount billed to the patient. The profit is considerably higher if the doctor uses one of the automated laboratories mushrooming around the country that do computerized blood and urine tests on a monthly contract basis.

The fabulous cash income possible from these medical services is explained by one general practitioner. "I do my own X-rays, as you can see. They cost me less than a dollar each, and I charge the going rate of ten dollars. I use a contract automated laboratory for my blood and urine tests, and pay only a flat fee of seventy dollars a month. For that I get all the usual blood and urine tests I want. They cost me only a few pennies each." Despite the minuscule cost, this physician—like many who use the automated laboratories—charges the full going rate ($5 to $7 for blood tests, $2 to $4 for urine) and pockets a Croesus-like profit from the growing medical interest in blood and urine sampling.

The pressing problem in nonsurgical fees is generally the doctor's reluctance to discuss *all* costs, regular and ancillary, with the patient in advance. The existence of any loose, undefined situation in which the physician can improvise his fee can be a hazard to the patient. "Many doctors have a defensive attitude toward fees and would rather not discuss it with patients in advance," says New York medical management man George W. Condit. "If he is concerned that the fee may be high, and the patient asks, he might say: 'Let's get well first, then we'll worry about the fee later.' That's his way of evading the issue. He'll send the bill out, then hope to God that the patient doesn't blast him on the phone. He'd save a lot of trouble if he would describe all his fees in detail in advance."

Physician reticence toward verbalizing about money (he has evidenced no other qualms on the subject) was shown in a series of

Medical Tribune interviews. "Fee discussions with patients are an essential, but personally distasteful, part of the practice of medicine for me," says an Albany cardiologist. "Whenever possible, I delegate this task to my office staff." A Baltimore dermatologist forthrightly states his attitude toward discussing fee. "I don't bring up the matter myself."

The existence of high fees has set off controversy between patient and doctor, and doctor and doctor. Most patient complaints to county grievance societies involve fees, many of which they help to adjudicate. The basic cause, they point out, is lack of initial agreement on *all* the fees.

Some physicians react defensively, almost hostilely, when fees are challenged, often with ill-developed counterarguments. One Detroit physician writes in a medical publication that in answer to fee complaints from workingmen, he asks the patient how much he makes a year, and how long he trained. "It's easy to show that on this basis most such patients are better off than their doctors," he writes. "Take a man making $5000 a year who requires only a few months of training for his job. Compare this with the nine years required for the doctor to make only four or five times that amount!"

This shallow sophistry has become near-epidemic. Pious official propaganda describes medical education as costing not only its tuition and board, but many thousand dollars a year in "lost income," a novel approach that is seldom used to evaluate fees of attorneys, the salaries of university teachers, and the delayed success of writers and artists, all of whom spend extensive time in preparation and reputation-building. One overexpansive Colorado physician estimated this cost of his education at $75,000! His "reckoning," detailed in the letters column of *Medical Tribune,* was as follows: 1. Loss of income, $5000 per year; 2. Cost attributable to education per se—tuition, books, equipment, etc.; 3. Return (lost) on investment at 4 percent compounded quarterly; 4. Amortization of investment over a period of twenty-five years.

Conversely, some physicians are frightened that any medical-fee excess will trigger public resentment and bring on the doctor's bogeyman, socialized medicine. "I figure we've only got ten more years to go before socialized medicine comes," one anxious physician comments. "I want to make all I can before then." This fear of "socialization" is regularly expressed in medical forums. "Doctors who overcharge are driving us right into socialized medicine," says Dr. Donald M. Dowell, former president of the Missouri State Medical Association.

Implicit in the traditional medical-fee structure has always been the concept that the doctor charged those who could pay so that he could spend charitable time ministering to the poor. This is now near-legend, for the modern doctor is not nearly as charitable. (In New York City, doctors have had to be *hired* to care for the poor in city hospitals.) The doctor working in poor neighborhoods was traditionally burdened with low fees and low collections in his office practice.

Today, doctors have only to contend with the bureaucracy which *pays* them for care of the poor. One Chicago physician has billed the Illinois Welfare Agency $8680 for one month's medical care of the indigent! The Veterans Administration now also pays physicians for the care of impoverished patients under a Home Town Medical Care Program. A *Modern Medicine* survey indicates that state and city welfare agencies pay doctors between $2.50 (Maryland) and $6 (Alaska) for each office visit of a welfare patient. The tendency, as in California, is to pay "charitable" doctors for the care of the welfare poor at the private-patient level. This is apparently not sufficient, says Dr. John Allen of the Wisconsin Public Welfare Department, who reports that some physicians seem to want "more" for their one-time charity cases, arguing that their care requires additional paper work!

The growth of the golden cult of medical economics has been nourished by doctor opportunity and the desire for great affluence. It has also been nurtured by infusion of business technology into the humane profession. There is little doubt of the success of its business values, but there is more fretfulness about its effect on the character of the profession, and on that of the doctor himself. So involved is the private medical practitioner in the mores of the small-business man, that he can scarcely challenge, let alone imagine, an alternative to contemporary medical economics.

More than one physician has. A Colorado general practitioner, for religious reasons, feels compelled to practice medicine without the intrusion of money. He sets no fees at all, and like the mendicant missionary, tells his patients, "Pay whatever you wish." Does the physician feed his own family? Obviously, more than barely. He grosses $36,034 a year!

The modern doctor is not expected to assume a religious guise if it is not comfortable for him, nor is he expected to forgo financial comfort and security. Traditionally, the doctor has been a reasonably affluent member of society. The ominous aspect of today's doctor-businessman is that his new technology of medical economics is a symbol of his overdedication to Mammon, a cultism that can only detract from his fervor for medicine. "Too often the practice of medicine is a business and not a scholarly profession," Dr. Frederick C. Robbins of Western Reserve University School of Medicine has warned the contemporary practitioner. "If medicine is to become a

volume business with an income based on numbers, it is not likely to
be a satisfying life, intellectually, and it will not attract the more
intelligent, idealistic and service-oriented youth."

The physician who kneels in obeisance to the golden cult of doctor
economics may be deaf to Dr. Robbins' portentous prognosis. The
nation of patients who maintain the cult with their generous offerings, may be listening more keenly. Should they decide that the
doctor-businessman has learned his medical economics catechism
too well, they have the potential indignation to teach him a morally
profitable lesson.

Chapter x

Our Medical Colleges: "Trade Schools" in Need of a New Revolution

"The medical student's present education is badly fragmented because his professors are not teaching him clinical medicine as it should be taught—mainly because they themselves are not usually clinical doctors," charges outspoken Dr. John Knowles, general director of the famed Massachusetts General Hospital, a major teaching institution of the Harvard Medical School. "The medical students are complaining that the professors are no longer professing. 'Why,' they ask, 'can't they teach us medicine?' The answer is that they have abdicated the responsibility of teaching and proper patient care to concentrate on research, where the rewards presently are. They claim they can do both. That's poppycock. The Renaissance man is getting rarer and rarer. And when you have a Clinical Department of a medical school headed by a research man—which is typical— what the heck have you got? A sad situation. At present the clinical teaching of medicine in our medical schools is spotty at best, fragmented, uneven, discontinuous, and haphazard."

This critique of contemporary medical education is startling, not only because it was made during a recent interview with one of medicine's most prominent participants. It is significant because it openly flouts the reputation of the sacrosanct medical college, the pearl of the doctor's establishment. Our eighty-seven medical schools receive the flattery of attendance by students from all over the world; their university hospitals provide some of the best patient care in the nation; and their 14,468 full-time faculty members (Ph.D.'s and

M.D.'s), buttressed by over a quarter of a billion dollars a year in grants, do most of the nation's medical research.

This aura of excellence stilled all criticism for some time. But inevitably the common-sense questions had to be asked: "If the American physician has faults, in ability and attitude, isn't the medical school that trained him greatly to blame? Shouldn't the medical college be examined for the core of doctor inadequacy, both in science and humanism?" The answer to both queries is apparently "Yes." Increasingly, these inquiries are being made by alarmed and annoyed physician critics who see the medical school as the unprobed center of almost our whole medical dilemma. The American medical school, in an important sense, has been a contemporary failure.

Scores of critics, from Dr. David Rutstein of Harvard to Dr. George E. Miller of the University of Illinois, are alarmed at specific aspects of medical-college failings which, when synthesized, explain many doctor deficiencies that have confounded observers. The algebraic sum of these criticisms is an apparent gross failure in curriculum, teaching and goals—a medical-college failure to train doctors in sufficient quantity and quality, as clinicians, professionals and human beings.

Understanding the revolution that created the modern medical college and its initial outstanding success is the key to probing its failures. Gaining an American M.D. degree in the nineteenth century was not difficult. It was possible to obtain one through subterfuge; to buy one; to invest a minimum of time and thought to gain the right to be called "Doctor" and be licensed to practice medicine in almost any state. The great European university-medical school concept had failed to grasp firm hold here.

American medical education had an auspicious start in the 1700's when King's College (now Columbia University), Harvard, Dartmouth and several other universities established medical schools. But the university movement failed to dominate doctor education. During the 1800's the typical American practitioner barely earned his familiar black bag. The majority were graduates of privately owned schools with incredibly low standards. The students paid their self-appointed doctor-teachers direct, then received "admission" slips for mass lectures, some scribbled on the backs of playing cards. The training was short, and some degrees were even awarded *in absentia*. Even the most respectable of schools required compulsory attendance only a few months a year. The proliferation of these medical diploma mills was staggering; Missouri alone had forty-two so-called medical colleges.

Scientific discipline and clinical instruction were virtually unknown, and Dr. Louis Lasagna of Johns Hopkins reminds us that even the Harvard Medical School had no stethoscopes or microscopes until after the Civil War. Not until 1892 did Harvard lengthen its course to four years and require written examinations for the M.D. degree. A generation before, the same suggestion was tabled because "most of the students could not write well enough."

At the turn of the century America boasted 150 medical schools. We did not boast that in the diploma-grabbing atmosphere of so many of them, science-poor techniques—leeching, cupping, even bleeding—were passed intact from doctor generation to generation. Few of the schools had educational prerequisites, and according to an aging practicing physician, one could enter a major medical college in New York at the turn of the century directly from junior high school!

Equally ruinous was the lack of research emanating from a profession of tradesmen without scope. The clinical research being done in Europe was hopelessly lost on the American practitioner, ill prepared to translate it into better medical care. In this dreary environment, two galactic spots appeared, William Osler and Abraham Flexner, one a Canadian-born Anglo-American who was later knighted, the other the son of a German-speaking Jewish immigrant.

A teacher of clinical medicine at McGill University in Canada, Osler possessed the rare blend of science, art and philosophy required for the proper practice of medicine. A Rockefeller aide, Frederick C. Gates, a Baptist minister, read Osler's tome *The Principles and Practice of Medicine* during a Catskill vacation, which reportedly led to the development of the Rockefeller Institute.

In 1897 Osler was called to the newly founded Johns Hopkins Medical School as the first professor of medicine, where he introduced the bedside method of clinical instruction, the teaching of medical students (called "clinical clerks") right in the hospital wards. Though Osler was not its originator, his excellence in its use and the high quality of Johns Hopkins graduates confirmed this system of medical education, one that exists to this day. He worked at Johns Hopkins for fifteen years, making it synonymous with the best in medicine, until he was named to the Oxford faculty and was knighted by the King of England.

Abraham Flexner was not a physician, yet he was to influence contemporary American medicine more than any living person. Born in Louisville, Kentucky, he graduated from Johns Hopkins University in 1886, then taught intermittently at the high school level. In 1908 he authored a highly critical survey of higher education entitled "The American College." Two years later, under the sponsorship of the Carnegie Foundation for the Advancement of Teaching, Flexner was traveling about the country intruding his person and intellect into our medical-education system. His finished report, "Medical Education in United States and Canada," documented in compelling terms the morass of the doctor diploma mills.

The profession had begun to take notice of the embarrassing situation in 1904, but this layman's uninhibited critique shook professional aplomb as no internal dissatisfaction could. Medicine began a much-needed therapy. Within twenty years most of the doctor mills were closed and a general reorientation took place in medical education.

The Flexner report changed medicine into a field of postgraduate university education. It stressed the scientific core of medicine and the necessity for research. It stimulated the hiring of full-time medical faculties. It made the university hospital the training center for the emerging doctor. The apprentice system, which had resolutely passed ignorance intact from practitioner to young doctor, was virtually eliminated. For most of the first half of the twentieth century the revolution precipitated by this brilliant Kentuckian made medical education in America a signal success.

Our American medical colleges are today, paradoxically, victims of the overextension and perhaps perversion of this Flexnerian revolution. The turn-of-the-century reforms have become static, transforming American medical education into an ineffective period piece, reflecting older, less compelling needs. A modern counterpart to the Flexner report is infinitely more difficult to visualize, for today's errors appear less glaring and less galling to common virtue. But the need for drastic reform—say outraged doctor-critics—is as real as it was over a half century ago.

The criticism of our medical colleges is varied and often shocking. Critics believe that the vocation of medical teaching is atrophying; research-conscious professors have made teaching future doctors a veritable side line; the schools have been attacked for producing less physicians than needed and in the wrong proportions of specialties; the medical colleges are prone to grant ineffective young men an M.D. degree rather than admit a misjudgment; the student is trained in institutional, "crisis" medicine, while the typical patient is ambulatory and apparently well, or chronically ill.

The research-oriented medical professor is often unqualified to teach clinical medicine; the working physician is locked out of the university; the research atmosphere dignifies non-practice rather than the practice of medicine; the schools are more interested in producing scientists than doctors; the curriculum is overloaded with abstract laboratory sciences at the expense of the care of day-to-day illnesses; the student's last two years of "clinical clerkship"—when he supposedly learns to be a doctor—are often unstandardized, haphazard, badly supervised experiences. The too-common result is graduate M.D.'s never properly taught the practice of medicine.

The medical schools' selection of students is arbitrary and misguided, say critics; the history and philosophy of medicine are sorely neglected; most medical-college curricula ignore the existence of patient attitudes, sympathy, or the doctor-patient relationship; the humanities are excluded from their training, helping to make the young M.D. an incomplete technician; the art of medicine is mistakenly de-emphasized in obeisance to an incomplete science. Perhaps most significant, the temper, methods and goals of the doctor's medical-school training are inconsistent with the actual setting of his life's work.

The Flexner reforms have dangerously over-tranquilized our medical colleges. This fear is expressed by several physicians, including Dr. George Rosen of the Columbia University School of Public Health. "Few medical schools are organized today to teach students to provide the comprehensive care needed by the patients with whom they will have to deal," says Dr. Rosen in the *New England Journal of Medicine*. "Although medical schools vary in the emphases given in their curriculums, they are all recognizable as variables on the themes established a half century ago during reforms influenced by the Flexner report. The time is ripe for a new look at the education and training of health personnel, to see whether the aims and goals of the schools that turn them out are consonant with the needs of society."

Before further probing the shortcomings in what and how the medical student learns, we should examine a typical four-year curriculum. Basically, it is divided into two parts: two years of theoretical medical science, plus two years of rotating "clinical clerkship" when the aspiring doctor finally meets the people he is going to spend his life with—patients. The first year is the student grinder, a fiercely intensive ten months of medical rote that taxes the young man's memory faculty, if not his soul.

The typical day runs from 9 A.M. to 5 P.M., during which the student takes approximately ten subjects, including anatomy. His introduction to the healing arts is the dissection of a cadaver, the symbol of inevitable medical failure. In addition to anatomy, he spends considerable time in the basic medical sciences of biochemistry, histology (microscopic study of tissues), human physiology, embryology, study of the nervous system, genetics, plus statistics, and perhaps a course in psychiatry. In the second year he learns clinical pathology, microbiology, immunology, pharmacology, neurology, epidemiology, parasitology and an elementary course in physical examination and history-taking. For these first two years the impersonal laboratory microscope, rather than the stethoscope, is his badge of belonging.

The third year is auspicious for the medical student, for he starts his "clinical clerkship" working on the hospital wards, generally

with indigent patients, blushing proudly as an unknowing (or winking) patient first addresses him as "Doctor." The faculty member
on the ward is *nominally* his preceptor. Today's research-busy preceptor does devote some time to students, but much of the student's
medical instruction is catch-as-catch-can from the internes, residents,
even the nurses.

The student "clerk" is given several of the internes' patients to
help care for. He participates in "rounds" and may be asked to
present his details of the case to the attending physician in charge
of the ward. Basically, the medical student learns his practicing
medicine by osmosis, by watching, and sometimes by doing. These
last two years are also his introduction to the specialties, from
ophthalmology to orthopedic surgery, presented to him piecemeal
on the wards and in lectures. The theory is quite simple: the sciences
are absorbed in the first two years and applied in the last two.

After a generation of smug satisfaction, the entire medical curriculum is coming under close scrutiny by concerned critics, with
call for drastic change. "It is improbable that many administrators
of medical schools are complacent about the present status of medical education," says Dr. Thomas Findley of the Medical College
of Georgia in a *JAMA* discussion. "The gap between national health
needs and the medical profession's ability to meet them is already
wide, and likely to become much more so unless radical changes in
pedagogical techniques are made."

A "top" student at Downstate Medical Center of the State University of New York, a relatively new but highly reputable medical
college, is one outspoken critic who believes that one aspect of the
curriculum—the integration of science and medicine—is badly done
in medical school. "In pharmacology in the first year, for example,
we study the chemotherapy of fungus and tropical diseases. The
only difficulty is that we have never been exposed to these creatures
before. When we finally learned them in microbiology, we studied
nothing about the therapy for the diseases they created. In radiology,
we were learning about X-raying of the skulls and bones, but we
hadn't yet reached the skeletal system in pathology. Perhaps the
best example is the muscle system. In biochemistry, we touched on
the biochemistry of muscles, then discussed its physiology three
weeks later in a different class, then still later on, its histology. It
should all be done together. The practicing physician is faced with
livers, heart, muscles and people, not physiology and biochemistry.
All the students get lost, but the student who lacks initiative or
interest is really in bad shape."

This student-observer is annoyed at the delaying of the appearance
of humans onto the medical-school scene. "We start by dissecting a
dead person, then spend two years in cold medical sciences. Finally,
in the third year we begin to work with patients, and I think it's too

late. I'd change the system entirely and walk the student over to the hospital ward the very first day of school. At the same time, the student would be going to formal classes. He'd be learning the art of medicine with patients while he went to class to learn *integrated* sciences. Now, by the time we meet our patients as clerks in the third year, it's too late."

The student's objection to beginning his patient indoctrination with a cadaver instead of a hopeful, live person is supported by anthropologist Ashley Montagu of Princeton. "A serious error, which is already beginning to be corrected in some medical schools," he writes in *JAMA,* "is that instead of exposing the beginning student to health and vigorous life at its best, we expose him at the very outset of his medical training to the ravages of death and all that the preparator in the anatomy morgue can do to render the very dead cadaver dissectible. The student is then supposed to reconstitute the cadaver as a living, functioning organism. This is absurd. The doctor should be prepared to minister to the needs of the living, and from the very first his studies should be conducted in relation to the living." Dr. Alan Gregg, the late medical philosopher, concurred, adding the dangers of lifeless medicine. "The result is a curious kind of callousness that need not be taken for maturity," he had said.

The student's shrewd observation about the failure to integrate science and the art of medicine is also supported by physician criticism. Dr. Tinsley R. Harrison of the Medical College of Alabama speaks of this failure as "the absurdity of the present medical curriculum." He adds, "Perhaps the most effective ultimate remedy will be long, loud, and continuous protest from the students."

The unreasoned overextension of the Flexner revolution has also created a curriculum top-heavy in the theoretical sciences, from biochemistry to genetics. It can, and often does, produce doctors more interested in a patient's enzyme levels than whether he has a fever or whether he slept the night before. Dr. John Knowles describes the honored "grand rounds" as now being an "excuse for launching into the biochemical mechanisms of disease." In fact, he states, the specialist himself, working full time in the university hospital, finds it increasingly difficult to understand what is going on.

Dr. David Rutstein, head of the department of preventive medicine at Harvard Medical School agrees, chastising the "medical-school curriculum [for] concentrating on minutiae of preclinical science, sometimes at the expense of clinical teaching." He recalls that in his early years anatomy was the false deity of the student curriculum that biochemistry and molecular biology are today. "For example, during my medical-school education, I was expected to learn the origin and insertion of all the striated [voluntary] muscles of the body," writes Dr. Rutstein. "This was the era of the anatomist—gross, microscopic, or morbid. When his influence declined with the rise of biochemistry, this anatomical requirement was deleted from the medical curriculum. But instead, students are expected to learn in the same unselective way the names and functions of all the enzymes in all the known chemical reactions in the muscles of the body."

The art within the imperfect discipline of medicine has suffered gravely as a result of this immature obeisance to the fiery god of science—a submission that may not be serving either science or society. Dr. Dwight Wilbur, noted San Francisco gastroenterologist, warns that the medical-college curriculum includes "too much lab work, test tubes and guinea pigs . . . and too little contact with professors and patients, too little contact with the art of medicine."

Some medical professors tend to dismiss annoyance from the lips of less prominent physicians than Dr. Wilbur as a sign of their scientific ineptitude—the shrill cry of the "local medical doctor," derisively known as the "LMD" in the "Town-Gown" fight that now grips medicine. This cheap motive does emanate from some quarters of incompetence, but not when the critique comes from outstanding medical educators and leaders, as it has. Explaining that there is a "renascence" of the belief in the art of medicine (no one has figured out a logical reason why it should have died), a report of the New York State Committee on Medical Education, for example, asks for a change: "The time is ripe, generally, for substantial revision of both concepts and curricula in medical schools, whose programs, while at variance with one another, have seemed static in their relative emphasis since the revolution influenced by the Flexner report a half century ago."

As we have seen, criticism has especially been directed at the often-chaotic last two "clinical" years of medical school, when the student comes face to face with a sick patient and is ostensibly learning the *practice* of medicine. "We should improve our approach to clinical training," says Dr. Frederick C. Robbins of Western Reserve University School of Medicine. "After a perfunctory presentation of the history and physical examination of a patient the instructor has never seen before, too often the discussion is conducted as a lecture and in generalities that may not be applicable to the immediate problem." Dr. Willis E. Brown of the University of Arkansas is direct in his biting critique on the failure of clinical education in the medical school: "Eventually the young physician graduates with the degree of medicine and a shining diploma, only to emerge upon the public totally unprepared for clinical medicine."

In theory, the student spends his clinical third and fourth years as an integral part of a tightly structured system in which he is taught and supervised by a vast hospital staff, beginning with the full-time chiefs of services, down through a multitude of attending professors and other faculty, and house staff. In actuality, says annoyed critic Dr. John Knowles, clinical medical-school training is badly *fragmented*. "If it weren't for the eager house internes and residents, I'm afraid the students would be lost," he states. Not every institution can boast a house staff of the caliber of Massachusetts General, and medical students are thus often "lost" in their crucial last two years. A chief resident at a New York medical school confides that he knew very little about practical care when he received his MD. He had taken his clinical clerkship in a non-university setting where he was not permitted to participate in patient care, supervised by a house staff or otherwise.

A graduate of a leading New York medical school, now a practicing internist, uses his trying first-hand experiences in medical school as a piercing deflater of well-merchandised puffery of American medical education, including the myth that the four years are so taxing.

"During the first two years, we were overwhelmed with the sciences and anatomy, much of which I now find we didn't need," the internist recalls. "After that there was little real work required of us at medical school. It was a breeze. The last two years, when we were supposed to be learning to be doctors, were often lackadaisical and unsupervised. The half year I spent directly at the university hospital was good, but I had clerkships at other affiliated hospitals where we were taught almost nothing. I spent one month on the chest service of one hospital, and had nothing to do. I almost never saw a teacher, and in the whole month I was given a total of six hours of teaching. I spent a three-months clerkship at another hospital, where we just wandered around because the hospital didn't know what to do with us. We didn't learn much medicine, but we played a lot of gin rummy. For part of the time, we were assigned to the emergency room. Usually the internes handled the work, and the only time—as far as I could see—that the attending physician, who was ostensibly our teacher, showed up was on insurance cases. If he had a spare five minutes, he would teach us. We felt that he had a deal with the hospital and was called in if workmen's compensation was involved.

"Ostensibly we received grades in our clinical two years, but no one ever flunked out," the annoyed physician continued. "The way to get a good grade in those courses is to hang close to the attending physician and ask an intelligent question at the right time. The real basis of ultimate determination of whether someone gets his M.D. degree, and whether he is considered a competent doctor at the university, is how well he did on his basic science courses in the first two years. This is tragic because so many students really don't understand the complex sciences such as biochemistry. They just cram and learn it by rote. Meanwhile the real training toward becoming a doctor—the last two years—is often handled badly by the school. When the university ships clerks out to other hospitals—which is common—they should make sure that the students will be well taught. Right now they assume that some place along the line, somehow, the students are picking up medicine by osmosis. Those of us who become good doctors do it in spite of our medical education."

A common complaint of third-year students who train in busy, understaffed metropolitan hospitals is the "scut" work—from laboratory tests to wheeling patients to X-ray—which does little to enhance their medical acumen. Their vital clinical training can be subsumed in favor of their more commercially profitable talents—that of providing cheap labor for the administration. "I spend so much time in the laboratory doing urinalyses, stool analyses, and white and red blood cell counts that I often can't get to my medical lectures," complains one eastern student. "After the first few days of lab work the experience is of little or no value to us, but it saves the hospital money."

It is apparent from student and professional comment that although conditions vary greatly from school to school, and even from ward to ward in the teaching hospital, one thread seems consistent: the table of organization for student instruction and supervision is often more wish than reality. In the typical medical-school organization, the student's *official* teacher is the attending faculty professor; however, he often has more pressing interests elsewhere and is seldom in direct control of the medical student's clinical education. "Unfortunately, we don't see our attendings very often," says one eastern third-year student. "Of all our superiors, he has the least to do with teaching us."

The next step on the clinical teaching level is held by the resident, but his instructional duties are merely *supplementary* to his many other responsibilities: his own specialty training, his supervision of internes, and his care of patients. The job of teaching, when it is done at all, often devolves onto him (if he has time) or the undereducated, typically unsure, overworked interne.

The sad experience of some medical students in their eagerly awaited clinical clerkships may explain one previously unfathomable riddle: how practicing physicians could successfully complete medical education, yet harbor such massive gaps in medical knowledge and technique. A top-ranking third-year student at a medical school in New York describes his clinical clerkships with clear evidence of the excessive variance in the quality of clinical training. "My clerkship in psychiatry and neurology was excellent," the student relates. "However, during my clerkship in pediatrics, very little clinical teaching was done. We met with our attending for an excellent hour in the morning, and had four other teaching sessions during the entire week. During most of the day we drank coffee and talked to each other. Every five evenings I stayed on pediatrics all night, and did nothing. I realized that I was kept on to do the urinalysis when a new patient came in. This may be of value to the hospital, but it was not clinical teaching. I know that one of the residents had given excellent lectures on pediatric problems to one group of students rotating through the service, but he never did it for us.

"Obstetrics and gynecology was somewhat better. We had ten students in our group, and we provided twenty-four-hour coverage for the obstetrics ward. I had a chance to do some uncomplicated deliveries. The supervision was good; the first-year residents were our principal teachers in the delivery room. An attending met with us three times a week for an hour each time, and we had seven or eight lectures a week. In gynecology, we had a forty-five-minute conference each morning, plus seven lectures a week, and worked in the gynecology and prenatal clinics three to four hours a day. At the clinics, we were the first to see each patient. We would work up the case and present to the attendings, who would examine the patient again. It was an excellent experience.

"My eleven-and-a-half-week tour of surgery, representing about one fourth of the academic year, was disappointing. It was a very unsatisfactory experience largely because the clinical teaching was insufficient. We met with attendings for two two-hour sessions a week, excellent sessions that dealt with specific cases. With four hours more of didactic instruction, this made a total of only eight hours of teaching per week—or an average of one and a half hours a day. It was not nearly enough. The rest of it was catch-as-catch-can, and often very frustrating. The failure of the house staff, as a rule, to contribute to our education added to the frustration.

"They told us that if we hung around, good things would happen. I found out that if I hung around, I'd see urine tubes to analyze, and dressings to change. I wouldn't even have minded changing the dressings, but I'd never been given proper instruction in how to do it—what sort of wound got what sort of dressing. I was often given worthless scut work to do. In fact, on four consecutive afternoons I tried to read the charts of patients in order to familiarize myself with the cases. Every time I went to the nursing station to try to read the charts I was sent chasing all over the hospital on errands. Because of the lack of clinical teaching in surgery, most of the students didn't hang around. By two in the afternoon at least half of them were gone."

The disparity of instruction in medical school is illustrated by the fact that the student's next clerkship—in medicine—proved to be "delightful." Despite the minimal contact with attendings, his clinical education was provided by the "incessant questioning, lecturing, and prodding of the house staff."

The constant conflict betwen "cheap labor" and clinical teaching tends to pervert modern medical education in some institutions. "We were told that every student should participate in an operation, and I have been to about fourteen," says the annoyed medical tyro. "Generally all I did was hold the retractors. At times no one spoke to me, and often I couldn't see what was going on. One of the surgical internes, in a rare display of candor, confessed that I was there only because they needed someone to hold the retractors. If I were really to learn from the experience, they would have someone else do that job and I'd be in a position to see what's going on."

The outspoken medical student, although disappointed in much that he has witnessed at medical college, has praise for the occasional house-staff officer who tries to educate the student despite the sacrifice in time involved. He describes one surprise. A busy chief resident took two hours, twice a week, to deliver lectures on differential diagnosis and treatment of various surgical conditions. "It was clear that the resident was doing this on his own, and that this was not one of his required activities," the student relates. "I know that most other chief residents did nothing of the sort. While this reflects the willingness of some residents and internes to go out of their way to teach us, it emphasizes the fact that under the present system they have to go out of their way to do it."

Rather than merely carp, this responsible student offers concrete suggestions to buttress the clerkship concept. "First, we need more contact with the attending physicians—at least twice as much. There should be more specific teaching duties for the house staff. Now they teach if they have time or want to, and don't if it is not their pleasure. Technicians rather than medical students should do more of the laboratory 'scut work'; messengers should run errands, and we should get more clinical work on the wards. It would probably also help if someone were put specifically in charge of each group of students—a real tutor, frequently available. We could use more supervision."

A reasonable synthesis of much of this student commentary is that the quality of medical-school education too often depends on chance rather than on a rigorous system of passing on the art and science of medical practice from generation to generation. Clinical medical education in the third and fourth years is often neither formal classroom education nor a master-apprentice system. The impressionable tyro is placed in a hospital-healing situation in which he usually has no recognizable position. What is referred to today as "clinical education" is often an ill-defined, hasty adaptation to a gnawing pedagogical problem. (In a recent survey, 57 percent of medical students gave attending physicians a failing grade in supervision and instruction in clinical education.)

In addition to a faculty rededication to teaching, what is obviously needed are superior *teaching residents,* who have been detached for three months from all their other duties, and have nothing to do but teach clinical medicine to students on the ward. "That would be marvelous," reacts one discouraged medical student elatedly to the obvious suggestion. "You can't have a man who is responsible for people's lives be responsible for a student's education at the same time."

The question of how one medical-college administration views the teaching in a clinical clerkship was put to a prominent medical educator, Abraham White, Ph.D. and associate dean of Albert Einstein College of Medicine of Yeshiva University. "It depends entirely on the degree of supervision and who's doing the teaching," Dr. White answered. "If there is not much available personnel, the fourth-year student may be working almost as an interne and receive experience but no teaching. With a maximum of personnel, each professor will have only six students and will teach in depth on the ward. I have heard of teaching hospitals where third-year clinical clerks are used as free labor, and spend a considerable amount of time doing blood and other laboratory tests, which is of little value to them. At the teaching hospital here, the students might do a maximum of a half dozen tests just to familiarize themselves with the technique. Despite problems, the third-year clerkship is a rewarding experience for students. For the first time, they are helping to take care of people.

"The fourth year in medical school, however, has mainly been a failure, a fact that is openly discussed at dean's meetings," Dean White continued. "At the end of the third year, the student is ready for more patient responsibility, but he generally doesn't receive it. I personally believe that if we had the student for five years— including his interne year—we could do a fantastic job, providing a continuing period of family medicine with each student handling a family or two for two years. He would be on the learning level the fourth year, and have responsibility for the fifth year. Since under the present system we can't do that, we are setting up a sub-interne system in which the fourth-year student will have patient responsibility—under teaching supervision—in pediatrics, medicine, or surgery for three months each." The plans of individual schools to improve their clinical training are important; however, *national reform* of the third and fourth year of medical school, including the creation of a standardized, comprehensive curriculum in diagnosis and therapy is long overdue.

Much of the criticism of our medical colleges is aptly directed at the research domination of the institutions, the result of a near-religious force that makes other education goals crumble. Plato believed that people accomplish what their communities honor, a thought that has not been lost on the research-oriented medical-school professor. The importance of medical research is not debated by serious observers, but its present context in the medical college is under fierce debate. Research was intended not only for its discovery value but to develop a climate of inquiry for the student, and to attract men of superior intellect to the faculty. Some of this has been accomplished, but in its single-minded ferocity, say critics, the bitch goddess "research" is now injuring the vocation of medical-school teaching, producing faculty men either unable or uninterested in teaching medicine to students.

Dr. Willard C. Rappleye, dean emeritus of Columbia University College of Physicians and Surgeons, has warned that some medical schools have already become research centers rather than teaching institutions. Professor Joseph C. Hinsey, ex-president of the Association of American Medical Colleges and until recently director of the New York Hospital-Cornell Medical Center, believes that the current emphasis on research by younger faculty men has caused them "to neglect their responsibilities in teaching."

The older, now virtually extinct professor of medicine was most at home with his students or at the hospital bedside of a patient, imparting his diagnostic acumen to a half dozen worshipful medical students and an entourage on "rounds" that might number twenty-five. Today's professor is more apt to be scurrying back and forth to his laboratory, or be involved in the preparation of a paper or delivering it to an out-of-town symposium.

"The current head of medicine at the university I attended has never practiced medicine anywhere except at that hospital, and the only time his hands were between the sheets there was when he could spare a few minutes away from his laboratory," says one New York internist who studied at one of the prestige institutions. "He may be an excellent researcher, but I couldn't think of anyone less equipped to be a clinical professor of medicine than he."

Medical educator Willis E. Brown of the University of Arkansas Medical Center savagely attacks those research-oriented colleagues who show little interest in teaching medicine despite their titles and obligation. "The goals of medical schools are, in a sense, a three-legged stool in which teaching, research and patient care form the necessary supports," he states in *JAMA*. "Unfortunately, recently most modern medical schools have had a hypertrophy [overgrowth] of the research leg, stimulated by the trophic effect of the over-abundant sums of money in the form of research grants . . . Many schools frankly state that they are attempting to teach only basic medical science and not clinical medicine. The full-time clinical professor has become primarily a research professor whose chief claim to fame is his 'grantsmanship' and whose hallmark is 'publish or perish.' " In fact, Dr. Brown adds to his indictment, some professors are "fundamentally lacking in an interest in teaching clinical medicine to medical students."

Dr. Clinton L. Compere, former president of the American Academy of Orthopedic Surgeons, verifies the consistent downgrading of the professor who can and wants to teach medical students. He is "seriously disturbed" by the trend of appointments and promotions at medical schools, most of which go to researchers rather than clinical doctors. "It is my feeling that many medical schools are placing undue and unwise emphasis on basic medical research, whether good or bad," he recently stated. " 'How many papers have you published during the past couple of years?' is usually the number one weighted question for an applicant for academic position."

Academic promotion based on research background rather than medical skill and erudition has become a virtual burlesque of the original concept. One full-time professor at a prestigious medical school in New York reveals that it has reached such extremes that promotion in his specialty department goes to the *basic science men*—the most theoretical of doctors, who usually have no clinical experience at all! "They would have no idea how to treat a sick patient," he says.

Others point out that medical status follows the dollar, and most medical-school dollars today are federal in origin. Forty-four percent of medical-faculty men have part of their salaries paid by federal research grants. The federal government, thus far, has failed to recognize the importance of teaching clinical medicine—the diagnosis and treatment of patients.

A 1958 survey of time-breakdown by the AAMC (Association of American Medical Colleges) shows that teaching of medical students took only 25 to 30 percent of the full-time professor's week, a figure that has undoubtedly diminished since. A living case history of how medical professors are diverted from teaching is described by a Dr. John Vender (a pseudonym) in a medical-journal revelation entitled "I Quit Practice to Teach." After describing the academic snubbing he had received because he had been a practicing internist —a lowly LMD (local medical doctor)—Dr. Vender told of the difficulty he had, sticking to his true interest—teaching. "I'm troubled by having to channel most of my efforts into a narrow subspecialty—the narrower, the better. And I dislike having to rush into print with every minor conclusion . . ." He expressed his annoyance at "time-consuming administrative chores," which include everything from an exhibit for a specialist convention to a charter flight to Europe. His medical-student teaching? "One effect of all this is that I have less time for teaching than I'd like."

"Why the relative neglect of the process of teaching?" asks an editorial in the *Journal of Medical Education,* which then attempts an answer. "We know it is unreasonable to expect satisfactory performance from someone who is not interested in what he is doing. Yet, habitually, we relegate the responsibility for teaching to the position of an ongoing initiation rite—a repayment for the privilege of a hospital or a school appointment, appointments that are often sought after for purposes of research interests, hospital admitting privileges, or prestige. Teaching becomes a tax that is levied, not the opportunity that is relished."

Research in medical school is a way of life for most faculty men. Naturally, they exert persuasive efforts to proselytize their best students away from medical practice and into the academic and scientific life. This eminently serves the goals of research, but does it serve society, which desperately needs superior practicing physicians?

Dr. George E. Miller, director of research in medical education at the University of Illinois College of Medicine, calls this the "heart of the matter." Dr. Miller candidly charges: "Some of our words and some of our actions suggest that we are far more interested in the few than in the many, that the practice of medicine is only for the clods who cannot aspire to the clouds of research."

With the elevation of the researcher in medical school has come the merciless downgrading of the clinician—the doctor, as Dr. Samuel Standard of New York describes him, who is primarily interested in "man-sick-today." "Until recently the clinician was the dominant figure in most schools and, as the expression goes, was highest on the pecking order," Dr. Frederick C. Robbins of Western Reserve University School of Medicine reminds us. "Today, there is almost a reversal, with the basic scientist—particularly if he is a molecular biologist or biochemical geneticist—occupying number-one position and the clinician coming last."

The personal tug of interest between clinical teaching and research that goes on within the innards of the typical medical professor is inevitably won by research, states Dr. John Knowles of the Massachusetts General Hospital who views the joust close up. "Progressively frustrated by wanting to excel at teaching and research, but seeing that his research in medicine is being removed farther and farther from the bedside and into the constant-temperature bath, he finds it increasingly difficult to teach clinical medicine as his research is no longer clinical research," Dr. Knowles says about his colleagues in the *New England Journal of Medicine*. "Furthermore, he notes that there is little federal support and even less approval or admiration by his colleagues for clinical research. And finally, the best experience for teaching clinical medicine, the actual direct care of patients and the *whole* patient, takes him too far away and for too long from his research." It takes little intellectual effort to calculate the result of Dr. Knowles's incisive words: medical professors poorer and less experienced in the art of healing—producing new doctors in their deficient image.

It is getting increasingly difficult to find the doctor who can teach, take care of patients and have an intelligent socio-economic viewpoint of medicine, warns Dr. Knowles. "Most professors of medicine know little about these vital things, yet they have tremendous power and are the models for students," he says. "The pendulum of medicine has got to swing back to teaching and patient care, and the medical professors must return to the bedside. A reward system must be established to encourage fine clinicians—to make the clinician who cares for the sick and teaches medical students, an elevated honorable pursuit. We must change our system to clearly make it obvious that it requires the highest powers of intellect and integrity to care for the patient and to teach medical students—rather than to devote oneself to biologic research. If our leaders display these values, the students will follow."

The increasing elimination of both the academic and practicing clinician from the medical-school environment has aroused other outspoken medical men, including the late Dr. Samuel A. Levine of Harvard Medical School, who found the future doctor weaker for it. The practicing clinician—whether GP or general internist—is typically the physician who sees patients at the first stage of illness, whether in the home, office or hospital, he points out. "However, the physician who did this kind of work was gradually eliminated from the important ranks of the medical faculty," he wrote in *JAMA*. "There have followed some unhappy, unfortunate, and harmful results in the training of undergraduate students, internes, and practicing physicians."

Despite such admonishments, faculty men who actually practice medicine daily find that their research colleagues have insufferably snobbish attitudes. "There is a sort of an odor about me here because I practice private medicine every day on people," says a brilliant thirty-five-year-old full professor of surgery at an eastern medical school. "I think that with all this chatter about better education, we're probably producing worse doctors all the time. The student today has trouble actually getting in touch with doctors who really practice medicine."

This perverse environment has a lasting effect on the typical medical student. Some medical professors admit a tendency to overstress those areas—whether cardiology, renal diseases, or some other subspecialty—in which they are involved as researchers and are therefore most expert. In many cases the research learning that the professor passes on—perhaps such esoterica as the molecular biochemistry of virus infections—may no longer be "clinical" at all.

Might this help explain why young doctors can triumph in a rote examination in complex biochemical enzymes, and yet not know enough to use the proper blood-sugar test to detect diabetes? The answers appears to be "Yes," especially if we observe some documented examples of distorted medical-school curriculum and clinical teaching.

The situation has reached such extremes, Dr. Solomon Garb, associate professor at the University of Missouri School of Medicine, informs us, that important diseases are "not fully considered" in medical school, while more esoteric ailments are given considerable attention. "As an example of the imbalance that sometimes results," he says in the *Journal of Medical Education,* "it may be pointed out that teaching and discussions of lupus erythematosus [a usually fatal disease related to rheumatoid arthritis] are fairly extensive, and medical students hear a great deal about it. Doctors in their clinical practice, however, see very few cases of lupus. By contrast, such conditions as cerebral palsy are hardly mentioned during the first two years of medical school, although the practicing physician will probably see many such cases."

Cerebral palsy is not the only common disease whose diagnosis and care is virtually ignored in many medical schools. The drug-induced diseases of the iatrogenic scourge are partially a by-product of the abject neglect of modern applied pharmacology in the third and fourth years of medical college, an educational failing stressed by Dr. Walter Modell of Cornell and others. Dr. Dickinson W. Richards, professor emeritus of medicine at Columbia, believes the "considerable upgrading of clinical pharmacology" would be his first suggestion for change in medical education.

Dr. Raymond J. Jackman of the Mayo Graduate School of Medicine points out that most medical schools offer little instruction in the diagnosis and treatment of common anal and rectal diseases, which are among the major causes of male death. Speaking at a section on proctology at an AMA convention, Dr. Jackman said that "fewer than a dozen" of the eighty-seven medical schools offer students any organized teaching program in proctology, the specialty of anal-rectal diseases.

The dilemma of why most physicians will not do rectal examinations with the metal proctoscope and diagnose curable cancer before it kills over forty thousand men a year is answered by Dr. Jackman's incredible report. Many physicians are never taught how to do it! Residents working at Mayo have told him, he reported to his colleagues, that in all four years at various medical schools and in the full year of internship at hospitals throughout the nation, they had not had even one opportunity to perform a proctoscopic examination. This, says Dr. Jackman, is symptomatic of the excess time the medical student spends on esoteric diseases to the detriment of care and cure of common ailments. "It is," he says, "only a truism to say that more emphasis should be placed on teaching some of the very common problems which every general practitioner will encounter. These surely will include diseases and states involving the anus, rectum and colon, and it seems the epitome of folly to ignore them in any medical school."

The failure of current medical education in the common chronic ailments often handled in the doctor's office is also lamented. "Very frankly, medical schools are not doing an adequate job of teaching the management of diabetics as office patients," Dr. Arthur Krosnick of the New Jersey State Department of Health says in *Medical Tribune,* adding that students are trained at the less practical "biochemical level."

The clinical curriculum—basically Osler's "learning by the hospital bedside"—has obviously been adversely affected by the new research stress. The medical school is constantly concerned about student contact with the LMD, lest he be contaminated by his "bad habits." The student, of course, may have as much reason to fear excessive research contact. As Dr. John Knowles points out, today's student learns clinical medicine at the bedside from a subspecialist-researcher, who may be able to instruct the student in the cardiology problems of a hospitalized patient but will not be able to answer his questions about her thyroid problem. "He must then go elsewhere for the answer," says Dr. Knowles. "This fragmentation gives the student a warped idea of the practice of medicine."

Dr. George E. Miller of Illinois relates another example of research-distorted teaching. "A student may witness vast batteries of clinical tests being ordered routinely without the faculty making clear to him that many of these tests are dictated by the investigative interests of the staff, with no relation to the diagnostic problem of a given patient . . . A case was cited where a senior medical student challenged the faculty, 'When will I be taught when *not* to order an EKG?' In another instance a vast battery of tests was being run on a service incidental to an intensive epidemiological survey, and no one had told the medical students that this was anything other than good medical practice."

It is becoming increasingly apparent to many medical critics that curriculum revision to reduce the amount of *theoretical* science while strengthening the teaching of clinical medicine is essential, if not inevitable, in the research-frenzied atmosphere of our medical colleges. Our most conservative observers concur that much of the biochemistry now taught, for example, is of little use to the practicing physician. In the direction of reform, Albert Einstein College of Medicine in New York has instituted a 10 percent reduction in the basic sciences for the 1965–66 year to allow more time for clinical and community medicine. Professor Rutstein of Harvard, however, has a more radical solution to the present distorted medical training: two distinct and separate medical curricula for future doctors. One would be enriched by heavy clinical training in diagnosis, therapy and preventive medicine for "general physicians."

The other would be a more scientific training for researchers, professors and specialists.

His idea makes excellent sense, but rather than develop two curricula that might be labeled inferior and superior by caste-conscious doctors, it would perhaps be even wiser to develop two *superior* curricula, one to train only researcher-scientists, the other to train *all clinical doctors,* GP's or specialists, whether to teach or practice medicine, or both. Every medical college would have parallel organizations with "research professors" and regular "medical professors," one to teach the theory and investigation of medicine, the other to teach the diagnosis, prevention and therapy of disease and to be in charge of the care of the patient. Any competition between the two could only be to the benefit of the medical student and the patient.

Dr. Osler's use of the hospital bedside provided a better setting for teaching scientific medicine than the doctor's treatment room it replaced. A half century later, the hospital ward still serves an irreplaceable function in medical school teaching. But its exclusive use—say critics—is probably a distorted introduction to the proper practice of modern medicine.

The young medical student sees the diabetic in serious coma; the dying myocardial-infarction heart case; the gall bladder patient awaiting surgery, the pneumococcal pneumonia victim fighting for life. His patients are supine, in their most dependent, childlike state, and often indigent and uneducated. They will stay in the hospital perhaps a week and never be seen again. For any help (or even unknowing harm) they are often vocally grateful to the god-figure doctor.

In actual practice, the physician sits at a desk facing a patient who looks and dresses much like him, may be as successful, or more, in his own line of work and is paying hard currency for the advice. He may be seeking management and therapy for a diabetic condition requiring twenty years or more of control; perhaps he has a heart murmur that needs proper diagnosis and long-term preventive management; he may have a chronic incurable arthritic condition, or an inexplicable pain in his stomach, a throaty cough or a generally chronic feeling of malaise. He may not be in need of hospitalization, but he does require diagnosis and therapy, a sage adviser and perhaps lengthy and considered medical management. He has been to physicians before and may be wary of the advice, annoyed at the fee, and gauging the physician's manner, intelligence and skill.

Is the young physician being trained for this type of medical combat? Is he prepared for this excursion into the real world of private medical practice where patients have free will, where there are no internes, residents or professors to advise him and where the illnesses may be challenging but usually not dramatic or academically interesting? Is he also learning, as one medical realist put it, to "sit and listen to an old woman's complaints about her bowel movements"? Sophisticated critics unanimously answer "No." "Since patients are seen only in the hospital," Thomas McKeown, professor of social medicine at the University of Birmingham Medical School, told a teaching convention of American medical colleges sponsored by the AAMC, "all that can be obtained from the teaching centre is a restricted view of the medical problems of a limited class of patients. With the predominant interest of teaching hospitals in the advance of knowledge, the methods exhibited are inevitably among the most complex, expensive, and time-consuming. Many of them are therefore inappropriate in the circumstances in which most graduates will find themselves."

One American commentator, Dr. K. L. White, describes the atypicality of conditions found in the university hospital. Of a population of 1000 adults, he states, 750 will experience some illness in an average month. Of these, 250 will consult a physician; nine will be hospitalized, five will be referred to another doctor, and only *one* will go to a university hospital. Drs. Charles H. Rammelkamp, Jr., and Edward M. Chester of Western Reserve comment on these enlightening numbers in the *New England Journal of Medicine:* "Thus, clinical training based primarily on inpatient services may present a distorted view of the type of disease encountered in the practice of medicine."

The articulate Dr. Knowles of Massachusetts General concurs, explaining that on "the ward services of teaching hospitals, the average patient is elderly and has been admitted through the emergency ward with one of the degenerative diseases or cancer. The signs of his disease and the results of special tests are more important to the diagnosis than the history. House staff and medical students are taught and learn here."

The student, he says, does not learn where typical patients are hospitalized and thus receives a distorted view of illness and care. The "great middle class" now has a semiprivate bed and a private doctor, and is therefore in the hospital's private, rather than ward, service. These patients suffer from a different complex of ailments, including more diseases in their beginning stages. "Here the history is more important to the diagnosis than the signs of disease. The patients are more articulate in their demands as well as in giving their histories. More preventive medicine is practiced here. The least teaching of house staff and medical students is done here, a peculiar paradox."

The medical student and his learning setting are obviously mismatched. *In addition* to bedside learning, should not the fledgling doctor practice in an office at the side of a *carefully selected* LMD, a board-certified "master" clinician, where he can learn to handle the insignificant, the baffling, and the long-term chronic conditions one sees daily in private practice? Despite the revulsion for private practitioners that exists in some medical colleges, this is the tourney ground of most contemporary medical practice. Not to train our future doctors in its *best* aspects may be disastrous.

The science, the clinical art and the *humanity* of the medical college have been challenged. If the practicing doctor is poor in the humane arts and letters, as is often the case, the poverty can be traced to the medical school where the student learns little to prepare him for the job of working in a complex society with varied patients. Even his medical heritage is ignored; the typical curriculum includes *not a single semester hour in medical history or philosophy*. The impressionable tyro is left to pick up distortions about his profession and his obligations from the pressures of his activity, rather than from the nobility of past heroes, from Hippocrates to Osler, and their sound ideals passed on. Thus unarmed, without a sense of professional fullness, they are flaccid patsies for any detail man, flamboyant therapy, human experimentation, bad medical habits or crackpot political ideology. Without a sense of profession, the medical school becomes a trade school, the physician a tradesman.

"It is time for medical educators to realize that the possession of medical philosophy and ethics is not simply a matter of instincts, emotions, sincerity, or premedical education," says Dr. Herbert Ratner of Illinois. "It is the great failing of modern medicine that it has developed for all practical purposes solely along technical lines. It has failed to incorporate, as Hippocrates and the great medieval medical schools did, medical philosophy and ethics as an intimate part of medical education."

Dr. Julius Comroe of the University of California School of Medicine gives an example of this dearth of ennobling learning at medical school. "A professor of pediatrics told me he deplored the inconsiderate attitude of present internes and residents in physician-physician, physician-patient, and physician-nurse relationships," Dr. Comroe explains. "I asked whether his department of pediatrics spent some time with medical students in teaching the art of medicine and emphasizing proper attitudes; he confessed it did not. Why don't faculty members fulfill their own objectives? Largely, I believe, because they assume that some other faculty member in some other department has taken care of it."

Patients who suspect that modern physicians are not fully molded and have an undeveloped sense of proper rapport with laymen, can find excellent confirmation in the medical-school curriculum, where the concepts of sympathy, idealism, compassion, ethics or even professional relationships with the sick are seldom, if ever, discussed. A recent impromptu session with six fourth-year medical students revealed that only one of them recalled ever hearing a professor discussing nonmedical attitudes toward a patient, and then only in passing! Any attitudes they held toward the sick were strictly imitative, an inferior guide to ideals. With no philosophical reference point in history or idealism, the ethically untutored doctor hardly knows how to cope with the demands put on him by patients, himself, his family and society. Unarmed, he may fall victim to the easy route.

The striking absence of ethics and morality in medical-school curricula is forcefully brought home by Dr. George E. Miller. "Faculty members may say with the greatest sincerity that they want to help students develop high ethical and moral standards; but if the educational program is built entirely upon the acquisition of information and skills, this objective is not a real one . . ."

The young doctor's education is devoid not only of medical philosophy and ethics, but contains not a single course in the humanities, the liberal learning that might help the physician identify with *people* and the society about him. "Perhaps our medical schools should have weekly courses in culture and the humanities," says Dr. Myron Prinzmetal in a *Medical Tribune* editorial. "It is important that our future doctors carry on in the Hippocratic tradition."

The atmosphere of most medical colleges blares out the absence of the humanities. Its incompleteness as a learning environment is evidenced by a campus generally devoid of student groups, athletics, newspapers, student magazines or journals. This is in contrast to other professional schools, such as law, where students produce mature journals of repute. The British medical school, contrary to its American counterpart, encourages the student as a person, and rugby and debating societies flourish alongside the dissected cadaver.

The dearth of humane education in the medical schools is not due to administrative neglect of demand from the students, most of whom are already honed into a technician mentality. An impromptu survey of a handful of Columbia College of Physicians and Surgeons students turned up only one who felt the absence of non-biologic thought. "I miss the humanities fantastically," said this fourth-year student. "I tend to take my intellectual pleasures seriously. I think they make one a better human being, and a better doctor."

This medical-school failure has a continuing, perhaps accelerating effect on the future doctor's idealistic atrophy. Edwin F. Rosinski, professor of medical education at the Medical College of Virginia, noticed some "distressing" views among the student body. As school progressed, students develop less and less interest in continuing education, for example, and a full 25 percent of the graduating class agreed with the statement: "A way to get through medical school is to sit in the middle of the room and say nothing." In their evaluation of their "respect for the dignity and value of man," the seniors scored *lower* than the entering students, a poor brief for medical-school teaching of human values.

Such attitudes can leave the student without the soul strength to fight off a stereotyped pseudoprofessional mold. "Though not intentionally exerted," Dr. Gregg wrote, "the pressures of expectation and example tend to convert the student into a stereotype. By the end of the fourth year, medical students resemble each other in manner, thought, and behavior much more closely than in their first year . . . The spontaneity, the naturalness, the self-reliance, and simplicity and homely originality of character that patients so rightly value in a doctor may or may not emerge from the eclipse. It is, I think, a close call for most medical students and young doctors: they all but prefer the protective stereotype." Other observers, including many patients, feel that the call has been more than close, and the accident fatal.

The medical schools' remedy for such spiritual anemia is usually their training in psychiatry. Unfortunately, in its concentration on human abnormalities it offers a distorted portrait of patients, and the disservice of overdetachment. "In addition to defining basic core material, we must not forget to foster in the student the concern for the patient as a person," Dr. Frederick Robbins reminds us. "The physician must understand man not only from the point of view of molecular biology, but as an organism functioning in society. There has been a tendency to delegate all concern for this aspect of medicine to the department of psychiatry, which is not necessarily desirable."

Many medical educators take a naïve attitude toward the absence of human enrichment in their curriculum. "We assume that as postgraduates, the students who enter here have already received a well-rounded education," says the associate dean of a nationally prominent eastern medical school, a man of learning who should know better.

The well-rounded pre-med student is another dangerous fallacy; his narrow-life focus begins early in training and prematurely deadens the embryo physician. "Once he [the pre-med student] has declared himself, two forces are set in motion, neither of which is entirely desirable," says Dr. Knowles in the *New England Journal of Medicine*. "The first is acceleration of the curriculum, and the second is an 'overwhelming obsession for science,' so that his interests are constricted and restricted and the liberal arts are not given the full measure of attention. What emerges from college may thus be an incomplete product, politically and socially naïve, and not optimally prepared to be, as Lionel Trilling has said, 'at home in and in control of the modern world' . . . the true purpose of study!"

Dr. Knowles then points out the further damage created by current medical training: "The medical-school curriculum accelerates the constricting effect of his premedical education by its complete emphasis on a foundation of basic science in the first two years of medical school. The opportunity still exists to introduce the liberal arts, humanities, and social sciences of medicine, but it is not seized."

The superior student interviewed at Downstate Medical College suggests that a liberal arts degree is superior preparation for a doctor of medicine, that basic college science is all the intelligent medical student needs. (He majored in philosophy.) Medical schools have tried to shed the blame for encouraging the "hot-house," overspecialized pre-med student, but more than one observer has hoisted them on this petard.

"For several years I have read articles in various medical journals to the effect that medical-school educators are looking for the student with a well-rounded premedical education, and not so much the student who is just scientifically oriented . . . Apparently all of this is simply verbiage, meaning nothing. I have a case in point," an Indiana physician writes to a medical periodical. The case is his son, a salutatorian in high school, with an A average in all the sciences. The boy made the dean's list at the University of Chicago, where he first majored in physics, then changed to literature, then to pre-med. During the journey he accumulated a vast background in mathematics, physics, chemistry, English, Latin, German, French, Hebrew, Greek, biology, philosophy and history. He did not, however, complete his advanced sciences, such as organic chemistry. When he was told by medical-school admissions officers that he needed a fifth year in "pre-med," the discouraged student entered a doctorate program in literature. "So medical educators on the one hand are crying for the well-rounded scholar to enter medicine, and on the other hand are slamming the door in his face," says this disappointed physician. "It's no wonder the humanities and sciences are now getting the bulk of the better students. Henceforth when I hear the moans and cries of the medical schools in this regard, I will answer to their insistent pleas, 'Hogwash!' "

In their selection and production of new doctors, the medical colleges border on callous negligence in three areas: the production of an insufficient number of new doctors; the production of the wrong types of doctor to meet patient needs; the selection of these doctors from a minute, unsatisfactory sample of eligible college youth.

The medical schools have refused to produce enough doctors to solve the obvious shortage. The AMA, among others, have been engaged in a statistical subterfuge to disclaim a shortage. ("I think," says the director of a Long Island hospital, "that there has been an unconscious conspiracy to keep the supply of doctors low.") The doctor population—variously described by sources as anywhere from 130 to 149 (typically 135) doctors per 100,000 of population—has been steady for a generation, states the AMA. They are superficially correct, but the trek away from practice into research, industry, defense and administration has altered the number of *available* doctors.

The number available in private practice drops to about ninety per 100,000 population, a chilling statistic when we consider that the average patient visits his doctor twice as often as he did thirty years ago. The profession, in announcing eight new four-year medical schools—from Mount Sinai in Manhattan to a state school in San Diego—plus six two-year schools and some enrollment increases, appears to be straining its production biceps. The Bane Committee report of the Surgeon General's office on the doctor shortage indicates that with a projected population of 235,000,000 in 1975, however, we will need 11,000 medical graduates a year by then just to keep pace with the present shortage!

How well have the medical colleges progressed toward this level? In 1964 the medical colleges graduated 7336 students and approximately 500 osteopaths. Counting two-year medical schools, we now have eighty-seven accredited institutions, with approximately twelve more planned.

The best estimates, including those made by the Association of American Medical Colleges and Dr. Howard A. Rusk, indicate a 1975 graduating class of 9000 to 9300. With osteopaths, and graduates of foreign medical schools, the figure will approach 10,500 new doctors a year. We can already peer a decade ahead and visualize a similar doctor shortage. In fact, with increasing medical usage and further subspecialization, we should anticipate a worsened situation.

The policy of one step forward and two steps backward is confirmed by the Association of American Medical Colleges. They report that in 1955 American medical schools graduated 4.2 doctors per 100,000 population; it dropped to 4.0 in 1957; 3.9 in 1960; and 3.8 in 1963. Only the licensing of over 1300 foreign-trained doctors a year has kept us from faltering catastrophically.

Broader overall planning for the erection of medical schools (at $20,000,000 to $70,000,000 each) is necessary by the profession, states and the federal government. Part of the shortage dilemma, however, can be traced to the reluctant medical dean who resists expansion. The entire yearly enrollment at a typical medical college is less than ninety-five students, and some medical administrators cherish this smallness the way their parent universities boast of their bigness. Columbia University College of Physicians and Surgeons, has had an unchanged yearly enrollment of 120 students for the past fifteen years. Physicians and Surgeons is now "expanding" due to a $1,052,300 matching Public Health Service grant, and will *during the next ten years* add a total of *ten* students.

With 32,000 medical students being "taught" by 14,468 full-time faculty members, and considerably more part-time men, the student-faculty ratio keeps *improving* while the doctor's population ratio keeps *deteriorating*. There are now three times as many full-time faculty men as in 1951, creating a situation of *almost* one teacher per student (1.6) in the third and fourth years, and only 3.5 students to one teacher in the first two years! Low student-teacher ratios may theoretically be desirable, but they are not our prime priority.

The class sizes of all medical schools, with appropriate federal aid, should be *increased* 15 to 25 percent, making the first sizable dent in the doctor shortage. "We do not want our school to become impersonal," states one medical school administrator, when queried on this suggestion. With a 25 percent student-enrollment increase, the student-faculty ratio will be back to where it was in 1955, when few deans were complaining that their schools were oversized, and a few faculty men were complaining of overwork. Support for immediate enrollment expansion of medical schools comes from Dr. John B. deC. M. Saunders, chancellor of the University of California Medical Center who proposes that each four-year medical school enroll an additional fifteen or twenty students per year. Such an expansion, he stresses, would produce as many new doctors as twelve to sixteen additional medical schools.

The factitious limiting of the medical-school-class size has a seldom-discussed deleterious effect: the incompetent student is protected from failure because of the necessity to graduate almost all in these truncated classes. Contrary to folklore, it is not difficult to get through medical school once the ponderous first year (when 7 percent drop out or have to repeat) is past. The image of a medical hatchet precipitously balanced to sever students from the profession at various stages of training is pure humbug. It has, in fact, been suggested that the curriculum is geared to the lowest student denominator. "The medical program is set to the slowness and intellectual activity of the least able but passable student," Dr. Robert A. Moore, president of the Downstate Medical Center of State University of New York has stated. "The abler student marks time, while the tail catches up with him. I was shocked two years ago when a small group of able freshmen told me that they found the first year of medical school less stimulating intellectually than the last year of college."

After the first year (or second, at the latest) minimal performance becomes sufficient because of the increased vested interest of the medical school in the student. "We don't fail anyone," says an administrator in a major medical school. "We do our screening of students at selection time, when we choose only 96 of 1700 applicants. If the student is not doing well, there must be other reasons." In this school's experience, which is reasonably typical, approximately ninety of ninety-six eventually graduate, even though a few may take an additional year to do it.

Protection of the not-so-competent is highly injurious to medicine. A much higher initial enrollment rate, plus a higher force-out rate for scholastic reasons—in clinical as well as science courses—would produce a finer M.D. product. In today's medical structure, once the student has passed the first-year obstacle, graduation, then internship, then licensing, then residency completion are virtually assured for the most mediocre, and worse, medical talents.

The medical-school product is also being created in inappropriate models for our civilization. As is commonly known, less than 18 percent of new physicians intend to become general practitioners. Those who expect to practice family medicine of any type—general practitioner, internist or pediatrician—still constitute a decided minority. (Only 8.5 percent of internes questioned intend to enter pediatrics, and 18 percent internal medicine.) The result is a constant decline in the number of doctors who will *take care* of adults and children. In 1931 there were ninety-four of these three categories of doctors per 100,000 population; today it has fallen below *sixty,* and is constantly declining.

Medical schools, with a few exceptions, have made no effort to avert this upcoming calamity. Medical-school administrators, when interviewed, are quick to point out GP medical inadequacy— probably with justification—but have no sensible replacement in their training schedule. "I would hope that the board-certified internist would take his place," states one eastern associate dean overoptimistically. The choice may be admirable, but our annual production of fourteen hundred doctors who *intend* to become internists of all types, including subspecialists, when measured against our need for family physicians, places this comment in the realm of near-nonsense.

Dr. David Rutstein of Harvard shows the impracticality of such fanciful wishes. "It has been suggested many times that the internist will be the general physician of the future. But, with our present medical education program, the number of internists providing personal health services cannot now nor in the foreseeable future meet the need," he states. He adds that over one quarter of the internists practice in New York and California, and that others have been diverted out of private practice. "Assuming that they were evenly distributed throughout the country, that they were all in general practice, and that pediatricians would continue to be educated at the present rate, it is estimated that by 1975, if general practitioners continue to disappear at the 1931–1957 rate, we will need *six times* [italics mine] as many internists as are now in practice in the United States to regain the general physician-patient ratio of the early thirties (one per 1100 of the population)."

The alternative to medical-school unreality is concrete federal grants and liberal "family physician" fellowships, to encourage the model of doctor the nation requires. (Dr. Edwin L. Crosby, executive vice-president of the American Hospital Association, has castigated the profession for not knowing its own needs. "We have never tried to find out," he points out, "how many neurologists, surgeons, dermatologists, internists, and so on, we need to assure that the highest possible level of medical care is being given.")

The third production-and-recruitment failing of the American medical colleges is the student himself. Of almost 500,000 bachelor's degree gradutes in the 1964–65 year, only 19,168 applied for admission to medical schools. Federal loans and AMA-secured loans, plus greater father-affluence and the lure of physician income have stemmed the precipitous decline in applications in the last few years, but medical-school applicants still make up a minute sample—4 percent of all college graduates.

Contrary to popular myth, it is not too difficult to get into medical school. Approximately half the applicants are accepted the first year, and many of the others enter foreign medical schools, schools of osteopathy, go into dentistry, or apply again the second year. Those who are accepted are an atypical group of young college graduates of twenty-one to twenty-three years of age. The medical student is generally an offspring of an upper- or upper-middle-class American, in the top two of five sociological classifications.

Professor Edwin F. Rosinski at the Medical College of Virginia studied the social backgrounds of students from five medical colleges. Even though he eliminated the Ivy League schools, the majority of students (58.3 percent) came from an upper- or upper-middle-class home. More than a third of them (34 percent) were offspring of the top upper category, which comprises only 3 percent of the population, and is composed of bankers, doctors, corporation lawyers, landed gentry, top executives and owners of large businesses. "Medicine is not recruiting enough students from the lowest social classes," says Professor Rosinski in a recent issue of *JAMA,* pointing out that "students from other social classes cannot afford the expense, so they select a career obtainable with less financial hardship."

Intellectually the medical student is in the above-average group, but exhibits little manifestation of academic genius. Twelve percent of medical students were A college students, about the same number had C grades, but the vast bulk were B students in undergraduate school. Much has been said of the decline from the 1950–51 peak, when fully 40 percent of new medical students had A grades. Dr. Ward Darley of the Association of American Medical Colleges explains that this was a result of having 50 percent more applicants than now because of the flood of returning World War II veterans and the financial support of the GI Bill. The higher student quality that accompanies more applicants and financial help should provide a hint of who could be drawn to medicine with proper incentives.

The medical student, say some observers, is also atypical because of his rarefied attitudes, possibly a by-product of his upbringing. Professor E. Lowell Kelly of the University of Michigan presents a dour portrait of this student as a materialistic and nonidealistic young man. He claims that if today's medical students were not becoming physicians, they would be "manufacturers, big business men, production managers or engineers." They are not, he states, the kind of people "interested in doing something for the good of mankind," adding that as a group they "reveal remarkably little interest in the welfare of human beings."

We have already observed one study of doctors-to-be, which revealed that "prestige" and "income" were the major impetus for medicine. Could this be a temporary outbreak of crassness that will be mollified by the surging new idealism of the younger generation?

Apparently not in medicine. A Michigan physician, Dr. E. C. Swanson, president of the Federation of State Medical Boards, surveyed members of a premedic club at an unnamed state university. He noted what he called "a twisted attitude about the practice of medicine" among these future doctors. "About 80 percent of the group seemed to be looking at the practice of medicine as one would view the merchandise behind a window pane at Tiffany's," Dr. Swanson stated. He added a discouraging peek into this nascent supermaterialism: about half expected to buy a Cadillac, on time payments, to gain prestige in the community.

Developing a new breed of doctors will require enticing a larger portion of the five hundred thousand graduates each June into medicine, and psychologically spicing the profession with young men of varied backgrounds and attitudes. Just as industrial recruiters boldly scour the campuses for prime corporate talent, it is now appropriate for the medical schools to shed their imperious isolation and actively compete for the superior students.

The cost to the student for a medical education is a mammoth deterrent to any reform. It is only softened, not crushed, by low-interest federal and high-interest AMA-guaranteed student loans. Although the legislation was almost blocked by the AMA, a student may borrow up to $2000 a year from Uncle Sam, repayable over a period of ten years, with interest, after he is in practice. However, the move may have failed in its attempt to attract less well-heeled youngsters. Some deans—who control the outlay of all loan funds—frown on students getting "excessively" in debt. Despite the student's ability to borrow, almost all medical schools insist on knowing how the applicant intends to finance his education. Federal largesse is not generally a satisfactory reason for selection.

The average cost of the four years of education, including living cost, was $11,642 in 1960 and is closer to $13,000 today. Despite loans, this cost makes the choice of medical school one generally limited to the more-than-comfortable classes. The determined student may surmount this adversity, but even the contemplation of these vast sums can deter most from medicine.

The solution to more applicants, better-quality students and a more humane outlook for the profession is obvious: nonrepayable, *full-tuition grants to all medical students,* from federal funds given as grants-in-aid to medical schools specifically for this purpose. The students' tuition, once a major item, now brings in only 5 percent of medical-school income! Replacing this lost school income with such a plan is minor, its significance major. The tuition costs of all thirty-two thousand medical students is $32,280,656 a year, a mere stave in the $309 million federal pork barrel now allotted to medical schools for faculty salaries, medical research and building construction.

The lure of free tuition should more than double the number (and quality) of applicants within three years, an excellent *beginning.* Blessed with a surplus of superior medical hopefuls, the medical schools should become more sage in their selection of future healers. The young doctor, too, should greet his new career more idealistically without worry about enforced penury.

Some astute schools are aware of their inadequacies and have at least toyed with innovations, a few of which may exert an influence on the medical school—and the doctor—of tomorrow. To tackle the doctor shortage, costs and lengthy training simultaneously, several schools, including Northwestern, Pennsylvania State, Johns Hopkins and Boston University, have experimental programs that condense the four undergraduate years and the four years of medical school into a total of five to seven years.

To answer advocates of "instant doctors," critics cite their youth, their lack of "seasoning," and the enormous amount to be learned. Associate Dean George A. Perera of Columbia University College of Physicians and Surgeons summed up the articulate opposition to "acceleration" in an editorial "All in Good Time," a plea for mature physicians. "In short," he says, "those who study medicine must be adult members of society; they must have gained insight through depth as well as breadth; they must be equipped with the understanding, the ability to communicate, the stability, the warmth and the stature of whole persons . . ."

Some schools are also experimenting with curriculum change, but several have limited innovation to the use of new "programed" teaching. The newer medical schools, such as Mount Sinai, will be introducing courses in electronics, physics and computers. Western Reserve University School of Medicine, however, has taken the lead in basic reform, in integrating the sciences and the human being, a pragmatic try at the "whole man" concept so flippantly mouthed by other schools. Rather than having the student learn the physiology of the heart independently of its gross anatomy, for example, the Western Reserve curriculum is "interdepartmental." The study of the cardiovascular system, for example, is integrated. The student is introduced to patients in his very first year. A half day a week (insufficient time) is devoted to early clinical experience with a family in the university hospital's family clinic, including aiding in the care of a pregnant woman. Once the child is born, the student follows its progress through the next few years.

In the third year the student makes a detailed study of a patient with chronic disease, key training that is usually neglected in medical school. In his final sixteen months of training the student completes six clerkships, including work in the group clinic for ambulatory patients, where the student is responsible for the management of their care. During the entire sixteen months, the student spends a day a week in his own "office" treating patients.

The Western Reserve reform program has attracted a flood of applicants and has been heralded by many medical educators. It answers only a portion of the critiques leveled against our medical schools, but it is at least an attempt to make the catechism of medical college conform to the desperate need for competently trained physicians.

Many other schools are making hopeful changes, but with the trepidation of the medical establishment. Several medical schools, including those at Cornell University, the University of Colorado, Temple and the University of North Carolina are trying to teach "comprehensive medicine," implying mobilization of all resources for the patient's care, including preventive medicine. At Cornell the "Comprehensive Care and Teaching Program" is primarily a twenty-two-week clerkship in ambulatory medicine, during the fourth year of training. Operating out of the New York Hospital clinics in Manhattan, each student receives either a family to follow in the clinics or a patient in the "home care" program.

Certain medical colleges, including the University of Wisconsin and the University of Vermont, are conducting pre-Flexner experiments in the master-apprentice system. Under these programs, students spend two or three months with their "preceptor" doctor in his office and on home calls, learning by observing and doing. In addition to a preceptor program for senior students, the University of Kansas conducts a "home care" program in which freshman medical students accompany a physician on house calls. The University of Tennessee has developed an entire department geared to "general practice," and are giving their students experience in the job of family care.

Other new programs are hopeful of stimulating the atrophied socio-economic awareness and conscience of the student. Albert Einstein College of Medicine expects to use the "giant laboratory" of New York City itself toward a community-oriented medical-training program. Beginning with the 1965–66 year, Einstein students meet patients, briefly, for two hours a week, from the very beginning of training. The school appears convinced that "group practice" will be the future of superior medicine, and states that "eventually," through gradual change, the "curriculum of the school will prepare the student to be part of this system."

Many of these medical college experiments are mere antimacassars covering the worn fabric of traditional medical education. The painful failure of one such experiment at Harvard is a case history in point. Several third-year medical students had been assigned as "family physicians" to Boston West End families living within ten minutes of the Massachusetts General Hospital, which was to be the "doctor's" care center.

"It proved very difficult to put the average third-year student at Harvard Medical School into the role of family doctor," admits a Harvard report in the *Journal of Medical Education*. The school points out that "the majority of students were unable to achieve a responsible position in medical care of their families." They then inadvertently explain the failure: "Students were required to care for their families during their *free time* [italics mine]."

Some experimental programs fail because of lack of commitment, but most suffer from the broader ailment of incomplete reform. Once the need for this reform—in curriculum, in faculty, in selection, in quality and quantity of M.D.'s produced, and in medical-school dedication to humanism and idealism—is recognized, the pedagogic devices for its implementation will follow inevitably. Meanwhile, the patient can only hope that the new, awaited revolution in American medical education which will transform the inadequate scientific "trade school" of today into a house to produce skilled and humane healers, is somewhere in the offing. Its urgency is not a whit less than it was in 1910.

Chapter XI

Internes and Residents:
From Innocence to Practice

"When I first began my internship, I wanted very much to have a warm and good relationship with my patients," says a first-year resident at Bronx Municipal Hospital who had just completed his internship at this university-connected hospital. "I was concerned about each and every case, and wanted to be sure to keep the family informed about what was going on. I felt that this was the duty of the 'personal physician,' and as their interne on the ward, that was my job while they were in this hospital. But after a while, I found I couldn't keep it up. I was a slave laborer, working around the clock. I worked five and a half days from 8 A.M. to 7 P.M. and every other night from 7 P.M. to 8 A.M. The way the night duty is blocked out, the night shifts overlap and I sometimes went for days at a time without any break.

"I guess that during my first three months I rarely got more than four hours sleep. A young interne feels important, but the old interne just values sleep. I found that the pressure of work can destroy a carefully built-up medical philosophy. I had hoped to be a warm doctor. Now, instead, I tend to be brusque and abrupt with patients. I have no time or energy for nonmedical matters."

This young man had been experiencing his trial-by-sweat, the traditional punishing, curing and ostensibly maturing process, which, once completed, older physicians take pride in. The theory of the internship—a one-year hospital tour for medical-school graduates which begins July 1 throughout the nation and ends each June 30, with two weeks off for good behavior—is that it is postgraduate education that will prepare him for licensed practice. From another point of view, the interne is a medical laborer, a "house staff" member who works for the hospital and private "attending" doctors cheaply. He may, or may not, learn (or be taught) to be a good physician in the process. Although the hospital bedside system ostensibly has scientific medical roots in the Osler system, internships are actually more like the old master-apprentice scheme in which today's fledgling doctor "picks up" his practical medicine—with both bad and good habits—as he works, with or without sleep.

The argument for both internship and residency in the making of the doctor is stressed by many physicians, including Dr. Eugene A. Stead, Jr., chairman of the department of medicine at Duke University School of Medicine. "Internship and residency years are the golden years in the life of a physician who practices medicine. They are the years when he first becomes a professional worker, the years when patients are first willing to entrust their bodies and minds to his care and the years of close association with bright young colleagues and mature doctors," he states in the *New England Journal of Medicine*. "They are important formative years, and they shape the future conduct of the young physician more than any other experience."

Because of the accuracy of Dr. Stead's emphasis, both the interne and residency concepts have stood the test of time. However, there is much critical evidence that between the theory of today's postgraduate training and its actual results in producing the most capable general physicians and specialists, there is a serious schism that is offensive to excellence. The hope of creating mature, competent doctors by thrusting them into the hospital inferno is often stronger than the planning and postgraduate training that accompanies it. The much-vaunted specialist training of the American doctor, for example, is often a slipshod three-year hospital residency without regimen or appropriate academic standards.

Immortalized in fiction, television and films, the junior "house staffer," the white-coated interne, has been drawn in such legendary proportions that it may be difficult to create a realistic portrait of him. He averages twenty-five to twenty-seven years in age, and contrary to legend, is neither single nor poverty-stricken—although he once was both. The fictionalized interne is not only overworked but oversexed and undersatiated, ever pursuing (or being chased by) ward nurses. Today an estimated 80 percent of internes are married, some with children. The tradition-bound profession had for a long time frowned on internes marrying and had steadfastly maintained that an interne did not need money. He was a "trainee" and his meager stipend was really a gratuitous "scholarship," a patronizing phrase still used at Duke University. This is a throwback to a half century ago, when some of the better medical schools required an internship toward a medical degree, and the interne was still a student. Today, the school merely turns him over to a hospital to complete his medical education.

With increased hospital admissions and less charity work by practicing physicians, the interne has become the backbone of care in many hospitals, and has been demanding better pay for his *work*. "Internes and residents deserve a living wage, and they are beginning to get it," says a Montefiore Hospital administrator in New York. "Years ago the better the hospital, the lower the stipend, on the theory that the interne was getting a great education and should pay for it, that he should 'sweat for the privilege.' But with a living wage the internes and residents can be freed from personal worry about their families, stop 'moonlighting' to make ends meet, and concentrate on what they are doing."

The pay scale at Montefiore is typical of the impressive advances made in the last few years that have been destroying the pathetic image of the penurious young doctor selling his blood for a mess of victuals. Internes at the hospital (now affiliated with Albert Einstein College of Medicine) receive $4120 a year, plus Blue Cross, malpractice insurance, uniforms and laundry. If he is married, low-cost housing in a hospital-owned apartment house is available. First-year residents receive $4620; second-year, $5120; third-year, $5620; fourth-year, $6120; and $6370 for chief residents of the Ben Casey ilk.

A survey of twenty-eight leading hospitals revealed that this dramatic new interne munificence is not unique, although some schools —such as Johns Hopkins—stick resolutely to the traditional theory that low pay is a privilege. Interne salaries as of July 1, 1964, averaged about $3500, with additional stipends of $600 in many hospitals for married men. The resident scale, which begins after internship, is typically in the $4000- to $5000-a-year range in leading centers such as Baylor University in Texas and the University of California hospitals. Even the New York municipal hospitals pay over $6000 a year for senior house staffers, a salary won after pressing their case with a hired attorney.

AMA reports on this new "affluence" show that almost 10 percent of hospitals offer internes an unprecedented $5000 plus. Over a hundred hospitals are luring residents with a *starting salary of at least $7000*—up to a once-incredible $11,500 a year! Dr. Richard H. Lyons of the State University of New York (Upstate) Medical School is one of many medical critics who see a $6000 minimum for house staffers essential.

"I think that within five years, house staffers will be making living wages for men their age," says one administrator. "By that I mean between six thousand and seventy-five hundred dollars for internes, and ten thousand dollars for senior residents. I think it has to come."

Another administrator puts it in philosophical perspective. "Perhaps it will eliminate the unhealthy feeling of resentment that many young doctors pick up in training, namely, that 'I was forced to starve for years. When I get out, I'm going to get mine.' "

The pressure of funds becomes most acute during residency years when the young doctor may be approaching thirty and has a wife and child or two to support. The unbalanced family budget can be rectified in only one way: moonlighting. According to surveys, the majority of residents take outside physician jobs: covering private doctors at night, on weekends and during summer and winter vacations; doing insurance-company physicals; evening and weekend work in emergency rooms or clinics. Busy obstetricians have been known to hire residents (who, unlike internes, are usually licensed doctors) to handle deliveries for them.

Moonlighting has been condemned by the AMA Council on Medical Education and is often prohibited by hospital regulations, but administrators have learned to blink at the indiscretion. Acknowledging its present financial necessity, a Chicago physician, Dr. Roland R. Cross, uses the pages of a trainee magazine, *RISS*, to warn against its damage. Dr. Cross describes a case history of four residents who have negotiated to "cover" for a private pediatrician on night calls and weekends for a guarantee of $1000 a month plus a percentage of the calls. Their income from moonlighting exceeds their hospital stipend.

The result of such free enterprise initiative may, however, be medically poorer house staff members, what he calls "a crew of tired, dull-eyed residents who've been up half the night." Medical moonlighting at all levels, he points out, is "undermining our system of medical education." He adds, "It's responsible, in part, for unnecessary dropouts, for residents who sack out when they should be on service and for the trouble medical schools have in recruiting enough students of the right kind."

Some institutions, including Bronx Municipal Hospital-Albert Einstein Medical Center, have been diverting Blue Shield insurance payments to a fund for internes and residents. With unbrotherly affection, organized medicine, from the AMA to Blue Shield, has attacked this diversion of money to their juniors. An AMA committee had recommended that a portion of fees paid to attending physicians be tapped for internes and residents, who after all do much of the attendings' work. The AMA delegates—most of whom are themselves attendings (private doctors on the hospital staff)—voted it down, 98 to 87, substituting a pious but breadless resolution for "appropriate methods of financial support."

To escape the financial dyspnea, some doctor-trainees find respectable escape in the Armed Forces, a "socialized" haven for physicians. The U.S. Air Force will commission a doctor while *still in medical school,* granting a fourth-year student a second lieutenant's commission and pay. After graduation he is promoted to temporary captain, and assigned an internship in a military or civilian hospital. After completing his internship, he is promoted to captain, and serves a year on active duty with a pay of over $700 a month. "Then," states the Air Force, "you apply for a residency in your specialty, which you may take in either a civilian or military hospital, without loss of pay."

The punishing work schedule of the typical interne can be as detrimental to medical idealism as penury. Most of the 9636 internes who work in 765 hospitals (a decreasing number of hospitals each year) work thirty-six hours on, then twelve hours off, then thirty-six hours on, with a lighter Sunday schedule. During this time the interne will be involved in delivering babies, sewing up wounds in the emergency room and admitting the acutely ill. It is baptism by full immersion into medical responsibility that takes him through the medical wards, obstetrics, and perhaps pediatrics or psychiatry. His own patients are often indigent and elderly, many of them in terminal illness. Since the one in nine hospitals that has interne programs tends to be among the largest and most general, internes and residents see three to six times as many deaths as in other hospitals. (A new trend toward a "straight" rather than traditional "rotating" internship may eventually restrict him to a specialty immediately after graduation.)

In his daily activities the interne rises to the height of the physician. He is also a simple technician drawing blood and urine samples, and sometimes doing the most menial jobs. The "scut" work and emergency-room coverage he performs make him invaluable to understaffed hospitals and to busy private doctors, to whom he is a gift of extraordinary proportions, an unpaid sweating assistant.

Interne responsibility and schedules vary, but the experience of internes at one university hospital is fairly representative. The patients are often admitted without a "personal" physician, a role the interne assumes. He does an immediate work-up with all essential (and some nonessential) tests, makes a tentative diagnosis and prescribes therapy. If the situation is not an emergency, the first-year resident—the interne's supervisor and mentor—will review the chart the following day, discussing the case with the interne. He may or may not re-examine the patient.

The dramatic daily "rounds," which represent the primary teaching ground for the interne, are most extensive in university-affiliated hospitals. They are likely to include the attending faculty member in charge of the ward, a resident, the interne on the case, and even a few medical students. The interne ostensibly learns from the reactions to his diagnoses and suggested therapies, and simultaneously serves in the role of teacher to the medical student, who may help him "present" the case. By working and walking on the wards, by talking to everyone from nurse to chief of medicine, over coffee, at bedside or in a weekly conference, the interne ostensibly learns the art of medicine by "contact."

The frenetic, nonintellectual nature of many internships is described by Dr. Robert Bigley of the University of Oregon Medical School. "From their desks the few nurses directed a wild traffic of aides, orderlies, and patients," he writes of his own internship. "The clinical laboratory seemed totally inadequate; internes drew blood for testing and did their own blood counts, urine examinations, and smears for bacteria. Internes took patients to and from X-ray, then stole the films from the guardian of the X-ray files and carried them to the ward for inspection."

Few hospitals, including university-affiliated ones, offer formal training for the interne. There are clinical conferences and an occasional lecture in a few hospitals, but the basic learning is by *case*. The "textbooks" are sick patients who are, by theory, to be discussed with the interne by his superiors. His teachers range from the first-year resident, who rides closest supervisory herd, to the attending (a private-practice doctor or faculty member) and up to the chief of service, if the hospital is alert enough to employ one. There is little scientific knowledge imparted except as it arises randomly—if at all—from the work the interne is doing. The interne whose wards are the last sanctuary of the aged, for example, may learn a considerable amount about a minor percentage of medical practice.

A retiring chief resident at Downstate Medical Center in Brooklyn described the training and supervision of internes as it theoretically functions. "At eight A.M. on the medicine ward, we have a full complement of four internes, two residents and four students. From eight to nine-thirty the interne sees all his patients, draws blood, takes gastric and fasting tests. He visits his patients, often along with the supervising resident, and two medical students. In the case of a heart patient, for example, the interne would ask how he spent the night. If his heart was beating fast, the interne would take an electrocardiogram before ordering the digitalis. He would also review the lab work, and make the plan for the patient for the next twenty-four hours. Later in the morning, the attending physician in charge of the ward would make rounds, and the interne would present his new cases, narrating the history, his diagnosis, and the therapy he has prescribed. The interne gets his direct supervision from the first-year resident, each of whom handles two internes.

"According to policy, the resident is supposed to be called on all new admissions. If it is an acute case, he calls the resident right in. If not, he'll wait to call him after he has done the work-up. As the year goes on and the interne matures, the policy tends to slide.

He doesn't call the resident at all if he thinks he has the situation under control. If the interne and resident have both examined the same patient and have come to a different conclusion, they bring the problem to the faculty member on the ward, and he decides.

"As chief resident, one of my duties is to check all new patients each morning, read the chart, perhaps check some physical findings. If I find that the interne has made a mistake, I will call him over and go over the case with him. Every chief has his own way of handling internes. The one before me used to get excited, and yell at the nervous interne: 'You almost killed that patient!' I handle it differently."

Is the system good enough for interne training? Does it provide the best in postgraduate education? "Learning on the firing line is the only way," states a graduate interne at Bronx Municipal, adding his opinion that the typical supervision of the first-year resident is generally sufficient. "His one year of extra experience is usually enough to get you through most cases," he states in what may be a highly debatable opinion.

This same young physician inadvertently offers one reason why current informal interne education often breaks down. The interne is never criticized at the bedside during rounds because of the presence of the patient. The "learning"—critiques and suggestions —comes instead in doctorly "chats" between residents and attending doctors in stolen moments in dining rooms and in the halls. But the precious learning moments are not always available. "Because of the volume of the work and the responsibility I had as an interne," explains the young first-year resident, "there was less and less time for me to chat about what I was doing."

The current training of internes and residents is quite analagous to the chaotic schooling of medical students prior to the Flexner reforms. Our postgraduate training programs are unstandardized, and the result—like the pre-Flexner medical school—encompasses every quality from exceptional to abysmal. The comparison is apt, for Flexner helped remove undergraduate medical training from the broad unevenness of the master-apprentice system and placed it under university control. Current postgraduate training is mainly a master-apprentice system in which the body of knowledge is passed on, by unexamined word of mouth, from medical generation to generation in hospitals of uneven quality and concern.

Its quality depends on the amount and intensity of teaching. Formal training is virtually nonexistent in the typical program. The learning, as we have seen, is basically by "walking and talking," whether on rounds, in conferences or in "chats." If economics, time and organization draw the attending doctors away from even this informal scheme—or if they are not sufficiently qualified themselves —the result is failure.

The interne's learning, from moment to moment, comes from

the youngest of masters, the first-year resident who has just finished his own internship. He may not be a provident teacher. If the young "master's" just formed habits are faulty, they may be passed on intact to the impressionable young interne. The system's reliance on the resident is illustrated by an interne profile published in the *Lilly Review*. "The ward is run by a resident," states a young interne at a Midwestern university hospital. "We're in constant contact with him. We have lots of questions on how to treat the patients, how much morphine to give a child who's four years old and two days postoperative, for example." This, the observer can see, is hardly the way to learn the intricacies of pediatric pharmacology.

The greenness of the new interne provokes a smile from the profession, but considerably less from the patient saddled with him. The interne's lack of basic doctoring ability, despite his proud M.D.—the failing of the medical school—is obvious to all who work with him. "Almost all internes are green when they begin," says one hospital administrator. An experienced chief resident adds that it takes at least a few months to "season" an interne, during which time he can be expected to make many naïve, perhaps serious errors. "In July, when the new internes come in," says a chief resident, "every electrocardiogram machine in the building is soon broken."

One doctor recalls asking an interne to "put the blood on the wall," a professional idiom which means to tape a tube of the patient's blood somewhere to check its clotting ability. The interne looked at the resident quizzically, then did what he was told: he squirted a hypodermic full of the patient's blood onto the plaster wall and all watched horrified as it slowly descended. The massive change-over which brings in almost ten thousand new graduates into the nation's hospitals simultaneously on July 1 each year can make summertime a most interesting learning experience for both internes and hospital patients.

The interne's medical unsureness may be matched by his growing insensitivity and lack of rapport with patients. "Not all internes are insensitive, but many are. There is a definite need to produce a more sensitive doctor than the present physician," says Dr. Peter Rogatz, director of the Long Island Jewish Hospital. "I don't want the young doctors to be social workers, but more has to be done to improve their relationships with people. Some have become so intent on scientific matters—which are important—that they have lost track of emotional factors." He sees the root of possible insensitivity in medical-school training, which, if properly reoriented, could enable the young M.D., he believes, "to survive the stress of internship without becoming a machine."

The foibles of current internship and residency-specialty programs appear to be numerous, and galling. One is the progressive promotion of the less competent or incompetent trainees, without any challenge, tutoring, drilling or examination. The present system, when faced with a weak interne who has undeservedly been graduated as an M.D., is to "cover" defensively for him, a professional gesture that becomes impossible when he graduates into unsupervised private practice.

A resident at a university hospital explains the unique protective system: "Often the chief resident identifies the internes without medical ability. He tells the resident supervising the fellow to check all his patients, no matter how minor the case seems. If the resident has two internes like this, the poor fellow will have to work his ass off covering. Right now we have three internes like that out of twenty-eight."

Projected nationally, the number of incompetent young internes is undoubtedly higher than in this university hospital, for in the contrary-to-logic, unco-ordinated world of medicine *the best medical students get the best internships in the best hospitals.* "If he is a good student and his acquisitive powers are strong," confirms Dr. Knowles of Massachusetts General Hospital, "he will receive the best internship."

Meanwhile, the mediocre, and worse, young M.D.'s who need training the most, get it the least. They are relegated to inferior, unaffiliated hospitals, where their ineptness or mediocrity is reinforced by bad supervision and training, and where their labor is often more important than their learning. The profession either "protects" or exiles them, but neither drops them from medicine or teaches them with added fervor. Meanwhile the talented young men —who need it the least—are constantly skimmed off the top of each class by the better institutions. While of benefit to the prestige hospitals, it is a disservice to the community, whose medical care is eventually provided by the bulk of physicians never so privileged.

Training at Peter Bent Brigham Hospital in Boston was "superb," says one of its graduates. "Learning was going on all the time, in grand rounds, in lectures, formal conferences, and informal conversation," says Dr. Eli A. Friedman, assistant professor of medicine at Downstate Medical College, who took his three-year internal-medicine training at Peter Bent. "So many exciting things were happening that it was a battle not to go to sleep. The attending faculty members love their profession and gave their time to the residents more than freely. In addition to their regular schedule, they might come in at one A.M. to admit a patient, and sit with us over coffee in the lunchroom and discuss the case. We had the man who wrote the textbook all to ourselves."

The gap between this type of institution and other training hospitals, where teaching of the house staff is often a side line rather than a dedication, makes the early identification of the less-than-competent interne and resident—and their more vigorous education—a necessity. Contrary to fictional opinion, internes and residents need not pass any hurdle or examination to be promoted or to practice subsequently as a specialist. The only criterion demanded is time put in rather than competence exhibited. It has been said that it is impossible to be dropped from internship unless the young physician rapes a nurse, or from residency unless the specialist-to-be goes thoroughly berserk.

It would perhaps be prudent (from a patient viewpoint), in a system without attrition which graduates almost all its medical students (92 percent), promotes *all* its internes, permits *all* those desiring to specialize to finish their residency, to concentrate the superior training in superior facilities on the *worst* students, instead of vice versa. If not this extreme, at least greater effort—and less protection—should be expended for the weak physician. This is medicine's last real opportunity to rehabilitate his medical habits: once he has completed his training, he has the expert camouflage of the institution's diplomas to confuse the inexpert patient.

Dr. James A. Campbell of the University of Illinois College of Medicine speaks of the current internship as "submerged in today's confusion," and calls for reform: "Hopefully the efforts to solve the problems of graduate medical education . . . will again be successful in restoring order in this chaos, as were those once directed toward elimination of the gross evils in the undergraduate medical education."

Surprisingly, the two- to five-year residency programs are cast in the same chaotic mold as interne training. Almost no residency program has a true curriculum, despite the mountain of information to be absorbed in any of the specialties. Learning is once more "picked up" from one's superiors as one works, depending on the curiosity and initiative of the resident, and the availability and skill of his superiors. Training in the specialties today consists too often of a meager academic program which includes rounds, conferences, a few lectures, and journal clubs—a monthly discussion of current medical literature.

The massive knowledge—whether in dermatology or orthopedics —is not passed down in any rigorous, coherent curriculum, nor is the resident ever examined on what he is learning. Only in a few prestigious institutions, where they have fewer places in the senior residency years, would an insufficiently competent resident be asked to go elsewhere, and residency vacancies are always available. (In the perpetual seller's market of medicine, there are 37,357 available residency places and only 29,485 residents to fill them, 7000 of whom are foreign graduates.) The only exceptions to this failing of formal education are three- to six-month basic science courses at *some* hospitals, in a few specialties such as ophthalmology. "The hospital assumes that we understand the unspoken code—that we are supposed to learn as much as possible," one resident explains about the honor system that controls, and often fails, their education. It is an unusual educational system that leaves the decision of competence level to the student.

An acerbic insight into the failings of some American residency programs was supplied by a vocal foreign student, Dr. Manuel F. E. Bonnemaison, a Fellow at the famed Mayo Foundation, who completed a residency at a Chicago voluntary hospital. In a frank "Special Communication" in *JAMA,* Dr. Bonnemaison describes the unstandardized nature of residency training, the gap between theory and practice of postgraduate education. "Particular programs in any of the three types of institutions (university, voluntary-charity, and private hospitals) may show deficiencies; however, charity hospitals and private hospitals are more apt to have unsatisfactory programs. Deficient programs may be such that not much teaching is done and residents spend a great deal of time doing unimportant chores that could be done by any well-trained member of the ancillary staff. Grand rounds may not exist; instead, the resident may be engaged sporadically in social rounds with different attending physicians. Anatomy, pathology, journal club, and other academic activities may be postponed for a special course. Also, the hospital may lack a library and study room for the benefit of residents.

"Residents who spend all their time in some private institutions are not thoroughly trained," the young Mayo physician continues. "Those who work in charity hospitals may acquire bad traits difficult to correct because of the lack of adequate supervision. Many times they find themselves alone when they have to make serious decisions, sometimes acting *not* in the best interests of their patients."

This close-up indicates a core deficiency of many residency programs. Rather than rigorous training leading to competence in a specialty, they can be nonacademic, low-paid house doctorships which relieve private physicians of much of the responsibility of hospital care of their patients, releasing them to earn more in their lucrative office practices. In a medical community where 82 percent of young doctors are becoming specialists, less-than-rigorous training for these specialties is unconscionable. Dr. Leland S. McKittrick of Boston reveals the tremendous variance in the training for different surgical specialties, pointing out in *JAMA* that "there is no central authority with the responsibility to stimulate, develop, and co-ordinate the tremendous effort necessary to assure success, and to evaluate the results." He offered the example of an OB-GYN specialist being able to do major pelvic surgery after only eighteen months of surgical residency, while the general surgeon would need four years of training before being "certified" to do a similar procedure. It is difficult, Dr. McKittrick says, "to look at the total picture in this area and not be aware of important inadequacies or, at least, inconsistencies and shortcomings in our present educational program." Dr. John Knowles is one medical critic who is convinced that resident training will have to become standardized and more formalized within the next five years.

The AMA Council on Medical Education does "approve" interne and residency programs in hospitals; in one recent year it withdrew approval from 117 residency-specialty programs and added 120 new ones. The AMA approval is not a sufficient guarantee, however, for postgraduate standards are low and geared to the practicalities of functioning hospitals. In addition, the true facts are apparently being withheld from the AMA approvers. Dr. Bonnemaison states that when American residents "encounter a difficulty in their training programs they are reluctant to express their opinions."

In a letter to *RISS,* an anonymous doctor who signs himself "Resident, Wisconsin" revealed the invidious pressure that stimulates this "reluctance." "Though well-intentioned, the AMA's internship evaluation program can easily turn into a farce," he writes. "Witness what happened to me: At the hospital where I interned last year, the administrator asked several internes, including myself, to discuss the training program with the AMA representative. But when I expressed some reservations about the program, the administrator quietly dropped me from the list of those to be interviewed. Incidentally, I was chairman of the interne committee at the time. If the evaluation program is to do any good, there should be some way that the AMA interviewer can hear criticism of the interne program without prior screening by the hospital." An approval program which interprets from censored interviews is not to be taken too seriously.

Dr. William R. Willard, vice-president of the University of Kentucky Medical Center, has also chastised the AMA approval program, charging that "the rules of the game" have forced "approval for programs not meriting approval." The present program of evaluation and approval of internship, he says, "is inadequate, expensive, frustrating and of doubtful value." Visits to charity wards, heavily staffed by foreign-trained, barely English-speaking internes straining to make do in poor medical surroundings, are live illustrations for Dr. Willard's critique.

Residency training has also been criticized as a not fully appropriate setting for the training of private-practice specialists. In the hospital the resident views crisis medicine, while in his practice he will concentrate on the ambulatory and chronically sick. The hospital provides a taste of this through its "outpatient" department, but as

Dr. Willard also criticizes, this may be an emergency-room situation "characterized by the pressure, confusion, and hurly-burly of a heavy patient load with much trauma and no follow-up on patient care."

Sixty-three former residents at the teaching hospital of the University of North Carolina showed forcefully that they had not received sufficient training for their private practice of medicine. The former residents asked for several changes, including "better and more intensive experience in ambulatory medicine."

Some community hospitals, fearful of losing their interne and residency programs, and hopeful of attracting American graduates, are trying to steel their academic programs somewhat, often with the help of local medical colleges. Albany Medical College has initiated a Regional Hospital Program that brings teaching talent to six community hospitals in upper New York and neighboring Massachusetts. University-faculty men visit each hospital each week, make rounds and talk to the hospital administrator about needed improvements. Two-way radio lecture series between faculty and hospital staff have been initiated.

The reluctance of private attendings to give sufficient time to interne and resident training is the community hospital's gravest educational problem. To circumvent this, many have hired a new medical entity, a professor-substitute—the director of medical education. There are 950 of these well-paid DME's, a hybrid between a den mother and a medical-school dean, whose goal is ostensibly to create a more academic atmosphere at the hospital. The DME can inject life into the learning environment by instituting lecture series, and prodding the attendings to donate more of their expensive time to making rounds and having direct contact with trainees.

Unfortunately, the DME concept, which is basically a stopgap, can be distorted by the hospital. One recent medical report warns that some hospitals feel the DME can take the teaching load off the attendings and give them more income-producing time. One DME admitted he had been hired simply as a recruiter. "I suspect that most of us are brought in because the attendings want house staffers around to do the scut work and cover the emergency room," he stated. "I wish every medical staff that votes to hire a DME could understand that he's not a labor-saving device. If he runs a good teaching program, the attending men are going to be working harder and donating more time—not less."

The DME has basically been used as a substitute for salaried full-time chiefs of service now employed by more enlightened hospitals—a program that has been opposed by some in organized medicine as the "practice of corporate medicine." However, warns an administrator at Montefiore Hospital in New York, "the DME cannot possibly take the place of a full-time man in each department in the teaching of internes and residents."

All attempts to provide better education for internes and residents are pertinent. However, even cumulatively, they skirt the necessary reforms Flexner brought to undergraduate medical education: training cannot be left to an uneven, unpredictable master-apprentice system. A standardized, formal curriculum is essential to ensure minimum competence. The establishment of a complex curriculum, including formal courses and examinations to provide the specialist-to-be with the involved knowledge of his field, is the first essential of reform. Given at the hospital, these courses should be devised and supervised by co-operating medical colleges. The present "honor code," in which the initiative of learning is left to the trainee, is unnecessary for the more talented and dedicated young doctor and a hopelessly inadequate stimulus for the uncaring or slow-to-learn student.

One medical-school faculty member critically points out that different residencies in internal medicine often stress particular areas of medicine, to the detriment of other essential knowledge. "A thorough, comprehensive curriculum could easily be set up in internal-medicine residency training," he states. "I think two to three hours of class a day would be sufficient. It should include classes on the most definitive information in cardiology, gastroenterology, hematology, chest diseases, neurology, kidney diseases, infectious diseases, and endocrine diseases such as diabetes. It probably wouldn't hurt either to give examinations in each course, and make successful grades necessary before the doctor could complete his specialty residency."

Dr. Osler Peterson of Harvard Medical School, in analyzing the "logic or systems" that enable doctors to diagnose and treat the sick, assures us that the medical school has left such training to the internship and residency, which are basically outside the school's control. "Whatever this process, it is seldom learned in medical school," he states, "since it seems to be a skill usually left for acquisition during the internship and residence years."

What is his solution to the dilemma of a student cast out too early, and perhaps thrust into incapable or uncaring hands for his most important education? His answer is a mild, if revolutionary, proposal not to certify this fledging as an M.D. too soon. Such a revolution would make *the granting of an M.D. degree conditional on the young doctor proving his competence as an interne and as a resident.*

"If the medical schools supervised the hospital training of their students and *withheld* [italics mine] the doctorate until they were satisfied that the individual physician was competent to practice," says Dr. Peterson, "they would be moving in the direction of the standards imposed by other university graduate schools, in which the doctorate degree is usually indicative of a minimum level of competence."

Dr. Peterson has made a gentlemanly proposal for interne and resident training that could begin to ensure doctor competence, a precious commodity the innocent patient thought he had been purchasing all along.

Part IV *The Family Doctors*

Chapter XII

The GP's:
Disappearing Family Doctor?

Some general practitioners, in a mood reminiscent of earlier, "oppressed" minorities, have developed a strain of private humor. "A lady called up a GP in the middle of the night yelling that her baby was choking to death," one GP recounts apocryphally. "The doctor was going to ask her the details, but she suddenly cut him off sharply. 'By the way, doctor, are you a board-certified pediatrician?' When he answered, 'No, I'm a GP, but—' her voice trailed off, and she hung up just as he was explaining, '—but I think I can help the child . . .'"

The 68,344 American general practitioners are a constant bane and wonder to the profession. They are maligned as vestigial in an age of superspecialization; held up to ridicule in front of impressionable medical students; forced out of major hospitals; periodically attacked by board-certified physicians for their lack of training coupled with no lack of medical activity. Their reputation among medical educators is base; their numbers appear to diminish each year. Between 1960 and 1964 there was a net loss of six thousand general practitioners. The nonspecialized family practitioners make up only 36.3 percent of all physicians in private practice, and only 23 percent of new physicians are GP's, two sets of figures that yield a graph ending in extinction. Even these glum figures may be optimistic. An inquiry of 256 internes and residents produced only eight brave youngsters who intended to become general practitioners.

Yet despite these dire forebodings, the GP flourishes in every community in the nation, attracting patients beyond his waiting room's capacity to hold them. The typical general practitioner sees 169 patients a week, sixty-three more than his medical-specialist colleague. He earns an income that his predecessor, "old Doc," would have viewed as the ransom of Montezuma. If ever a profession harbored a living paradox, it is American medicine's general practitioner.

The famous North Carolina survey that dissected the medical behavior of eighty-eight general practitioners, concluded that much of their doctoring was more alchemic than scientific. Dr. Osler Peterson of Harvard, one of its authors, has since found a damning statistical correlation that implicates the general practitioner as the medical-school "goat." Following up two classes at six medical schools, he concludes that of those students in the bottom third of their classes, there are four or five times as many entering general practice as among those in the top third.

Suspicions about the general practitioner's competence in scientific medicine have been strengthened by a report on Canadian general practitioners, first cousins of their American counterparts. According to Dr. Kenneth R. Clute, who surveyed eighty-six general practitioners in Canada, 40 percent were practicing inferior medicine and "were thought likely to expose their patients to serious risk." The six-year study substantiated prior results on American general practitioners.

The upsetting North Carolina survey reported on eighty-eight GP's at work in their practices, with several revealing insights. The necks of patients were not examined by one third of the general practitioners, and 43 percent never bothered to inspect the vital lymph nodes. "Indeed, one physician made the diagnosis of measles in a child, but failed to search for enlargement of any lymph nodes," the University of North Carolina report states. "Specific examination of regional nodes draining an area of infection was seldom seen."

The disillusionment with their lack of scientific proficiency was infused throughout the report. Ophthalmoscopy, the instrumented examination of the eyes for signs to many diseases, was never done by 66 percent of the GP's!

"Despite the acknowledged value of ophthalmoscopy in following the course of hypertensive vascular disease . . . relatively few hypertensive patients were subjected to this evaluation," state the saddened surveyors. "Hypertensive disease is prevalent; however, in assessing the severity of the disease, it appears that the emphasis has been misplaced on determining the height of the pressure rather than actually observing the evidence of vascular damage [in the "eye grounds" with the ophthalmoscope]. The same criticism applies to the management of diabetes. Some doctors owned ophthalmoscopes but never appeared to use them, while a few apparently did not possess one."

Rectal and vaginal examinations were "not usually done" (omitted 83 and 64 percent of the time) by the general practitioners, a neglect that contributes to the high death rate of curable cancer. Such

examinations were even omitted in the presence of obvic
cations. "One physician had hospitalized a young Negro
who gave a story of gradual onset of progressive pain in tl
abdomen with fever, chills and leukorrhea [white vaginal discharge],"
the report states. "Examination revealed that the patient had fever
and marked tenderness over both lower quadrants of the abdomen.
Treatment for infection had been instituted but bimanual examination of the pelvis had not been performed."

Even the doctors' sterile techniques, accepted hallmarks of modern
medicine, were questionable. Almost half (43 percent) of the GP's
showed "evidence of breaks" in sterility of their work, either in inadequate sterilization of the skin, or the use of unsterilized needles
or stylettes. "The improper practice of using an unsterile instrument
for acupuncture was observed," the Peterson report states. "The
same instrument was sometimes used repeatedly for successive patients, and inadequate sterilization was done between each use. An
occasional physician used sterile instruments with unwashed hands,
while others failed to wash their hands after obvious or presumptive
contamination."

Such studies are a constant affront to GP's, and their reputation.
Compounding the injury are the comments of specialists who inventory the general practitioner's doom in any available medical
forum. One fierce internecine battle developed when internist Dr.
Alfred P. Ingegno used his column in *Medical Economics* to announce "The Twilight of General Practice," an epitaph that aroused
the ire of GP's from San Diego to Boston. He drew a dodo-bird
portrait of a family doctor whose place is already being filled by
the internist-pediatrician-obstetrician-surgeon team, which, with some
additional training, will collectively function as the general practitioner of the future. "Let's wake up to realities—and stop wasting
our energies in futile and emotionally motivated efforts to perpetuate
the ghostly pattern of practice [family doctor] of a bygone era," he
charged his colleagues.

"The hell you say!" rallied scores of general practitioners, who
felt that their offices, bursting with ailing patients, belied this dire
prophecy. "This lively corpse refuses to lie down," stated one aroused
family doctor. The twenty-five printed answers, all defending general
practice, covered the full range of anger, piety, surprise and defiance.
A Woodbine (New Jersey) doctor questioned the motive of medical
specialization, implying that the ensign of medical sincerity flies only
over the GP's modest office. "Does it [the trend] really spring from
an earnest interest in specially practice?" he asks. "Or does the
trend to specialism arise from the new generation's quest for shorter
office hours, fewer working days, freedom from home visits, and
maximum fees for minimum time?" A Chicago doctor echoed this
noble sentiment: "There are still many family doctors whose goal in

life is not a title but the satisfaction that they gain from their work."

To Dr. Ingegno's claim that "the jack-of-all-trades is no longer possible or needed," the GP's took violent exception. "A family internist [specialist in internal medicine for adults] would still have seen the same forty-odd patients a day," argues a Lorain (Ohio) doctor. "To whom would he refer them? To a 'super-internist' who's spent ten years in residency? We *do* need a jack-of-all-trades; the more specialized we become, the greater the need for a co-ordinator."

General practitioners claim that specialists have no real desire to be part of the family; that neither internists nor pediatricians have the training (or the desire) to care for cuts and bruises; that it would take a tremendous number of obstetricians to deliver the two million children GP's now bring into the world each year; that the public needs considerably greater medical availability than that provided by specialists.

The most salient point of all is emphasized daily by the medical buying public itself, which has voiced—with cash for doctor visits— its insistence on having its own family physician. They obviously have little concern for his intraprofessional label, other than that he be a licensed M.D. A Portland, Oregon, physician believes that the public, if pushed, will subsidize even incompetence or quackery in order to have their own family doctor. "Exterminate the general practitioner, and the public will make GP's out of osteopaths, chiropractors—and even, for that matter, out of board-flunked internists and surgeons," he writes.

We had only to visit the office of a family doctor in a lower-middle-class neighborhood, a Long Island suburb whose income approximates the national median of almost $7000 a year, to verify why the public insists on supporting "vestigial" GP's. The physician's office was on the main residential road, with a sizable, well-lit shingle reminding the townspeople that his office was open and primed for patients each evening, a chore he shared with a partner. The waiting room was humanity in microcosm, and the physician good-naturedly, if quickly, dispatched the patients' complaints with a prescription, a suture or a homey word of advice. No appointment was necessary, and the basic fee was the venerable $5. He worked without interruption or rest, seeing six to eight patients an hour.

Emergencies were intermixed with a kaleidoscope of normal complaints. A child had a forearm break placed in a cast; a mother in her mid-thirties complained of neck pains; a man in his forties, distraught with symptoms of impotence, received an examination, a placebo prescription and good-natured advice; a housewife complaining of chest pains and fatigue received an examination, including an X-ray, and a nonspecific diagnosis and therapy; a hernia was diagnosed in a ten-year-old-boy, and an appointment was made for him to see a surgical specialist for possible surgery. In the midst of this activity an elderly woman who had cut her hand badly on a knife was rushed into a treatment room. The doctor left his other patients, and while he maintained a friendly neighborhood patter, he sewed the opened hand back into recognizable form with his semicircular needle and thread. By 10:30 P.M., office hours were over, and the cash box resoundingly full. Scores of patients had been seen and most of them were apparently pleased with their care, both personal and medicinal.

"You know, eighty-five to ninety percent of the people we see here have self-limiting conditions or aren't sick at all," stated the homeward-bound practitioner, who had had much of the afternoon off. "We seldom have a patient that we have to send to a specialist. Our patients seem quite satisfied solely with our care."

Like most patients, they are convinced of their doctor's skill out of total ignorance. The present general practitioner in typical private practice is pitifully trained and organized to handle the total health of such vast numbers of people, especially sick ones. His training usually consists entirely of medical-school orientation—during which the embryonic doctor gains bare recognition of diagnosis and therapy —and a year as a confused hospital interne. The GP's role as a diagnostic and treatment screen permits many patients to assume, wrongly, that they have the security of full medical care.

Despite gnawings of scientific and status inferiority, most general practitioners are well pleased with their practice, including its family contact, and its obvious financial rewards. Many other physicians are dissuaded from general practice because they falsely consider it a $5-a-visit penury. Actually, the volume aspects of general practice have made it extremely remunerative. During 1965 general practitioners in a national survey admitted a gross of $40,620, only $3000 less than their medical-specialist colleagues. As we have seen, it is usual for general practices to gross over $50,000.

Much of this affluence stems from his bravado in handling almost any variety of disease, despite his short training. This intrepidity surprised a visiting British observer, in whose country GP work is specifically circumscribed. "He sees himself as a complete physician and surgeon, limiting his activities only to his own estimate of his capabilities," Dr. Ronald Rorie of Dundee, Scotland, commented recently after an extensive American tour. "I witnessed a speculum examination of the cervix, followed by manipulation of a cervical disk under hypnotic anesthesia, with some psychotherapy thrown in for good measure—all in the same patient."

With such versatility and pecuniary success, why haven't young medical graduates been bleating for admission to the general-practice ranks? One reason is that within the profession, the GP is undisputed occupant of the status basement. Any deference to the general practitioner by his better-trained colleagues is usually only transparent hypocrisy. "Lip service to general practice is given everywhere," says Dr. G. R. Foster, Jr., of Georgia in *JAMA*. "Medical assemblages of all sorts are frequently outspoken about the need for more general practitioners. Yet none of this is translated into any real action. On the contrary, the forces of organized medicine are inexorably eroding the state of general practice."

The medical college, accurately state GP's, is the prime villain in the atrophying of their professional status. "Any medical school that shows an increasing productivity of general practitioners would be branded as having an incompetent faculty," admits Robert S. Alexander, PhD., of Albany Medical College.

General practice as a medical way of life is constantly downgraded to students, who hear the GP derided as the lowly LMD. "Consciously or unconsciously, he [the medical-school professor] disparages general practice," writes Dr. John S. DeTar, former president of the American Academy of General Practice. "The lifted eyebrow and the slighting references aren't missed by his students . . . Of course not all professors are guilty. But I believe the majority are. Dozens of young specialists have told me the same story: They entered medical school planning to become family doctors but were talked out of it and into specialties by their professors."

Dr. Martin Markowitz of Brooklyn, New York, who made the GP-damning survey of local-hospital residents, reports how effective this campaign has been. "In the eyes of his fellow physician, the GP is low man on the totem pole," he quotes one resident as stating. "General practice is discouraging at every turn," adds another.

One prominent young doctor, Robert O. Voy, then president of the Student American Medical Association, believes the GP has become the scapegoat for all charges of medical incompetence as a face-saving device for the specialists. "There is an atmosphere in many of our medical schools where each proclaims his field the most important, each points the finger of incompetence at the general practitioner, whom they consider the obvious 'scapegoat' for the human errors in medicine," he writes in the journal *GP*.

Error is overly common in all medical fields, but it is stressed more fervently against the *enemy*—the GP. "To them [specialists] it is an article of faith that no general practitioner is sufficiently trained to attempt a diagnostic work-up, deliver a baby, do any surgery, look at a fracture, and so on, according to the specialty in which the critics have proprietary rights," writes Dr. Edward Liston of the Palo Alto (California) Medical Clinic. "The general practitioner is doomed to remain the LMD—the local M.D.—whom the resident has learned to look on as the lowest form of animal life."

Despite specialist acrimony, public interest in patronizing the general practitioner is unflagging. It is not out of idealism or sympathy for his underdog status but a matter of personal convenience and economics. Using an accessible general practitioner is cheaper and more convenient than co-ordinating a team of specialists—a sorry, unsound job that often befalls modern patients. One patient who "hires" an internist, a pediatrician, a psychiatrist, a dermatologist and a proctologist has half jocularly considered holding an annual "medical conference" about his and his family's health at a local hotel.

Financially, the specialist "team" concept is peculiarly suited for the upper-middle class, who typically patronize a pediatrician, an internist, an obstetrician-gynecologist, a recommended surgeon and a series of subspecialists (ear, nose and throat; proctologist; cardiologist, etc.) as specific situations arise.

Although this splintered scheme of medicine is growing, patient support for a family practitioner has not abated. In fact, strong patient desire has created a paradox in which so-called specialists do what is, in essence, family-practice work. The pediatrician was originally a specialist in children's diseases who was to be called in by the GP to advise on a difficult diagnosis or therapy. Similarly, the internist was the family doctor's backstop in adult medicine, a system that still prevails in most nations. America has developed a unique situation in which *basic* illness—from the running nose to the rheumatic pain—is cared for directly by specialists, without referral. Rather than a more highly trained adjunct to the general practitioner, as they were originally envisioned, the pediatrician and internist are now his competitors. In a sense, many of them practice not as traditional specialists, but as general practitioners for either children or adults.

The Opinion Research Corporation confirmed the trend toward this "specialty" family practice and recommended that since GP's, pediatricians and internists are, in effect, all "family physicians," they merge into a combined "American Academy of Family Physicians."

The cash register value of general practice—through the immediate avalanche of sick humanity that appears at almost any wide-open medical door—has attracted many newly hatched specialists who need to build their bank accounts. A medical-publication survey of 105 recent graduates of residency programs showed that nearly one-third admitted to doing some GP work. One South Carolina GP claims that over half the general practice in his town is handled by surgeons, one of whom even treats "heartburn." A general surgeon in a small Iowa town frankly admitted that his patients insist on his practicing general medicine in addition to surgery. "If I didn't take care of the stiff back, colds, and bellyaches they bring me, I wouldn't have a practice," he told surveyors from a medical publication. The lure is not all financial. Other specialists, including obstetricians, confided that they felt both qualified and interested in handling the "whole person" rather than just using the specialized procedures for which they were trained.

The need for a medical mentor (whatever his title) to supervise the family's entire health is virtually undisputed, despite our present lemming-like lunge in the opposite direction. The most eloquent spokesman for the "personal physician" and his indispensable place in medicine is Dr. Zale Yanof, whose lively contributions on the subject have filled the pages of *JAMA*. "Never has the time been more propitious and the need greater for the reconstitution of the personal physician," he argued recently. "The patient needs an expert pilot to steer him through the maze of specialists and sub-specialists; to see the illness in its entirety vis-à-vis the total patient; to make the important decisions; to show comforting concern for him; to assume the final responsibility; and to be *his* personal physician."

Dr. Yanof made the convincing argument that the "great" are seldom without a personal physician close at hand: "Heads of state from ancient times to the present day, including Presidents of the United States, have always had full-time personal physicians in attendance—a testimonial to the indispensability of the personal physician in safeguarding and preserving a valued life."

This *desire* to have one doctor must be implicit in the patient, for over 74 percent of patients still call their family physician first, despite specialization, states the Opinion Research Corporation. The *need* for the GP, and the resultant shortage, has even been expressed statistically, by *GP* magazine. This excellent official organ of general practitioners has developed a POS (Physician's Opportunity Scale), which converts information from the AMA Placement Service into an index of job opportunities. It is formulated by dividing M.D.'s looking for jobs by the number of openings available. While surgeons are not currently in demand (.130 POS), the general practitioner is being wooed with more positions than he can handle—a smacking POS of 1.617.

The patient's annoyance at the specialist's formalities and fees, and his adherence to age and body-part limitation at patient expense, has helped buoy general-practitioner acceptance. For example, a girl whose skate sore had become infected on a Sunday was taken to a nearby internist when her pediatrician could not be reached. The internist, much like a suspicious ticket salesman on an airline, asked if the child was twelve. When he was told "eleven" he shook his head, and reminded the parents that "internal medicine is only practiced on adults." He suggested that the child be taken to a hospital emergency room. Only after the troubled frowns of the parents penetrated his pseudo-academic mien did he agree to treat the infection, but only as a one-time "favor."

The GP's desirability is, of course, enhanced by nostalgia. The general practitioner once represented the *Gemütlichkeit* of doctor and patient, the availability and closeness—both physically and spiritually—that the patient admired. The new general practitioner has been corrupted by the Lorelei of specialist comfort—of days off, truncated evening hours and the virtual elimination of house calls. Although still closer to the family, and more "one" with his patients in class structure (or better at simulating togetherness) than the specialist, his eventual estrangement from the patient as a result of modern practice management now appears equally inevitable.

The "need" for a family doctor may usually be emotional in origin, but it may also be scientific. The most sophisticated patient who patronizes a series of subspecialists—whether psychiatrists or cardiologists—without "front line" diagnosis by a *superior* overall diagnostician, may be inviting body neglect. Case histories of patients under psychoanalytic treatment who were actually suffering from a neurological disease are no longer rare; patients who brought their "choking" and "breathing" problems directly to nose-and-throat specialists and who were later found to have coronary insufficiency are among the many victims of misdirected ailments. The need for a family diagnostician and for a medical co-ordinator and manager, whatever his title, is apparent. The salient question is: *Is the present general practitioner the man for the job?*

The considered answer appears to be an almost unqualified "No." Doctors themselves, when choosing physicians to care for their family, overwhelmingly rejected general practitioners, seeking out hospital-connected internists and other subspecialists. A sample of 468 New Jersey physicians, questioned by the Columbia University School of Public Health and Administrative Medicine about medical care for their family and themselves during a three-year survey period, had chosen specialists to care for their family in 99 percent of the medical cases! Even New Jersey GP's had eschewed the services of their colleagues in favor of specialists.

The general practitioner's rebuttal to charges that he is incompetent to manage this central medical role revolves about two arguments: (1) 85 to 90 percent of ailments do not need expert specialty attention; and (2) the better of the GP's have been maintaining medical competence through the American Academy of General Practice. The AAGP, which has twenty-eight thousand members, operates a noteworthy but hardly sufficient attempt at intensive re-education of the general practitioner in view of his multiple challenges.

The "85 percent" statement may be theoretically true (although probably overstated in view of extensive chronic ailments), but is

actually a meaningless sophism. Just sorting out the minority of
seriously ill from his multitudes of supposedly "well" patients requires extreme acumen and skill. Even if we ignore negative surveys
of the general practitioner's skill, the present patient-burden and the
manic scope of the GP's activities—from obstetrics to surgery—
makes accurate screening and labeling of the seriously ill *15 percent*
of his patients an almost theoretical impossibility.

A further liability of today's GP as the ideal family physician is
not of his making but is, nevertheless, crippling. "I enjoy general
practice," says one GP, "but I do miss the absence of intellectual
stimulation in my work." This enforced estrangement from the university hospital and even his lockout from the better voluntary hospitals has made today's GP a virtually isolated "tradesman."

In retaliation, he has become the backbone of the staff of many
proprietary, profit-making hospitals. This cuts his isolation from the
backwaters of medicine a little, but as we have seen, further penalizes
his patients, who are denied potentially superior hospital care. "I am
committed to general practice," Dr. Leon N. Zoghlin of Ohio writes
in the *New England Journal of Medicine*. "I believe that it best
services the need of the people. I want the future general practitioner
to be inspired to intellectual excellence and inquiry by the devoted
educators of the great universities. Why is this denied to us?"

The denial injures the general practitioner's competence, writes
Dr. Richard D. Baldwin of New Jersey, in another publication,
claiming that modern scientific tools for diagnosis such as "endoscopy" and "organ biopsy" are denied to them through "arbitrary
restrictions." Cases such as cystitis (inflammation of the bladder),
a common complaint seen by family doctors, are, he says, usually
cured by antibiotics. If not, a general urologic work-up is necessary,
but general practitioners generally have no facilities to do this.
"Unless he can look at what is going on, the general practitioner
cannot be sure what is going on," he states in a medical publication.
"He can continue to treat—but this is a mistake (for both patient
and the doctor). Since he is not absolutely sure of what he is doing,
he becomes burdened with doubt, anxiety, and guilt. If he is wise,
he refers the case. He thus falls victim to ignorance (the legacy of
his medical education). Such enforced referral, for a common diagnostic procedure, is called a 'ringer.'"

The stubbornness of the general practitioner is also his consistent
enemy. His idealization of himself too often includes the distorted
image of a virtuoso of both medicine and surgery, equally at home
with an opened abdominal cavity and in treating a cold. Many
GP's carry a heavy load of surgery, operating wherever such
privileges are granted them—often in voluntary community hospitals
in small towns or in proprietary hospitals in both small towns and
larger cities. Despite the surplus of board-certified surgeons, the

general practitioner is an indefatigable, scrappy competitor (in rates and instant availability to patients) and still does almost half of all the surgery in this country, "specializing" in the bread-and-butter procedures of hemorrhoidectomy, tonsillectomy, appendectomy, and even more complex procedures such as ulcer and gall bladder surgery.

His competence in surgery has been rudely attacked through reliable surveillance, but he apparently has no intention of relinquishing this lucrative income or using the time to provide better diagnosis and care for his mass of patients. The very charter of the American Academy of General Practice—generally a progressive organization—certifies to GP intransigence on relinquishing the "cutting" to specialists. Under "objects and purposes" of the group they state: ". . . to promote and maintain high standards of the general practice of medicine and surgery."

Those general practitioners who do no surgery sometimes participate indirectly as "assistants," receiving a separate fee from their patient for the service. In other situations the GP will receive his fee directly from the surgeon, a practice denounced by the American College of Surgeons as "fee-splitting." One general practitioner who "assists" the surgeon on all operations performed on his own patients at the local hospital, bills the patient an extra fee and defends his practice as very ethical and sensible. "I'm not a surgeon, but I do know the patient's condition and can help medically." Most surgeons and patients would fail to support his strained logic, preferring a skilled surgical assistant on the spot, a man who can sometimes tilt the balance away from death with his trained hands.

The time and talent (but not the income) of the general practitioner are further diluted by the practice of obstetrics. About half the children in the United States are still delivered by general practitioners, and controversy about his competence in this area, especially in difficult deliveries, still rages. Because of the obvious shortage of trained specialists, his services as an obstetrician are still essential, if not of service to the remainder of his patients. A physician supporting a 1000 to 2000 patient load certainly cannot be diverted by the continuous delivery of children and still maintain rigorous care of the thirty patients he now sees a day.

In attempting too much, the contemporary species *"Homo medicus GP"*—despite its unquestioned fortitude—may yet be exercising itself into early extinction. Dr. Dana Atchley of Columbia Presbyterian Medical Center recently dealt with this GP overstretching, defining the ideal family physician as a man trained in both medicine and pediatrics. "The busy GP with his surgery and obstetrics usually finds it difficult to fill the role," he says in a masterful understatement.

The contemporary general practitioner, simultaneously wielding four arms of modern medicine, may, in a paraphrase of the military cliché, be waging the wrong medical war in the wrong place at the wrong time. His skills and presence are desperately needed, but not on his traditional terms. What, then, is the profile of the *ideal family physician?* How can he be fashioned, even in embryo, in the hostile womb of medical specialization?

To the public the answer is obvious: they want a physician with the availability and warmth of the best general practitioner, blended with the awesome science of the most highly trained specialist. The answer has been contemplated by medical critics: to reduce the GP's roles and to make him exceptionally well trained in a somewhat smaller, but still broad, area.

Producing the better-trained GP is the plan of certain medical colleges, including the University of Tennessee, University of Oregon and University of Kansas, where concentration on family medicine has produced startling figures: 50 percent of the graduating classes have become general practitioners. Hospitals have begun family-practice residencies, such as an AMA-approved program organized by New York Medical College and St. Joseph's Hospital in Paterson, New Jersey. Other institutions, including Harvard Medical School, have instituted similar programs, but the attrition of tradition is slow. Of the 29,485 residents in the nation, only 370 are training in general practice!

Medical surveyors have advanced dozens of plans to revolutionize the GP, the synthesis of which spells out the obvious solution: a highly trained *specialist in family medicine,* a board-certified "personal" physician who would care for the entire family. His patient age span would be from birth to death. His duties would be pediatric and medical, and although definitely *not* a surgeon, he would have sufficient training to suture cuts and lacerations. To ensure that his office would be the first line of medical care, he would have sufficient orthopedic training to set a simple fracture. Although not, as now, a functioning obstetrician, he would have sufficient training to deliver a child when necessary.

Rather than the butt of the medical fraternity and sophisticated patients, the new family doctor-specialist would rightly be its diagnostic star. He would be more intimate with the family, its habits and heredity than any other physician, and versatile enough to turn to his intuition and/or science to provide the maximum in health care. His training would span four years of postgraduate-hospital and disciplined outpatient work instead of his now meager one year. In addition to the one-year rotating internship, he would complete a three-year residency in family-practice medicine: one year of internal medicine, one year of pediatrics and a third year of advanced training, including orthopedics, dermatology, obstetrics, nose and throat, etc. Hopefully, this promising scientist-healer would retain the best of medical tradition and reinvigorate what has atrophied—from the house call to freely offered compassion.

As a specialist (with as much built-in logic as the specialties of internal medicine and pediatrics, depending on age), he would command the respect of the academic community and his colleagues. He would regain entrance to the medical universities' halls and hospitals —gaining from them needed stimulation, and adding to them the stern pragmatics of clinical family practice.

Lest the current family doctor (and his patients) be viewed as "persecuted," it should be kept in mind that a three-year attempt to create such a specialty was voted down by the membership of the American Academy of General Practice in 1963, mainly because GP's—in their private arrogance—were afraid it would "restrict" their activities. Members who now successfully compete with board-certified surgeons would probably have been limited to nonsurgical family practice, and had no intention of forgoing this income. Dr. James D. Murphy of the AAGP, one of the opponents of the family-practice specialty, raised this point. "About half our doctors do major surgery," he stated. "Having dealt with the AMA Council on Medical Education and Hospitals on several occasions, I don't think it would ever approve a board of general practice that encompassed any surgery. Yet a board that didn't include it would be absolutely unacceptable to the academy men who do surgery. No, we can't buy that idea."

The dissonant GP-specialist battle has made ideal medical care a wistful illusion for many Americans, and physicians may yet be forced to "buy" a sensible plan that more befits their oath. "There needs to be a meeting of the best minds in the leadership of general practice, the AMA, and those who determine the shape of things to come in medical education," warns Dr. G. R. Foster, Jr., in a plea in *JAMA*. "Otherwise we shall be yielding passively to the spectrum of forces that is sweeping us to an unknown and likely undesirable destination. General practice will die and, with its death, the public as well as the medical profession will be the losers."

The public desperately needs a family, or general or personal, physician to co-ordinate their medical care. The demise of the current overbusy, undertrained general practitioner will prompt no professional tears. Neither should it provoke any from patients *if* he can be superseded by a new family doctor who can blend the soul of healing with the power of science.

Chapter XIII

The Pediatricians:
Grandma or Scientist?

The suburban pediatrician's waiting room reverberated with the deafening sound of twenty children, each determinedly adding his effort to the controlled bedlam. Eight-month-old infants crawled across the bunny-decorated linoleum, flinging any toys that cut across their path; babies as young as six weeks old screeched in discomfort; four-year-olds banged compulsively on the progressive toys designed to vent their early hostility. As a quiet backdrop to this high-decibel mayhem was the soft, continuous chatter of the mothers, trading baby formulas and prideful exaggerations about their child's weight gain— brilliantly aimed to make the other competitive mothers shudder with insecurity.

"Mrs. Gray!" The nurse's call brought a young mother, impeccably decked out for her monthly visit with her pediatrician, toward the nurse's desk with her six-month-old child in hand. The young matron was led to an examining room and asked to undress the youngster. Ten minutes later, just as the anxious parent was about to cover the crying infant's chilled body, the pediatrician entered. His opening question, "How is the big boy doing?" triggered a series of counter-queries from mother about the child's growth, spitting up, bowel movements, behavior, alertness, diaper rash, crawling and formula. The pediatrician made reasonable attempts, many of them obvious guesses and clichés, to answer the questions; then he weighed and measured the child with a touch of ritual as the proud mother looked on. Comparing the height and weight with last month's, he smiled broadly and said, "He's gained more than average. No need to change the formula. Doing just fine." Checking the immunization chart, he saw that a shot of DPT (diphtheria, whooping cough-pertussis, tetanus) was due, and appropriately jabbed the surprised youngster. Moments later the mother—her face beaming with reassurance—left the office with her child.

"The American pediatrician is taking the place of the grandmother," says an assistant professor of pediatrics at Columbia University College of Physicians and Surgeons. His surprising comment alludes to the "well baby" care that has become the core of many pediatric practices, comprising anywhere from 40 to 80 percent of the pediatrician's daily effort. The pediatrician is an anomaly in the modern medical species. While most other physicians work in a constant crisis of illness, he is heavily committed to (virtually bogged down in) the normality of young, vibrant, squealing life. As a combination of a public-health nurse administering shots, a general physician making routine examinations of healthy children and the grandmother-counselor so desperately sought by anxious mothers, the modern pediatrician and his well-baby care are the subject of professional controversy.

"I think well-baby care is valuable for the patient, but I'm bored with it," says an East Side Manhattan pediatrician. "The time that it takes to do routine examinations and immunizations brings a relatively small fee. I find it deadening and intellectually stultifying, but with pediatrics the way it is, I couldn't get rid of it and survive."

Pediatrics has been the quickest growing of the large specialties, expanding rapidly after World War II to satisfy the baby boom and the "specialized" care demanded by the newly affluent mother in city and suburbia. It is the fifth largest of the specialties (after surgery, internal medicine, obstetrics and psychiatry) and now boasts some ten thousand physicians in private practice, over two thousand of whom entered the profession in the past four years. In addition, there are almost three thousand more pediatricians in hospitals, government, medical schools and other salaried positions.

Pediatricians have been the *Wunderkinder* of American medicine, springing from a minor offshoot of obstetrics and gynecology into the darling of the young American matron. While physicians in general have increased in number 73 percent in the past forty years, pediatrician ranks have risen 1425 percent, almost twice the growth of other specialties. Pediatrics has been called *genus Americanus* because nowhere in the world is the child so closely under the medical aegis of specialists. While America boasts one pediatrician per 15,000 population, there is only one pediatrician per 200,000 people in the British Isles, which has created no apparent difference in the two nations' child-health statistics. The difference is in the responsibility: the British pediatrician is a "consultant" who cares for only the sickest children, while the American pediatrician cares for his giant flock, healthy or sick.

Why, then, do we support so many pediatricians, and are they really necessary? The answer lies in the philosophical attitude toward the growing child. To the general practitioner, the pediatrician is not really a specialist, but rather just another general practitioner "who takes care of little people," as *GP* magazine has phrased it. The pediatrician counters that the child is not a small adult, but a person with different physiological problems, on which he is ostensibly an expert.

The party line, expressed recently by three prominent pediatricians in *New Physician,* is resonant: "It [pediatrics] is the study of the growth and development of the child from the moment of conception through adolescence, and the science and art of the prevention, diagnosis, and treatment of all diseases from the moment of birth through adolescence, whether these disturbances be on a physical, emotional, or mental basis."

Good pediatrics, these doctors state, requires constant checks— once a month during the first year, every three months in the second, every six months until the sixth year and once a year thereafter— to ensure that the child is "progressing at normal rate physically, mentally, and emotionally." This strict regimen, of course, also ensures the continued, healthy growth of the American pediatrician.

This triumphant advertisement can be translated into two basic claims: that the preventive "well baby" care catches ailments and congenital defects that might otherwise be missed; that in case of sickness the pediatrician is better trained in the biologic idiosyncrasies of the young and their diseases, from measles to croup.

Claims that most pediatricians can better handle emotional disturbances of children are, by and large, ridiculous. Claims for superior organic diagnosis of *certain* childhood ailments—although not scientifically established—are more reasonable. "The picking out of obscure illnesses in youngsters is the point of the whole thing," says one New York pediatrician. "The average GP can catch the communicable ailments in youngsters. But I think we do a better job in endocrine, metabolic and genetic problems in children. I see only one case of infant diabetes in perhaps every five years, but other problems—including heart defects in the newborn, infantile hernias, cross-eyes, and feet turned in—are more common."

Few, if any, pediatricians would fail to justify their specialty, but some are less chauvinistic about the calling. "Much of pediatrics can be done away with," states a salaried pediatrician in a teaching hospital. "I would say that in the care of children the pediatrician has an edge in a small number of cases. In tonsils, for example, I think the pediatrician is less likely to advise their removal. Most important, the pediatrician is aware that children change with growth, and so do their blood counts and chemistry levels. A general practitioner may treat the youngster by adult standards. An anemia that is diagnosed by adult standards may not exist in the child at all."

Pediatric activity covers a broad health base, some of which the pediatrician does well. In other cases, including the newborn, he has shown surprising gaps in his therapeutic knowledge which have elicited acid criticism from doctor-critics, including prominent pediatricians. One critique involves iron-deficiency anemia, which has been routinely treated with pleasant-tasting iron preparations by many pediatricians. Its shocking ineffectiveness has been stressed by the *New England Journal of Medicine,* whose editors warn of the "inadequacy of an iron preparation for oral use that seems to have achieved widespread popularity, especially among pediatricians, in the treatment of iron-deficiency anemia." The *NEJM* quotes reputable pediatric authority to support its stand, then adds: "Other pediatricians have had the unpleasant experience of seeing infants and childen remain anemic and iron-deficient after taking this 'pleasant-tasting' elixir for several months." The proper medicine, ferrous sulfate, is not sweet or innocuous, they advise pediatricians, but "these attributes are no standards for selection of therapeutic medications."

Allergy diagnosis and attempted control is another burgeoning activity of the pediatrician, some of whom maintain special "allergy rooms." The necessity for allergy treatment is not debated; allergic disease, from eczema to allergic asthma, is an increasing phenomenon now affecting at least 10 to 15 percent of all children. Children can be allergic to cow's milk, and even to the common substitute, soybeans.

The difficulty in allergic management of children may be the pediatrician's inability. There are "two types of problems that pediatricians are least qualified to handle," states Dr. Lewis Fraad, professor of pediatrics at Albert Einstein College of Medicine. "One is behavior disorders and the other is allergic disease." The average pediatrician, he states, is "confused and frustrated" because of insufficient allergy training in both medical school and at the resident level.

The area of congenital (inborn) ailments, in which the pediatrician can save a young life *if* alert enough, is perhaps the most significant pediatric work being done today. Congenital malformations are said to affect more than three in each hundred children. In many hospitals the family pediatrician or resident will examine the newborn child for congenital ailments that might impede its future or its life. In addition to heart malformations, there are others that bring on death quickly. A bowel obstruction makes the intake of nourishment impossible, but if spotted quickly, can be surgically repaired. A fistula, or opening, between the trachea and esophagus, can bring foreign bodies into the lung, causing death unless it is discovered and closed.

Are pediatricians astute enough to pinpoint this pathology in the apparently healthy infant? There are no statistics available, but one critic—a teaching pediatrician in a large hospital—believes that such lifesaving diagnosis is inadequately performed. "The main problem in the diagnosis of the newborn is that it is like the peacetime army," he states. "There are so many normal children that the doctor assumes that they are all normal. It is hard in such a situation to stay alert."

The debate over the skills of the pediatrician, and the advisability of a specialty-trained physician weighing and cooing at youngsters from birth to fourteen years of age, is unresolved. The American mother, however, long ago resolved any debate in favor of her medical *amour,* the pediatrician. In such a child-centered culture, what possible general dissatisfactions (although she may be piqued at any one pediatrician) could a mother have with a profession geared to salving her anxiety and devoting its medical perspective to her child? How can a mother be cynical about a physician with seven years of training (including two years of pediatric specialty residency, the shortest of any specialty), who recites the nursery rhyme "Twinkle, twinkle, little *car*," to all his patients and makes a fuss as the children correct him?

Despite such adoration, many pediatricians have not returned her love in kind. One survey shows the pediatrician to be the least satisfied of all specialists, with discontent admitted by 37 percent of baby doctors. One of his gripes is common to certain family practices: occasional long hours. But his Achilles heel is a tender one: the nervous, cloying, inquisitive, overprotective, neurotic woman —in short, the typical American mother.

The anxious mother—what he calls the "shook" or "hyper" female —irritates him beyond normal bounds. Some pediatricians are fond of repeating "crank" stories about their more persistent mothers, especially those who are armed with a yard-long list of questions, and others who they believe reach for the phone at any provocation, from slight constipation to the spitting up of milk. To avoid onerous telephone calls, many pediatricians have a "calling half-hour"— often from 8 to 8:30 A.M.—when mothers with routine queries can question him as they would have Grandma in prior generations. (Only the speediest can get through the busy-line before the allotted time is up.)

The constant irritant of worried mothers makes some pediatricians almost permanently irascible. Dr. R. James McKay, Jr., chairman of the department of pediatrics at the University of Vermont College of Medicine, believes such pediatricians—not the mothers— may be temperamentally unsuited. "Actually," he says in a guest editorial in *New Physician,* "I believe that most *over*anxious or *over*protective mothers exist only in the minds of *under*interested or *under*sympathetic physicians. Therefore, in considering pediatrics as a career, it is important that the prospective pediatrician not only like children, but also that he like and be sympathetic toward parents, especially toward worried mothers."

Are there any special requirements needed to become the exemplary male "grandma"? "It takes a special kind of person to make a pediatrician," says an eastern board-certified baby specialist. "Usually the pediatrician is a more passive type of man. He likes children, and he has sought out pediatrics because it's an optimistic profession. Most of the diseases he deals with are preventable or curable, and the great majority of his patients live. Some doctors are frankly attracted to pediatrics because they are afraid of trauma or involvement, and because death—which is always present in surgery or internal medicine—is less of a problem in pediatrics."

Whatever his attributes, some critics believe he is overinvolved in the "grandma" aspects of pediatrics, to the detriment of scientific care of the sick. His failure in the handling of "strep" throat and rheumatic heart disease has already been noted, as has Dr. Herbert Ratner's statement that the pediatrician shepherds youngsters when they are well, while the general practitioner cares for them when they are ill. This may be an exaggeration, but there is evidence that the talent of the pediatrician is being badly utilized. In the current masterful nonorganization of medicine, the board-certified pediatrician may be cooing at an obviously healthy youngster for the tenth continuous month, while another child may be dying in the same community under less trained care.

In the second Trussell report, two university pediatricians surveyed twenty-four cases of pediatric care in hospitals. Only two turned out to be under the care of certified pediatricians. The quality of child care was not encouraging: nine children received "good" or "excellent" treatment, but twelve received unsatisfactory treatment. (Surveyors could not agree on the other cases.)

One seven-year-old girl was hospitalized for her first acute episode of rheumatic fever. "However," states the report, "no evidence that penicillin was given or that prophylaxis undertaken." A two-year-old boy with severe respiratory infection is reported as a case history in classical slipshodness. The condition "became worse after admission," and medication fluids were given ineffectively under the skin (clysis) rather than intravenously. A five-year-old, hospitalized because of chronic headaches, was a victim of diagnostic neglect. States the damning report: "No complete neurological examination, fundoscopic [study of eye grounds by light], or study of refractive error [lack of ability to focus pupils, which can be a sign of brain tumor]. No spinal tap, no electroencephalogram. No blood pressure recorded."

The *individual* pediatrician cannot be held responsible for the malorganization of his practice, for his well-baby business is his marketing lure to his customer, the American mother. Without it he cannot survive under present conditions. Further, certain aspects of well-baby care, such as regular immunizations, are valuable. (The fact that a trained specialist is responsible for immunizations is surprising; it could be a simple, well-organized public health function.)

The better baby hospital, specializing in care of the sick child, apparently shares this concern over the available amount of the pediatrician's "sick child" time. As insurance, some have turned away from the community pediatrician to the full-time pediatric scientist to ensure on-the-spot quality care when needed. "Kids tend to go from well to sick much more quickly than adults, and can develop 105 fever in virtually moments," states one pediatrician, adding that complications such as meningitis can come on when least anticipated.

One specialized institution, Babies Hospital at Columbia Presbyterian Medical Center in New York, employs a sizable staff of full-time pediatricians, research fellows, and even teams of pediatric subspecialists in cardiology, endocrinology, liver, kidney and metabolic disorders, neurology, hematology, and the newborn. Private patients whose pediatricians are on the attending staff receive care from their own doctor, but are backed up by the hospital staff.

Some pediatric hospitals are concerned that the general pediatrician is not competent to handle the serious problems of the newborn (neonatal), whether premature or so-called full-term babies. Paradoxically, the danger of dying is greater at the period directly after birth than at any time except advanced old age. Almost two thirds of all infant deaths occur in the first week of life. (An estimated 100,000 infants a year die in their first year.) Newborn infants, for example, who do not breathe regularly within two minutes of birth, must receive tracheal intubation or risk death.

An estimated five to ten thousand infants and unborn children perish each year in America because of Rh disease (erythroblastosis fetalis) despite the ability of medical technology to save many of them through proper exchange-transfusion of blood. Rh disease occurs when the mother's blood is Rh negative and her baby's is Rh positive. The failure to save many such children is often due to the lack of proper transfusion equipment in the newborn nurseries of many hospitals. A report by Dr. Herbert F. Philipsborn, Jr., described the survival of over four hundred infants in Illinois who were born with this hemolytic disease. The death rate was up to three times as high for babies born in a hospital not equipped to perform often lifesaving exchange-transfusions. Children rushed to another hospital, generally after they were already six hours old, had much smaller chance of surviving the procedure. (A possible contribution to unnecessary infant death is also the insufficient co-operation between obstetrician and pediatrician, a general failing recently stressed by Dr. Sydney S. Gellis, chairman of the pediatrics department at Tufts University School of Medicine.)

A tragic case history of one needless Rh death where equipment was available but neglected was dramatically described in a report in *Medical Tribune*: "Early one morning on the obstetric service of one of the larger New York City hospitals, a woman was delivering uneventfully of her second child. The one possible complication foreseen during pregnancy, erythroblastosis fetalis—resulting from Rh incompatibility—had been given careful heed, and the woman's Rh antibody titers had been measured and precisely recorded on her chart at each prenatal visit. Only no one had made certain that exchange transfusion equipment would be immediately available at the time of delivery in case it proved necessary to save the baby's life. It did, and the baby died."

The measure of the struggle during the first year of an infant's life is termed infant mortality, a scale of inappropriate death in which American medicine weighs woefully heavy. Our death rate of twenty-five per 1000 live infant births is eleventh of fifteen graded nations, lagging behind Czechoslovakia and Ireland, and 40 percent higher than Sweden and the Netherlands. Much has been made of the fact that the nonwhite population distorts this figure. It is an irrelevant comment, since all countries include their poorest population, and America's happens to be a racially poor. Even discarding the nonwhite figures, America is still over 30 percent behind leading European nations, and out of the first ten. The reasons are complex: genetics, prematurity, faulty obstetrics, inadequate hospital facilities, prenatal care, poverty. Dr. Margaret M. Hutton, after studying perinatal mortality in Canada, attributed some of the preventable death to the late transfer of Rh-negative pregnant women to centers with exchange transfusion facilities; to the elective Caesarean sections being done in hospitals with inadequate anesthetic or pediatric care; and the failure of doctors to give needed hospital care to mothers with toxemia because of improvement shown after diuretic therapy. The infant, Dr. Hutton points out, is still in danger.

But both critics and discouraging figures also implicate medical care shortly *after* birth, the province of the pediatrician, as responsible for much of this high death toll.

An indictment of general pediatricians as insufficiently trained and self-maintained to handle the life-and-death problems of the newborn comes from Dr. Hans G. Keitel, head of the department of pediatrics at Jefferson Medical College in Philadelphia. Using the editorial page of the *Medical Tribune* to vent his concern, Dr. Keitel states that "infant mortality in the United States is still excessively high," and that "pediatricians and generalists are finding it increasingly difficult to keep abreast of developments in neonatal medicine." His conclusion: in the crisis days immediately after birth, the general pediatrician should be replaced by a well-trained specialist, the neonatologist, who would care for the child from birth until release from the hospital. (The neonatal period is generally defined as the first twenty-eight days of life.)

"Since many illnesses in newborns progress from the initial symptoms to a critical stage extremely rapidly," stresses Dr. Keitel, "only the most conscientious, specially trained, on-the-scene physician can provide optimal service. The neonatologist, on twenty-four-hour call, would be available to identify disorders in minimum time. This, many of us are convinced, would be reflected in a decrease in infant mortality and morbidity."

Dr. Keitel noted that he expected pediatrician "hostility," a prediction that proved accurate. Angered by a challenge that would nudge them closer to their unstimulating "grandmother" role, pediatricians stubbornly defended their competence in handling the newborn and damned his suggestion as "unnecessary."

Dr. Keitel countered by asking if pediatricians within eyeshot could handle vital inquiries about the newborn. He asked: "By what hour of life do most infants first pass stool? urine? What are the possible causes of gastric perforation in the neonatal period? List five common causes of persistent hypotonia [below normal strength] in the first five days of life? Which of the following diseases can be recognized in the first week of life: congenital hypophosphatasia; nephrogenic diabetes insipidus; phenylketonuria; cretinism; galactosemia; glycogen storage disease; Pierre Robin syndrome; idiopathic hypercalcemia of infancy? What is the dose of the following drugs for a 6½ pound, two-day-old infant: chloramphenicol; nalorphine; kanamycin?"

The professor was armed not only with the questions and answers, but with a failing grade for the American pediatrician. "These are but a few of many questions we have found that general pediatricians have difficulty in answering," he reveals.

The current diagnosis and salvage of sick infants also has its brighter side: incomplete esophagus made normal through surgery; repair of some congenital heart defects; correction of many with hydrocephalus (water on the brain); and saving of most children with intestinal obstructions.

However, it is becoming obvious that the current practices and training of the pediatrician may not be sufficient to meet the scientific challenges being presented. A sharp schism between the pediatrician's oft-superficial well-baby care and the sorely needed improvement in the care of sick children may be the next reality of the pediatric world. The extravagant use of medical manpower in a plethora of mother-purchased attention may not be the ideal future for the American pediatrician.

"Perhaps the answer," offers a Columbia Presbyterian Babies Hospital doctor, "is that we need two kinds of pediatricians: the grandmas and the scientists."

Chapter XIV

The Internists:
Tomorrow's GP's?

The "professor" of medical legend, whose acute intuition immediately recognized the esoteric "Goodpasture's syndrome" in a patient whose symptoms had baffled a multitude of physicians, is the internist of medical lore. Garbed in bulky tweeds or nondescript attire, and invariably immersed in medical journals and laboratory reports, he is the master clinician whose image—whether lecturing a medical-school class or at a bedside consultation—represented as much the superlative of medical skill as the neurosurgeon. He is the Leonard Gillespie of fiction; the Sir William Osler of medical past.

Armed with this concept, the patient ardently seeking expert medical acumen, and willing to pay for it, has beaten a path to the door of the internist, the specialist in internal medicine of adults. The sophisticated patient has increasingly learned the meaning of "internist," that it is not related to the junior "interne" just beginning postgraduate education, and that it is a term representing a higher degree of training than that achieved by the typical general practitioner. This recognition, and hope for excellence, has made internal medicine the largest of American specialties with more than twenty-five thousand physicians who describe *themselves* as "internists."

In the morass of modern medical organizational chaos, the "internist" may fit any one of a dozen descriptions: a suburban family physician virtually indistinguishable from the GP; a full-time clinician in the "medicine" department at a large hospital; a faculty member of a medical school; a diabetic specialist; a gastrointestinal subspecialist on Park Avenue; a $50-a-visit general internist whose initial medical examination requires an hour or more; the member of a staff cardiology team of a major institution; the "fellow" in endocrinology in a research center; or the cancer specialist.

Internal medicine is the broadest of the specialties, and like the general practitioner, the internist faces almost the entire scope of human death and disease, a variety of ailments that include cardiac conditions, liver diseases, tuberculosis, pneumonia and other chest ailments, diabetes, kidney ailments, blood disorders, infectious diseases, arteriosclerosis (hardening of the arteries), hypertension (high blood pressure), cancer, diseases of glands (thyroid, etc.), and any and all abnormalities not codified as the province of other specialties. This breadth of disease in the adult makes the internist the most needed and most vulnerable of all specialists.

He may have his own patient clientele, or in the classical image, his practice may consist mainly of "consultations" dependent on referrals from other physicians. The difference may be calculated in prestige, or in the gap between a $5 office visit and the $50 to $150 consultation, the closest the internist ever comes to the expansive fees of his surgical counterpart.

Who is the internist, and how does he differ from his colleagues? The typical private-practice internist sees considerably fewer patients than the general practitioner: ninety-six a week as against 169, reveals a survey done by a medical publication in collaboration with the American Society of Internal Medicine. In the eastern states, where internists are more usual, he treats even fewer patients—seventy-nine a week. Time—the unhurried attention to patients' complaints—is the good internist's effective sales lure. Assembly-line medicine is atypical in *good* internal medicine practices, and the internist devotes an average of thirty minutes to each patient visit, considerably more than most other physicians. (Another, more recent survey indicates 112 patient visits per internist, as against 169 for the GP. The time crush in contemporary medicine is apparently beginning to affect the internist as well.)

Forty percent of private-practice internists do some teaching, but his academic involvement is not usually substantial. (Today, most academic internists are not in private practice, but are full-time university men.) In all, the private internist devotes only five hours a week to the instruction of internes and residents at hospitals, his own education and professional reading, writing and research.

Some internists' fees stagger the patient imagination, especially those for his comprehensive physical, which average between $25 and $50, and can soar up to $150. His typical office fee is $10 rather than the general practitioner's $5, but his overall income is only slightly higher than the GP's and smaller than other specialists' because of his patient-time involvement. In fact, internists in solo practice average less than general practitioners.

His general demise as the "doctor's doctor" is illustrated by the fact that only ten of his weekly roster of patients have been referred by other physicians. Increasingly, he is being sought out directly by sophisticated patients who have learned that, if nothing else, their complaints *may* get undivided—if not necessarily sympathetic or expert—attention in his office.

"Is the man I'm going to an internist rather than a general practitioner, and how does the doctor define what he is?" the patient may ask. The strict definition of any "specialist" requires certification by a board—in this case the American Board of Internal Medicine. Another possible definition is election as a Fellow of the American College of Physicians.

"Remember that a doctor can call himself a specialist or by any other medical name he wants to as long as he holds an M.D. and a license to practice," an astute internist and faculty member of an eastern college reminds us. Being connoisseurs of prestige, doctors are prone to make their status as elegant as possible. The spread between the number of self-proclaimed and board-certified internists substantiates this cynicism.

At latest census, there were twenty-one thousand "internists" in private practice. The total number of "board certified" men, states the American Board of Internal Medicine, is 16,616. Several thousand are occupied in teaching, hospitals, research and salaried positions, yielding estimates that only half of all "internists" in private practice have passed their specialist accreditation. The approximately ten thousand physicians who call themselves internists but are not "certified," usually do so on the strength of having completed a residency in internal medicine. Some older "internists" (including some professors and hospital chiefs of medicine) have neither residencies nor boards, but trained instead under the prior "preceptor" system.

Is the absence of the framed "Diplomate" on the internist's wall visible proof of a masquerade? It can be interpreted several ways: he may have failed his "boards" one or more times; if young, he may be in the midst of taking them. With a fancy of personal peevishness unknown outside chaotic medicine, it can also mean that the "internist" has just ignored them. "I know several successful internists, including medical school faculty members, who refuse to take their boards," says an examiner for the Board of Internal Medicine. "They don't like the idea of anyone testing their ability or knowledge."

After completing a three-year residency in internal medicine, the board candidate must practice or teach for two years. He can then take his written examination—an entire-day multiple-choice test. If he passes, the candidate later presents himself for his "orals." Oral examinations are held in four or five leading centers each year. The candidate travels to the nearest one, where he is watched and questioned separately by two examiners as he does the work of an internist on two hospitalized patients. If one internist-examiner is doubtful of his ability, the candidate gets the benefit of this doubt, and he is passed. If both are doubtful, he fails. Then the candidate must wait at least another year before he can take the test again.

What is his hope of success? "I saw 80 to 100 candidates a year for eight years," a medical college professor who examines for the Board of Internal Medicine relates. "About two-thirds pass the written examination the first time, and approximately two-thirds of the remaining men pass the orals. That means about half the candidates get their boards in the first attempt. Eventually two out of three of those who try become Diplomates."

What of the failures and those who simply shun this academic trial by fire? Are they bled and expunged from medicine? Are they restrained from handling the complex tasks of serious internal medicine—whether liver disease or cancer? Hardly. In actual practice, there is little difference in passing or failing, except in the language of medical sophism: "board-qualified" for those who for any reason don't have their Diplomate, and "board-certified" for those who do.

"Some major hospitals won't take a man who doesn't get his boards, and some agencies—like the VA, I understand—will pay more for a board-certified man," explains an internist. "But overall, the board-qualified man can often do as well, in private practice and in many hospitals, as the certified man. One of the good features of the 'boards' is that they have made the hospitals improve the quality of specialty training, and thus improved the standards of medicine. One of the bad features, though, is the frustration created in the souls of people who don't get them."

If the intramural designations and standards are not explicitly applied within the profession, is the public amply protected? Are the "boards" less significant because the candidates have been thoroughly screened and tried during the crucial three years of residency-specialist training in internal medicine? It would be reassuring—but false—to say so. The facts indicate that a young doctor of less than average talent can become a "board eligible" internist through a series of progressive incompetencies, culminating in his failure or avoidance of the "boards." The inept student graduates to become the inept interne, who then functions as the inept resident, who finally matures into practice as the inept "internist."

Residency training, as we have seen, is a passive situation in which the profession *hopes* the aspiring specialist will learn. It neither forces him to, nor evaluates him. "Doctors don't flunk out of residency training," states one frank medical educator.

There are almost twice as many residency openings in hospitals as there are American candidates, and the mere desire to specialize is the *only qualification* the young M.D. must possess. Any selection of quality takes place at the better (more prestigious) institutions, where applications for residency appointments exceed openings. Those rejected there are eagerly absorbed by other AMA approved and understaffed residency programs.

The mere presence of a physician in the noncommercial environment of a hospital for three years is, of course, touched with beneficence despite its unstandardized training. The group (if not the individual) superiority of the internist, over the undertrained general practitioner, is thus apparent. The involvement of internal medicine in the grand image of healing, makes the development of the specialty an asset to medicine, and something to be further nurtured and exploited. *However,* the lack of stringency of much of this specialty training—and the ease with which a medical poseur can thrive within it—casts doubt on what may be the exaggerated repute of many internists. The reputation of many of them as broad healing specialists, may—if current surveys are accurate—be another modern medical chimera.

To place the criticism in perspective, it might be wise to visit the office of a practicing board-certified internist, a member of the attending staff of New York Hospital-Cornell Medical Center. (After an appointment was made for a week hence, the doctor's secretary dispatched, by mail, a standard several-hundred-question medical-history form.) After a wait of only five minutes the patient was ushered into the physician's office. Except for two phone interruptions, the next half-hour was the reserve of the patient. The internist methodically used the medical-history form to ask pertinent information; the physical examination that followed was as careful as the history. Although not a full diagnostic procedure, it was a reasonable introduction to a new patient. The vital factor was the physician's singular concentration on the person at hand, an invaluable commodity in today's oft-bedlam medical practice. The luxury of this specialist's time and concentration cost $30 for the first visit, $15 thereafter. The patient could only guess at the physician's acumen, but could not fail to be impressed by his regimen.

Such punctilious methodology may not ensure medical genius, but thoughtful procedure, careful history-taking, examination and testing are the hallmarks of the better internist. Despite its current high cost, such medicine is to be complimented and encouraged. Not all internal medicine, unfortunately, is as stoutly maintained as this specialist's tight little office. The inherent difficulty in internal medicine is the breadth of disease it encompasses and attempts to check. When blended with a failure of thoroughness or regimen, it produces a state of internal medicine that is far from sanguine.

The most recent medical-quality survey, the second Trussell report, substantiates much of this pessimism. Published in 1964 by the Columbia University School of Public Health and Administrative Medicine, its findings indicate grave medical failings.

The most perturbing statistic incriminates "general medicine"—the nonsurgical treatment of adults—as the *weakest of all care*. Of 120 surveyed cases of internal medicine, only *31 percent* of the patients received "excellent" or "good" treatment by physicians. The remaining 69 percent suffered from "fair" or "poor" ("less than optimal") treatment.

The caretaker of general medicine is either the GP or the internist. The Trussell report shows that the internist's medical-care average is somewhat higher than the general practitioner's, but still alarmingly low: an intramural contest in which the patient is the loser. General medical care in proprietary hospitals is most often done by general practitioners; in university hospitals it is almost entirely board-certified-internist controlled; in the voluntary hospitals it is sometimes mixed, but generally internist-inspired and controlled, especially in the "better" voluntary hospitals with interne and resident programs. "It is virtually impossible for anyone except an internist to admit a patient here in general medicine," confirms a staff member of a New York voluntary hospital which participated in the Trussell report.

Of the 108 general-medicine cases on which the two surveyors agreed, only thirty-three were considered as having been "optimal" (good or excellent) care. Seventy-five cases were judged as consisting of basically unsatisfactory treatment. The cases were split between four grades of physicians: board-certified internists or "fellows" (Class I); men without boards (or not "fellows"), but with voluntary hospital appointments (Class II); men without voluntary hospital appointments (Class III); and the house staff of voluntary and municipal hospitals (Class IV).

The record of internists and internists-in-training was more than unsettling. The house staff (Class IV), operated by internal medicine residents and internes, performed satisfactorily in *only seven cases out of twenty-six*—incompetence "surpassed" only by the general practitioners (Group III), who had sixteen in eighteen failures. The Class II physicians, an unknown conglomeration of board-eligible internists and general practitioners, scored about as badly as the house staff—fourteen satisfactory cases out of forty-three. The board-certified internists, generally practicing in the best available hospitals, with the finest staff support and technology, did better, but only miserly so. Less than half their cases—ten out of twenty-one —were graded as comprising good or excellent medical treatment!

The case accounts are a potpourri of the failures of all four classes of physicians in general medicine, but they include the sins of neglect and commission of board-certified internists. Case No. 205, that of a fifty-seven-year-old male, narrates an encyclopedia of medical failure. His first hospitalization lasted fifteen days. A diabetic, he suffered from the common symptom of an ulcerated great toe. No complete analysis of his diabetes was made, and he was discharged with the ulceration still present. Over the next four years the same patient was hospitalized six more times, receiving perfunctory and endangering medical care each admission. The second admission, six weeks after the first, also involved a great-toe ulceration "with superficial evaluation and management." The third hospitalization was prompted by acidosis (air hunger and eventual coma) caused by his diabetes, plus a mid-thigh abscess. "Handling of acidosis inadequate," the Trussell report states. "Discharged with a temperature of 101."

The fourth admission of the same patient involved congestive heart failure and severe anemia, about which the surveyors commented tersely: "Cardiac status not fully explored. Etiology of anemia not determined. Discharged without cardiac drugs." Four months later he was readmitted to a hospital with a knee condition, and again given questionable treatment. At the age of sixty-one, he entered a hospital again, this time "as a diabetic with rectal hemorrhage and anemia." The criticism of this next-to-the-last medical diagnosis and therapy was the most piercing: "Although ulcerated hemorrhoids found, no treatment instituted. No further search for anemia. No overall medical evaluation. No chest film."

One month later the patient was admitted to a hospital for eleven days, at the end of which time he died. A chest tap had produced 3500 cc. of bloody fluid, along with malignant cells. The surveyors end this log of the patient's painful journey through a world of medical omission with a comment of muted despair. "Signed out as carcinoma of the lung. No chest film."

Does the failure at thoroughness exhibited by more than half of the internists in this study spill over into their office practice? An in-the-office peek at internists' record-keeping shows deficiencies that may mirror medical failings. Physicians at the Graduate School of Public Health at the University of Pittsburgh have recently published, in *JAMA,* a survey on "The Office Practice of Internists," covering interviews with 125 internists. Patient records were examined by non-physicians, who found that the patient's chief complaint was recorded as such in only 40 percent of the records. One quarter of the time the doctors did not even describe the patients' symptoms; one third of the time there was no family history; only 40 percent of diabetic patients had a vital fundoscopic (eye grounds) examination recorded; only 12 percent of the female patients had a Pap smear recorded.

Physician-surveyors judged that thirty of the ninety-one internists they sampled kept inadequate records. Family history was not taken 41 percent of the time; diagnosis was not stated in 24 percent; and treatment was omitted in 16 percent. On those records judged unsatisfactory, physical examination was missing 32 percent of the time. "Some men never recorded diagnoses and gave various explanations to the surveyors for this practice," state the Pittsburgh researchers.

The widespread deficiency in internal medicine can partially be blamed on the specialty's anatomic ambition: it tries to cover almost the entire medical being of the adult. With such a broad range of disease to treat—from bronchial to rectal disturbances—only the most astute doctor can maintain adequate proficiency. This has logically led to the development of several *subspecialties* within internal medicine, a narrowing of interest that could raise proficiency in certain areas.

An American Society of Internal Medicine survey indicates that 51 percent of all internists have a subspecialty, from cardiology to rheumatology, although only one in three of their patients will fall into their subspecialty category. The most common subspecialty is heart disease (20.8 percent of internists), followed by gastroenterology (7.1 percent), rheumatology, hematology, endocrinology, allergy, and others. At present there are four subspecialty "boards" under the aegis of the American Board of Internal Medicine. *After* qualifying for the main board and practicing additional time, members may try for further qualification in cardiology, gastroenterology, allergy, and pulmonary diseases.

Concurrent with this trend toward narrow subspecialization is, paradoxically, the growing "GP syndrome" among internists. Especially in suburban areas, there is a growing tendency for the internist to assume the role of the adult personal physician. Mated with the pediatrician and obstetrician, this modern internist provides the personal family care that challenges the general practitioner's province, especially in upper-middle-income areas from Santa Barbara to Scarsdale. The phenomenon began less than twenty years ago when, as internist Dr. Richard C. Bates states, the "laymen discovered the internist." As he puts it: "After World War II, large corporations began sending top executives to big clinics and universities for a yearly overhaul—by internists. Many executives returned home and purchased the same thing for their wives . . . The word 'internist' began to catch on at cocktail parties; patients worked the phrase 'My internist tells me' into conversations as a status symbol."

The financially able patient still wears his internist-family doctor as a prestige pendant, but carries it comfortably because it represents perhaps slightly better medicine than he had previously. The internist's popularity has raised the thought that this might be the shape of that oft-heralded "doctor of the future," that super-physician all patients are anticipating as avidly as the messianic second coming.

Dr. Mahlon Delp is one of the enthusiastic supporters of the "general" internist as the "new front-line medical representative." The professor of medicine at the University of Kansas Medical School encouraged the membership of the American Society of Internal Medicine: "The general internist is the personal physician of the future. His broad training in both the science and art of medicine makes him the best equipped for this responsible assignment." When the "hapless victim of severe complicated" illness finds himself lodged in the modern medical center, Dr. Delp points out in example, the patient "truly needs the general internist as a buffer between himself and the super-scientific representatives of the profession."

The public's need for such a physician is hardly debated, and Dr. Delp eloquently restates that desire: "They [the patients] want and deserve a talented, thoughtful, and scholarly physician capable of reburnishing the blemished image now under attack."

Will the internist be tomorrow's super-practitioner? Except for the contradictory subspecialization, this has been his tendency—to compromise between the academic necessity for thoroughness and the growing patient demand for services—a crush that may move him even closer to family medicine. There have already been proposals to have the internist take additional training in pediatrics, to "round out" his family competence. This converted image could well prove an identical twin of the "family-practice specialist" now being groomed in the medical wings by certain general-practice groups.

From this vantage point, the future of internal medicine appears secure, but highly schizophrenic. The specialty—with its ridiculously limited manpower—cannot even begin to satisfy the pressing medical needs if it tries to fill both the GP gap and the urgent need for good subspecialists and academicians. The answer appears to lie in two distinct groups: the subspecialists, who might further organize into several separate "boards" (the American Board of Gastroenterology); and the family practitioners, who will retain the work and title of "general internist." The latter, larger group will then have ample opportunity to prove whether they can provide desperately needed, better medicine as the GP's of tomorrow.

Chapter XV

The Osteopaths:
Medical Manipulation

The legend on the door read "Dr."; the framed diploma on the wall was an unrestricted license to practice "Medicine and Surgery" in that state. The patient was a mild diabetic who had just moved into town; he had sought out the physician on his neighbor's recommendation. The doctor proceeded with the usual diagnostic technique, including a physical and a blood-sugar test. On the patient's return, he prescribed a diabetic diet and oral diabetic drugs, a therapeutic regimen virtually identical with that used by the patient's previous physician.

Before he left, however, the physician ushered the patient into an unfamiliar-looking room and toward an awesome treatment table, an apparent hybrid of a masseuse's platform and an operating table. On the physician's instruction, the patient mounted and was astonished as the doctor performed back "manipulation" not unlike that the patient had received from a chiropractor for back pain a few years before. "Doctor," the now-shaken patient asked, "what has this got to do with my diabetes?"

The explanation mystified the patient, who had never heard such a philosophy expounded by any doctor. The human body, the doctor told the befuddled patient, cannot be divided into two simple systems of the internal and the external—the visceral and somatic. The body is a whole, united by the musculoskeletal system, which in turn can influence the internal economy of the body. Manipulation of areas of the back, he explained, can have a beneficial effect on diabetes in several ways: by maintaining the body tone; by improving the blood circulation, which may be especially pertinent if diabetes and arteriosclerosis coexist in the patient; even by helping in the assimilation of sugar. Equally important, he informed the now-alert patient, manipulation improves the overall body health, which is vital to a victim of an endocrine disease such as diabetes.

This unusual meeting of patient and doctor is not such a rare adventure in America. The doctor was an osteopathic physician, a peculiar native phenomenon born in the Midwest during the 1860's which has flourished in the twentieth century as an unloved cousin of the conventional medical physician. He boasts the D.O. (doctor of osteopathy) degree instead of the M.D., but legally is neither medical quack nor poseur in thirty-nine states of the Union and the District of Columbia, where he has full medical and surgical prerogatives.

He is not an M.D., did not graduate from a conventional medical school and is not qualified for membership in the AMA. But in most states of the nation he may legally do anything permitted of an M.D., including the prescribing of narcotics and other drugs, the setting of broken bones, the delivery of children, and even complete brain surgery. In addition, he carries on the theory and technology of body "manipulation" developed by a former Civil War officer, Dr. Andrew Taylor Still, the founder of the osteopathic profession.

Although unknown to some and enigmatic to most, the osteopath must be reckoned with in American medicine, for he cares for the health of approximately 6 percent of the population, for many as their regular family doctor. The 12,266 osteopaths are spread across America, but more than half of them practice in towns of less than a 50,000 population, where the D.O. is often the only general-practice physician available. He is far from absent in the large city: the Manhattan phone directory, under the heading "Physicians & Surgeons–Osteopathic (D.O.)," lists fifty-seven osteopaths. In some areas of the country the D.O. is such a popular healer that he has become a serious competitor to the M.D. In Michigan, patients support 1781 osteopathic physicians; Pennsylvania has 1413; Texas, 725; Ohio, 933; and Missouri, the profession's birthplace, 1062.

To the M.D.—officially or unofficially, depending on the state—osteopathy is a "cult," a non-science devoid of merit. Since many osteopaths practice an equivalent of the M.D.'s scientific medicine in addition to his various body manipulations, he may receive begrudging acknowledgment from the M.D. as a "second class" physician, much like the European "feldsher." This low esteem has traditionally placed the osteopath in a strange medical demi-world where he operates as a mutant offspring of the M.D., but without his full status.

The M.D. community may look down their noses imperiously, but to millions of patients the osteopathic "Doc" is the man who assisted at the birth of their child, removed his tonsils and was in the house devotedly caring for Grandma when she passed away. Osteopathic medicine has copied almost the exact structure of orthodox medicine, making the patient—who may not even know that his doctor is not an M.D.—more secure. Osteopathy operates 311 osteopathic hospitals, with 15,804 beds, from a four-bed hospital in Kentucky to the 425-bed Detroit Osteopathic Hospital, institutions which look and behave basically like any other hospital. In a typical year they handle 660,000 patients, deliver 110,000 babies and perform 310,000 operations, whether simple tonsillectomies or total gastric resections.

Eighty-nine of the hospitals maintain interne and resident training for the specialties—near word-for-word duplicates of those developed by orthodox medicine (which, incidentally, is generally referred to derisively by osteopaths as the "allopathic," or countersymptomatic, profession). Eleven percent of osteopaths specialize full time, and many are members of boards such as the American Osteopathic Board of Proctology, American Osteopathic Board of Internal Medicine and even the American Osteopathic Board of Neurology and Psychiatry.

The profession operates five osteopathic colleges, with entrance requirements only somewhat lower than the best medical colleges: three years of undergraduate school instead of the conventional bachelor's degree. (Seventy percent of their entering students, however, do possess a degree.) It is difficult to distinguish their curriculum from that of a typical medical college. It has been carefully fashioned after conventional medical schools, and students receive five thousand hours of instruction during their four-year course in a full range of basic science, medicine, obstetrics and surgery, plus 320 hours of their own osteopathic theory and manipulative therapy. In the states where he has unlimited medical privileges he must pass the same medical-license examination as M.D.'s, but the lack of an M.D. after their name at the end of their training does not seem to deter applicants, for approximately five apply for every available space at osteopathic schools.

The amalgam of modern medicine and "back-cracking," as cynical M.D.'s are wont to describe osteopathy, began shortly after the Civil War, when Dr. Still developed a deep dissatisfaction with contemporary medicine, which had failed to save the lives of three of his children who died of spinal meningitis. Osteopathy was the offspring of this discouragement, a hopeful therapy in an era when conventional medicine offered little hope.

Dr. Still's theories had a metaphysical ring, and to this day, although staunchly defended by many osteopathic physicians, are difficult to convey accurately to others. The human body, said Still, was a self-healing mechanism which required an unimpaired structure to maintain adequate functioning. The normal functioning of the body was dependent on an uninterrupted nerve-and-blood supply to the body tissues, a system of balance that could be reachieved through manipulation during lapses of sickness. "Still had a flair for practical invention and was mechanically inclined," states the American Osteopathic Association. "With ingenuity and no precedent he worked out a system of manipulation intended to realign functional deviations and abnormalities. Such was the beginning of the 'osteopathic manipulative treatment,' which, added to all other proved theories, has distinguished the osteopathic school of medicine."

A tall, impressive, bearded man, Still traveled the small towns of Missouri, bringing his hatred of the conventional medicine of his time right into the streets. Often seen carrying a bag full of symbolic bones, and attracting sizable crowds wherever he went, the "tramp doctor"—who had one of the easily secured M.D. degrees of his time—set up osteopathic shop on the spot and massaged the musculoskeletal system of delighted townspeople, many of whom shouted his praise as a "miracle healer." In addition to his therapy of manipulation, he preached damnation of drugs and denied the existence of many specific diseases. "There is no such disease as fever, flux [flu], diphtheria, typhus, typhoid, or any other fever," the old heretic insisted. Modern osteopaths know better about these diseases than their ancestral mentor, but many still revere the intuition and joint-popping manipulation of Dr. A. T. Still.

What, if anything, can manipulation do today for the ailing body? Current osteopathic claims are broad, almost to the extent of visualizing a medical Nirvana of perpetual health. One booklet published by the American Osteopathic Association makes the following immodest statement: "The use of musculoskeletal manipulation in diagnosis and treatment is an integral part of the osteopathic concept. Manipulation has proven particularly valuable in the treatment of pneumonia, upper-respiratory infections and certain types of cardiovascular disease. In addition, osteopathic treatment during hospitalization helps prevent atrophy of muscles, stimulates the body while it is existing at 'low gear' and helps normalize body functions including elimination, circulation, and respiration."

Osteopathic literature makes claims that manipulation can improve ulcers, diabetes and other serious internal disorders, diseases that the D.O. has the unique choice of handling with conventional medical management or his own unusual therapy. Enthusiastic osteopaths see their ubiquitous "back rub" as a scientific therapy for treating asthma, sinusitis, migraine and even angina pectoris, the painful cardiac condition. "Many of us are amazed at what can be done with manipulation," states a Manhattan osteopath. "I personally believe that manipulation should be used much more than it is today."

As an illustration of such sublime confidence, a New York osteopath (whose practice is almost entirely "manipulation") explains that he treats hypertension with manipulation of the upper back and neck, and gastric ulcers with similar therapy applied "a little lower." Osteopathy even has psychiatric capabilities, says this adherent. "In addition," he states, "manipulation of the upper dorsal [back] helps eliminate nervous instability."

Is osteopathy, then, simple massage—a form of physiotherapy or chiropractic? D.O.'s say, "Hardly." However, pinning down an osteopath to the *exact* nature of his art and its effect on the body is often more strenuous than some of his more aggressive manipulations. ("This business is harder physical work than allopathy," says one successful osteopath.) The language of osteopathic theory rings exasperatingly vague to someone attuned to the semantics of conventional medical thought.

The osteopathic vocabulary is rich, if nebulous, and their theory of disease and therapy is exotic. His osteopathic "lesion," unlike the injury we usually associate with the word, is part of a "structural fault" in the body and is ostensibly evidence of a disease process. The "lesion" cannot be seen or X-rayed, or evidenced in other objective ways, but osteopaths swear that it exists. Some practitioners state that with the sensitive fingers that osteopaths develop, they can feel the "lesion" and remove it. "A good osteopath must be able to feel a dime through a book," they say allegorically.

In the semantic wonderland of osteopathy, a "reflex" is the influence from a diseased or damaged internal part or organ back to the surface of the body. This reflex can supposedly pass over the nerves to distant regions of the body to produce the "lesions," which then result in a slowing-up of the circulation of the blood or lymph glands, causing edema and acidosis. The nerves themselves can thus become irritated and affect the circulation in other parts of the body. The vital processes of the body organs are interfered with, and the body's natural remedies to fight illness and infection are blocked. The body's natural state of homeostasis—perfect balance—is disrupted, but it can be righted by osteopathic manipulation.

According to their theory, the trained manipulation of the proper portions of the body (soma)—muscles, joints, ligaments, tissues and the spine—improves the circulation of the blood and lymph, and restores the body's structural integrity. The hand manipulation can include virtually every external part of the body—arms, legs, chest, back, neck, even the head. Thus, says osteopathic dogma, it brings healing therapy to the inside (visceral) of the body where the illness may be centered. Osteopathy has also utilized modern technology, and manipulation is sometimes accomplished mechanically by machines such as the Spinulator, which massages the spine through a long hole cut into the treatment table.

While M.D.'s insist that this is pure rhetoric and anatomic obfuscation, D.O.'s consider it as plain as simple muscle tension. "If M.D.'s can't see the connection between nerves, the circulatory system and disease," says one D.O., "it's just because they are pig-headed." Although most osteopaths use antibiotics as standard treatment for pneumonia, osteopaths state that prior to the modern drugs, osteo- pathic treatment of peumonia was often the only successful treat- ment. They claim that it is still valuable in some cases. Pneumonia and other respiratory ailments are osteopathically treated with a movement called the "thoracic pump," a rib-cage manipulation which ostensibly breaks up the lung congestion.

One prominent osteopath, Dr. J. Marshall Hoag, states that be- fore the antibiotic revolution, his record of cure for pneumonia was far superior to the M.D.'s, who had almost no method at all. "A person who has pneumonia is breathing rapidly and with difficulty," he states. "He breathes as much as forty thousand times a day, as opposed to the twenty-five-thousand rate of a normal person. The first step in treatment is to slow down the pneumonia victim's res- piration by manipulation of the muscles of the back behind the lungs, permitting easier breathing and recovery."

Sinuses, too, osteopaths believe, can be treated, by pressure on the neck and temples, which ostensibly helps to drain the clogged hollows. Swelling of the legs, according to osteopathic theory, can be alleviated by a manipulation movement called the "lymphatic pump." Although many osteopaths deny that there are specific body manipulation points related to specific diseases, osteopathic texts have been published claiming this simplistic connection.

"It's all cultism and has no scientific healing value," says Charles C. Mangi, M.D., of Queens County, New York, a vociferous med- ical opponent of the osteopathic profession. "I personally feel that osteopathy should be abolished for the protection of the public. Osteopaths talk about an osteopathic lesion that causes disease, but if you ask an osteopath to show you one, he can't. The reason is quite simple: it doesn't exist. Why has osteopathy succeeded? I sup- pose it's because there's a sucker born every minute. Also, illnesses often cure themselves, and if an osteopath is the last one to see the patient, and manipulate him, he gets the credit. But what the patient doesn't know is that manipulations can often be dangerous. I remem- ber one person who was brought to a hospital with a dislocation of a vertebra of the neck after receiving manipulation from an osteo- path. In addition, the time and effort spent on manipulation can cause neglect of the true diagnosis of the case."

Traditionally, organized medicine's attitude toward osteopathy has been a duplicate of Dr. Mangi's cynicism. Past resolutions at many medical conventions have, in effect, stated that osteopathy is quack- ery, and that M.D.'s associating professionally with D.O.'s were guilty of unethical behavior. Although osteopathy and manipulation are still almost universally derided as cultism by medical doctors, the osteopath himself is achieving new-found dignity in medical eyes. His traditional entry into the medical world—surreptitiously, by the back door of the hospital—is now being altered to a near-welcome in many localities.

A recent about-face by the Medical Society of the State of New York is evidence of the shifting attitudes (or strategy) of organized medicine toward osteopaths, if not osteopathy. In 1961 Dr. Mangi's resolution defining osteopathy as "cultism" and making association with D.O.'s unethical was passed by the New York State House of Delegates, only to have it repealed at the February, 1965 meeting. The latest interface in the M.D.-D.O. relationship is restrained, but has at least the trace of a Gioconda-like smile. Under a new AMA policy, M.D.-D.O. relationships are a matter of state option. Now doctors of osteopathy can be members of regular hospital staffs in several states, without the hospital fearing that it will lose its accreditation.

The new policy of the New York medical society is typical: "We further suggest to the physicians practicing in areas where there are osteopaths requesting admission to hospital staffs that if these hospitals change their bylaws to admit such osteopaths, and if in the opinion of the medical board they practice scientific medicine and are otherwise qualified, association with osteopaths is not unethical."

The manipulative theory of "Lightnin' Bonesetter" Andrew Still has not been welcomed into the House of Hippocrates, but in many areas his medically trained descendants are increasingly receiving long-sought reputability. Since it started as an offshoot of conventional medicine, osteopathy has always insisted on some scientific medical training as a bulwark to "manipulation" and "lesions." Osteopathic schools such as the profession's fountainhead, the Kirksville (Missouri) College of Osteopathy and Surgery, have historically maintained a medical curriculum in addition to extensive training in their musculoskeletal dogma. The medical-school reforms of Abraham Flexner, however, were not fully implemented in osteopathic schools until 1940, and some middle-aged and older osteopaths tend to rely much more heavily on manipulation than scientific medicine.

But despite this scientific education, his debt to Andrew Taylor Still is still heavily extracted: the future D.O. must take his hours of manipulative theory and therapy, and swear obeisance to the memory and system of the old eccentric. In their version of the Hippocratic oath, osteopaths affirm at graduation: "I will ever be alert to and adhere to and develop the principles of osteopathy as taught by Andrew Taylor Still."

Estimates indicate that adherence to Still's dogma is still reasonably high, despite rumors—perhaps inspired by D.O.'s seeking fuller acceptance—that the new men are practicing full scientific medicine. Approximately eleven hundred osteopaths limit themselves to only manipulative therapy; about an equal amount use no manipulation; while the great majority of D.O.'s practice the curious hybrid of conventional medicine and manipulation.

The mere existence of the D.O. is a persistent lesion in the psyche of organized medicine, which is restless about the presence of a legally recognized splinter group. Competition is always a possible motivation, especially when the doctor shortage in small-town areas gives the D.O.'s an opportunity to earn as much as the prideful M.D. (Under New York's workmen's compensation laws, D.O.'s receive more than M.D.'s per patient visit.) Equally galling is the prize patient who is a devotee of the profession, such as Nelson Rockefeller, whose private physician is reportedly an osteopath, and whose family has donated over $1,500,000 to osteopathic research and training, and to the Kirksville College in Missouri.

Respectability is catching. General Motors has donated $625,000 toward a giant osteopathic hospital in Michigan. A $40,000,000 osteopathic college is being constructed in Lansing, Michigan, and two more are planned for New Jersey and Texas. Mamie Dowd Eisenhower has lent her name to an osteopathic hospital in Colorado. The federal government now grants commissions to D.O.'s entering the armed forces, and employs them in the Veterans Administration and Public Health Service. Federal legislation, including National Institutes of Health grants, now include D.O.'s as well as M.D.'s. Ironically, annoyed M.D.'s blame the osteopathic acceptance on the fact that D.O.'s stayed at home during World War II taking care of the "people" when M.D.'s were overseas "fighting with the boys." They conveniently forget it was medical lobbying that convinced the government to withhold medical commissions from D.O.'s.

The price of this newly won success is that it has attracted the covetous eyes of the medical profession, which now apparently plans to kill off the competition by marrying it into the family. This maneuver succeeded so well in absorbing the "homeopaths" in 1903 that it is being refurbished for an osteopathic encompassment. (The homeopaths were followers of Dr. Samuel Hahnemann, who revolted against medical purgatives and relied heavily on nature's remedies— from starfish to toads. They also believed in creating sympathetic symptoms like those of the disease itself. Several homeopathic institutions, including Flower & Fifth Avenue Hospitals in New York, were absorbed with the rebellious physicians.)

The acquisitive instinct of the AMA was ironically whetted by the osteopath's striving for excellence. In the 1950's AMA official Dr. John Cline visited osteopathic schools. He reported back, with some apparent surprise, that the scientific training was good, and that the emphasis on "cultism" was decreasing. A more recent example of the new scientific profile of osteopathy is the March, 1965 issue of *The Journal of the American Osteopathic Association,* none of whose medical articles involved the theories or practice of Dr. Still's "bone-crackin'." Its only osteopathic-related advertisement is one small insertion for a folding-type treatment table.

Many medical doctors still insist that D.O.'s practice "second-rate medicine in second-rate hospitals." "I can't think of one medical advance that has come out of osteopathic training," says one M.D. "Osteopaths may be of some value in treating backaches that medicine can't help, but that's about all. Mostly, they are just people who couldn't get into medical school and are willing to settle for less. Can you imagine a young fellow having his choice of becoming a D.O. or an M.D. and choosing osteopathy?" (Osteopaths deny that most of their students are medical-school rejects.)

Despite the bickering, many influential medical leaders feel that D.O.'s might be sufficiently well trained, and sufficiently plump and powerful, to be organizationally gobbled. Officially, the osteopaths have been reluctant. The American Osteopathic Association has defiantly affirmed its desire to remain "a separate and complete school of medicine," fearing that merger would be a euphemism for the profession's extinction. The rank and file, especially the younger men, are torn between allegiance to the memory of Still and the tantalizing status lure of an M.D. added to their name. "It's no fun at cocktail parties explaining to people what a doctor of osteopathy is. They think I'm a chiropractor or a chiropodist," says one D.O. In fact, one D.O., Dr. John C. Button, so valued the older initials that he voluntarily gave up a $100,000 annual income as an osteopath in suburban New Jersey to go to medical school!

Other osteopaths are concerned that a merger might be scientifically premature, eliminating osteopathy as a profession before it has had a full chance to proselytize its unique ideas to the conventional medical world. Still other osteopaths, fierce with the pride of any minority that has successfully survived, even prospered despite opposition, refuse to consider merger.

The status gnawings of many D.O.'s and the appetite of the AMA have already been victorious in California, where the two professions were recently merged into one—that of the conventional M.D. After semisecret negotiations fought by the national AOA, most osteopaths and medical doctors in California agreed on a merger plan that might be a model for the eventual demise of osteopathy. The Los Angeles College of Osteopathic Physicians and Surgeons was renamed the California College of Medicine, and an M.D. was appointed as its new dean. In a series of unprecedented academic moves that brought cries of "diploma mill" from some sources, the

college—with state-government and medical-society agreement—
then bestowed M.D. degrees on virtually its entire D.O. faculty. In
less than a year the new medical school was approved by the
Association of American Medical Colleges and the AMA.

The next step was the most crucial: for $65, an osteopath prac-
ticing in the State of California could *write* in and almost automatically receive an M.D. degree from this new school. Since
March, 1962, the California College of Medicine has granted M.D.
degrees to over two thousand former osteopaths, leaving barely two
hundred D.O.'s still practicing in the state. The profession will
eventually be extinct in the state, for California will no longer grant
new osteopathic licenses.

What has been the effect on these newly minted California M.D.'s?
A medical-publication survey indicates general satisfaction, with the
possible exception of 267 osteopathic specialists who have not received reciprocal board certification. One general practitioner in Los
Angeles expresses typical joy at his new status. "It used to take me
ten minutes to explain to new patients the difference betwen a D.O.
and an M.D. Then, when I'd get all through, they sometimes say
to me, 'Well, you're just like a chiropractor!' No more of that now."

Controversy within osteopathy rages in other states: osteopaths
in Pennsylvania have temporarily voted merger down, but some
Washington State osteopaths have received medical degrees despite
opposition by the Washington Osteopathic Medical Association. The
state-by-state situation is becoming even more chaotic as D.O.'s receiving M.D. degrees are being cut out of their osteopathic associations, and are not finding easy reciprocal acceptance as M.D.'s
should they leave the state in which they originally merged.

The organizations of the two professions are now engaged in a
bitter political fray, in which the mammoth AMA has the wealth
and prestige, but the osteopaths have the wile they have accrued
in their hundred years as a minority, fighting a variety of opponents
including organized medicine and rural sheriffs. The struggle occasionally becomes nonsensical, as in the osteopaths' current usage of
the small "md" in discussing medical doctors. But basically, it
evolves into the issue of whether or not there can be two accepted
medical schools of thought.

The osteopathic attitude is *Yes.* "It may be true there cannot be
two sciences of medicine," says the AOA in a white paper on AOA-
AMA relationships, "but AMA fails to recognize that while medicine employs scientific knowledge, the practice of medicine is not
science *per se.* It is equally unrealistic to insist only one system of
medical practice, that approved by a political body, can be valid.
The AOA firmly believes that AMA has chosen to depreciate the
osteopathic profession, not because of its scientific concepts but for
purely political motives."

The AMA counters with little comment, but with the aggressive activities of a strategy group, the Committee on Osteopathy and Medicine, whose membership includes an ex-osteopath. The committee has made forays into various states, attempting to build the climate for eventual merger, and with it the demise of osteopathy. In a recent editorial, *The Journal of the AOA* accused the AMA of attempting "to roll its Trojan Horse into such osteopathically strong states as Michigan, Pennsylvania, New York, and New Jersey."

Which group serves the public interest in this fracas? Should osteopathy remain as a profession and osteopaths remain the family doctor for millions of Americans? It appears obvious that with the necessity for further stringent upgrading of lagging medical quality, the existence of any medical practitioner who is legally licensed, but operating on the fringe of the medical establishment, is not in the public interest. *Under certain conditions,* the return of D.O.'s to the field of medicine through merger is essential.

If medicine can *satisfy* the public about the truth of their argument that osteopathy is cultism, then osteopathy obviously should be eliminated as a separate profession. Despite pronouncements on either side, the argument is not a political one, but one entirely of science. Neither expansive claims by the osteopaths, nor the obstinacy of the AMA will alter the basic question: either "manipulation" is therapeutic, or it is not. It is not a complex dilemma, but a medical problem that cries out for controlled therapeutic studies over a period of several years. Validation studies, financed jointly by the osteopathic and medical professions with assistance from federal research funds, are essential if we are to reveal the truth of osteopathy.

If, for example, any of the sixty thousand who die yearly of pneumonia (despite all the scientific attempts of modern medicine) can be aided by osteopathic manipulation, then the intuition of Andrew Taylor Still will have left a legacy for all physicians, both D.O.'s and M.D.'s. If this and other serious organic ailments can be healed by manipulation, the discipline undoubtedly deserves a place as an important separate medical specialty. If its balm is curative in only specialized skeletal and muscular ailments, such as back pain, perhaps the discipline could prove an asset to physical medicine specialists. And if osteopathy proves to have been purely a medicinal delusion of a frontier doctor with more imagination than command of science, it can find its place in history with other cults that piqued man's inherent healing impulse for a time, then passed into memory.

The millions of Americans who now rely on osteopaths as their family physicians have an urgent need to know.

Part V *The Doctor As a Professional*

Chapter XVI

The American
Medical Association:
Our Most Potent "Labor Union"

The young physician who has just completed a residency at a university hospital and decides to open a practice in a suburban area, quickly absorbs the reality of organized medicine. Patient-and-scientifically-oriented, he may have little interest in organizations, whether the Democratic Party or the American Medical Association, whose Mesozoic socio-economic programs, including the ill-fated opposition to Medicare, leave him unmoved. Before establishing his office, he makes vital inquiries, to find a good voluntary hospital staffed with internes and residents where he can bring his patients, and to protect his future against bankruptcy by taking out malpractice insurance.

An official of the voluntary hospital in his community welcomed his academic qualifications and recommendations, then asked, "I assume that you are a member of the county medical society?" The startled young physician was informed that according to the bylaws of the "Community General Hospital," staff appointments are open only to "members in good and regular standing" of the county and state medical societies, the local constituencies of the American Medical Association. His inquiry to an insurance agent helped to shade in any undefined parts of the emerging picture. "Membership in the county medical society is normally a criterion for the underwriting of medical malpractice policies," the agent told the young doctor. "It is an indication of your reputation and that you have been evaluated and accepted by a professional group. If a doctor was not a member, we would want to know why." A physician-friend confirmed this in less evasive language: "It's damn difficult, if not impossible in many places, to get a malpractice policy if you're not a county society member."

The internist needed little more persuasion, but it was freely provided by a senior physician-friend who educated him to the facts of community medicine: the county society is often the informal focus of referrals to specialists from other doctors. The internist went to the next society meeting and joined, at an annual fee of $100 a year. He found that he was automatically a member of the state medical society at $45 a year and that membership in the AMA was *compulsory*. "We're one of the thirteen states [including New York, California and Illinois] whose House of Delegates have made it a requirement that all county members also join the AMA," he was told by the membership chairman.

In medico-political parlance, he was not offered a "free choice." Having paid his $190 in annual dues, and prepared to pay them for the rest of his life—a total of over $7000—the young internist had lent his name, his degree, his repute and his funds to an organization whose views and methods he did not support.

"The AMA is a federation of 54 state and territorial medical associations," states a recent AMA brochure distributed at its annual New York convention. "These in turn are composed of more than 1900 component medical societies. The representative government principle applies throughout, with authority moving up from the component society through the state and territorial associations to the national body, through the process of elected delegates."

The AMA appears to have the prescribed requirements of a democratic professional group. A House of Delegates, composed of 234 members, is the chief policy-making body. Between its twice-yearly sessions the AMA is directed by a board of trustees, composed of the president, president-elect, immediate past-president, and twelve trustees elected by the House for a three-year term.

The AMA *face* is a superficially pleasant and democratic one. It is ostensibly a noncoercive organization whose good services have effectively attracted doctors to its ranks. To the noncritical physician eager to conform to the dicta of organized medicine, this benign profile is accurate. To any critical observer, however, the AMA, its constituent county and state groups, and related activities, badly fit the brochure's sonorous phrases. As no other professional group, organized medicine bears an unflattering resemblance to the type of organization for whom several of its leaders have expressed contempt —the sometimes oligarchic, closed-shop labor union.

Like most labor unions, and unlike most professional societies, its political goals are specific and polarized—in this case generally to the right. Its vociferous support of issues and political candidates thought likely to enhance the doctor's aims, especially his pocketbook, can conflict badly with the needs of society. In terms of power over its membership, its film-thin veneer of democratic process, its self-perpetuating minority control and its *ad hoc* but effectively coercive tactics, the AMA and its local groups are easily the peer (if not the superior) of the most hidebound of the old-line trade unions. Its visible methods are more impeccable and its tone more professionally reassuring, but its steel grasp on those few physicians who dare contest it can be punishing. Whenever the AMA itself has found it expedient to maintain its aloof, imperious stature, as in its attitude toward prepaid group medicine, the local society members have been boyishly willing to provide the persuasion.

While its massive power has stilled the tongue of most of its membership, an increasingly vocal minority of physicians are becoming openly critical of its monolithic stance, its political leadership and its nonprofessional obsession with doctor income. "The AMA is not led by medical leaders, but by medical politicians," says Dr. Richard Lee of the respected Palo Alto Clinic in California, which provides medical care for Stanford University. Dr. John Freymann, director of medical education at Memorial Hospital in Worcester, Massachusetts, decries the AMA's general backwardness. "No longer a positive force," he writes in the *New England Journal of Medicine,* "the AMA, and with it the entire medical profession, has for forty years been in the negative position of supporting or opposing programs conceived by the laity and carried forward on the fitful winds of public demand."

A young, anonymous faculty member at Downstate Medical Center in New York who refuses to join the county medical society believes that for all its pretended interest in medical affairs, the AMA "is all the time thinking about those bucks in the doctor's pocket." Dr. Samuel Standard, former chief of surgery at Morrisania Hospital in New York, concurs, stating that the AMA judges a medical program by "the extent to which the physician's income is assured."

Our young internist attending his first county elections was undoubtedly taken aback by some of the realities of AMA life, especially the typically self-perpetuating AMA elections, which effortlessly push hand-picked physicians into office through the "nominating slate" technique. The nominating committee, appointed by those already in power (including the president), chooses a slate of county officers, plus the delegates for the State House of Delegates. No anti-administration nominations are usually offered from the "floor," say critics, and the "one party" election usually proceeds on precise schedule.

From that moment on, the democracy of organized medicine takes place outside of the doctor's purview and without his participation. The state delegates elect the state officers. The state officials, in turn, nominate the national delegates. At the annual convention the national delegates elect the AMA president and officers. The official slate carries not only the imprimatur of organized medicine, but soliciting of votes and electioneering is considered ungentlemanly, and contests are thus uncommon. At the turn of the century the AMA passed such a non-electioneering rule, and although it has been declared unenforceable, Dr. Morris Fishbein, former editor of the *Journal of the AMA,* has found it to be an "effective moral force."

The formal structure of the AMA is custom-made for minority control. The "real power structure," according to a study of the AMA in the *Yale Law Journal,* is concentrated in a small minority of forceful, apparently conservative hands. "Thus the few doctors who are interested in medical politics can easily wield power and influence out of proportion to their numerical strength," says the Yale study. "The nominating process, in combination with the apathy of the average doctor, assures domination by a single faction within the AMA."

The autocracy of the AMA at the local level is verified by a California doctor, Dr. Andrew S. Markovitz, who gives a vivid picture of the pseudodemocracy of organized medicine. He explains in a medical publication that the traditional secret ballot never took hold in the medical establishment. "The usual medical society and hospital staff elections are about as democratic as Genghis Khan's council meetings," states the courageous physician. "An *appointed* nominating committee *appoints* all the officers, committee chairmen, and committees. There's a perfunctory request for nominations from the floor. But in case anyone is so nominated, he nearly always either declines to run or is defeated." His solution for an "honest" vote in local AMA meetings: announce elections two weeks in advance; abolish nominating committees; open nominations from the floor; and use secret ballots.

Another AMA critic, a Connecticut physician, writes a letter to the editor of a medical publication to express his resentment over AMA failure of "democratic processes" in the handling of Social Security for doctors, since passed by the government. "We resent the parliamentary tricks long used by the American Medical Association to block this legislation," he states indignantly. "The AMA has subverted our freedom of self-determination. In all fairness, they should hold a secret vote and act according to the opinion of the majority."

Criticism of AMA oligarchy does not prove that the organization does not reflect the typical doctor's views, but free dissent is not encouraged. Surveys of doctor opinion on Social Security retirement for themselves generally showed that a majority disagreed with the AMA position. Most opposing doctor opinions have little opportunity for exposure, however, for the publications of the AMA and the medical societies are careful censors of attitudes which might be a rallying point for opposition.

JAMA, though an increasingly valuable scientific journal, is not a forum for dissent. When a nonmedical publication tried to place an advertisement for an article on compulsory health insurance, it was reportedly turned down. Doctors claim that controversial letters submitted by members are almost always "circular filed." The *AMA News,* the monolithic house organ of official policy, is apparently as restrictive. "It seems that there is no effective organization or voice for the liberal physician," Dr. Jan Polissar of Massachusetts writes in a letter to the *New England Journal of Medicine.* "His minority views are seldom printed and almost never in the AMA publications. Even a doctor-sponsored advertisement in favor of medicare was refused by *AMA News.*"

An exception to this censorship is the *New England Journal of Medicine,* official organ of the Massachusetts Medical Society. This unique medical group has resolved on freer discussion, urging that "the *Journal of the American Medical Association* welcome and provide space for the presentation of considered discussion from varying points of view." The columns and the letters page of the *New England Journal* regularly (and atypically) present a ferment of oppositional opinion.

The *New England Journal* provided an opportunity for a distinguished pediatrician, Dr. Alexander Nadas, clinical professor of pediatrics at Harvard Medical School, to publicly announce his resignation from the AMA. The resignation was made because of several AMA stands, including what he called "the autocratic attitude toward editorial policies of the AMA publications as exemplified in the editorial upset of *AJDC,*" referring to the *American Journal of Diseases of Children,* an AMA-published pediatric magazine. The rhubarb involves an alleged hammer-handed censorship of the journal by the AMA over the opposition of its own editor. The proceedings of two pediatric research groups were regularly published in the *AJDC* and the editor made plans to print the Presidential Address of one of the societies as scheduled, despite the fact that the organization's president had made some critical mention of drug-firm advertising. The "higher echelons" of the AMA, however, stepped brusquely in, and demanded that three offending items in the speech be changed, or it would not be published. The changes were made under this extreme pressure and the piece published. Shortly after, the journal's editor, Dr. Warren Wheeler, professor of pediatrics at the University of Kentucky, was "not reappointed," and several members of the staff resigned in protest.

If the AMA were pure Neanderthal, it would be considerably

easier to criticize its methods and aims. Its vintage goals, promulgated to ensure the doctor's dollar flow, disguise an occasionally enlightened scientific interest in medicine. The AMA's concepts of quality medical care and how to achieve it have gorge-sized gaps, but their generations-past policies did help elevate American medicine from its nineteenth-century frontier crudity.

The founding of the AMA—on May 5, 1847, in Philadelphia at a meeting of 250 doctors representing twenty-two states—was stimulated by the poor quality of medical care in the country and by the need for a recognized national association of doctors. Earlier attempts to organize medicine had failed, and even this effort, led by the AMA's founder, thirty-year-old Dr. Nathan Smith Davis of New York, was not the last. American medicine later nurtured many divisive movements, including the International Hahnemannian Association, which espoused homeopathy, a revolt against the harsh (now comparatively tame!) therapeutics of the day. Several other general medical groups, including the American Medical Union, also made brief appearances. Today, except for the tenacious osteopathic association, only the American Medical Association remains. It boasts 206,000 members, or 74 percent of the doctors, including many whose national membership is compulsory.

Its fierce attacks on quackery have aided American health, as has its help in the reformation of abysmal medical schools. It approves medical schools, helps in the accreditation of hospitals, appoints physicians to recommend state discipline, inspects and approves interne- and resident-training programs. It was the major sponsoring group of the specialty boards. It has also taken a leading part in continuing education for doctors. All of these programs currently cry out for crucial improvement, but their initial establishment was of radical benefit to earlier medicine.

These multiple functions give the AMA and its local groups their basic powers, controls so strong that organized medicine is quasilegal, often exercising power of professional life and death over many of its doctor subjects. Part of this control is exercised through the AMA's "Principles of Medical Ethics," which governs the conduct of its members. Its tenets are clear, with the exception of those ostensible "ethical" matters involving economics: types of medical care and payment systems that may be in conflict with the AMA policy, or even the prejudices of local society members. The controversial "ethics" which seem to bring unemotional physicians up to the pitch of warriors are the "fee for service" and "quality of medical care" clauses of the ten-point "Principles." The pertinent part of Section 7 reads: "His fee should be commensurate with the services rendered and the patient's ability to pay." Section 6 prohibits dispensing medicine under "unethical" conditions which "tend to cause a deterioration of the quality of medical care."

The wording of sections 6 and 7 has been interpreted—or stretched—as armament against various medico-economic plans, including Medicare and group plans with prepaid health insurance, such as HIP (Health Insurance Plan of Greater New York). Some vocal spokesmen claim that these plans violate the ancient medical tenets of "ability to pay" and fee for "services rendered" which have served doctors' pecuniary interests so well. When aroused (or frightened) by such supposed threats, doctors can cause offending colleagues grievous harm. "The physician who is suspected of 'unethical' practice may be subjected to professional ostracism," states the *Yale Law Journal* report on the AMA. "This may involve denial by member physicians of patient referrals and consultations, and the loss of advancement in hospital and other professional appointments."

The most coercive of organized medicine's powers is the refusal or loss of hospital staff privileges, and expulsion from the county medical society, or refusal of entrance into its ranks. Equally effective is the ability to wield "spontaneously" the combined professional power of doctors against a dissenter—sometimes with a cruel vengeance.

A Buffalo, New York, radiologist, Dr. Angelo S. D'Eloia, learned this when his nonconforming opinions riled his uncharitable colleagues sufficiently for them to ruin his twenty-year practice. "It began in 1962 when I was an active member of the Erie County Medical Society," Dr. D'Eloia opened his description of those fatal weeks. "We received a notice that Medicare would be the subject of the next meeting of the county society. I didn't agree with the official policy on Medicare, so I wrote up a short statement and came to the meeting prepared to read it. Instead of the discussion, they played a recording against Social Security put out by the U.S. Chamber of Commerce. I wanted to criticize the handling of the subject, and to read my statement, but when I asked if there would be any discussion, the chair said 'No' and I was called out of order. I walked out of the meeting."

Dr. D'Eloia's rebuff to the medical establishment's view on Medicare, and the verbal fracas at the meeting, made the next day's newspapers and catapulted the physician into public notice. "I got a call from the Democratic Party asking me to run for the Congress," he relates. "It was a Republican area and I didn't expect to win, but I accepted. As soon as my candidacy and support of Medicare was announced, my trouble with the local doctors began. They were also angry at me because I had planned to develop a new type of health plan. My practice just disappeared all at once. As a radiologist, I was dependent on referrals from other doctors, and they just stopped suddenly.

"With my practice gone, I was forced to take a job in Allegheny as an assistant to another radiologist. That didn't last long, for he was soon called by doctors and told to get rid of the SOB. I don't think there was any concerted effort on the part of the county society. I think the individual doctors became hysterical and acted without rhyme or reason. When it comes to official policy, they are just a bunch of sheep. I have rebuilt my life now, and I don't hold any malice against them."

Vendettas against physicians whose conscience veers them from the official path takes many tortuous forms. Dr. Paul O'Rourke, Harvard Medical School graduate and currently special assistant to Governor Pat Brown of California on anti-poverty planning, found that circuitous methods of doctor-squelching could be replaced by an open frontal attack, one which he courageously met and bested. Had it succeeded, says Dr. O'Rourke, it probably would have ruined his medical career. O'Rourke vs. organized medicine had its inception in Marin County, California, and its climax in Imperial County, the lush area which is often temporary home to migrants.

"It began in the early 1950's in Marin County, where I settled to practice as a GP," Dr. O'Rourke relates. "I went to join the county medical society, but was told I would have to take the whole package, including the AMA. I didn't want to pay my twenty-five dollars, but a county society official told me to 'go in and change the society' if I could. I took him up on it, and was eventually elected to its board of directors as a dissident. As a GP I could afford to be independent and speak my mind, because I didn't need any referrals. Some of the young specialists in the society agreed with me, and they became my silent partners."

Dr. O'Rourke helped conduct a vociferous program, including debates on Medicare, and on the end to one-slate elections—what Dr. O'Rourke refers to as the AMA "Stalin ballot." His prime antagonist in the Medicare debates was a fellow physician, whose disagreement with Dr. O'Rourke, he believes, was the impetus for what he calls the harassment that followed.

In 1960 the Harvard-trained physician's opinions finally brought the expected retributions. In Imperial County, where he was chief public health officer, his request for transfer of his AMA membership from Marin County to the Imperial County Society was greeted with significant silence. Unknown to him, his Marin County debating antagonist, who had been elected president of the California Medical Association, was corresponding with the local medical society. The correspondence contained innuendos which were later to cause organized medicine grave embarrassment.

"Meanwhile my relations with some of the local doctors were strained," Dr. O'Rourke explains. "Many of the local men wouldn't accept the federal payments for care of migrant youngsters, so we started treating the children ourselves for free. I had a pediatrician working with me, and we planned to examine every poor child in the county. The referrals of crippled children alone went up eight-fold. The local doctors were annoyed at this, and I was a perfect target—they thought—because of my family. My wife is a Quaker pacifist, and we have five adopted children, including one Chinese-Hawaiian child and one who is part Indian."

The letters from the new president of the California Medical Association to the local medical society, and the pressure from local physicians were followed by his being voted out as public health chief by the county board of supervisors. One letter stated, in part, that O'Rourke held "an attitude towards the medical profession that is not only hostile but also indicates that he is basically interested in massive social changes that from my point of view would be most disruptive . . ."

"The following week was a dramatic one," says Dr. O'Rourke. "I had insisted that the hearing be public and that everything be part of the record. The *San Francisco Examiner* took my side, and doctors—who didn't agree with me on Medicare—put pressure on the CMA president-elect at the convention. They just didn't like the hatcheting. Almost immediately, I was reinstated by unanimous vote of the supervisors, and some of the local physicians apologized. I left Imperial County about two months later, and went to northern California. I made it a point to visit the president of the California Medical Association and strongly remind him that I expected to be admitted to the county society and had no intention of being harassed. I haven't had any trouble since. I'm one of the few guys who have beaten them, perhaps because I was willing to fight."

The American Medical Association seldom, if ever, sullies itself by using coercion against individual doctors who stray from national dogma. The national organization is involved in massive propaganda, legislative lobbying, political-candidate support (through AMPAC) and resolutions to direct the local physicians and their organization. The "enforcers" of organized medicine's catechism are either the county medical society or "vigilante" groups of physicians.

AMA officials, of course, deny the existence of coercion in medicine. At a congressional hearing, union leader Walter Reuther charged that many doctors were afraid to speak their true mind. Congressman Cecil R. King of California, co-sponsor of the Medicare bill, suggested that doctors opposing the AMA viewpoint were afraid "that they would be put on an unfavorable list of their state or local societies." Dr. Edward R. Annis, forceful spokesman for organized medicine, acknowledged that some doctors are fearful to speak out because they might be "ostracized socially or within the profession." However, he attributed this to misunderstanding.

"Some people are not aware of the AMA policy or misinterpret it or misunderstand it," he told the congressmen. Others might phrase it less delicately: the AMA trods the philosophical high road knowing that its constitutent local societies are, if nothing else, earthy.

Control of physicians is achieved by county societies in many ways: expulsion, censure, suspension and denial of membership to applicants, whether new members or transfers from other counties. Expulsion can be appealed to the AMA Judicial Council, but denial of membership is arbitrary and the AMA declines jurisdiction. One county medical society, just to divest itself of a member, completely *dissolved* the organization, then re-formed without the dissenter.

The county medical society generally represents the local private-practice physicians, the "Town" portion of the classical Town-Gown controversy, in which the local doctor and the medical academician often have opposing views on socio-medical problems. It has been known to use its punitive powers against doctors to fight the suspected encroachment of the livelihood of the private practitioner by outside forces—whether by group practice or by the university hospital. Only an estimated one third of the university physicians are members of the AMA, and many do not even belong to the county medical society.

The doctor-academicians have relinquished the medical associations to others by default, only rallying occasionally—as in a recent case in Massachusetts. "I hadn't been to a medical meeting in some time," says a member of the Harvard medical faculty. "But when I and others heard that the Massachusetts Medical Society was considering making AMA membership compulsory, as in New York, about four hundred of us turned out. We defeated the proposal soundly."

In one Town vs. Gown clash in Houston, Texas, the community voted in favor of academic medicine, but not without the county society claiming the opposing physician as a casualty. City-county authorities wanted to move Jefferson Davis Charity Hospital to a new medical center and affiliate it with Baylor University's College of Medicine, a plan almost guaranteed to improve the medical care usually found in municipal hospitals. The Harris County Medical Society (Houston) opposed the move, hoping to keep the hospital downtown and unaffiliated so that its staff membership would be open to all practicing doctors. Dr. Abel J. Leader, professor of surgery at Baylor, attacked his medical-society colleagues for "a degrading mess of power politics," adding that any "physician who would knowingly do injury to a medical school—and there can be no doubt as to what is intended—differs little in my opinion from the man who beats his parents."

The local doctors lost the county-wide referendum, then set about to avenge themselves on Dr. Leader. The county medical society tried Dr. Leader for "unethical conduct" and censured him, a ruling upheld by the equally "Town" dominated Texas Medical Society. Dr. Leader, when interviewed, charitably considers the local society's "vindictiveness" the results of a deep doctor frustration over being locked out of the university.

There is an unfortunate AMA tendency, at all levels, to denigrate any medical change as either "unethical" or "socialized." During the last forty-five years the AMA, or its constituent groups, has been in almost constant conflict with contemporary attitude, yet invariably the giant slowly veers its head toward eventual agreement. In an eerie imitation of Orwellian "Newspeak," it then denies that it ever opposed such moves.

Over the past forty years, organized medicine (or its leaders) has been guilty of an abysmal lack of foresight. Their record of disapproving or trying to thwart obvious boons to medicine has been staunchly backward—a 100 percent score of faulty judgment. They have spoken out against voluntary health insurance (later to become Blue Cross and the doctors' own Blue Shield), medical groups of all kinds, prepaid health clinics, full-time salaried hospital chiefs and, more recently, federal low-interest loans to medical students, a measure supported by the Student AMA over its parent body's opposition.

Prepaid group health plans such as HIP and Group Health Association of Washington generally have been accepted despite medical-society antagonism and guerrilla-like, harassing activities. Yet today the AMA, questioned at its national office, blithely denies that it ever opposed prepaid group health plans. Any such opposition is attributed to a few "local doctors," officialese for the "enforcer" activities of the local medical society.

What does the enemy—the group plan—look like? Many prepaid group plans provide a reasonable level of medical care, but are not necessarily the panacea for American medicine. They do solve most of the economic problems of medical care, especially for working-class families. Their physicians, however, are products of the same medical schools as other doctors, often have the same aversion to house calls, and quality varies from physician to physician and from group to group. Most groups, like their private-practice colleagues, believe in five- or five-and-a-half-day medicine, an immaturity that dominates American doctors. Some patients enjoy the group's concentration of medical skill in one building, while other patients shy from any institutional setting for medicine, fearing a failure of doctor-patient relationships.

HIP provides care for seven hundred thousand New York subscribers in thirty-one centers. Those HIP groups, staffed mainly by *full-time* specialists, are capable of providing excellent medical care. Other HIP groups, which rely on local doctors to care for their patients for a yearly "head fee," in addition to their regular patients, may provide inferior care. "It's obvious that if a doctor has already gotten paid by HIP, and has both the HIP and regular-fee-paying patients, he will discriminate against the HIP patient," says a Long Island doctor under contract to HIP. "They become second-class patients in our practice." In fairness to HIP, which tries to maintain quality control and can boast a lower surgery and hospital utilization rate than is prevalent elsewhere, it is aware of the problem and encourages full-time practice by paying a bonus to such groups.

The local physician's animosity toward these prepaid plans is fired by consistent "free enterprise" statements by organized medicine. By implication they draw the group clinic doctor as an underpaid bureaucrat in the army of socialism. Actually, doctors are not salaried at HIP; the physicians own their practice and divide the profits. "The new doctor gets a fourteen-thousand-dollar annual wage for his first year, after which he enters our profit-sharing plan," reveals a spokesman of the East Nassau Group, which has twenty-three full-time staff doctors. "A typical senior man nets about twenty-eight thousand to thirty-five thousand dollars a year, plus retirement and disability programs, and paid vacation." The director of the Jamaica Medical Group of HIP describes a clinic-doctor affluence that will probably stimulate green envy in his colleagues rather than economic fear, and will undoubtedly surprise HIP patients. "Our typical doctors make thirty-five thousand dollars clear for a thirty-five-hour week," boasts Dr. Ben Landess.

Organized medicine's internecine war against group clinics, like its battle against many innovations, is a by-product of the AMA's staunch free-enterprise concepts. Surprisingly, prior to World War I the AMA had a golden era of concern. In 1916 an AMA committee investigated European methods of health insurance. Its reports urged co-operation between the medical profession and legislatures in setting up health insurance laws, then prophetically warned the profession against blocking necessary change.

"Blind opposition, indignant repudiation, bitter denunciation of these laws is worse than useless; it leads nowhere and it leaves the profession in a position of helplessness if the rising tide of social development sweeps over them," stated the committee. The report was adopted by the House of Delegates on June 5, 1917. In 1919 a resolution opposing compulsory health insurance was tabled, prompting Dr. John Freymann to comment recently in the *New England Journal of Medicine:* "This was to be the last liberal act of the House of Delegates for many years to come."

The post-World War I AMA has been more recognizable. In 1932 an AMA committee surprisingly recommended group medical practice financed by voluntary health insurance, but the minority report called health insurance "thoroughly discredited" and replete with "great dangers and evils." The *minority report was accepted,* and in the next few years the House of Delegates repeatedly opposed voluntary health insurance, later slated to become Blue Cross and Blue Shield, and other now-popular plans.

In 1933 a *JAMA* editorial referred to group hospitalization insurance plans as "half-baked experiments in changing the nature of medical practice." (*Probe,* an insurance newsletter with a long memory, recently warned its readers not to support the AMA blindly against Social Security Medicare, reminding them of these rash early AMA attacks on voluntary health insurance. "When it was not so dependent on our support," *Probe* recalls, "it screamed that we were about to commercialize medicine!")

In 1932 *JAMA* labeled group practice as "medical soviets," but opposition to prepaid plans had started even before this. In 1929, when Los Angeles city employees contracted with the Ross-Loos Clinic for health coverage, several of the clinic's doctors, including a former county medical society president, were expelled from that society—which cut them off from hospital practice. The AMA Judicial Council reinstated them in 1934, but the rage of local medical societies did not subside. In 1935, physicians associated with the Civic Medical Center in Chicago (a doctor-run prepayment plan) were refused membership in the county medical society.

The mere threat of action was often enough to stop medical groups before they were fully hatched. In Williston, North Dakota, such hints allegedly kept the Farmers Union Medical Service from acquiring a sufficient staff of physicians. In this early period, organized medicine permitted no rebuffs. In one case, when the county society was an ally of a disapproved group plan, as it was reported in Logan County, Arkansas, the state society just *expelled all its members* by revoking the county society charter!

A highly experimental plan combining prepaid group medicine and a salaried hospital staff so alienated the medical society in Elk City, Oklahoma, that they expelled the plan's founder, Dr. Michael Shadid, by dissolving itself and re-forming without him, then reportedly attempted to have his medical license revoked. In 1950 the group's staff physicians, who had been refused membership, sued the Beckham County Medical Society for $300,000, also seeking an injunction for "restraint of trade." Faced with power greater than their extralegal ostracism, the society buckled.

The most direct confrontations between the AMA and the "groups" appropriately took place in Washington, D.C. In 1937 a group of federal employees had organized Group Health Association, a low-cost, nonprofit plan which hired physicians on salary.

The livid district medical society expelled some of the physicians and disciplined others, while still others resigned from the GHA staff rather than face stern medical discipline. The district medical society then called on organized medicine's trump card of persuasion—a "white list" of approved organizations and individuals, from which GHA was conspicuously absent. In a now-familiar pattern of harassment, the county society crippled GHA by convincing local hospitals to deny GHA doctors the privilege of bringing in patients. The federal government, which had not before, and has not since, moved to break the medical monopoly of the AMA, criminally prosecuted the AMA and the Medical Society of the District of Columbia under the Sherman Anti-Trust Act, and won a conviction in court for "restraint of trade." The AMA appealed to the Supreme Court, but on January 18, 1943, the august court upheld the government. The AMA humbly sent in its check for $2500 as a federal fine.

Despite the conviction, similar harassing action was taken by other monopoly-minded medical societies. After World War II the doctors of Group Health Cooperative of Puget Sound, Washington, faced the same pattern—hospital privileges and their society memberships revoked for association with an "unethical" plan. Several physicians found they could not even be certified as specialists by certain "boards." (Present specialist "boards" still consider medical-society membership "desirable.")

Once again the courts acted against the pugnacious medical fraternity, enjoining the county society against harassing the doctors. "There can be no question but that the purpose of the combination in the instant case is to pre-empt and control all contract practice of medicine in King County," Justice Hamley of the state supreme court declared. "The result will be a complete monopoly of the product throughout the country."

By removing the fees of seven hundred thousand patients from doctors' pocketbooks, HIP has been the main target of organized medicine's enmity in the New York area. In many cases HIP physicians have been denied hospital privileges. In suburban Queens County, the contention erupted in the early 1950's when the director of HIP's Jamaica Medical Group was expelled from the county society because of "advertising," a charge leveled for institutional ads inserted by the HIP organization. (The charge, not surprisingly, has never been proffered against doctors' participating in heavily advertised Blue Shield, medicine's own competing plan.) The Medical Society of the State of New York upheld the expulsion, but on final review by the AMA Judicial Council—whose organizational memory may be seared by the Washington, D. C., prosecution—it was reversed.

"I'm convinced that much of the membership of the county societies and the AMA is based on coercion," says Dr. Ben Landess, the Jamaica Medical Group director who later resigned from the county society after his victory. "If the county society didn't have control of hospital affiliation, both they and the AMA would be depleted of members, especially now with their Medicare loss. Many doctors outside of HIP have told me this—that the AMA does nothing for them, and they wouldn't belong if they had their way."

The latest act in the battle was dramatically staged only a few years ago in Nassau County on Long Island, with the law again having to restrain organized medicine. "We were turned down by several hospitals in Nassau County, usually on the excuse that they did not have bed space," states a physician at the East Nassau Medical Group. "We couldn't get into either of our local hospitals. I had a personal interview for staff privileges with the chairman of one of the credentials committees, who is personally friendly with me. I never received a rejection, nor did I get an appointment. At one hospital when I went to find out what happened, the director told me the applications of our staff were still in his desk drawer. They were gathering dust."

The petty machinations against HIP in the Long Island suburbs allegedly cost at least one life. An aggrieved husband wrote a local daily that his wife died during the long car ride to a hospital in New York City. Her physician, as a HIP doctor, could not bring her to the local hospitals, where he had no affiliations. "The current fight of Health Insurance Plan doctors for admission to Nassau County hospitals leaves this subscriber in a fury and with the 'short end of the stick,' " the bereaved husband wrote to the daily newspaper. "My wife died August 25 of a spontaneous cerebral hemorrhage en route to the Midland Hospital in Jamaica, Queens, where HIP doctors are admitted and therefore can admit their patients. It is a long ride from one end of Nassau County to the other, made longer when prompt hospitalization is so near, yet so far."

The local HIP patients themselves picketed a local hospital, drew up petitions, and presented them to Nassau County officials, who held a public hearing. The resulting county ordinance, issued on October 29, 1962, prohibited "the practice of refusing hospital staff appointments and privileges because of group participation," a legislative spark that resulted in the recent passage of a similar law by the New York State Legislature.

The next challenge to AMA control may come in Detroit, where a prominent pro-Medicare spokesman, Dr. Caldwell B. Esselstyn, is in charge of Community Health Association, a prepaid group with seventy-one thousand subscribers. "We are in one local hospital, The Children's Hospital, now," says Dr. Esselstyn. "We hope to be in others very shortly. If we are refused, we will go to the state, and ask for a law such as New York's."

Without settling the question of whether prepaid plans or private practice is superior—a Solomonesque dilemma dependent on doctor's skill and patient preference—it is clear that the use of "un-ethical" to describe such plans is a typical medical-guild distortion. "Unethical" would perhaps better describe the action of organized medicine in maintaining a neck lock on physician allegiance by making many hospital appointments dependent on medical-society membership. Breaking this coercive hospital hold is the first impera-tive for a democratic medical community.

Medical associations are persuasive about the patient's "free choice of doctors" while violating the doctor's own freedom to reject organized medicine. To permit hospitals supported by state-super-vised health insurance funds, tax exemptions, and constructed largely with federal Hill-Burton money, to continue this discriminatory prac-tice would be folly. The legislative course of action to break the AMA monopoly is obvious: fifty state laws making it illegal for hospitals, formally or otherwise, to require medical-society member-ship of their doctors. The state, not the AMA, the physician should be reminded, licenses the practice of medicine.

In private conversations several physician-critics have accused the AMA of more heinous actions than those of which the Justice Department has convicted them: of purposely controlling the pro-duction of doctors to maintain the doctor shortage. With fewer physi-cians, the law of supply and demand will naturally insure doctor income. The documented history of AMA action in creating the current doctor shortage would tend to lend credence to such shocking rumors.

The AMA power over medical schools stems from its quasi-legal status as a medical-school approving agency. State licensing au-thorities require graduation from an "acceptable" medical school. The term is almost always defined as a school approved by the AMA and/or the Association of American Medical Colleges, whose lists are the same. In fact, nineteen states rely entirely on the AMA as a guide. Because the states relinquish their prerogatives (without citizen knowledge or approval) to the AMA, organized medicine can arbitrarily discipline any school which does not conform to its "standards," presumably including the number of students. "These standards, of course, fix the quality of medical education, but they also indirectly determine the size of classes in each school," says the *Yale Law Journal* report.

AMA control of doctor supply has historically been less covert. During the Depression, when physician income sank to $3700 a year (still several times the national average), the AMA moved quickly to curtail the supply of doctors in the nation—guild-inspired damage from which this nation has not yet recovered. In 1933 the AMA's Council on Medical Education enlisted the "active support of the Association of American Medical Colleges in bringing about a substantial reduction of their enrollment." The council's secretary concluded forcefully: "The time has come when we must still further *limit* [italics mine] the enrollment of our medical schools," a policy which was reiterated by AMA's president-elect in 1934. "The limitation of schools is possible," he stated, "and here the Council on Medical Education of the American Medical Association can do much. There can also be a district curtailment of certain schools."

The council was soon able to report phenomenal success: schools were decreasing enrollments "in adherence to the council's principles." There was an immediate decrease of 584 future doctors in the freshman class of 1935! "This is a most encouraging sign," the council reported, "and it is due to the efforts of the Council on Medical Education of the American Medical Association and the Association of American Medical Schools and the Federation of State Medical Boards."

During World War II the AMA once more set itself against national needs for increased doctor supply by not co-operating with proposals to increase sizably the number of medical schools. Instead, the Council on Medical Education supported only a modest expansion, repeating its perennial rationalization that the problem was in the distribution of physicians rather than in the supply! (The AMA would resist any bureaucratic attempts to tamper with the *distribution* of doctors.) It is of course appalling that our community leaves virtual veto power over its doctor supply to a nonlegal body such as the AMA, which eventually answers to its narrow guild interests rather than to the public weal.

If these narrow guild interests were ever thought to be nonexistent, they have become explicit through organized medicine's crass, unprofessional foray into partisan national politics. AMPAC, the American Medical Political Action Committee, is the muscle of doctor political conservatism. With it, they hope to shape a new federal government responsive to AMA wishes by electing pro-AMA candidates to Congress.

AMPAC was founded in the fall of 1961, when organized medicine decided to risk its already tarnished image on a massive campaign for political victory, much in the style of the activist labor unions of the 1930's and 1940's. It has been active in two congressional and senatorial campaigns since (1962 and 1964), in which it backed over a hundred "conservative" candidates with both cash contributions (approximately $5000 to $10,000) and grassroots volunteer doctor-and-wife campaign support through its fifty PAC state offices. "Although membership figures are restricted, it can be said that a substantial percentage of all U.S. physicians and their wives are now members," stated an official spokesman.

AMPAC is nominally a bipartisan group, but its insistence on "conservative" candidates (in the words of its national chairman, Dr. Frank Coleman) tends to funnel AMPAC funds into conservative coffers, especially those of Republicans. During its first campaign in 1962 AMPAC had outstanding success, either picking winners or influencing their victory. According to Dr. Gunnar Gundersen, former AMA president, then AMPAC chairman, "better than seventy percent of AMPAC-supported candidates won office." Entering four Senate elections, AMPAC backed two winners: Republican Senator Peter Dominick, who unseated a pro-Kennedy Democrat, and incumbent Republican Senator Wallace F. Bennett. The doctor-politicians lost to archfoe Abraham Ribicoff of Connecticut, and to George McGovern in South Dakota. In Congress, their strategy included support of House Ways and Means congressmen who were opposed to the Medicare bill.

AMPAC's beginner's luck vanished in the 1964 campaign, when the Johnson landslide defeated most of their doctor-dollar-backed candidates. Of fourteen physicians who were candidates for Congress —almost all of whom expressed anti-Medicare attitudes—eleven were defeated. "We have had better years," understates an AMPAC spokesman in Chicago. One close counter-landslide victory, that of Senator George Murphy over incumbent Senator Pierre Salinger in California, allegedly involved AMPAC support. In fact, Senator Murphy reportedly has given AMPAC a sizable portion of the credit for his unexpected victory.

What is AMPAC? Is it a euphemistic front for the AMA? A staff member at the Chicago office indignantly denied the connection, claiming that it was an *independent,* nonprofit group registered with the Clerk of the House of Representatives. It was *not,* he stated, connected in any way with the AMA. Dr. Frank Coleman, who is a Tampa (Florida) pathologist as well as chairman of AMPAC, was more circumspect, repeating that AMPAC has its own organization and board of directors, and that its connection with the AMA is "information we do not discuss." This privileged information, so hushed by AMPAC insiders, is *supplied in a widely distributed AMPAC brochure.* It plainly describes the strong, direct ties between the medico-politicos and the AMA. After protesting its independence, the brochure openly states: "However, AMPAC's directors are appointed annually by the AMA's Board of Trustees." Further, these AMA-picked AMPAC directors, according to Dr. Coleman, make the final decision on all candidates. To answer a prior rhetorical question, *AMPAC is a front for the AMA.*

AMPACer Dr. Coleman, who answered most inquiries with, "We are not in a position to give out that information," sees their fortunes improving along with anti-administration sentiment. "Doctors have been quite interested in AMPAC and quite generous in its support," he states. "After 1964, things are bound to get better.

Off-year presidential elections generally show improvement in the success of the minority party."

AMPAC is the AMA's boldest political move, but not its first involvement. The National Physicians Committee, with whom they also denied a connection, fought President Truman's national health insurance plan with a vast lobbying effort costing $353,390, more than any other registered lobby of its day. This was but the prologue for a massive, successful public relations campaign costing over $2,000,000. A Florida senator revealed that he had checked the origin of anti-national health insurance postcards he was receiving and found they had been distributed by doctors to *hospitalized patients*. It was during this campaign that a now-ironic caption was placed by the AMA on a nostalgic portrait of a worried physician at a sick patient's bedside. The caption read: "Keep Politics Out of This Picture."

Senator Abraham Ribicoff, during his term as Secretary of Health, Education and Welfare, called the AMA lobby "the most powerful" in America. Its size is incontestable: in the first three months of 1965, the AMA spent $951,570.13 in lobbying against Medicare, a figure declared in its quarterly report to Congress. The sum, of course, is *exclusive* of money spent by AMPAC or related groups.

The non-professionalism of their lobbying is apparently not felt by the insensitive AMA. It is imbued with a rightness of action even when opposing such charitable causes as Social Security payments to the disabled, or federal loans to medical students. To critics, realistic hope for its regeneration into a more public-devoted body is mixed. An abortive revolution called "Physician's Forum" began twenty-five years ago in Manhattan and still has less than a thousand doctors nationwide, although it does claim much of the credit for convincing Congress of the rightness of (and doctor desire for) Social Security coverage for physicians.

Some physicians see the solution in greater AMA participation by anti-AMA-policy doctors, who could attempt to reform its organizational behavior and nudge the giant closer to the twentieth century. There is some evidence that this is beginning to happen. "Surely there is room for a dissident minority within the ranks of the AMA," writes Dr. Vincent Mazzarella of Oklahoma in the *NEJM*. "It is true they have no room for us in the *AMA News*, or in the editorial pages of the *JAMA* for that matter, but we can write 'letters to the editor' of other magazines and newspapers, we can publicly express our views calmly and rationally, even if they are unpopular. Admittedly, this is not a great deal, but I have decided that it is better than resigning."

Dr. Irvine H. Page, editor of *Modern Medicine,* hints that a new dimension of medical authority may be necessary—that "grumbling hostility between the AMA and Washington" seriously jeopardizes proper national planning on health issues. He asks for the establishment of a prestigious National Academy of Medicine around which, he states, "some harmony could develop while concurrently providing the scaffolding for medicine to probe its intellectual, economic and administrative future."

The case for such an academy is impressive. The many quasi-legal functions, from approval of interne and resident programs to influencing the supply of physicians, could better be accomplished by an impartial, science-oriented medical authority not overinvolved in self-motivated political and economic action. Such serious affairs should not be entrusted to an organization whose concept of responsible action is massive support of partisan political candidates who are almost uniformly of a conservative bent.

Motivated by such undisguised vested economic and political interest, the AMA could never assure society that its medical overseeing (as in the case of the doctor shortage) reflects the public, rather than their private, good. For the future of medicine, we should divide the responsibility of medical affairs into two distinct parts: a National Academy of Medicine whose doctor-leaders would function with lay advisers in the control of all medical affairs, and a "guild-union" such as the AMA to protect ferociously the pocketbook of the doctor.

The future of the American Medical Association is not predictable, but it takes less than a seer to see that continuation of its policy of "hold and fight," of employing economics-tinted glasses in viewing many modern patient needs as doctor dangers, will bring organized medicine to the edge of a precipice for which it is not prepared.

Chapter XVII

The Doctor and His Drugs: *Ignorance, Detail Men and Four-Color Promotions*

"In recent years we have seen postgraduate medical education taken over by the siren song of advertising with illustrated brochures, wholesale distribution of samples of powerful drugs, and the ventriloquism of the detail man spouting his spiel like the barker at Madam Snakehair's sideshow . . . The detail man is a lineal descendant of the medicine man of pioneer days. Why does he come praising his brand of drug or placebo? His personal knowledge is obtained by a brain bathing which leaves him to feed back echoes . . . The drug may be powerful and good; it may be powerful and harmful—good drugs are harmful if used too much, too long or too vigorously. Long-delayed sequels are hard to judge. Instead of the costly solution of going back to school, the harried and hurried physician swallows the brochures, pictures, and often the pills."

The commentator is Dr. William B. Bean of the State University of Iowa, whose homey wisdom describes the bizarre behavior of the contemporary American physician when faced with the expanding galaxy of drugs.

Besieged by "ethical" drug advertisements screeching therapeutic balm from the pages of medical journals; inundated by four-color, three-dimensional direct-mail literature; offered the riches of pharmacopoeia free of charge as samples; high-pressured by sixteen thousand drug detail men extolling their wares; confused by trade names, generic names, six-syllable chemical applications of some 12 thousand current drugs; and apparently unable to digest the academic material on drug composition, effects and side effects awaiting him in 440 medical journals, the doctor has become an often unthinking, untutored, anti-cautious participant in the drug revolution that carries, as we have witnessed, unseen death and disease as a partner of its therapeutic benefit. Drug sickness incidence *in* the hospital totals over 3,500,000 cases a year, including those admitted for drug iatrogenesis and patients who suffer drug reactions while hospitalized. How many *millions* are ambulatory victims?

A recent four-week admitting schedule of the public medical service at Johns Hopkins Hospital, where 5 percent of admissions were due to sickness caused by drugs, is one eloquent illustration of the situation. The new patients suffered a variety of drug-induced illnesses, including digitalis toxicity which had aggravated a heart condition; sulfadiazine crystalluria (sulfa particles in the urine which can cause serious blockage of the renal tubules); bromism, or bromide drug poisoning; erythema multiforme, a serious skin disorder that was caused by phenolphthalein; a case of penicillin serum sickness; a serious blood disorder, thrombocytopenic purpura (hemorrhages within the skin) attributed to sulfisoxazole, a sulfa drug; coma brought on by a popular sedative-tranquilizer, glutethimide; and a case of hypokalemic dehydration (loss of potassium) caused by the popular diuretic chlorothiazide.

The physician scanning a contemporary medical journal is thrust abruptly into a far different medical world, one of pinker, warmer hue. He perceives a visual sermon in limitless optimism, part of a heady drug climate that he is unable to control, sometimes even comprehend. The thalidomide horror, the subsequent Kefauver-Harris amendments which tightened the Food and Drug Administration control over the drug industry, the Humphrey hearings and the recent Fountain Committee investigations, made deserved headlines.

However, critics say, neither the government nor the medical profession have yet joined with the basic problem: *the physician's mishandling of prescription drugs.* Through his almost layman-like gullibility, he has permitted the marketing-manic pharmaceutical industry to maintain a mesmeric control over his drug-prescribing decisions and, therefore, his patients' bodies.

Medical criticism of the doctor as a prescriber of drugs has been considerable and biting. "How is the physician doing his job in relation to drugs?" Dr. Harry F. Dowling of the AMA Council on Drugs asks rhetorically. "Not as well as he could," he answers in *JAMA.* Vocal Dr. Charles D. May of the New York University School of Medicine, pediatrician and outstanding pharmacologist, sees the doctor as currently unable to cope with the drug maker's onslaught of both products and hectic promotion. The physician is often involved in an "illogical and excessive use of drugs" prompted by the "promotional machinery" of drug makers, with resulting danger to patients, Dr. May has stated.

Dr. Walter Modell, the outspoken Cornell pharmacologist, blames the hard-sell pharmaceutical industry for enticing the physician into a promotion-induced ignorance. "It is beginning to look as if the success of a new drug will depend less on how well it works and more on how well it is promoted," says Dr. Modell, editor of *Clinical Pharmacology and Therapeutics*. "This is why physicians are led to use drugs when the indications are lacking, to use drugs that are not the best available or even those which do not apply. It is because of this that the rate of serious drug reaction is mounting."

The physician's propensity to dose patients with drugs with which he is scientifically unfamiliar is abhorrent to New York pathologist Dr. David M. Spain, who notes that doctors have "daily prescribed drug after drug for which only the flimsiest of evidence exists as to their value." The doctor's innocent *assumption* that the drug is safe is noted by Dr. Leighton Cluff of Johns Hopkins, who states that with "most preparations," the "physician may not consider the possibility of adverse reactions seriously, as they appear to be infrequent or insignificant."

One of the angriest criticisms of doctors' penchant for using drugs carelessly was made by the late Dr. Lawson Wilkins of Baltimore in his frank presidential address to the American Pediatric Society. Dr. Lawson asked his colleagues to adopt a "cold, scrutinizing, skeptical state of mind" about new drugs "which would make them leery of accepting any therapeutic claim without proof." He then shocked the physicians: *"Wait, wait, wait—and then wait! Let the other fellow poison his patients—or learn the drug is worthless."* If it is truly valuable, he assured them, the drug will make itself known and survive their skepticism.

The *appearance* of drugs, so neatly packaged in pills or gelatin capsules, and so unassumingly small, belies their power to disrupt the human body, for balm or bane. The knowledge required of the doctor to knife through that innocent appearance is formidable and still unacquired by most physicians, a condition unchanged by congressional hearings, albeit their necessity. "Often the doctor does not know a great deal about the drugs that he uses," Dr. Walter Modell stated when interviewed in his office at Cornell Medical College. "As a result, there is too much not well thought out drug therapy."

Dr. Karl H. Beyer, Jr., past president of the American Society for Pharmacology and Experimental Therapeutics, warns of its implications—that doctors' knowledge on how to use drugs safely has not kept up with the industry's proficiency in new drug development. Unless physicians learn, he adds, it will become increasingly dangerous for the drug industry to produce new complex therapeutic compounds.

Sir William Osler noted that man is the only species that ingests medicines, a proclivity that seems to grow each year. There is no doubt that America is currently involved in a massive, promiscuous addiction to the concept of medication. Having oversold itself on the miracles of pharmacology, it is hypnotically ingesting as much chemical matter as gracious physicians (who, naturally, do not pay the exorbitant bill) will prescribe. The drug binge costs us $4,-300,000,000 a year for 782,000,352 drugstore prescriptions (four for every person, not including drugs received in the hospital) and an additional $1,800,000,000 sold over-the-counter in more diluted form.

The doctor's participation in this national medication orgy, especially for self-limiting illnesses, is scoured by medical critics. "People want to be dosed, and doctors unfortunately feel obliged to yield," Dr. May stated in his office at New York University's new University Hospital. "But it is a pseudosophistication on the part of the doctor to prescribe toxic drugs for his patient in the treatment of minor ailments."

The charge that the American physician has overdosed his patients by being too facile with his prescription pad can hardly be denied. His most annoying drug habit is this treating of self-limiting ailments with a potentially dangerous Rx, even when patience and conservative regimen are the more logical prescriptions. "It is especially in the use of agents offering only symptomatic relief that the physician must carefully consider the side effects of therapy," says a stern editorial in the *New England Journal of Medicine*. "Certainly he is not justified in prescribing an agent for the relief of pain, loss of sleep, muscle spasm in a host of conditions if it has inherent possibilities of causing serious damage."

The record clearly shows that the doctor has eschewed the thoughtful drug policy, and has yielded to a compulsion to drug every symptom of the complaining patient—replacing the benign, sometimes curative hot-water bottle, the ice bag, the bed rest, the heat lamps, the changed living habits, the tender loving care and limited exercise with powerful, body-disturbing chemicals. Equally damning is the fact that he has kept his patient in ignorance of the potential danger of the drugs he prescibes. Without knowledge, the patient *himself* cannot decide whether the anticipated comfort is worth the risk.

We have already witnessed the steroid excesses. Another anti-inflammatory, phenylbutazone, is often prescribed by doctors for minor muscular ailments (strains and spasms), even though the drug is potentially quite harmful. A manufacturer himself lists the awesome possibilities: it accentuates bleeding in patients taking anticoagulants; it produces sodium retention and edema (swelling); it can produce ulcers; it depresses the bone-marrow function and lowers the red cell count; it may produce the serious blood disease agranulocytosis, and even leukemia has been reported. An unusually frank statement adds: "Thrombocytopenic purpura and aplastic anemia must also be considered possible side effects of therapy." A report in the *NEJM,* and another from Katharinen Hospital in Stuttgart, Germany, show the drug implicated in several cases of acute kidney failure. What good can it do for a muscle strain for which it is often prescribed? Little or nothing. It merely makes the muscle "feel" better, much like a powerful aspirin.

The debacle in which unsophisticated doctors futilely dispensed antibiotics for the common cold is a case of negligent dispensing whose ramifications are first being felt. The careless physician has helped to create a nation of twenty to forty *million* sensitized individuals in constant danger of possibly fatal allergic reactions from penicillin and other antibiotics. The setting is so fertile that the slightest contamination of *other drugs by penicillin dust* is becoming a medical problem. The contamination takes place in drug factories when air currents carry the penicillin dust to areas where other drugs are being made. In the period June 1964–1965, there were ninety-five incidents of penicillin contamination involving pharmaceuticals of every description produced by dozens of manufacturers, including several of the most prestigious.

The doctor's overuse of antibiotics has stimulated nature's contrary side in many ways. Penicillin sensitivity, then bacterial resistance to penicillin were the initial results. Streptomycin seemed to conquer hospital staph, until its frequent use helped develop bacterial immunity. Tetracycline, a potent agent against Gram-negative bacteria such as E. coli in urinary infections, may now—says Dr. Trevor Franklin of England—be following the frustrating path of its predecessors.

There is new evidence that doctors may be repeating this discouraging history—helpfully goaded by the drug industry. The British-developed semisynthetic penicillins (oxacillin, methicillin, cloxacillin) have provided medicine with a new weapon against deadly penicillin-resistant staphylococcus bacteria. But once again the potent drugs are apparently not being husbanded with care. Their overuse by doctors as an unneeded *general* antibiotic could *end* their singular power to save victims of certain antibiotic superinfection. Rather than reserve the drug for this use, a distributor of one, sodium cloxacillin, has apparently been successfully beseeching doctors to use it for minor infections. Alluring black-and-gold ads in medical journals proclaim that the drug is more "economical" for "tonsillitis, pharyngitis, otitis media, bronchitis, sinusitis, pneumonitis," even though antibiotics of less strategic value are widely available.

A warning against this new antibiotic debacle is made by the *Medical Letter,* the authoritative nonprofit "drug and therapeutic" bulletin which attempts to educate physicians in the mature use of modern remedies. (Its editorial and advisory boards include such leading medical personalities as Dr. Louis C. Lasagna of Johns Hopkins Medical School; Dr. George E. Moore, director of the Roswell Park Memorial Institute; Dr. Louis Goodman, head of the department of pharmacology of the University of Utah College of Medicine.)

The outspoken *Medical Letter* warns about the abuse of two relatively new "staph" fighters. *"NOT FOR ROUTINE USE—*It would be unfortunate if either oral or parenteral oxacillin (or methicillin) were routinely used for infections suspected of being caused by staphylococci," says the *ML.* They report that a few strains of the germ resistant to oxacillin or methicillin have already been noted, adding: "Because of this possibility and because of the toxicity of other antibiotics used against resistant staphylococci . . . *all of these antibiotics are best reserved* [italics mine] for serious infections caused by penicillinase-producing staphylococci."

The widespread "cosmetic" prescribing of diuretics to take off a few offending pounds is indiscriminate prescribing at its worst. The *ML* reminds doctor readers that drugs always produce reactions, and that diuretics are not excepted. Although valuable in indicated illnesses (hypertension, congestive heart disease), "they are by no means innocuous," they state, "and should not be used for trivial indications or in larger doses than necessary."

The cold-and-pain remedies prescribed in massive volume by doctors with a compulsive urge to do "something" are further examples of generally needless overmedication. One cold remedy, says the *Medical Letter,* is quite safe for most people. But if one of its ingredients is involved sufficiently to do its job of drying respiratory secretions, it "could also increase intraocular pressure in narrow-angle glaucoma or cause urinary retention." The decongestants in many cold remedies, the *Letter*'s authorities also caution, often produce a "rebound turgescence"—a drug-induced congestion that may be more unwelcome than the original.

The massive tranquilizer-psychochemical drug binge (which rivals the fast hypodermic of the penicillin era), in which doctors are now libidinously immersed, may prove to be their most erratic adventure in drug overprescribing. The general practitioners and internists are the targets of a massive multimillion dollar psychochemical promotional campaign. Exploiting the concept that "the family doctor is the front line against mental illness," the drug makers, aided by naïve physicians, have built it into a $300,000,000-a-year industry. The annual business in "mood" drugs amounts to almost a thousand tons of ingested psycho-pharmaceuticals. (The maker of one tranquilizer boasts that it has been taken by ten *million* patients!) Some undetermined portion treats the seriously mentally ill, but much of it is for the pseudoscientific treatment of simple "nervousness" with potentially toxic chemicals. An undue tonnage of psycho drugs are being dispensed with abandon by doctors to patients unsophisticatedly diagnosed as being in need of chemical manipulation—"calming down" or "pepping up." Doctors have even been advised by drug makers to prescribe these powerful chemicals to allay the symptoms of attending a funeral or a fight with the boss!

The ambulatory patient has been given them all—the sedative-hypnotics, the phenothiazine tranquilizers, the rauwolfia derivatives of the snakeroot, and the antidepressants, with all the attendant physical danger we have witnessed. Overdoses of the simpler-acting drugs such as meprobamate have "hooked" him, while the phenothiazines have many opportunities for harm, from Parkinson-like syndromes to increased libido in women to the *creation* of psychological disturbances to the chance of blood disorders such as agranulocytosis and jaundice.

Doctors have been warned—often futilely—against their common habit of prescribing potent tranquilizers such as phenothiazines, for simple anxiety. Dr. Leo E. Hollister, of the AMA's Council on Drugs, uses *JAMA* to caution physicians: "Phenothiazine derivatives should not be used for trivial purposes, for symptoms such as anxiety and vomiting when other less potent and less hazardous agents may be effective." Not only is there danger involved, but the drug may be virtually useless in such situations. A researcher at a New York mental institution explains that despite wholesale prescribing, phenothiazines are antischizophrenic and are not even effective against "the usual range of neurotic and situational anxieties." Similarly, he adds, antidepressant drugs should be reserved for severe depressions; minor depressions are generally self-limiting and best treated with "time."

Some doctors naïvely accept all "miracle" claims made for drugs while the more skeptical prefer to challenge drug effectiveness. The drug industry's persistent gadfly, the *Medical Letter,* contests the ability of the popular psychochemical, Librium, to handle anxiety better than any plebeian sedative available to physicians. There is, states the *Letter,* "no reliable evidence that Librium had any special usefulness; it is a sedative drug which causes drowsiness, and its value in anxiety and tension was judged to be no greater than that of other sedatives." To substantiate this charge, *Medical Letter* later quotes a controlled study reported in the *British Journal of Psychiatry:* "Anxiety was not significantly reduced when the results, using a dosage of 10 mg. (t. i. d.) were compared with the changes observed during the use of a placebo."

The libertine prescribing (and willing patient ingestion) of too many drugs for minor ailments may create a "contaminated" body atmosphere that will diagnostically confuse the physician. Instead of well-delineated organic disease, the doctor may instead find a morass of conflicting symptoms precipitated by the drugs the basically well patient has been given. Dr. Walter Alvarez, sage editor emeritus of *Modern Medicine,* reminds his colleagues that "a drug or a chemical can cause the disease" that is baffling them, and that they can sometimes provide miraculous cures simply by stopping *all* the remedies! "In the past few years, I have been so impressed by the number of patients I have seen, in my now small practice, who had some puzzling symptoms that had stumped all of us physicians who had studied the problem," says Dr. Alvarez in *Modern Medicine.* "In such cases, I try to remember to do something that is essential, but which in a physician's busy afternoon can easily be forgotten— and this is to insist that for a few days the patient stop all medicines that he or she is taking."

He describes a woman with a "very curious" set of symptoms who was taking six drugs simultaneously: one to reduce her blood pressure, another to soften her arteries, plus one for depression, and two barbiturates and one tranquilizer. He asked her to take nothing for a week, at the end of which time the overjoyed patient called to say that she was a "new woman."

Without the pills her suicidal desires and depression had vanished, the metallic taste in her mouth which has been "driving her crazy" disappeared, and the terrible itching in her skin and the dizziness were gone. "What interested me," observes Dr. Alvarez, "was that she had been referred by a good friend, an able internist, who should have known to ask her to stop the drugs for a few days to see if her illness was due to any one of them." Apparently, the internist had neither Dr. Alvarez' common-sense faculty, nor had his medical school tutored him in the amazing modern cures made possible by not dispensing drugs.

Dr. Alvarez' report on drug intoxication contains several such miracle cures. A woman of fifty suffering from sore breasts recovered when he reduced the dosage of stilbestrol hormone she was getting for menopause to 1/20th of its original amount. A jittery, sleepless woman taking thyroid—apparently a casualty of a laboratory girl's misread PBI or basic metabolism test—was taken off it, and found a swift recovery.

The drug explosion has created another antiscientific habit in the physician, that of treating before diagnosing. Why learn what ails the patient, the indolent doctor asks himself, if a shot of penicillin may clean up the unknown infection? "Doctors today are prone to utilize therapy and treat before diagnosing," Dr. Raymond Villey of France told an International Conference on General Practice. Clinical care, he stated, is "less conscientiously practiced by many of our colleagues because we have at our disposal powerful drugs."

The doctor is enticed, he said, into practicing "heads or tails" medicine in which he prescribes potent and dangerous drugs without first being sure of the patient's illness.

Dr. Harry F. Dowling, head of the AMA Council on Drugs, is saddened at doctor proclivity to "use a drug in place of a diagnosis," calling it both "reprehensible" and "dangerous." In *JAMA,* he expounds on why this is unsound therapy. "In such instances, physicians do not study their patients carefully in order to make a diagnosis; instead they prescribe a drug or a succession of drugs in the hope that one of them may cure the patient," he says. Dr. Dowling then added a literate insight to the grave problem. "Matthew Arnold said in 'The Wish':

> Nor bring, to see me cease to live
> Some doctor full of phrase and fame,
> To shake his sapient head and give
> The ill he cannot cure a name.

"But instead of giving the ill they cannot cure a name, these physicians give the ill they cannot name a drug."

Insufficient knowledge of proper drug dosage can be another physician vulnerability. An excessive dose of oxytocin, a birth-inducing drug, contributed to the death of a twenty-four-year-old woman who had a resulting tumultuous birth followed by a postpartum (after delivery) hemorrhage. During the malpractice trial, a $60,000 settlement was made for the drug overdose.

Infants are, of course, the most vulnerable victims of dosage ignorance. The problem of drug dosage in infants is complicated by missing detoxifying enzymes in their bodies, and an insufficiently developed kidney and liver "cleansing" operation. One young mother (and, hopefully, one young doctor) received a practical if frightening lesson in pediatric drug dosage when she called in a physician to examine her crying three-week-old baby. Her regular pediatrician was away on vacation, and a young general practitioner was engaged instead. He examined the child, could find nothing wrong and suggested a sedative to solve the "crying" problem. He prescribed phenobarbital in liquid form, with a dosage of a half teaspoon. Almost immediately after the child had swallowed the drug, a severe respiratory depression set in. The infant could not get its breath, starting a gasping wheeze toward impending death. The mother acted quickly and began a vigorous mouth-to-mouth resuscitation, which probably saved the child's life. When the family pediatrician returned and heard of the incident, she remarked that the sedative should have been administered to an infant by the "drop" rather than by the teaspoon.

The danger of overdose in young children can never be exaggerated, by parent or cautious physician. Physicians at a Montreal hospital have reported on ten cases of poisoning from overdoses of aminophylline, a therapy for asthma often given to children. The widespread ignorance on pediatric doses is a failure of both doctor and drug maker, who often, say critics, naïvely base their dosage on the child's age. "Age is almost completely worthless, useless, and often dangerous basis for determining dosage—dangerous because it may yield insufficient dosage at a time of critical need, or result in an overdosage that may produce toxicity," Dr. Harry C. Shirkey writes in *JAMA*. "Drug manufacturers frequently disregard these facts in making children's dosage recommendations."

The variability of drug effect on the newborn is frightening. Dr. Shirkey explains that a dose of chloramphenicol that may kill a child less than a week old may be insufficient as an antibiotic two weeks later. The answer, states *Medical Letter,* is to withhold all drugs from the newborn except in "response to pressing need." Seldom, they state, is there "sufficient clinical evidence, when a drug is introduced, on which to base reliable and safe dosage recommendations for the newborn, young infants, and elderly patients." They quote the experience of one of their consultants who administered a drug, methacholine, to children in a clinic. A dosage only *10 percent* of adult strength produced cardiovascular side effects in the children.

A small boy suffering from pneumococcal meningitis was given less than the adult dosage of tetracycline intravenously (along with sulfisoxazole injections and chloramphenicol by mouth), but it was apparently more than his four-year-old constitution could stand. He died, and at autopsy, physicians found the same fatty metamorphosis of the liver seen in other cases of tetracycline overdose. As *Medical Letter* states about pediatric drug doses, *any formula,* although helpful, should be "regarded critically." To those who would dose infants they invoke a solemn warning: "For the newborn, no table or formula can be safely applied."

The American physician has somehow assumed the omnipotence of pharmacy. He has not yet learned, as the Commission on Drug Safety has so sagely stated, that "life is not a drug-deficiency disease" requiring constant chemical nourishment. The doctor's only opportunity to use drugs with integrity is to use them with knowledge, for the most esoteric pharmacological information can spell the difference between patient death and life. Eight deaths involving a little-known drug, dithiazanine iodide, that have been reported in the past four years are cases in point.

In a New Orleans hospital, a three-year-old girl was seen in the outpatient department and diagnosed as harboring T. trichiura eggs, a parasite. The child took three of the purple dithiazanine pills for five days, and was admitted to the hospital on the sixth day because of vomiting and seizures. Her urine was blue. She was given antibiotics, intravenous feedings and blood transfusions, but she died the next day. On autopsy, doctors saw that her small intestines had turned green, as had the wall of her gall bladder and the surface of her kidney; the heart and liver were greenish gray. In their report on the case in *JAMA,* the physician-authors, Drs. Abadie and Samuels, offer a piece of pharmacological information—that *there is a safer method of using the drug*—which might have saved her and the others. "An alternative to oral medication with dithiazanine may be its use in the form of an enema made up in a solution with gum acacia," they state. "This method of administration has been found, in limited trials, to afford good therapeutic results, with apparently less hazard."

Is the contemporary doctor too ill-equipped to digest and intelligently implement the drug revolution? How carefully does he study pharmacological information, and where does most of it come from? Although it seems like a well-laid plot of calumny against the doctor, there is conclusive evidence that the American physician gains most of his information on which drugs to use to treat his sick patients not from academic professional sources, but either from *drug salesmen,* euphemistically called "detail men," or from *drug advertisements* written by professional agency copywriters.

Verification of this "libel" comes from various sources, including the American Medical Association itself. The AMA, with the aid of Ben Gaffin and Associates, conducted "The Fond du Lac Study," which polled all fifty-five practicing physicians in the community of Fond du Lac, Wisconsin. The foreword to the study drew attention to a prior survey, "Advertising and the American Physician," completed in 1953. "This study emphasized the importance of pharmaceutical advertising in physician education," states the AMA with candor. *"It showed that physicians receive a large proportion of their postgraduate medical education from advertising and detail programs of pharmaceutical companies* [italics mine]."

Having exposed their membership for its reliance on hucksterism, the AMA accented that fact to potential advertisers in the *Journal of the AMA.* It was done through a comprehensive survey of how the fifty-five doctors learned about five drugs: Serpasil, Achromycin, Pamine, Furadantin and Butazolidin.

The disheartening figures show that between *half and two-thirds* of the doctors received their drug information from detail men, advertisements and direct-mail pieces. Only a minority of doctors learned from more objective journal articles and medical conventions. Of fifty prescribers of Achromycin, boasts the AMA report, thirty of the doctors—including all five of the heaviest users—admitted that the detail man was "instrumental" in getting them to prescribe it for patients. Nine more learned of it through drug

advertising in journals or from direct-mail pieces sent by the manufacturers. A total of thirty-four of fifty doctors apparently felt that
commercial sales messages constituted medical education.

The physicians could not even be embarrassed into denying their
reliance on the drug firms for their so-called education. Even when
questioned on the theoretical concept of postgraduate pharmacological education with the query: "Which of these methods do you
find most important to you personally in learning about a new drug?"
more than half chose detail men, ads and direct mail. *Significantly,
only one of the apparently advertising-washed doctors thought "postgraduate courses" was the proper milieu in which to learn about
new drugs.*

This perilous submission of the American physician to the drug
industry was confirmed by still another survey, "Attitudes of U. S.
Physicians Toward Pharmaceutical Industry," and quoted with candor by Dr. Harry F. Dowling of the AMA Council on Drugs. "And
yet, when physicians were questioned regarding a drug they had
recently prescribed for the first time, 48 percent stated that they
had learned about it from detail men; 20 percent from direct-mail
advertising; and 8 percent from other doctors," he states. There are
"sound" and "unsound" reasons for prescribing a drug, Dr. Dowling
is convinced, but apparently *at least 76 percent of physicians* are
dominated by the *unsound.* "Among the unsound reasons, listed in
the left-hand column, the most unscientific is suggestion—suggestion derived from a fleeting look at an advertisement, the receipt
of a sample in the morning's mail, the chance remark of a colleague
in a doctor's lounge," Dr. Dowling declares.

His list of sound and unsound reasons should be an inspiration
to the undertutored American doctor. In addition to reacting to
"suggestions" and using drugs in place of diagnoses, Dr. Dowling
lists the nonscientific impetus of four fears: "Fear of not doing anything; of being 'behind the times'; of displeasing the patient; of malpractice suits." The modern doctor's neurotic fear of inaction—a
severe personality failing—is possibly one of the major causes of
drug accidents, and deserves the emphasis Dr. Dowling places on it.
"Doctors are active men," he states. "They chafe under the restraint
of taking long histories, doing complete physical examinations, waiting for results of laboratory tests and poring through the literature
to find out what has happened in similar cases. They are restive
under inaction; to them inaction smells of defeat. But whereas, as
men of action, we know that we must often act before all the evidence
is in, we can all remember times when action taken too soon has led
to catastrophe."

Being the first to dispense a new drug is another unsound motivation. "The best way to gain this [colleagues' respect] is by understanding what he is doing and by following the example of those

who have had more experience with a particular drug. To be 'the first by whom the new is tried' may bring momentary satisfaction; it will hardly win lasting respect," Dr. Dowling advises. The wise doctor motivated by sound reasons will learn "all he can about the absorption, metabolism, and excretion of the therapeutic agents he uses," and will seek "the advice of experts, either through consultation or by reading what they recommend," states the University of Illinois physician. With obvious chagrin, Dr. Dowling asks rhetorically: "These procedures are elementary, but how often are they followed?"

The doctor's avoidance (perhaps abhorrence) of scientific-learning principles and his reliance on commercial-drug puffery meets with determined indifference from organized medicine. The question was raised at a Fountain Committee (one of the successors to the Kefauver Committee) hearing when former Food and Drug Administration Commissioner George P. Larrick had testified on the problem of getting physicians to read available material on drugs. Despite the existence of AMA-sponsored surveys admitting that physicians *do not* maintain continuing pharmacological education, and do rely on biased detail men and ads, the AMA's Director of Scientific Activities, Dr. Hugh H. Hussey, stubbornly contended that doctors do keep up. "Physicians are generally reliable," he told the committee. "Physicians are generally aware of the need and fulfill the need for continuing their own education." Such Pollyannish attitudes are the greatest obstacles to proper education of the physician in intelligent drug prescribing for his patient.

Dr. Dowling's definition of "suggestion" as unsound" doctor learning has not deterred the pharmaceutical industry from making drug suggestion to doctors into a massive undertaking, budgeted at an estimated $750,000,000 a year, more than is expanded on drug research. It dazzles, entertains, confuses and allegedly "educates" the American physician in the mysteries of "ethical" (prescription) drugs. That he daily succumbs to this pharmaceutical carnival is the greatest deterrent to his pharmacological education.

In his powerful essay "Selling Drugs By 'Educating' Physicians," Dr. Charles D. May of the New York University School of Medicine explains that "education" of the doctor is a euphemism for selling brand-name drugs. "How much of this sum [$750,000,000] was truly directed to 'education' is a moot question. Advertising in medical journals and by direct mail to physicians amounted to $125,-000,000," he reveals. "The expense of maintaining the army of 15,000 detail men busily engaged in spreading 'education' must account for a huge portion. The remainder went for exhibits, films, trade publications, lectures, televised clinics, samples, etc. All this huge sum was in the last analysis devoted to one purpose—to get the physician to prescribe products of particular firms by brand names."

The opening advertising campaign for the antibiotic Furadantin is a sample of a new-drug promotional effort. Two hundred and ten advertising insertions were placed in eleven medical magazines. *JAMA* received the largest support (sixty insertions), with most others—from the *Journal of Urology* to *California Medicine*—receiving twelve insertions. The direct-mail campaign for Furadantin, according to the Fond du Lac study, was even more impressive. One hundred and fifty mailings on the drug were made to urologists, pediatricians, GP's, and to obstetricians and gynecologists. (It might be significant to note that several years later, a *Medical Letter* chart on the antibiotic choice for forty-five infections excludes the antibiotic as either the "first choice" or even as an "alternative drug" for any of the infections.)

In "detailing" the drug, the company representative visited the Fond du Lac area eight to ten times a year, staying two days each time. On his first trip he stopped at the largest pharmacy, made an inventory of competitive drugs and left free samples with the druggist. He scoured the list of local physicians and eliminated the unlikely sales candidates—surgeons, pathologists, radiologists—then further restricted his efforts to potential "heaviest users." (Should not all doctors benefit from his "educational" effort?) Having isolated his superior doctor-markets, he visited each of them three or four times, pausing at all the drugstores and at the local hospital on each visit.

How well does this dollar-dominated "university" of ads, brochures and detail men serve the doctor? In his office in the mammoth white-stoned Cornell University Medical Center in New York, Dr. Walter Modell, who is also editor of *Clinical Pharmacology and Therapeutics,* addressed himself to this controversial medical issue. "The only culprit in this issue is the medical profession itself," he states. "Doctors ought to protect themselves against the detail man and the advertising man by insisting on getting their medical information from unbiased sources. By welcoming the easy kind of information of the detail man and the attractive drug-house brochures, the medical profession itself is undermining the practice of medicine."

Although aiming his philosophical barb at doctor submissiveness, Dr. Modell also singled out the detail man for special culpability. "The detail man is a more insidious force than the drug brochure. The brochure is seen by the FDA, but what the detail man says in the doctor's office no one knows. When I was in private practice, I did not let them into my office. I felt my postgraduate education should be left to better hands." (Some detail men believe that the FDA is now eavesdropping on them by having co-operating doctors tape their sales pitches. Others are skeptical, considering it too resourceful a gambit for the FDA.)

The detail man is a phenomenon of unusual dimensions. Without a medical education he is expected to instruct M.D.'s in drug choice and therapy. (Years ago many were pharmacists, but this is no longer true; medical students are sometimes employed over the summer.) He accomplishes this by careful memorizing and vigorous spieling back to the doctor of what he is told. The salesman-customer relationship is doubly unique in that no matter how much the doctor-customer "buys," it costs the doctor—who scribbles a brand name on his prescription pad—nothing. (Perhaps if the doctor, rather than the ultimate customer, the patient, were to pay the oft-exorbitant bill for overpromoted drugs, he might become more wary—even more scientific—about his choice.)

Two veteran detail men, now in the drug advertising field, describe some of the finesse of selling physicians. "The first thing I learned is that the doctor is a busy man," says a detail man who worked for a major drug house for fifteen years. "When I started, I used to detail the doctors on three items in our line, and remind him on two. Then one doctor told me it was too much. After that I restricted detailing to one big item."

Some drug companies have developed formal training programs for their detail men; others train the men directly in the field by having a sales manager spend a few weeks with the recruit. "The detail man is told exactly what he can speak about, and he's not expected to be expert in how to use the product. Under the old law, promotional literature did not necessarily contain mention of side effects," says one veteran detailer. "They do today, but detail men don't go out of their way to bring it up. Dealing with the doctor is not easy. Status and ego is his whole way of life. He doesn't like to admit that he's ignorant about anything. He wants to pick up the information about the new drug from us but doesn't want to show that he needs it."

Sales success depends equally on availability of the drugs at the drugstore, which, often, is also the detail man's responsibility. "Before I went to see doctors in a neighborhood, I would visit the drugstore," explains a former detail man for an ophthalmological drug house. "I would tell him I was detailing his area and would like him to stock a certain number of pieces. He generally did, because if he didn't sell them, he could always return the unopened packages to the manufacturer."

The detail man shares the frustration of all salesmen, getting in to see his customer, the doctor. They grumble about the waiting and about the fact that some physicians leave lists with their nurses as to which of their drug teachers they will entertain. "I knew one doctor who would see only detail men from two companies," a veteran drug salesman recalls. "Other doctors especially young ones and 'sample grabbers' like to see everybody." Sample grabbers come in varying forms: those who give them to patients as public relations offerings; those who donate them to charity missions; and others who (some detail men swear) *sell* them, generally to repackagers.

Sample largesse is a vital part of new-drug economics, for once a suggestible physician is "hooked" by a free medication, he invariably keeps prescribing the fully paid variety of the same drug. "We dish it out like water. I once gave 20 cases of vitamins, each containing 48 one-ounce bottles to one GP with a tremendous practice," recalls a detail man. "From the re-orders at the drugstore, I know that it generated a lot of business." (Although not professional cricket, friendly pharmacists will often tell detail men whether Dr. A has really been prescribing his drug, and in what volume.)

The multimillion-dollar therapeutic giveaway ($200,000 of a $1,900,000 antihypertensive drug-promotion campaign was allotted for samples) has become a major medical headache. A *Medical Tribune* "Pulse of Medicine Report" shows that over 80 percent of physicians use samples for their patients, and that *almost half use the samples to test the efficacy of the drug in their office practice,* an ability that medical critics do not believe the average physician possesses.

A Massachusetts pathologist is quoted by the *Tribune* as stating: "This is absolutely not a method of testing new drugs"; a New York GP believes that "testing should be done in hospitals and clinics"; a Tennessee GP calls "efficacy testing without controls next to impossible." One annoyed physician later wrote *Medical Tribune* criticizing the drug-company sample bonanza as exerting undue influence on the susceptible physician. "I believe that one of the most basic criticisms that may be leveled against the drug companies' sampling practices is that many physicians are thereby prompted to treat patients with medications that they would not otherwise feel to be drug of choice in the individual case involved," he wrote. A Cambridge (Massachusetts) physician has sent a form letter telling drug companies to refrain from sending him unsolicited samples—suggesting that his colleagues follow suit.

Few physicians would admit selling their samples, but the FDA has announced that fifteen seizures of mislabeled drugs in one two-week period involved doctors' samples that had been turned over to fly-by-night repackagers, who often work under unsanitary conditions. The FDA advises doctors not to just throw away the unused samples (janitors also sell to repackagers), but to flush them down the toilet.

Some drug firms have instituted a sample-by-request plan, while others are experimenting with preprinted prescription pads containing the name of the drug. The patient brings the "sample" prescription to the pharmacist who fills it, then collects from the drug maker.

These attempts to improve the image of drug-sample promotion are interesting, but most physicians still welcome regular samples as a cheap, convenient—if unscientific and dangerous—way of introducing new drugs simultaneously to themselves and their patients.

A repelling aspect of the doctor's relationship with the drug industry is its overclose personal relationship. It is an "ethical" (in medical jargon) but nevertheless disturbing breach in medical objectivity. Drug companies are aggressive, but too many physicians have quietly acquiesced to the easy fraternization. The "courtship" manifests itself in innumerable ways, including the personable detail man's attention, drug-company-supported clinical trials, physician ownership of drugstores, drug advertising in medical journals, exhibits at medical conventions, drug-firm-sponsored medical "symposia," and even in open-handed gift-giving.

"Is it prudent for physicians to become greatly dependent upon pharmaceutical manufacturers for support of scientific journals and medical societies, for entertainment, and now also for a large part of their education?" Dr. May has asked. "Do all concerned realize the hazard of arousing the wrath of the people by an unwholesome entanglement of doctors with the makers and sellers of drugs?"

Medicine has an unhealthy vested interest in the health of the pharmaceutical industry through acceptance of advertising in *JAMA* and other AMA journals, and a profitable direct-mail tie-in with the drug companies. The relationship, in fact, appears to be fiscally essential to the AMA, which now receives over $9,000,000 a year from pharmaceutical advertising. (A black-and-white page in *JAMA* costs $1840.)

The AMA's membership list of 206,000 names has become a dollar-making accommodation for the drug industry. It has been placed on computer tape, and is leased to drug makers for their direct mailings to doctors through AMA-franchised mailing-list houses. One of them revealed that clients pay approximately $6 a thousand for the use of the names, plus $3-a-thousand royalty to the American Medical Association. In addition to the drug makers (90 percent of all mailings), doctors' names are also rented to book publishers, retirement plans, automobile manufacturers and almost anyone who wants to sell the doctors a product—whether antibiotics or annuities.

The advertising concordat between doctors and drug firms has been taken for granted, despite the medical profession's own ethical edict against promotional activities. Dr. Charles May is one critic who is less than sanguine about the AMA's active role in such obvious commercialism. "The medical societies have less independence because of their acceptance of drug advertising," he says. "I find the AMA's acceptance of pharmaceutical advertising in

JAMA a very strange arrangement. It is as if the Supreme Court of the United States had a journal and accepted advertising from those presenting their cases before them."

As a prominent medical witness before the Kefauver Committee Dr. May, former editor of *Pediatrics* and former head of Physicians' Council, was former Commissioner Larrick's candidate for Medical Director of the FDA. "The appointment was dangling for a full year," Professor May explained in his office. "Then finally it fell through. I understand the objection came from some people within the drug industry."

Dr. May's initial discord with drug makers began prior to the Kefauver hearings when as editor of *Pediatrics* he cast a jaundiced eye at some superextravagant drug ads, refusing to publish them in his journal. "I turned down several drug advertisements while I was editor," he recalls about this still-unconventional behavior. "The typical journal does not screen drug advertising. There is a sort of perfunctory scrutiny by some, but in no case is there strict concern."

Prior to the Kefauver-Harris amendments to the FDA Act, which went into effect in 1963, drug ads were not required to contain the simple caveat of listing side effects and dangers. "The AMA Journal of March 5, 1960 carried a scientific article by Dr. Lawson Wilkins documenting 36 cases in which girl babies were so masculinized that they would have been reared as boys, because their mothers were treated early in pregnancy with a synthetic hormone to reduce the risk of spontaneous abortion," Dr. Martin Cherkasky told the Kefauver Committee. "Yet for months after, the *Journal* carried advertisements of this drug . . . which contained no word of warning as to the possible catastrophic effects."

The Kefauver amendments have cleansed the drug-advertising atmosphere somewhat, but have not faced the basic issue involved: doctor gullibility in the face of overexpansive drug ads, and his well-established pharmacological ignorance. The new law requires that all contraindications and side effects be published in advertisements in "brief summary" form. But this has hardly throttled the drug advertiser's challenge to "educate" physicians into underwriting a larger share of the market for their drug—irrespective of its scientific value. The challenge is more difficult today, but is even more rewarding. "Puffery," says Dr. Walter Modell, "is not regulated by the FDA."

Today, much of the creative energy in many drug advertisements is spent allaying the meager suspicions of practicing physicians. Knowing their customer well, they have unleashed an inventory of evasive literary devices that apparently satisfy not only the current law about listing unwanted reactions, but reassure the easily assured physician.

The "side-effect" flimflam currently used in some drug advertisements to befuddle doctors can be summarized briefly: 1. Start with a disclaimer of innocence. 2. Put the inconsequential side effects first to set a mild tone. 3. Vigorously point out any lack of proof-positive, even if all indications point to the drug's involvement. 4. Remember that all reactions are "rare." 5. Bury the worst side effects anyway possible, especially by jamming them into a paren-thetical phrase. 6. Utilize obfuscation and sophism to increase confusion. 7. Keep the paragraph as a whole from sounding the way it should sound—like unadulterated *danger*.

A two-page journal ad for a meprobamate sedative is a classic use of No. 5—the clever, if specious, reasoning of sophism. The drug has been implicated in addiction, and the drug maker must therefore comment on the fact. "Excessive prolonged use may result in dependence on habituation in susceptible persons—as addicts, alcoholics, severe psychoneurotics," the ad states. How does the doctor go about identifying the patient who is a susceptible "severe psychoneurotic"? Obviously by watching. If he becomes addicted after "prolonged use," the ad copy has been confirmed!

The words "rare" or "isolated cases" are mainstays of the creative drug copywriter, for no physician can interpret such words statis-tically. The "rare" ploy (in combination with many of the seven rules of drug-advertising prestidigitation) was recently employed by a manufacturer of a phenothiazine tranquilizer. The ad appropriately appeared in *JAMA* about the same time as a *JAMA* article entitled "Sudden Death during Treatment with Phenothiazine Derivatives."

The "Precautions and Side Effects" section of the ad, designed to lead the doctor into cautious thought, begins instead with a thump of reassurance stating that from a clinical experience of more than ten million patients, it is apparent that the tranquilizer "has a wide range of safety" and that "jaundice has not been observed." Having tranquilized the physician, it proceeds to hastily list fifteen side effects, saving some of the more serious—leukopenia, agran-ulocytosis, convulsive seizures—for the end. It adds the meaningless value judgment that they are "extremely rare." The AMA's Council on Drugs has stated that agranulocytosis may occur as often as one case in 150 during phenothiazine therapy, making the interpretation of "rare" a philological debate over whose white cells are being gored.

The most gleeful gambit in the drug advertiser's copybook is his trumpeting of a new drug's supposed lack of side effects. This ab-sence is not generally a matter of pharmacology, but only of time. The *Medical Letter* advises doctors not to be prematurely swayed by the "safety" of new drugs. "Relative freedom from side effects is often reported in early trials of a drug, but not later."

(The *Medical Letter* is one of the few effective counterweights to massive pharmaceutical hucksterism. Initiated in January, 1959, the nonprofit drug *Letter* now has 30,000 subscribers, most of whom are physicians. The *Letter* is apparently unconcerned about law-suits (none have been instituted), for its critiques are written with ramrod forthrightness. In describing a new weight-reducing agent, for instance, the *Letter* claimed that its was "capable of causing serious toxic damage to the heart," and asked that it be taken off the market.)

An increasingly popular puffery technique is to lard the journal ad well with "clinical references," calculated to heighten its scientific allure to impressionable doctors. This is one of the "tricks of the trade," says Dr. Charles D. May, who reveals that "inferior" articles in the medical literature may be selected to support the claims "even when superior work is available to refute them."

Critics are concerned that "references" are often used as the drug maker's version of the soap-ad testimonial, with quotations taken from many inconsequential or even biased sources. "Reference is often made to unpublished data from 'personal communications,' 'case reports in the company's files' which are collected at random, and even individual testimonials," Dr. May writes in the *Journal of Medical Education*. "There are a few privately owned magazines published in the format of medical journals that are favorite repositories for superficial studies and common sources for references in promotional material. One of these was edited and published by a drug company that then used the references in its advertisements, thus having a handy closed system of quotation."

The *Medical Letter* recently used a psychochemical ad as a case history of the manipulated reference, warning doctors that it may have no scientific relation to the subject.

"The advertisement in question was captioned 'When anxiety and tension create major discord in parent-child relationships . . . ,'" the *Medical Letter* reports. "It bore a picture of a small boy and his distraught mother, and a solid panel of 188 references appeared at one side. A study of 177 of the references, made since the advertisement appeared (eleven references could not be traced), shows that only three or four clearly had anything to do with young children and their parents. In another ten or so, the 'children' were adults whose parents were still living." In summary, they warn: "In a word, a drug may have great value or no value; long lists of references, at least for the busy reader who cannot possibly check them, have no value."

The *Letter,* and other riled critics, have called attention to another ploy that trips unwary doctors: references that apply to animals rather than people. The makers of an appetite depressant recently purchased a massive amount of medical-journal advertising. The color ads were distinguished by professional layout and copy, and a calculatedly impressive number of clinical experiments. "The only trouble with the ads," a prominent pharmacologist explains, "is that you have to read the material very carefully before you learn that most of this work was done on cats—not on people."

Advertising bravura that rivals extravagant "strength" claims for pills on television, finds its way into medical advertisements to perplex the working doctor, who has neither sufficient technical competence nor inquisitiveness to untangle the truth by himself. One drug firm recently claimed: "It takes 5 mg. of the most widely sold agent to control drug-induced extrapyramidal reactions," adding that it takes only 2 mg. of their drug. Such attempts to over-sell the doctor with claims of potency and economy are often specious, says the skeptical *Medical Letter*. They divulge that the 2 mg. advertised tablet costs "exactly the same" as the 5 mg. tablet of its competitor, and that there is no relationship between "milligram potency" and therapeutic effects. A 6 mg. dose of one tranquilizer, they illustrate, produces more side effects than 200 mg. of another popular psychochemical.

"Learning" from drug ads, which is the industry's institutional propaganda line, can create a distorted curriculum for the pliable doctor and danger for his patients. Dr. J. Polissar of Massachusetts upbraids a drug company for advertising a sulfa remedy for a disease which experts are convinced it does not control. He points out in a letter to the *New England Journal of Medicine* that a recent American Heart Association booklet on prevention of rheumatic fever warns that the sulfonamide drugs should *not* be used for treatment of streptococcal infections. "In spite of this long-held opinion by leading medical authorities, a producer of sulfonamides has conducted a very intensive campaign over the last year urging physicians to use sulfonamides in the treatment of upper respiratory infections." Dr. Polissar's comments are penetratingly accurate, but we should not fail to indict the pharmacology-poor physician who has to rely on such advertisements for advice on proper "strep throat" therapy.

The physician who owns his own dispensing outlet—a drugstore —is another potential source of abashment for his more sensitive colleagues, who shudder at the thought of still another possible negative influence on the physician's prescribing habits. The doctor trapping of the patient at both ends of the prescription gives the physician a vested interest in drug marketing, which may conflict with his interest in the patient's health. "We're not in favor of physicians owning drugstores," *GP* magazine states editorially, even though, they point out, it is currently "ethical."

"Ethical" so used is a semantic anachronism that has nothing to do with morality. It refers only to doctor-guild regulations, and apparently vacillates vigorously. Owning a drugstore was *not* "ethical" for a doctor in 1954, but in 1955 the AMA Judicial Council apparently had a change of ethic. "It cannot be considered unethical for a physician to own or operate a pharmacy, provided there is no exploitation of the patient," they told the relieved doctor-entrepreneurs.

The National Association of Retail Druggists reveals that physician-owned pharmacies total twenty-two hundred (involving considerably more doctors) and are "steadily increasing." In California during hearings on the subject, a county welfare spokesman testified that one physician had been writing prescriptions for welfare patients averaging $10,000 per year. When he opened his own pharmacy, in 1960, stated the welfare officer, the same drug-prescribing rose to $50,000 a year.

Doctor ownership of a pharmacy is an obvious galling conflict of professional interest, despite AMA dollar-blindness on the subject. There are also *illegal* methods by which doctor or druggist may increase profit at the patient's expense. The method, explained during the California hearings, is simple: the physician prescribes a drug by brand name, but the drugstore fills it with a "generic" drug of the same composition, which costs half or a quarter as much. The pharmacist, meanwhile, charges the higher brand-name fee.

California expects to eliminate doctor temptation by removing the physician from the drugstore business. Its new legislation makes it illegal for physicians to hold drugstore interests (except in hospitals) after June 1, 1967. Other states might find it expeditious to adopt similar legislation rather than wait eternally for the AMA to reconsider its distorted "ethical" philosophy on this issue.

The dedicated physician-prescriber flourishes best in isolation from any pressures or temptations except the therapeutic needs of his patients. Drug makers have a converse concept of his interest, one to which he is unfortunately not opposed. They implement it with a mammoth program of physician-courting that has no bounds— from elegant publications, convention exhibits, symposia, fellowships, scholarships, to outright gift-giving.

Dispensing small gifts to the receptive doctor is the job of the detail man, who, like contemporary salesmen everywhere, eases his way with gifts of fountain pens, desk blotters, desk calendars, plastic paperweights, phone dialers, metal telephone indices, most emblazoned with the name of the charitable drug company. The accomplished detail man can sometimes offer such unusual premiums as baby food, drugs for the doctor's own family, or even a plastic heart with removable ventricles. One cunning drug firm gives away a desk set and appointment calendar strangely limited to two months. The pleased detail man must return that often just to refill the calendar!

More sizable gifts, calculated to implant eternal brand loyalty in young physicians, are dispensed with a flourish by knowing managements. Eli Lilly has for years given medical students new diagnostic instruments at various periods of their education. The gift is sometimes accompanied by a fond note pointing out the "co-operation of the dean of your college" and the "close association of our two professions." The Lilly gift of the young doctor's first black bag with his initials etched in gold is calculated, possibly accurately, to influence him toward Lilly medications.

Effective gift-dispensing combines the need to give with the desire to receive. No audience of young men is as receptive to such blandishments as relatively poor doctors in training. One drug company has periodically entertained internes and residents at an elegant club or restaurant, anticipating more future prescriptions than the cost of the night out.

"They invited me and my wife to a good-will dinner for residents at the Tavern-on-the-Green," a resident in New York recalls. "I turned them down. I don't need a night out that badly." Other young doctors are less strong-willed about such innocent-appearing invitations. One medium-sized drug firm in the southwest flies tired young residents out to "see its plant" and to receive an expense-paid weekend vacation at the same time. Drug-company entertainment is provided for senior physicians too, including an all-day golf outing for an entire county medical society. Several firms "chipped in" to supply such amenities as green fees, golf balls with the doctors' name printed thereon, lunch, cocktail party and dinner for physician and wife.

The doctor is not only seen, entertained, "educated" by attractive journal ads, flattered and plied with petty gifts. He is resolutely bombarded through the U. S. mails. He annually receives 3636 pieces of promotion (twelve every mail day) from drug makers, an avalanche of beautifully designed, ornately colored brochures. "We believe we use more advanced design techniques than other advertisers," a spokesman for a leading drug advertising agency states. "We have to get the doctor's attention, which sometimes is not too easy." For several years the challenge was solved by expensive gimcracks, including pop-outs and die cuts.

"That era is over," says the drug-advertising spokesman. "Since the congressional hearings, there is less effort put on gimmicks, and more on science and concepts." Some of these more conceptual gimmicks include a Salvador Dali-designed walk-in human cell exhibited at the AMA convention; a Terramycin brochure printed in a new process that makes a color drawing of bacteria appear three-dimensional; and a socio-economic promotional program that exults for special mention.

Physicians opening their morning mail recently were greeted by an apparently hand-typed letter from the executive vice-president of Roche Laboratories. In part, it read: "Once again, we are privileged to pay our tribute to you as a member of a profession which has traditionally cared for the indigent on its own time and its own cost.

We do so by announcing an extension of the Roche program of free medication for the economically and physically handicapped . . ." The physician was asked to send in a brief report of an indigent patient and the amount of drugs needed. Enclosed was a wedding-like invitation, which included the statement: "Librium—for indigent patients with anxiety." It is difficult to criticize such an effort, but its promotional motivation may be less pure than the truly charitable would prefer. Similarly, the "scientific" physician should be sufficiently confident of his pharmacological knowledge not to be influenced—for or against—a drug because of such studied persuasion.

A single drug mailing may reach 150,000 physicians, or as few as 300 gastrointestinal subspecialists, with a hand-typed, personalized letter. The average mailing, states one agency, is 75,000 to 100,000. Knowing what the physician is currently doing in his treatment rooms, and what prescriptions he is actually writing, is a matter of dollars-and-cents curiosity for the drug maker, who feels he must target his mail campaigns pointedly. The drug industry's efforts to learn how doctors actually use their license to practice exceeds any made by the medical profession.

The National Disease and Therapeutic Index, a Pennsylvania market research group, has some fifteen hundred co-operating physicians who keep a diary record of all their patients, their diagnoses and treatments. For an annual fee of $40,000 each, the NDTI regularly reports to their thirty drug-firm clients on the drugs, the number of prescriptions, the dosages being written by which type of doctors and for which ailments. (This is a program that doctors might well duplicate for healing statistics rather than direct-mail promotion.)

Several survey firms intrude into the doctor-pharmacist privacy by auditing several hundred drugstores. The stores report which drugs doctors are prescribing for patients and in what quantity, including such detail as dosage and the number of capsules and injectables. New Era, a New York mailing firm, is attempting the ultimate. They have mailed a questionnaire to every AMA member in the United States, asking him the quantity and name of all the drugs he prescribes. A manufacturer of antihypertensives, using this inside-the-doctor's-office intelligence, could ostensibly zero in his promotional literature only to those doctors prone to prescribe such drugs—missing the opportunity to "educate" the others.

The purpose of all this adroit promotional activity is to convince the suggestible doctor—a program that is apparently quite successful. An important aspect of the sales message to the physician is the drug's *newness* and *distinctiveness*—attributes the critical often tend to be skeptical of. Drug makers often insist on developing a "new" drug, whether or not it is truly new or medically needed, then sell it to physicians. Enhancing the drug's significance, obfuscating its sameness and registering its computer-born brand name in the physician's psyche are the theme of this multibillion-dollar game.

The American physician has not only been sold, but hopelessly confused by the constant duplication of drugs, mutations of drugs, and drug combinations, some of which appear to be invented by copywriters rather than doctors. George I. Freedman, a hospital pharmacist, wrote the editors of the *New England Journal of Medicine* that a supposedly "new" tranquilizer was the same drug that had been marketed for years under a different name. Another drug, he says, had been introduced under three different trade names for three different indications. When side effects were noticed, he adds, "it was combined with antacids and put on the market for peptic ulcers . . ."

The overwhelming plethora of newness (not unlike the *new, new* offerings of soap manufacturers) has been criticized by Dr. Walter Modell, who explains that needless drugs are being created by "structural roulette," the making of a minor molecular change in a competitor's patent. The resulting near-cousin is then rushed to market before it is economically too late—but in time to confuse the practitioner further. In *Clinical Pharmacology and Therapeutics,* Dr. Modell describes one manufacturer "who sells one drug entity in this country and a congener [chemically related drug] in another country," yet claims in both countries that "each is the best for the same purpose." The *New England Journal of Medicine* adds its anger in the form of an editorial comment: "There are in addition a multiplicity of identical or similar drugs that have no good reason for being on the market except to help their promoters recover some of the investment that went into their production."

Many physicians have pointed out that of the current twelve thousand drugs in use, only seven hundred are listed in the *U. S. Pharmacopoeia,* a blue-ribbon glossary that they believe is quite sufficient for the modern practice of medicine.

"As a matter of fact," says Dr. Charles May, "the really new drugs of material assistance in treatment, and requiring advancement in the knowledge of the physician for their use, probably amount to *less than six compounds a year* [italics mine]." He adds the cogent comment that partially explains physician ignorance of today's prescription drugs: "The physician might not need so much 'education' if there was not so much duplication in brands produced for profit rather than to meet the real needs of the patient."

The drug firm has a vested interest in the drug's brand name, a pseudoscientific alphabetese spewed forth by a computer or copywriter. It usually is as unrelated to the chemical involved as a soap or girdle brand name, but has been so successfully merchandised to the physician that he suspends scientific description and usually prescribes by brand name—much like the housewife in the supermarket. Drugs have two other identifiers, the simplified generic name, and the complex chemical name, both of which are descriptive to the knowledgeable.

The ever-poetic *New England Journal of Medicine* published a lilting rhyme on the generic-brand-name confusion, written by a concerned Boston doctor. It begins with the stimulating thought, "Come let a thousand flowers bloom," then lampoons the drug names:

> . . . Amylofene and Gardenal
> Peribar, Numol, Blu-phen
> Barbivas or Liquital
>
> Hail brand names, profits and confusion
> Circumlocutions' gay profusion!

The brand-conscious doctor is a modern phenomenon. The older physician elaborately scrolled Latin phraseology on a prescription pad, after which the pharmacist "mixed" the ingredients. Today, the pharmacist's deliberations behind the high counter are mostly clerical. The doctor's brand-name prescription is all carefully pilled and packaged, waiting to be personalized by the pharmacist by having him repackage it in his container. Why is the physician so intent on brand-name drugs when many hospitals buy the same drug much cheaper under its generic name?

A veteran detail man tries to explain the doctor's attitude. "When he writes a trade name of a drug on the prescription he feels secure," he explains. "He figures he has enough to worry about, and feels better about the quality of an advertised product—just as we all seem to. The difference in price is tremendous. Serpasil pills run around $4.50 for 100, and I can get generic 'reserpine' at 75¢ for *one thousand*. But the doctor feels better not taking a chance." Some major hospitals are less diffident or impressionable than doctors. "We buy few brand-name drugs," says the assistant administrator of a large eastern hospital. "Most of our drugs are bought under generic names from quality sources. It saves us a great deal of money."

Creating a previously nonexistent need, then filling it, is high art in the advertising industry, and may even have a salutary effect on the economy. But the comparison of drug promotion to other forms of advertising is specious. While it is of little import which brand of soap or breakfast food one uses, it may mean death or ill health if a physician is influenced to use a well-advertised but ineffectual, or unnecessarily toxic, drug on his patients.

The parallels of the needs of a free economy and those of healthy patients depart radically at this juncture. Should facile drug advertising be permitted to convince an ill-informed doctor to prescribe a potentially toxic phenothiazine tranquilizer for a "nervous" patient who does not need an anti-schizophrenic? Is the size and impact of a drug-advertising budget in any way related to the crucial issue—the effectiveness, superiority and safety of a drug?

The physician has proved himself an insufficient barrier against drug hucksterism, but neither has he been aided by his learned journals. Dr. Charles May has shown that medical journals are an indifferent control against drug puffery, a comment that has apparently been confirmed. The counsel to a Senate investigating committee has reviled the AMA for its reported *backtracking* on the screening of drug advertising. In 1955, he told the committee, the seal of acceptance of the AMA was discontinued, after which their advertising lineage rose. The move was apparently in response to an advertising-marketing survey conducted for the AMA by Ben Gaffin and Associates of Chicago. According to the counsel, the pharmaceutical manufacturers who did not agree with the standards the American Medical Association had maintained under their advertising seal of acceptance stated that they would place their advertising in other media and were not dependent on *JAMA* as long as they maintained relatively strict drug-advertising standards.

What possibility is there for objective pharmaceutical truth which the complacent, confused and undertrained physician so desperately needs? "I would change the whole system of communication between the drug company and the doctor," says thoughtful Dr. Walter Modell. "The *Medical Letter* is an attempt in the right direction in keeping physicians informed about drugs, but it is insufficient. We need something like that, but on a grand, massive scale. The medical profession must do something on the same order as the drug houses now do, but of course more objectively." Dr. Modell's suggestion for a sponsoring group is *not* the AMA's Council on Drugs, which as an ex-member he feels is not effective enough. His candidate: the U. S. Pharmacopoeial, a quasi-official group founded in 1820 whose volume, *U. S. Pharmacopoeia,* sets the U.S.P. standards for the manufacture of drugs.

The abdication of the medical profession in the proper education of the doctor about the drugs he uses disturbs Dr. Charles May. "The profession's influence is not inserted effectively in the kind of information disseminated in drug promotion or in the decision of authoritative bodies," the outspoken medical authority stated during a recent interview. "What is required is an independent body with independent access to media. The industry now spends $750,000,000 a year on promoting drugs, and is therefore a pretty large body to buck. At present, the information on drugs is not manageable for the typical doctor.

"There is no objective, systematic method of sifting opinion or documentation, or teaching the doctor about drugs," Dr. May continues. "He needs authentic information provided methodically. I visualize a properly constituted body of authorities in clinical medicine, pharmacology, industry, and government, acting as a Board of Overseers on the questions of drug safety and the dissemination of proper information to doctors. Neither the medical profession or the pharmaceutical industry have yet come to grips with the problem. Once the country understands the cost in money and health hazards, perhaps they will act. I believe the public has a great capacity for indignation, but it has to be aroused."

The supra drug body visualized by Drs. Modell and May can help screen the physician from the most insidious intrusion of drug promoters. The doctor's ignorance of modern pharmacology, though, is a heritage of an insufficient medical education, one that refuses to face the drug realities of everyday medical practice. "The boys in medical school are learning the principles of drugs, but they are not learning how to prescribe," Dr. May states. "Try an experiment. Pick out a group of senior medical students, and choose ten common drugs in current use. Ask them to give you their generic names, their trade names, the chemical compounds, the dangers, and proper dosages. I know they will not do it successfully. Our education process in pharmacology in medical school is not adequate."

Dr. Walter Modell concurs. "One area of medical knowledge given the least expansion in the third and fourth years of medical college is pharmacology and applied pharmacology. I think it is anticipated that it will be 'picked up' by the student in internship. But I'm afraid by that time the blandishments of the detail man become attractive to the busy interne. Much more time has to be given to applied pharmacology in later years of medical college in order to keep the doctor abreast of rapidly increasing new and potent drugs. Here at Cornell we have some courses—but not enough—in the third and fourth years. In some medical schools they have none."

Dr. Louis Lasagna, associate professor of pharmacology at Johns Hopkins and an adviser to *Medical Letter,* has added his concern about the pharmacologically undereducated American physician. He sees an urgent need for more and better teaching of pharmacology and applied pharmacology among medical students, internes and residents. Speaking to a recent White House Conference on Health, Dr. Lasagna stated: "It is a sad fact that as of this date there are only a handful of clinical pharmacology programs in universities throughout this country. Clinical pharmacology units devoted to first-class, imaginative, creative research on drugs and to the education of medical students and physicians in regard to drug usage should be established in every medical school in the country within the next decade."

The practicing doctor has an equal need for continuing education in drugs, but no co-ordinated system exists. The physician has also shown himself to be a callously indifferent student. Dr. Maxwell Finland, professor of medicine at Harvard, who has delivered postgraduate lectures on how to evaluate drugs, is distressed by this failure of doctor interest. "I would like to see some method of developing continuous education in the use of drugs," he told the medical press at one such meeting in Boston. "There is so much talk that only detail men are teaching the physicians. Yet, unfortunately the sum total of the people in practice who attend these meetings and are interested in attaining knowledge of this rapidly developing field is such a small percentage of the practicing community that it is distressing."

This failure of doctor education produces the ideal drug-company setup: a physician able enough to comprehend its pitch, but not discerning enough to see through it or knowledgeable enough to know the drug's history and drawbacks. This is especially valuable to the manufacturer during a drug's first two years on the market when the drug company tries to stimulate enough doctor prescriptions to recoup most of its investment—before the side effects or competition appears, or lack of efficacy is determined.

"The pharmaceutical industry finds the prompt establishment of its new drugs essential. It cannot afford to wait," Dr. Walter Modell told the American Association for the Advancement of Science. "In this kind of rat race it is simply sound business practice for industry to attempt to recover a large portion of its investment in a drug immediately after the drug is introduced . . . It does not allow time for the practicing physician to learn about the drug through the scientific journal, which is slow to publish, or through experience, which is even slower. The drug is promoted from the very start as if its use were a part of standard and accepted practice."

Safety for the patient can hardly flourish in this environment. Although apparently unknown to doctors, any new drug is still an experiment despite FDA approval. As Dr. Modell states, it is just beginning its two- to three-year "trial by ordeal" by inducing untoward, perhaps fatal, reactions in patients. In *JAMA,* Dr. Modell reminds doctors of the intelligent security of older drugs, whose risks and advantages are better understood by the physician. "Remember there is no guarantee that a new drug is better than an old one, the chances are less than even, and if you throw the weight of your experience into the balance, the odds against it are still longer," he advises doctor-readers. "Therefore, until the evidence is in, until a drug's probationary period is over, I suggest that the value of experience be held in proper esteem and take precedence over shakily established claims and hurried use of new drugs."

Dr. Modell proposes a plan that would make FDA approval only an initial step in drug acceptance. It would be followed by a two-to three-year probationary period before a drug would be considered "standard therapy" and widely used by all doctors. "Delayed drug reactions, if they occur at all, are noted within the first two or three years," he said, "and might be watched far more carefully if drugs were considered to be in a probationary period prior to their introduction as established medication." Full implementation of this would require new congressional action, which is undoubtedly called for.

To be transformed into an educated prescriber, the doctor must receive more objective drug information on a systematized basis. Adverse reactions are part of this knowledge and—on paper—noteworthy attempts are being made to collect this information. In May, 1963, following the thalidomide situation, the AMA announced a Registry on Adverse Reactions, to be part of the Council on Drugs. Elaborate plans were developed, and reporting forms with self-addressed envelopes were included in copies of *JAMA.* Advisory panels of fifty physicians, including some of the nation's most prominent pharmacologists and clinicians, were named. The nation sat back and awaited the vigorous drug reporting and warning system.

The AMA may well be receiving voluminous correspondence from doctor-readers, but the Adverse Reactions reports in *JAMA* reflect a medical mouse begot by a noisy lion. *JAMA* continues to publish excellent full-length articles on particular drug problems as experienced by physicians, and the Council on Drugs publishes short articles in *JAMA* that vary in quality from mediocre surveys to brilliant, short, objective reports.

The *master* AMA information center, feeding adverse effects on specific drugs in substantial, no-holds-barred doses back to the practicing doctor, has not materialized, however. The AMA material too often attempts to cover a massive number of drugs and reactions in one or two pages, such as their overbrief wrap-ups on kidney toxicity and photosensitivity, with tables of drugs arranged like a supermarket list, as if their reactions and toxicity were all comparable. *Few drugs are singled out* for any special study of particular concern. The articles are usually quite distinguished by their brevity, occupying perhaps one-tenth the space in *JAMA* they deserve.

Medical observers of the program have thus far been disappointed. "If a few people can band together to produce *Medical Letter,* staking their reputations on their statements," asks a former, disillusioned member of the Council of Drugs, "why can't the giant AMA do the same and better?"

Despite the bounteous number of protagonists involved in the contemporary drug story, from the FDA to drug advertisers, the man responsible for all prescription-drug consumption—the doctor—must be singled out as the one requiring the sternest rehabilitation. By drawing on the comments of medical critics and on other constructive opportunities, it is not impractical to visualize a plan for correction. The doctor's education for drug usage must be *quadrupled* in medical college, especially in the last two years of clinical training. Internes and residents must receive formal training in applied pharmacology in every hospital. Practicing physicians must be required to take similar courses on a continuous basis. The incestuous kinship of doctors and drug makers must be dissolved; one's motive is, hopefully, patient health, the other's is profit. Gift-bearing of the most innocent-appearing variety—whether the sponsorship of a symposium, a desk blotter or a black instrument bag—must be discontinued.

Perhaps most important in such a plan, *drug-product advertising to doctors should be totally eliminated.* The naïve, intellectually suggestible physician must be protected from its blandishments. Its replacement should be true doctor education in the form of detailed academic text pieces on each new drug, prepared by a "joint commission" composed of the medical profession, the pharmaceutical industry and the FDA. On the introduction of a new drug, such information should be mailed (first class!) to every physician in the nation. Advertising income lost by the journals should be replaced by institutional advertising, and federal grants-in-aid.

The detail man should be abolished as an affront to the medical profession, and as an unscientific, biased—if convenient—source of drug information for the susceptible doctor. In the same manner, *promotional literature, and direct-mail correspondence between drug companies and doctors, should be prohibited.*

As the major source of continuing drug education for the practicing doctor, a joint body of the medical profession and the FDA—this time purposely excluding the drug makers—should publish a weekly *comprehensive drug bulletin* (much like the weekly "Morbidity and Mortality" bulletin now issued by the Communicable Disease Center of the U. S. Public Health Service), listing all adverse drug reactions received or reported in the literature that prior week; cumulative lists of drug reactions; objective evaluations of particular drugs by leading academic authorities; notes on new-drug introductions; current journal bibliographies on various drugs and drug therapies; news of FDA actions; information on continuing pharmacology-education courses; and comprehensive articles by physicians on drug therapy. When an especially pertinent drug article—whether on therapy or reactions—appears in a medical journal, it should be reprinted in the official bulletin, thus bringing it to the attention of every physician in the nation. The bulletin, paid for by government funds, should be mailed free of charge to every doctor. Semiannually, the new drug information and the bulletin could be bound and distributed to physicians.

Such a program of change should pique the interest of the sensitive physician, and challenge organized medicine and the drug makers. Its intent is to make the patient more assured that someday his physician's scribbled prescription will be safer and more knowledgeably written than it is today. In the final analysis, the patient deals neither with government nor drug makers, nor the AMA. His life and health have been placed—for fee-for-service—solely in the hands of his doctor. "It is he [the doctor] who must observe carefully every patient whom he treats with any drug," says Dr. Harry F. Dowling, "and it is he who must bear the ultimate responsibility for the effects of the drug he has used."

Chapter XVIII

Malpractice:
The Patient's Recourse

The successful malpractice attorney's office overlooked New York Harbor, from which vantage point he remarked about the multitude of physicians within a sweep of his hand, whose errors were the grist for this specialty of American jurisprudence. "There is far more malpractice being committed by doctors than there are legal malpractice cases," attorney Charles Kramer opined. "I would estimate that for every case of malpractice that a lawyer handles, there are ten others that don't come to light. Some doctors have attacked malpractice attorneys, but I personally feel like a crusader. Malpractice is the most difficult of all torts to prove. But without us, the patient would never have any redress against doctors."

The extent of malpractice suits is not as fearsome as some beginning practitioners—who dread such legal action more than they do their own unpreparedness for healing—believe. It has, however, become a substantial phenomenon as patients sorely learn that organized medicine and state licensing authorities have absolutely no interest in disciplining the incompetent physician. Of the 14,616 physicians surveyed by the Law Department of the AMA, one in six physicians (17.8 percent) revealed that malpractice claims had been made against them. Most had had only one, but one in four of these doctors had been legally challenged by two or more patients with what the AMA euphemistically calls "professional-liability claims."

Attorneys estimate that there are more than six thousand malpractice suits filed against physicians each year. The most recent data, compiled by physician-attorney Sidney Shindell of the University of Pittsburgh, indicates damages of $34,000,000 in 1960, with evidence that it has since passed the $50,000,000 mark. William J. Curran, director of the Law-Medicine Institute at Boston University, points out that the number of satisfied malpractice claims increased 84 percent from 1954 to 1959, and that "the trend will continue." Suits against hospitals are perhaps the fastest-growing malpractice claim: in a recent year the cost of hospital-liability policies rose up to 20 percent in thirty-four states.

No area or physician is immune to suit, although California is the undeposed leader in malpractice-suit frequency (more than 50 percent greater, proportionately, than the country at large), with Oregon, Minnesota, New York, Massachusetts, bunched in second place. Malpractice is not a threat that strikes only the relatively untrained doctor. The American College of Surgeons has cited an unpublished survey indicating that board certification as a surgical specialist is not a factor in malpractice frequency.

What chance does the patient have of winning such suits? They are apparently higher than rumored, for an AMA survey shows that aggrieved patients win a *majority* (53.1 percent), with judgments ranging from a few hundred dollars to recent record decisions that cost physicians up to $725,000. This financial substitute for Hammurabic eye-for-an-eye vengeance is typically absorbed by the doctors' insurance companies, which protect over 94 percent of physicians. "Those physicians who have no professional liability insurance are running a serious risk," the AMA understates to its journal readers.

Malpractice has its peculiar manifestations, but is basically a civil-law case in which one party claims damages for injury done to them by another, or that a contract or warranty has been breached. The parties are entitled to a jury trial, and the contest rests both on the facts and the persuasiveness of opposing counsel. The basic difference between malpractice and other civil suits is the difficulty of proof, and an emotional factor. The plaintiff is a patient (or surviving family) who sought medical help from the defendant, and is now claiming that the doctor, through negligence and/or incompetence, has injured or killed. The doctor is virtually immune from professional or legal discipline, and this attempt at pecuniary retribution is the layman's only current recourse.

"The greatest volume of our cases involve anesthesia complications, general surgery, orthopedics, and obstetrics and gynecology, but there is no limit to the variety of malpractice," attorney Kramer estimates. "Fistulas following hysterectomy seem to be a common surgical error. The surgeon cuts the bladder by mistake, and if it is not recognized at that time, urine leaks out continually, and repair is difficult and dangerous. Often the fistula just doesn't heal. We have cases of maternal death too. I just tried one case in which a woman delivered twins, and had a postpartum hemorrhage. We won because of the failure to treat the loss of blood promptly. The woman died twelve hours later.

"About half our cases involve doctors alone, and the other half involve hospitals and doctors. Judging from our cases, there is a lot of carelessness in hospitals. We get about a hundred new cases a year in this office, and the same hospitals keep cropping up over and over again. It's not just proprietary hospitals, which account for about twenty-five percent of cases. There appears to be just as much neglect in the supposedly good voluntary institutions whose names we are all familiar with."

The potential for medical and surgical harm should, by now, be apparent. But despite any supposed sophistication, leafing through one malpractice attorney's docket of cases is a reintroduction to the underside of the medical corpus. The file, encompassing over a hundred malpractice cases, was medically encyclopedic, including claims of injury from allergic reactions to ulnar-nerve (forearm) damage.

"Anesthesia" was an active category of malpractice claims: a "spinal" resulting in paralysis; the use of Xylocaine local anesthesia with a fatal reaction; spinal injection with a "dropped foot," resulting from injury to the peroneal (side of the leg) nerve. Under "cardiology," a girl had allegedly died from an internal laceration created by cardiac catheterization. The "drug" heading was expectedly busy: penicillin death despite warning from a patient; antibiotic injection with death; arsenic effects from carbarsone for treatment of dysentery; death from treatment of psoriasis with a steroid.

"Ear, nose and throat" malpractice claims were frequent: tympanoplasty (middle-ear surgery) resulting in total deafness; bronchoscopy with perforation and death; injury to vocal cords from tube insertion during a gall bladder operation; injury to vocal cords from excision of throat polyps (case settled); cancer of the tongue with the patient unable to speak—allegedly from doctor failure to diagnose nodule in neck. The eye, too, can be susceptible to medical-malpractice suits: glaucoma resulting from use of atropine; cosmetic eye operation on patient with Bell's palsy—allegedly made worse; cataract with infection, loss of vision.

A score of obstetrical and gynecological cases catalogued the reported injury to female organs, the death of mothers during delivery, and damage to the newborn child. Several cases of maternal death were similar: charges that delivery was followed by fatal hemorrhage. During delivery other mothers allegedly developed rectovaginal or vesical (bladder) fistulas, from forceps and other instruments. Children were reportedly injured during delivery in various ways, from severance of the spinal cord to creation of Erb's

palsy, a shoulder disability. In one case the delivering physician
was being charged with contributing to the child's mentally retarded
condition.

The medico-legal category of "hospital negligence" is a malpractice
catch-all. In this giant docket were included charges that a nurse
pushing a crib overturned it, fracturing the child's skull; a $90,000
settlement for a fall out of a hospital bed; a refusal by two hospitals
to admit an asthmatic child who died the same day; injection of a
tranquilizer with resulting paralysis of the legs; a patient confined to
a wheel chair due to injection injury to the sciatic nerve; a catheter
that broke off, then entered the blood stream.

This one attorney's pending cases against hospitals include
charges involving the premature discharge of a heart patient who
died soon after being sent home; collapse of an examining-room
table with injury to a child; several fatal cases resulting from mismatched blood; failure to provide needed oxygen; infection contracted from a hospital roommate; the administering of glucose to
a child without tests. The child proved to be a diabetic, and died
($7000 settlement).

Orthopedic errors are writ-and-butter for many a malpractice
lawyer. This *one* attorney was filing suit on a dozen claims: repair
of a leg fracture with a Smith-Peterson nail and rectangular bar that
broke; failure to take proper X-rays, including postoperative ones,
on several fractures; injury to an ulnar nerve ($48,000 in damages)
during orthopedic repair; tight casts causing ulceration. Judging from
malpractice cases, the too-tight cast applied for bone fracture appears to be near-epidemic. It can cause death of the tissue, gangrene,
and even amputation. "Much of it," says one malpractice lawyer,
"stems from the fact that doctors and nurses are inattentive to complaints from patients about pain. The patients tell them that the cast
hurts, but they just push them off by answering that it's to be expected. Actually the cast should be sliced to allow for swelling.
If there are complaints, the cast should be loosened and inspected
for pus or other signs."

Several surgical-malpractice charges on the attorney's docket had
the added degree of finality. Two appendectomy patients died, one of
ruptured appendix, the other of postoperative hemorrhage. A gastrectomy was followed by complications and death; another ulcer
surgery with perforation of the esophagus. A venous ligation was
followed by pulmonary complication and death; artery and nerves
were injured during stripping of varicose veins; a melanoma (type
of pigmented malignant cancer) was allegedly removed without
biopsy. It spread after surgery, causing death.

Proving medical malpractice is considerably more trying than
listing pending complaints. Demonstrating the fact of negligence—

that the doctor involved did not follow the *customary* practice or use the *usual* skill or judgment of other physicians in the community —generally requires the co-operation of an expert witness—another doctor. Doctors' reluctance to point the finger of culpability against their colleagues has made malpractice attorneys cry that there is a "conspiracy of silence" blocking justice. Bernard D. Hirsch, director of the Law Department of the American Medical Association, has called the "conspiracy" of silence a "false phrase," a comment that has aroused the ire of trial lawyers who feel they must put up with its restrictions daily.

"There most definitely is an informal conspiracy of silence among physicians," states Jacob D. Fuchsberg, former president of the American Trial Lawyers Association, the national body of trial attorneys, many of whom handle or specialize in malpractice work. "Of course, it does not mean that doctors have organized not to give out information to attorneys and their clients. But it does mean that doctors—who privately are often highly critical of each other— have voluntarily decided not to testify in court to one another's errors, generally for fear of professional sanctions in the hospital and rebuke from their colleagues. Mr. Hirsch also believes that the majority of malpractice suits are not justly founded. In my experience, this is patently untrue. By the time claims get to us, much of the evidence has disappeared, and the trivia has been eliminated by time. We are generally left with only those cases where the damage and the malpractice are obvious."

Prominent trial attorney Alfred S. Julien charges that when the medical community refuses to testify in malpractice cases, it "does not live up to its professional or legal obligations to its citizenry." Without such protection, he states, "the victim whose surgeon cuts off the wrong leg, or leaves a sponge in his abdomen, or whose obstetrician delivers but one twin, allowing the mother and other baby to die of neglect, is without redress."

John J. Tullman of New York, reputed to be the only attorney who limits his law work to malpractice, has coined the apt phrase: "The gauze curtain put up by doctors can be as impenetrable as the iron one." When interviewed, attorney Tullman elaborated on the frustrating situation, which he believes "may sterilize our system of jurisprudence" if not corrected. "There is no question that there is a pattern that has almost grown into a tradition with doctors, that insists on silence in a malpractice situation," he comments. "They will speak to you privately about the case, give you a factual account, and sometimes even a frank opinion of the previous doctor's work. But they will refuse to say it in court. To subpoena the doctor into court, which we can do, is an empty gesture. Once in the witness chair, it is legally his right to absolutely refuse to give his expert opinion on the case.

Attorney Charles Kramer recounts an example of doctor fear. "I had a medical expert who agreed that the defendant's work was bad medical practice," he recalls. "He told me that he was going to say so on the stand. When he was on the stand, I outlined what the defendant doctor had done as a hypothetical question, then asked him if this was good medical practice. You can imagine my shock when he answered without hesitation: 'Yes.' A few days later he apologetically explained why he had suddenly changed his answer. Just as he was starting to testify, he noticed that the chief of service of his hospital was seated in the courtroom. He assumed that he was a defense witness and was afraid to antagonize him."

One attorney describes another case in which pressure was put on a doctor to maintain his silence. "A doctor who was going to testify for my client in a malpractice case was approached by a prominent physician who was active in the county medical society and told that there might be serious difficulty if he testified," he related. "I wanted to go to the district attorney about this threat, but I didn't only out of concern for the doctor's peace of mind. I wouldn't blame this situation on the county medical societies in particular. It's part of a larger pattern in the profession."

While medical organizations vehemently deny the "conspiracy of silence," physicians themselves openly admit it. The Boston University Law-Medicine Institute asked physicians if they would testify for the plaintiff in a malpractice case in which the surgeon had mistakenly removed the *wrong* kidney. Seventy percent of the physicians admitted that they would refuse despite the obvious merit of the case.

The weight of evidence seems to support the "conspiracy" charges of malpractice attorneys, who some doctors feel are "harassing" their profession. The actual trouble appears to be harassment by doctors of other physicians who co-operate in malpractice suits. Attorney Paul W. Brightmire of Tulsa, Oklahoma, recounts a case of tragic medical harassment that almost ruined a doctor's well-being. "A urologist decided to file a malpractice suit of his own because of injury to his eldest daughter," attorney Brightmire recalls. "The girl had vaginal difficulty, and was scheduled for minor surgery by an obstetrician. During the operation she went into cardiac arrest and it was several minutes before they could find a surgeon, have her chest opened and the heart massaged. She had permanent brain damage and loss of intelligence.

"The doctor waited almost until the two-year statute of limitations was up, then came to see me to file suit. Immediately after, the local doctors started to put pressure on him. His urology partnership broke up. His wife was snubbed, he was given the cold shoulder by other doctors, and even a friend anesthetist told him he couldn't operate with him until the malpractice suit was dropped. The doctors had jumped on him to put him out of business. He finally made arrangements to relocate out of town, but the pressure was as great there. He received a letter from a leading doctor in the town where he was planning to settle, flatly telling him that he was not wanted, and that if he wanted to get along in the medical profession anywhere in the country, he had best drop the malpractice suit. Finally, another lawyer was engaged to draw up a dismissal of the malpractice suit. I filed a conspiracy action against several of the doctors by name, and the insurance company too. It has just been settled. I collected twenty-two thousand dollars." Now that the physician has acquiesced, attorney Brightmire explained, he has been accepted back in the medical community.

The notes of the Superior Court of New Jersey contain an illuminating case history in doctor failure to testify to medical truth. On learning that his expert witness, a prominent obstetrician, had suddenly refused to appear in court, the plaintiff asked for a postponement. When it was denied, it was appealed to the superior court, appellate division, where the plaintiff was upheld with an enlightening decision. The Saturday before trial the expert witness, a professor of obstetrics and gynecology at a New York institution, had suddenly declined "on second thought" to testify against a "brother practitioner," even though he still thought the defendant was negligent.

Judge Clapp commented historically, "The circumstances of the case must be looked at in the light of—the matter is of sufficient public concern for plain speaking—*a shocking unethical reluctance on the part of the medical profession to accept its obligations to society and its profession in an action for malpractice* [italics mine]." He then added: "A charge of malpractice is a serious and emburdening charge upon a professional man, but it is not answered by an attempt to throttle justice."

This unethical, fierce resistance by doctors crushes many attorneys. They either give up their cases or refer them to malpractice specialists skilled enough to circumvent medical opposition. "There's no doubt about the conspiracy, and some lawyers throw their hands up when faced with it. But if you know how, and are persistent, you can eventually get a doctor to testify as your expert witness," says Henry H. Dillof, law partner of Charles Kramer. "It's generally impossible to get the men we would prefer, the chiefs of staff of various leading hospitals, but that doesn't block other possibilities. We're constantly meeting new doctors. Some have malpractice cases involving their own family; others are friends; some have testified in accident negligence cases.

"None are really willing, but some are less unwilling than others.

Sometimes a doctor will say, 'I'll testify if you subpoena me,' which perhaps lets him off the hook a little. Sometimes you have to beg—reminding them of the social aspect, of the aggrieved wife or parent. Often, I find, the doctors who are willing to testify are independent, by personality or circumstances. One doctor who has testified in perhaps ten ophthalmology malpractice cases is a retired old-timer in his seventies. He is not intimidated by the medical hierarchy."

The doctor's compensation for being an expert witness runs anywhere from $150 to several thousand dollars. Many attorneys claim they never pay physicians more than $500 for both consultation and testimony. One attorney speculates that there are "professional witnesses," doctors who earn a considerable portion of their income by appearance at malpractice trials.

"There are a few doctors who testify fairly frequently in court. But this should not be a reflection on them. It merely means they are willing to testify on medical matters, and are therefore consulted frequently," attorney Fuchsberg explained. "I try not to use them, not because they are not telling the truth, but because it is best not to give opposing counsel any diverting points to discuss. If I do use a doctor who has been in court several times, I bring it out myself as a positive factor—that he is called upon frequently to advise lay people on the merits of medical matters.

"Typically, though, getting a doctor as a witness for a malpractice case is a hunt. I have a letter on my desk from an attorney in Albany who needs a doctor for a witness. What can I tell him—getting each one is an involved project." Attorney Fuchsberg relates some mechanics of the intricate search: checking with an outstanding doctor as to the medical merits of the case ("He is willing to tell us if there is merit to the complaint but does not want to be personally involved"); researching the medical facts and journal articles in a medical library; securing the patient's hospital or medical record; preparing an extensive medical brief from the material.

"Armed with this, we go to those physicians who have written on the particular subject—say, gastroenterology—and who have shown concern with the best medical practices," Mr. Fuchsberg explains. "If possible, we try to find experts from the medical school or the hospital where the defendant trained or is associated. It is difficult for him to repudiate his teachers or colleagues. I use the strongest intellectual and moral pressure to convince them that it is best for medicine for them to testify—which it is. It is very difficult to get the most prestigious doctors, but eventually we get someone. Only about half the time, though, are our doctor witnesses specialists in the same field as the malpractice action."

The defendant-doctor has no such problem. "The other side often has such a powerful array of physician witnesses that I am forced to tell the jury not to be swayed by that fact," says attorney Fuchsberg. "I explain to them that we do not have the same access to, or co-operation from, doctors." This initial handicap does not deter the aggressive lawyer, who, says Mr. Fuchsberg, "must make himself as expert in the limited medical subject as the most qualified specialist."

Attorney Charles Kramer maintains a "medical room," where in addition to his library of medical texts and journals he keeps a breakaway model of the human body. Each of the parts and organs are detachable and can be viewed individually or in relation to the body as a whole. "When we finish researching a case, we know quite a bit about the medicine or surgery involved," states attorney Kramer. "Of course, it is not always best to show the jury that you are too expert, but neither should you let the opposing counsel or doctors trip you up on anything."

The obstacles placed in the way of patient victory go beyond the difficulty of obtaining medical witness. Contrary to popular belief, legal malpractice is not present each time a doctor errs, even if the error is costly enough to cause the patient's death. Malpractice has been defined as a "deviation and departure from accepted and approved standards of practices, procedures and techniques." It has also been termed "the failure of a physician to exercise the required degree of care, skill and diligence." If "standard" or "required" medical practice includes expected human errors or even ignorance, some courts (legal custom varies) have held the improper technique not to be malpractice.

In one case involving aplastic anemia resulting from the prescribing of chloramphenicol antibiotic for a minor infection, a doctor-defendant pleaded that he was not negligent. He pleaded that *it was and still is* standard practice for doctors in his community to use the potent antibiotic that way despite warnings against it from the drug company and the FDA. The bizarre but apparently legal argument was successful, and the patient lost.

This edict that determines what is *usual,* rather than what is *proper,* has strange ramifications. A patient in Boston had his appendix "removed," but learned several years later that a segment of it had been left in. His doctor had not told him about it, or about the potential risk to his body. The court ruled against the patient because there was no proof offered that doctors in Boston at that time typically informed patients of such incomplete appendectomies!

A mother sued a Memphis hospital for a staphylococcus infection contracted by her newborn child. A lower court awarded the family $25,000 for injury, commenting that hospital regulations were violated, contributing to the infection. On appeal, however, the verdict was overruled in the hospital's favor. Following such hospital rules absolutely, the court said, would be asking for a "hospital utopia." The court quoted an earlier decision that it is only the duty of the hospital to "exercise that degree of care, skill and diligence used by hospitals generally in that community . . ."

Not all errors in diagnosis are actionable either. In a malpractice suit against the government, a parent charged that federal doctors had falsely diagnosed appendicitis in an eleven-year-old child. After the unnecessary operation the child developed internal bleeding and was operated on again. Surgeons discovered a generalized peritonitis (infection of the intestinal lining) which had caused a strangulation of the intestine. Blood poisoning and permanent brain damage were the final result. The court ruled that there was a failure to prove negligence. Although there was a mistake in the original diagnosis of appendicitis, it was, said the court, within the range of reasonable medical judgment to proceed with the operation. The failure to discover peritonitis was not significant, they ruled, since there was no proof that the treatment of it would have been successful!

The law is concerned about negligence, but asks proof that medical oversight caused the damage. In one case in Iowa, a steel shard that had pierced a patient's eye and later resulted in loss of the eye was not discovered by the treating doctor. Despite the oversight, the state supreme court decided in favor of the doctor. They decreed that there was no proof that had it been discovered in time, the eye would have been saved.

The nature of the malpractice law unfairly places many doctor errors outside the reach of patient recovery, but we should not infer that courts are typically pro-doctor. Given a case of provable negligence, juries and judges often bring in sizable verdicts for the plaintiff; and for every case tried, another is settled by insurers.

The "community standard" concept may even penalize under-trained physicians. "In any large metropolitan area, the standard for medical performance is that of the specialist in the field," says attorney John Tullman. "If a doctor does not have the training to do a procedure, he's safest—legally and medically—in not doing it at all."

The climate of some malpractice courts is changing. "Doctors are beginning to be treated just like any other tortfeasor [wrongdoer]," says one attorney. In fact, where doctor negligence is *obvious,* courts are increasingly holding that hard-to-obtain doctor-witnesses are not essential. The phrase *res ipsa loquitur* has become a magical Latin litany to malpractice lawyers and their patient-clients. Its meaning— "the thing speaks for itself"—implies that the damage is so obviously the result of medical negligence that only the recitation of the facts are necessary. In the State of Washington a patient entered the hospital for a hysterectomy and was placed in a Trendelenburg position (on her back with her head down and body up, then lower legs down), making the administration of anesthesia more difficult than in other operations. When she awoke after the operation her arm was paralyzed. She sued under the doctrine of *res ipsa* and received a jury verdict of $25,000. The court held that "surely to emerge from abdominal surgery with a paralyzed arm is so extraordinary an occurrence within the general observations of mankind as to raise an inference of negligence." Without expert evidence, the paralyzed arm "spoke for itself."

The *res ipsa* concept jars many in the medical world. They envision an endless, endemic surge of multimillion-dollar malpractice judgments against them based on apparent results of treatment rather than on medical proof of doctor's negligence. The concept is sweeping California and a few other states, and making initial inroads into the more staid New York judicial system despite attempts to stop it. "There is no doubt about it: it is the conspiracy of silence which has given impetus to *res ipsa* in malpractice cases," states Tom Lambert, editor of the *American Trial Lawyers Journal.* "Some medical or surgical errors are so extreme, abnormal and 'wild' that on the basis of ordinary experience, *without* eyewitness evidence or expert testimony, we know that the medical practitioner made a bad and blameworthy mistake."

He offers examples of recent *res ipsa* decisions: cast too tight, followed by infection and amputation (Iowa); common bile duct severed during gall bladder operation (California); doctor concealed that 12″ filiform, attached to a catheter, had broken off and passed into plaintiff's bladder (Michigan); cloth sack left in patient's body (Arizona); child's uvula (conical tissue hanging from the soft palate) removed during a tonsillectomy.

Malpractice is not just an anatomic concept. It is present whenever the "contract" between patient and doctor—unwritten but binding—is broken by the physician. Failure of the doctor to produce a *promised* cure is one breach of the medical pact. Most physicians imply that their therapy is valuable, but refrain from making concrete promises of "cures," especially quick ones. One doctor agreed to remove a patient's growth, reportedly promising that the patient could go back to work in one or two days. Instead the doctor punctured an organ, and a major operation and a month's hospital stay was necessary for repair. "The courts will enforce such an agreement just as any commercial contract by permitting money damages for its breach," says *GP* in reporting the case. "Liability would result from failure to perform the contract and not from any failure to perform up to standard of care as in tort cases."

One form of malpractice seldom discussed outside medico-legal circles is "abandonment," in which the physician fails to maintain treatment of his patient. The doctor is under no obligation to *take* a case, but having done so, must not abandon the patient without sufficient notice or a qualified substitute. "Abandonment cases are increasing," says Herman B. Glaser, dean of the New York Academy of Trial Lawyers. "Unfortunately, the old-time doctor whose only concern was his patient is rapidly disappearing from the medical scene. While many doctors still practice the ancient credo of dedication to the patient, others are making a business out of the profession. With nine-to-five hours, abandonment can be the result."

Mr. Glaser also points out that a doctor cannot merely place his patient in the care of a resident house staffer at a critical time without risking suit. "The doctor who is employed by the patient is his only doctor. The resident can help the regular doctor, but if the doctor leaves his patient in full care of the resident or interne—as is sometimes done in childbirth—that is abandonment."

The absence of the patient's doctor at the delivery of a child is abandonment at its most dramatic. At a recent American Trial Lawyers Association meeting in New York, attorneys expressed concern over the increasing abandonment of obstetrical patients. Physicians with two patients under induced labor at the same hospital have been forced to leave one delivery to an interne or resident; other doctors with obstetrical patients at two different hospitals have been forced to abandon one.

In a western state a physician decided to deliver a child with instruments after the woman had been in labor for some time. The woman shrank back in fear. After two or three unsuccessful attempts, and a warning to the woman to be quiet lest she cause harm, he gave her an ultimatum: if she did not quit, he would quit. Without arranging a substitute, the angry physician abruptly left the hospital, with the husband following him into the street, imploring him to return. He would not, and the husband finally secured another doctor. The baby was born several hours later, but lived only eight minutes. "He [the doctor] can never be justified in abandoning it, as did this defendant," said the court, "and the facts show a negligence in its character amounting well-nigh to brutality . . . Such conduct evidenced a wanton disregard, not only of professional ethics but of the terms of his actual contract."

The crushing emergency-room situation has increased the possibilities for doctor abandonment. In a classic case a man who had been shot in the neck was taken to an emergency room at 1 A.M. and a doctor was summoned. The doctor, who arrived clad in pajamas covered by a coat, found a punctured trachea and a bullet in the neck. He gave orders to prepare the patient for a blood transfusion and a tracheotomy to create a breathing opening in the neck. Before either was accomplished, he left for home to change his clothes. Within an hour the man's son had secured another physician, who arrived at 4 A.M. The new doctor examined the patient and realized that he was dying. He called the first doctor at home, asking him to release the patient, which he at first refused to do. The bitter phone conversation reportedly lasted a half-hour. Finally, at 5 A.M. the new physician attempted to save the patient's life with surgery, but the patient died in cardiac arrest.

"This case is, of course, a flagrant example of abandonment of a patient at a critical time," says Neil L. Chayet of the Law-Medicine Institute of Boston University. "The physician who attends any patient, either in a hospital, at home or in an office, must be sure to provide continuing medical care for the patient who is seriously ill."

Although abandonment of a regular patient has the most immoral overtones, the physician is legally (often morally) bound to a new patient even by a simple telephone call. A patient awoke at night with severe chest pains and walked over to a hospital emergency room accompanied by his wife. Unfortunately, he mentioned that he was a member of HIP, the New York group health plan, and the nurse told him they did not care for HIP patients. (This frankness from group health subscribers is not advisable when on other medical premises.) Instead of getting him medical aid, she dialed a HIP doctor and gave the patient the telephone. The physician listened to the complaint and allegedly told him to visit the HIP office at eight in the morning.

His wife then again asked the nurse to get a doctor because this was an emergency. The nurse reportedly refused again, and said the patient would have to see his own doctor. He returned to his apartment, and while undressing for bed, fell to the floor and died. The appellate court held that by virtue of the phone conversation the doctor "undertook to diagnose the ailments of the deceased," and that, in effect, a doctor-patient relationship was established.

The negative result of a doctor's treatment is more likely to be malpractice if the patient is not properly forewarned of possible repercussions of the therapy. In such cases the malpractice law states that the patient did not give the doctor his "informed consent." A doctor's patronizing edict, "Don't worry, you'll be fine," should be insufficient for the sophisticated patient being asked to undergo potentially harmful treatment.

Doctor evasiveness can be a legally dangerous trait for physicians, as was confirmed by a recent case. A woman suffering from rheumatoid arthritis was treated by her physician with injections of gold compounds without his informing her of the possibility of serious complications. A complication, a serious skin condition known as exfoliative dermatitis (shedding of the skin), did develop and the patient sued for malpractice. "We are of the opinion that, under the facts and circumstances disclosed by this record, including the fact that no immediate emergency existed," the appeals court stated, *"defendant was obligated to make a reasonable disclosure to his patient of the known dangers which were incident to or possible in the proposed use of gold* [italics mine] . . ."

An important "informed consent" decision took place in Kansas in 1960, in a case involving a patient whose left breast had been removed because of cancer. After the operation the surgeon suggested radiation therapy at the site of the mastectomy. Cobalt treatments were given which, she claimed, produced a sloughing off of the skin, flesh and muscles beneath her left arm. Her suit against the radiologist and the hospital on grounds of negligence was denied. On appeal, however, the court reversed the decision and ordered a new trial on the grounds of possible failure of *informed consent.* "Anglo-American law starts with the premise of thorough-going self-determination," they decreed. "It follows that each man is considered to be master of his own body, and he may, if he is of sound mind, expressly prohibit the performance of lifesaving surgery or other medical treatment . . . We think, upon all the facts and circumstances here presented, Dr. Y was obliged to make a reasonable disclosure . . . of the dangers within his knowledge which were incident to, or possible in, the treatment he proposed to administer . . ."

Within the contested arena of malpractice, some doctors heap abuse at malpractice attorneys who, they claim, are getting gluttonously rich off patients through "contingency fees." Under the current system the attorney takes the case without a retainer in the hope of winning and legally dividing the judgment (by formula) between himself and the patient. Because of this often-outsize fee, cry angered doctors, attorneys seek outlandish judgments and encourage dissatisfied patients to sue. Attorneys rebut that they handle only a fraction of the true malpractice committed by doctors. Without the "contingency fee," they add, the typical patient could not afford to retain them to press a claim of malpractice. "Just the expenses that we lay out for research and documents would be impossible for many patients to handle," says one plaintiff's attorney. "What should the poorer patient do. Forget about his injury?"

In the charge and countercharge, doctors accuse lawyers of occasional courtroom histrionics, and some attorneys level a more serious charge at some doctors: that of *purposely altering medical records to cover up malpractice.* "There is no way to know how extensive it is, but I know that some doctors do change and destroy records which might prove them negligent," says attorney Charles Kramer. "I tried a case recently in which my client developed osteoporosis [bone brittleness or softness] of the spine with spine fractures as a result of steroid treatment of a skin disorder. It crippled him. We found after investigation that the doctor had added to his records, making it appear that he had done more urine tests—to check for effects of steroid excess—than he had actually done. We have photostatic copies of the original records, and copies of the record after it had been altered. The doctor's insurance company settled with us for a substantial amount."

Dr. Don H. Mills of the University of Southern California and John J. Harris, an expert in questioned documents, delivered a paper on altered records at a forensic medical meeting. Mr. Harris, who has handled approximately twenty altered medical records during his career, found that most of them involved "expanded" office records. "Hospital records are more difficult to alter," he pointed out when interviewed. "When a patient's office record is altered, it is done because the doctor usually adds more details that tend to mitigate something that has happened."

He and Dr. Mills described one case in which they believe the word "penicillin" was added to numerous entries on the patient's record. The patient had sued the doctor for inadequate treatment of an upper respiratory infection. The document examiners found that the "penicillin" entries were written with the same kind of ballpoint pen and ink, while the original entries were written with many different ones!

The size of recent malpractice judgments unnerves physicians, who fear it might exceed their liability insurance. Since the cost of malpractice insurance is usually not high, some physicians have purchased $1,000,000 coverage. A Michigan physician who does no surgery, for example, pays approximately $60 a year for $5000/$15,000 liability coverage and twice that for $100,000/$300,000 coverage. (The smaller amount is for a single claim; the larger amount for all claims in one year.) For a small additional premium he can be covered for a full million. "Class 4" surgeons (including anesthetists) —those who engage in major surgery—must pay substantially more: $212 for the basic coverage, and twice that for the $100,000/ $300,000 protection.

In certain communities the major surgeon who seeks full protection becomes aware of the cost of his malpractice insurance buffer. In San Francisco the *basic rate* for the Class 4 surgeon is $468 a year; in Los Angeles it is the same $468; in New York City, $315. Sizable surgical malpractice protection in these lawyer-rich patient-sophisticated, doctor-rushed communities can cost the anxious surgeon $1000 a year.

Rates rise perceptibly and steadily as courts seem more inclined to grant substantial awards. "There was a time when a dead patient was worth nothing in court," explains attorney Jacob Fuchsberg. "The statutes provided only for pecuniary loss of the recovered patient. Even today, in Massachusetts the maximum recovery for death resulting from malpractice is approximately twenty thousand dollars."

A great injustice in our malpractice system is the miserly amounts usually awarded to parents for the death of a child. "Because the malpractice law is based on money damages, a one-day-old child is theoretically worth nothing. In such cases any damages awarded would be nominal," Mr. Fuchsberg explained. "In fact, in Nebraska the jury brought in a guilty verdict against a doctor in the death of a child, but did not award the parents any damages at all. They felt that the parents would have put more money into bringing up the child had it lived than they could expect to receive back! We estimate that in court a child's life is worth about three thousand dollars for each year that it has lived. I think it's shocking. The courts should value sentiment and other non-pecuniary values—as I understand Florida courts now do."

The size of malpractice awards seem to resist any logical pattern. There are, however, some guide lines that attorneys use to estimate what medical damage is worth in court. A recent malpractice award to a young Army veteran details how the more sizable awards are determined. After lung surgery for service-connected tuberculosis in a federal hospital in Baltimore, he became paraplegic. The $650,211 malpractice award, given to him at the age of thirty-four, was broken down as follows: $42,314 for loss of past income; $110,352 for loss of future income; $200,000 for future medical expenses; $350,000 for pain and suffering; $52,455 deducted for past disability payments.

The rich man is worth considerably more to a malpractice court than a poor man. "If a man of thirty-five with a wife and two children were to die as a result of medical malpractice, the award would depend on how much he was making per week, and his future potential," attorney Fuchsberg explains. "If he were making 80 dollars a week, I would estimate the award at one hundred and fifty thousand dollars. However, if he were making forty thousand dollars a year, it would probably reach a half million or more."

The concept that housewives do not "earn" money has traditionally dampened awards for the death of female victims of medical malpractice. The low value that courts have traditionally placed on their lives was characterized by a Pennsylvania nonmedical case in which a jury awarded a husband $46,059 for wrongful death of his wife and the mother of his three children, only to have the judge insist that it be reduced to $17,618. The plaintiff refused, and on appeal of the case, received a more enlightened decision from Justice Musmanno of the state's higher court. The judge stressed the mother's value to her family through her "incessant activity, tireless energy, and never-flagging concern."

One intrepid attorney circumvented the problem recently by presenting a malpractice court with what was, in effect, a financial bill itemizing the cost of replacing a wife and mother. The wife of a Navy serviceman died in a Florida hospital from an incompatible blood transfusion while her sixth child was delivered by Caesarean section. Expert testimony was presented to illustrate the cost of maintaining the children with "substitute mother" care. It was figured at $8500 per year for eighteen years, including the cost of domestic help, after which time the youngest child would be of college age. "The present value of an annuity of $8500 per year for 18 years compounded at 4 percent (discount rate) is $98,838," their brief estimated, which exact amount was awarded. Her added value as a wife of fourteen years was described as "far above rubies," but an arbitrary $25,000 was awarded in addition, for the "love and companionship" of a "steadfast and devoted wife."

Suing for malpractice must be done speedily, within the typical one- to three-year statute of limitations. The law may be specific but illness is less conforming, and injuries suffered from negligence may not show themselves for years after the statute has expired. Rather than begin from time of *discovery* of the malpractice, the statute of limitations in many states begins from commission of the negligence.

Physicians and hospitals have been known to conceal injury from patients, hoping that the statute will expire before the harm is discovered. Because of this, several courts are permitting postlimitation cases where doctor deceit or concealment of facts is involved. In Georgia a woman treated for a broken arm was told by physicians that it was healing satisfactorily, even though medical records showed that it had been improperly set. More than two years afterward, when the statute had expired, she filed suit in federal court. An expert witness testified that the patient's arm was now permanently disabled. The court ruled that the doctors' concealment of facts from the patient warranted postponement of Georgia's two-year statute of limitation.

The restrictive time span normally permitted patients is underscored by attorney Joseph W. Campanella of Long Island, who recounts a narrow squeak with New York's malpractice statute of limitation. "A woman twisted her foot on November 30, 1961, and had an X-ray taken on December 1, after which her doctor informed her that it was not a fracture," relates the attorney. "She suffered pain in that foot for years, favoring it constantly. Finally on a visit to another doctor for varicose veins three years after the accident, he noticed the pain in her foot and insisted that she take another X-ray. This time the fracture was obvious on the X-ray plate. A serious operation including bone removal was required to repair the foot. The discovery of the break wasn't until October, 1964, and she contacted me in November. We filed a malpractice suit against the original doctor and radiologist on November 30, 1964. Had this woman discovered the fracture just a few weeks later, she would have had no case. In fact, the insurance companies tried to claim that we had filed too late. I am convinced that the laws throughout the country should be changed to make the statute begin to run from the time of the patient's discovery of injury rather than its commission. Nothing less is fair to the patient."

Malpractice involves sharp philosophical conflicts between doctor, patient, malpractice attorney and our legal system. Sixty-three percent of physicians queried by *Medical Tribune* are convinced that malpractice suits are a threat to good medical procedures. An equal number of patients and attorneys are undoubtedly convinced that without the deterrent of malpractice suits, cautious medicine would suffer even more. Physicians believe that the increasingly vast awards are the handiwork of extravagant attorneys and sentimental juries. Attorneys have complained about a current "first cousin" campaign among doctors. Physicians are reportedly being asked not "to talk their colleagues into court" by making negative remarks about the treatment of a previous doctor. This is most often a patient's first hint that he is a malpractice victim.

Several attempts are in progress to soothe the most trying medicolegal ulcers. One of the "cures" is a panel of doctors and lawyers to screen malpractice cases beforehand, as has been set up in some communities in Nevada and New Jersey. Other remedies will be forthcoming in time, but none may ever reach the basic malpractice problem—doctor negligence and the deteriorating doctor-patient relationship that stimulates lawsuits.

Some medical error is unavoidable, but certain physicians and hospitals appear to be more malpractice-prone than others. Other physicians invite malpractice suits because of congenital inability to be frank with the patient. "Doctors too often try to conceal their mistakes from the patient," charges attorney Fuchsberg. "Patients inevitably find out about it later from another doctor, and are determined to bring suit for malpractice. It is not only the injury, but the fact that they have been deceived about it. If doctors said afterward, 'I made a mistake. Let's see how we can repair it,' I think there would be fewer malpractice suits."

The failure of human relations, says Dr. Charles B. Wheeler of the University of Kansas School of Medicine, "is the primary cause of malpractice suits." He explained that poor operative results account for 25 percent of suits; poor medical results for 20 percent; errors in diagnosis, 10 percent; foreign bodies left in surgery for 9 percent; alleged assault (treatment without permission) for 7 percent. One third of cases are settled out of court, one-fifth are dropped and approximately 40 percent actually go to trial. Whatever the action, he believes that if physicians would "keep the lines of communication open" with their patients, they could avoid many of the suits. (This human breakdown and subsequent lawsuits can be accelerated, says one California attorney, when a doctor attempts to force bill collection in a case which turned out less well than expected. Such collection attempts, he says, have provided him with some of his best malpractice cases.)

In the final analysis, malpractice suits can be restrained only by a more *humane* concern for the patient by the doctor, a concern that expresses itself in warmth, frankness and *good, mature medical care*. A medico-legal consultant for physicians studied one thousand malpractice cases and published his considered observations in *JAMA*. "There has been considerable publicity about the threats of malpractice facing the medical profession today," he stated. "Most of the emphasis has been on prevention of suits and on legal requirements for professional protection. Little has been said about the medical problems involved, except for the observation that gross errors do occur now and then. Is this the limit of true medical responsibility, or are there more subtle shortcomings which have not been sufficiently identified as yet?"

Those subtle shortcomings have occupied many of these pages. Examination of them, here and in the myriad other avenues available to the profession, will hopefully increase medical responsibility and decrease both malpractice and the patient's only present recourse—the lawsuits that follow.

Chapter XIX

Disciplining the Doctors:
A Conspiracy of Laxity

"We get lots of complaints from patients or their families about doctor incompetence, but there is nothing we can do about it," says the physician-secretary of the New York State Board of Medical Examiners. "Under the law, we grant licenses, and we discipline physicians for 'unprofessional conduct,' but we have no jurisdiction over the gross incompetence or gross negligence of a doctor. I have never heard of a doctor's negligence being involved in a disciplinary case."

George Bernard Shaw acerbicly referred to the medical profession as a conspiracy to hide its own mistakes. Today he might accurately have added that this conspiracy operates not only with the sanction but with the knowing aid of public law developed by the patient himself. The futility of a complaint by a patient who believes he has been wronged by a negligent doctor is testimony to the expertise with which medical incompetence is kept silent and unpunished, both by the secretive medical fraternity and the law itself.

It is part of an expert defense system established over the years by medicine against its natural enemy—the dissatisfied patient. While once the physician feared imprisonment, physical harm or exile for gross error, the modern doctor is immune to the complaints and pressures of society. Unless he breaks the law, is found "insane," becomes addicted to narcotics or commits sexual immorality with patients, his license to practice medicine is a lifelong contract with his state which permits him to practice ignorance, mayhem and impardonable blunder without legal reproach.

The otherwise effective Division of Professional Conduct of New York's Department of Education, which investigates physician behavior for possible disciplining, confirms its lack of police power over medical bungling. "We regularly receive complaints from the public about medical treatment," says a senior investigator of the division. "I remember one about a child that died from a routine tonsillectomy, and another patient who died from anesthesia in a minor toe-nail operation. Sometimes we look into these things, not from the points of view of medical negligence, over which we have no control, but to see if the doctor was drunk or a narcotics addict, which falls into our area.

"The doctor's medical competence is not under the state's jurisdiction once he's licensed," he continued. "Some of the calls come in to us from the state attorney general's office, and I guess they don't know or haven't the heart to tell these people that no one in the state government can help them. I advise patients with complaints to go to the county medical society and present their grievance, or to go to their own lawyer. The only recourse against a doctor in such a situation is a civil malpractice suit."

Surveys of states indicate that New York's laxity in granting official *Lebensraum* to the incompetent physician is part of a nationwide folly, with the singular exception of a recent historic change in the California law. Even those states (such as Texas, Oregon, California, New York, Massachusetts) which are fairly strict with physicians straying from the law—whether for income-tax evasion or lascivious conduct with a patient—have never had the legal ability to punish the ignorant, slothful or negligent doctor.

"Since I joined the Medical Board of Registration in 1958, we have never had a case of discipline against a doctor for incompetence," says the physician-secretary of the Commonwealth of Massachusetts. "Under our present law, we are not able to set ourselves up as a judge of professional treatment." The doctor's treatment of a patient, he pointed out, would only be legally pertinent if it involved misconduct such as fraud or offensive language or assault. In Massachusetts, as in virtually every state in the union, it is more dangerous for the doctor to slap a patient than to kill him.

A symbol of the strength of the medical "conspiracy" is that *other* health professionals in New York—dentists, nurses, veterinarians and pharmacists—can have their licenses revoked for *incompetence,* negligence or inefficiency. "We have taken action against a nurse who was no longer able to function properly," says a state spokesman. "We couldn't do that with a doctor and get away with it."

The bald refusal of medicine and government to police doctors guilty of gross incompetence is basic to the laxity of the profession and our laws. Even in the discipline of ethics and morality, many states have failed to exercise simple prudence to protect the public. State medical examiners, says Joseph Stetler, former general counsel of the AMA, are sometimes "too cautious" in handling discipline cases.

The underpublicized Truman report of the AMA forthrightly states the truth about this oft-whispered conspiracy: "We conclude from these studies that the present supervision of organized medicine over the ethical standards of doctors is not adequate to protect the public, or the good name of the profession." The AMA's Medical Discipline Committee has concurred. "All too seldom," they state, "are licensed physicians called to task by boards, societies, or colleagues."

Some states seem inherently incapable of discovering evil in physicians. From 1960 to 1963, New York disciplined 334 physicians and California chastised 203 for various ethical reasons, exclusive of incompetence. But physicians in many states, including giant Illinois, either have unblemished psyches, or more likely, the state and the medical fraternity are overzealous in safeguarding his feelings. The State of Illinois disciplined a total of three doctors during this period, and none *at all in three of the four years!*

Despite gaps in state enforcement, the record is strict when compared to the medical societies, typically nonchalant courts of the doctors' peers. Medicine jauntily carries an undeserved reputation as a "self-policed" profession. "I do not believe the AMA is sponsoring self-policing in the same way as the legal profession," Dr. Robert E. Shank, then an AMA committee chairman, testified before a Senate subcommittee hearing. "I know in my state I have seen examples of gross medical negligence go uncensored, and the victim could not even get an award in court from the damages resulting from negligence."

The published statistics of the AMA itself show a shocking indulgence, a tendency of local groups to shield rather than censure offending colleagues. That doctors scrupulously avoid "lowering the boom on their golfing partners," as one physician states it, is supported by a comment from a spokesman at the Division of Professional Conduct in New York. "Very rarely," he states, "does one doctor turn in a report against another doctor." Dr. O. J. Johnson, past president of the Michigan State Medical Society, would remove the camaraderie from the serious business of censuring guilty doctors: he would have "regional panels" made up of strange physicians judge violators rather than the sham jury of colleagues.

A board of censors member of a county medical society gets pointedly at the failure of doctors' self-policing. "We are afraid of the embarrassment and the anger that will result," he admits. "Also, I am a busy practicing physician, and I have no time for any real disciplinary hassle that might develop over a colleague's actions. I would have to spend weeks in court. If our group became a real action one, I'm afraid I would have to resign."

The disciplinary lists from 1960 through 1963, published in *JAMA,* show the result: amazing disparities between official state action and discipline by the medical societies. In New York in 1960, when the state government took action against 216 doctors, the Polly-annish medical societies punished *zero* doctors! In 1963 in California, the state took fifty-nine actions, the local medical societies two; in Oregon fifty-six, the medical groups four; in Texas thirty-four, the doctor organizations one; in Florida, the state fourteen, the doctors themselves zero. Against a total of 401 state actions that year, there were only eighty-two medical-society actions—*none at all in thirty states!*

The discrepancy perturbs the AMA's Judicial Council, who may be fearful that the profession's self-policing privileges may be withdrawn by exasperated patients, through the law. "It is understandable that the figures for state boards should be higher than those of state medical societies, because not all physicians are members of the state medical societies," they state with anxiety in *JAMA*. "However, the discrepancy in the data still appears to be too great."

A few successful lawsuits instituted by doctors forced outside the pale have left some medical societies trembling; however, state government action against a doctor makes medical societies virtually damage-proof. That it is possible is shown by the few intrepid state medical societies which account for most of the nation's disciplining. During 1963 the Massachusetts, Maryland and Nebraska medical societies were responsible for *over half of all the doctor expulsions and suspensions* in the country! Surely doctor chicanery and misconduct is not that geographically erratic.

Although totally oblivious of doctors whose carelessness and incompetence can kill, some state governments are effective policers of nonmedical indiscretions. New York is a prime example. Its disciplinary act for doctors lists causes for action: fraud and deceit, conviction of a felony, habitual drunkenness, drug addiction, "secret" methods of treatment, advertising, criminal abortion, fee-splitting rebates and "unprofessional" acts such as being drunk while treating a patient. The law does not include "gross negligence" or "medical incompetence," and other state laws are virtually identical.

When the state disciplines a physician, it is typically done in the protective semiconspiratorial atmosphere that cocoons doctor-to-doctor proceedings. The hearing is attended only by the physician involved, the state-appointed doctor panel and the attorneys. The public is kept effectively ignorant even if action is taken. A sparsely worded press release is issued, listing only the physician's name, address and the result: censure, suspension or license revocation. The listing is published in some medical-society journals and in obscure half-paragraph notices by a minority of newspapers.

In Texas, by unique ten-gallon contrast, the press are invited in; public pillory is the norm, a technique that state officials believe has a deterring effect. "The doctors hate the idea of having their dirty linen aired in public," an official of the Texas board has stated. For a public not privy to medical matters, the linen indeed seems soiled. "Accuse Three From Houston Area of Drug Addiction," blares one Texas headline.

As in some states, Texas authority over physicians has been increasing, but not to the point of controlling incompetence. Up until 1953 the state medical examiners could only have a license revoked by court action—a limiting statute still in force in many states. After 1953, however, the Texas board itself could act after a formal hearing. From *no* cases the year before, doctor disciplining rose to approximately thirty cases. California has a budget of over $500,000 for medical disciplining, which supports a staff of fifteen detectives who aggressively seek out leads to errant physicians.

Physicians who violate the law were discussed in detail by a senior investigator for New York's efficient Division of Professional Conduct. "The biggest problem we have with doctors is narcotics addiction. We must have five to ten cases a year in this state," he revealed. "After that, I would say it is income-tax evasion, then abortions. If we think there is enough evidence against the doctor, a private hearing is held before a three-man subcommittee of the Medical Grievance Committee—doctors appointed by the governor on recommendation of the medical societies. The doctor and his lawyer appear before them, and an assistant attorney general prosecutes for the state. The decision of the doctors—who are acting as state officials with immunity—is passed on to the State Board of Regents, who make the final decision."

The image of a physician enslaved to narcotics while ministering to patients is an unsettling one. Too often it is an accurate portrait, for it is estimated that approximately two thousand doctors now practicing are, or will become, narcotics addicts. The etiology of this unusual doctor disease is typical human weakness compounded by facile access to drugs.

"Sometimes the doctor gets involved in narcotics because of the pressure of his work, or for some physical disability," says a physician-member of New York's Medical Grievance Committee. "Rather than see another physician, he treats himself, and as the saying goes —has a fool for a patient, and a fool for a doctor. He may take Demerol to ease recurring headaches or other pains and then find that he can't continue without regular use. If he runs out of narcotics, he can order more on his federal narcotics form. Other times, he will write a false prescription in a patient's name and fill it himself in the drugstore."

The unearthing of the doctor-addict comes in several ways, says a state investigator. "The State Narcotics Control people make periodic inspection of pharmacists' narcotics registers, and look for any doctor who is ordering a suspiciously large amount. The pharmacist personally may have information on certain doctors. They also check hospitals, and the federal government, too, provides us with valuable leads. If the doctor can show that he has completely stopped taking narcotics, he might be put on probation. He would be allowed to continue in practice, but would have his privilege of prescribing narcotics taken away. He might be required to go to a psychiatrist for treatment, and would be spot-checked with the nalline test, which can tell us if he has really shaken the habit." (Incidentally, the doctor's patients are not informed that their doctor is an addict. The patient could only learn about it if he is astute enough to notice that his doctor never prescribes codeine, morphine, Demerol or other narcotic for pain.)

Patients and authorities in California appear to have a formidable doctor-addiction problem. Approximately *fifty cases* of doctor addiction are uncovered each year by diligent state authorities. Dr. William F. Quinn, a former member of the California Board of Medical Examiners, explains that all narcotics prescriptions must be filled out in triplicate, one of which the pharmacist sends to the State Bureau of Narcotic Enforcement, which maintains a file on each doctor in the state. If a physician's file "bulges suspiciously," Dr. Quinn has stated, it generally hurries an investigator into the area.

Several state authorities offer an optimistic sidelight: the cure rate for doctor-addicts is much higher than in the general population. California estimates that 92 percent of them are rehabilitated, usually by self-discipline that begins with the threat of license revocation. Tragically, of those who return to the habit, a majority have committed suicide.

Physicians stricken by mental illness present perhaps the thorniest dilemma (aside from medical incompetency) in the discipline of doctors. Several states suspend a physician's license if his illness is accompanied by a court commitment to a mental institution. But what of the ill doctor who voluntarily seeks out psychiatric treatment or admission to a mental hospital? How does society protect his rights and yet shield the patient from the by-product of a doctor's injured emotional balance? At present the doctor, but not the patient, is protected in many states. New York State contemplated temporarily suspending a doctor's license until he had recovered, but medical-society intervention successfully thwarted such sensible action. "The medical society sent a delegation of psychiatrists to the state and they testified that any action taken against a mentally ill doctor could prove to be 'traumatic.' After that the idea was dropped, and now we do nothing," a state spokesman reports.

The errant physician is especially well represented in the income-tax-evader ranks, and the states and the medical societies are considerably more understanding than Uncle Sam. Between twenty-five and thirty-five physicians are indicted for income-tax evasion each year, and almost all convicted. Most are fined, but five or six are jailed each year as a deterrent to the physician addicted to pocketing unrecorded $5 and $10 cash payments. Nationally, one in approximately sixty-five evaders are doctors, who of course represent a much smaller segment of the population—closer to one in 750. The federal government's attitude is often punitive in such cases, but state disciplinary groups tend to be lenient (short suspensions or just reprimands), while the medical societies generally look intently the other way.

Abortion is a consistent headache, and a melange of other doctor impieties—from drunkenness to insurance frauds—illustrates the full range of his human frailties. "One complaint that we almost never get about a medical doctor is immoral conduct with female patients. They seem to be scrupulous about that," reports a medical investigator. "We get the most immorality complaints, surprisingly enough, about dentists. It's not just in New York. I have had the same comment made to me by investigators from other states. Dentists seem to be the 'sexiest' of professionals. The only physicians that we receive immorality complaints about are psychiatrists, who rank next to the dentists. These are generally not from the female patients themselves, but from parents or relatives."

Doctors are not permitted to advertise, and serious violations of this are disciplined by some state governments. In one major scandal a group of plastic surgeons were advertising in wide-circulation movie and fan magazines under the "cover" of a publishing house. The ads offered free booklets on remolded breasts and reshaped noses, and the printed material was sent out with a cordial note from the ambitious surgeon. A half dozen physicians involved had their licenses suspended.

Certain unethical doctor traits have almost been accepted as inevitable, unpunishable transgressions. One common doctor flair has been the "kiting" of medical bills in liability cases to help the attorney impress the insurance company that the illness is severe. "The bigger the doctor's bills, the bigger the settlement," a trial attorney comments. This incessant tapping of insurance-company funds has resulted in a massive scandal in which legions of doctors are being charged with "fraud and deceit" in the practice of medicine.

"We have been investigating fifteen hundred doctors involved in these so-called 'ambulance-chasing' cases," states a New York investigator. "So far we have handed out disciplinary action to a hundred doctors, including taking away many doctors' licenses. It started in Brooklyn, and we are now working on Manhattan physicians. We also expect some cases to break upstate. The way the fraud works is that the physician files medical bills with the lawyer for treatment of injuries the patient doesn't have, and for medical visits that were never made. We have seen medical bills for twenty patient visits, and after questioning the patient, we learned that he went to the doctor only once after the accident. Almost all the cases involve car-injury suits. The fraud usually starts with a lawyer, who gets a GP or an internist involved. Sometimes a medical team of three men—a GP, an orthopedist and an X-ray man—work together in building up the bills.

"They list phony diagnoses such as synovitis [inflammation of the membranes of joints] to build up the claim. In one case the patient had eight stitches taken for a head cut, and the doctor submitted a bill for plastic surgery that was never done. One doctor actually gave his blank stationery to the lawyer and let him fill out any medical bills he wanted. We have had more than one case in which the patient never saw or heard of the doctor submitting the bill.

"What did they get out of it?" the investigator continues. "Well, no doctor got rich as a result. Sometimes, when the car insurance policy covered medical costs, they did receive all the money; sometimes they split with the lawyer; and sometimes I think that they made very little. The typical bill is between one hundred and ten dollars and one hundred and eighty-five dollars. For the large risk involved, it was really very petty crime."

The reflexes of some doctors when faced with a medical insurance policy is one of the sorriest behavior patterns of our time. The fact that the insurer is often the doctors' own plan, Blue Shield, has not stilled certain greedy physicians. The *New York State Journal of Medicine* has lamented those who undertake unnecessary procedures in order to collect insurance fees, or who fraudulently enter claims for medical service never rendered. "There is no question that [this] is being done," charged the editorial. "The only question lies in determining what to do about it—how to stop it."

The editorial, in a futile plea, hoped that it could be done by self-policing "within our own ranks." One ophthalmologist submitted *170* claims for the removal of foreign bodies from patients' corneas—foreign bodies he reportedly had both conjured up, then magically removed. One general practitioner ostensibly had a massive onslaught of 157 carbuncles, all of which he incised and drained. Actually they were less serious lesions which were not covered by the surgically oriented and generally inadequate (from the patient's viewpoint) Blue Shield plan.

In New York the Group Health Insurance plan found it necessary to submit fifteen complaints a week against physicians who often had contributed more bookkeeping imagination than needed medical service. In Oregon one errant physician found that the common practice of bilking Blue Shield can be a federal offense. The general practitioner had patients sign blank forms of the Oregon Physicians' Service (Blue Shield) in case they needed subsequent visits. Many never returned and the doctor filled out the forms with fictitious dates and treatments. Since the fraudulent claims and checks eventually traveled through the mail, the physician was convicted of federal mail fraud and given an eighteen-month suspended sentence.

Potential abuse of fees is indigenous to the medical tradition, for the doctor can ethically charge *whatever he wishes*. He is supposed to base it on such demi-metaphysical factors as *his evaluation of his own skill* and the patient's supposed ability to pay, a form of biologic blackmail. This latitude was created in the non-insured past when the "ethics" were partially based on charitable impulses. Although outdated, they are retained for the doctors' convenience, converting modern health insurance, especially major medical policies, into a succulent feast for the greedy medical gourmand.

"Let's get you well first, then we'll talk about money," some accomplished physicians answer to patients' crass money questions. Other patients even fail to ask, assuming the existence of some tight professional control of doctor exorbitance. The result can be, and has been, a surgeon's bill for $2000 for the repair of a broken bone, and vast bills to the estate of deceased persons. In the current lax medical environment, neither the medical societies nor the state have any control over these fees. Most county medical organizations, who are desperate to retain the wispy trifles remaining of the doctor's "money" repute, will, however, *mediate* fee conflicts in their grievance committees.

"We have no power over the doctor, who has the right to set his own fees and can charge as much as he wants," says the president of one county society in New York State. "Buying medical service is like buying anything else. If the patient goes to Tiffany's he doesn't expect to pay Woolworth prices. He knows he has to pay more for Martinson's coffee than for the A&P brand. It's the same with medicine. A doctor has the right to say, 'I charge so much,' and the patient can take it or leave it. It's up to the patient to accept or decline the doctor's fee. Unfortunately, many patients don't ask the fee, then they get socked with the bill." The spokesman had scrupulously avoided mentioning that physicians seldom offer fee information the way supermarkets and jewelers do, and that unlike prices in other businesses, the price of medical service may have no relation at all to "quality." In medicine, it is a sharper index of the doctor's office location, his ego and his business acumen.

The grievance committees of the county medical societies are the patient's only opportunity for arbitration of disputed fees. "We suggest a change of fee in about half the cases. Doctors usually abide by our decision, but they are still within their rights to charge what they want," one society president comments. What are the criteria for such fee decisions?

"I agree that it's a knotty problem," states the medical official. "It depends on the time the doctor puts in, the complexity of the procedure, the financial circumstances of the patient, and the reputation and training of the doctor. If a cardiologist makes a home consultation in a good section and charges a hundred and fifty dollars, it doesn't mean it's exorbitant. It's nothing but a house call, but if he is known to charge this rate for consultation, we probably wouldn't consider it unfair."

A member of the Board of Censors and Mediation of the Westchester (New York) County Medical Society, whose group hears some three dozen fee complaints a year, explains that the patient's complaint is put in writing, and that the doctor, but not the patient, is present at the committee meeting. Most complaints involve fees "somewhat higher" than patients anticipated, but occasionally the board receives cases involving exorbitance: one case involved a well-to-do patient whose doctor thought his "ability to pay" equaled a $5000 fee. An unusual overfee is the "punitive" bill, a case of pure doctor vengeance. "We have had a case of a physician who was so angered by a patient's behavior—that of going to another doctor —that he multiplied the bill by ten times as much," the Westchester physician recalls.

It may or may not pay the patient to vent his annoyance to a grievance committee: his success depends on the attitude of the particular group. The sixteen-doctor Wayne County (Detroit) Fee Mediation Committee is one that has boasted of its successes in arbitration. As in other cities, Blue Shield abuse by doctors is a recurring problem. A physician who had given a patient hospital care and assisted at the operation billed him $250 over and above the $133 allotted by Blue Shield. The $250 was broken down as follows: $100 over the Blue Shield allowance for hospital care, and $150 for assisting the surgeon. The committee found the extra $100 unjustified, and reduced the assistant's fee to $75.

Health insurance—the cornucopia of capital which beguiles the greedy doctor—is central to many elevated fees. The overcharging of insured patients, even by small amounts, has had a deleterious effect on the voluntary health insurance system. "While the amount of any individual case may be small, the large number of such cases represents a substantial [sum]," says Raymond F. Killion of the Health Insurance Council. In Texas an attorney reported to a meeting of the Federation of State Medical Boards that one insurance company has recovered more than $150,000 from physicians who had padded their bills.

Many grievance-committee complaints involve doctor abuse of

major medical insurance. Unknown to most patients, major medical policies do not blanketly cover the patient. They pay only what is "usual and customary," leaving the patient responsible for the rest. "We have made a deal with the insurance carriers to set the 'usual and customary fee' on a case but they must abide by our decision," explains a spokesman of the New York County Medical Society, which has one of the nation's thirty-five insurance review committees. "As an example, an orthopedist had charged an insured patient two thousand dollars for setting a broken arm. The customary fee is about two hundred and fifty dollars, but it turned out that it required a complex 'open reduction' of the arm, and that the patient had the most expensive room in the hospital with nurses around the clock. In addition, the orthopedist is a top man. We decided that a thousand dollars was a fair fee."

Superficially it would appear that the patient had saved $1000, a wishful interpretation of organized medicine's motivation. "The insurance company pays the doctor only a thousand dollars instead of the two thousand, but the patient still owes the doctor the thousand dollars," the doctor-spokesman underlined. "In our experience, about fifty percent of the doctors accept the fee the county society decides on as full payment. The other patients either pay the balance, or their physicians collect or sue them for the amount."

Grievance committees are by no means impartial boards to which patients can bring other complaints against physicians and expect them to be heard objectively. Medical societies tend to "see no evil" in a reasonable imitation of the insensate monkey. Fee disputes make up about 60 percent of patient complaints, the balance covering doctor treatment, availability, rudeness, inattention and incompetence. The off-hand disposition of such complaints is obvious from the comment of one society official. "Almost all of these complaints come from psychos," he states brusquely. If not a fee dispute, patient anger against a doctor expressed to a medical society is a voice thrown into an unheeding wind.

In areas *not affecting patients,* the profession demands strict conformity, backed by strict discipline. These areas are covered by the term "medical ethics," a seductive euphemism that bears little relationship to its philosophical connotation of morality, and may even be damaging to the health and care of patients. Medical "ethics" are actually a fastidious code of guild manners that binds one doctor-guildsman to another with propriety. Physicians' seminars discuss the convoluted but basically insignificant subject endlessly, as if their petty regulations were a medical Koran or ancient kabbala. When stripped of their mystique, many medical "ethics" are revealed as canons against patient-stealing and advertising; how to refer a patient correctly; whether a doctor's picture can appear in the newspaper; how to pay a covering physician; and such essentials as whether a lawn shingle may be lighted. As Dr. Herbert Ratner of Illinois has stated: "It may further help organized medicine to realize that what they pass off for medical ethics and professional morality is for the most part none other than medical etiquette and professional courtesy."

The ramifications of "ethical" medical minutiae would be humorous if they did not detract from the truly grave moral problems affecting doctors today, including human experimentation, iatrogenic death, insufficient availability and dedication, patient-punishing egotism, and life-failing medical ignorance and omission. Advertising and publicity are favorite "ethical" tussles within the profession, and medical societies vary in their masterful interpretations of these dilemmas. The Bergen County (New Jersey) society, for example, states one doctor's wife, permits the doctor to send out press releases on a three-week flying trip to California for a postgraduate conference, while the New York group insists it is "unethical."

The learned doctor quickly absorbs the essentials of "ethical" medical practice: that his name should not be displayed on too large a shingle; that it should be lighted (discreetly) only during office hours; that he can buy a "Compliments of . . ." church ad, but not in a doctor's "section" or "directory"; that he can chair a fund drive, and have his picture and name published in the paper as an "ethical" way to attract patients. (A few courageous newspapers confound such "ethical" ambitions by referring to all doctors in nonmedical context as plain "Mr.") The Judicial Council of the AMA has handed down some epochal "ethical" decisions, including one stating that a doctor handling an emergency case may have his name mentioned in the news story!

Part of the "ethical" code contains a scrupulously observed guild tradition—"professional courtesy." It is a compulsory bond to provide free medical care for other doctors and their families no matter how extensive or complex. Fees are only permitted if travel time is involved. Much of the doctor's unrealistic attitude toward medical fees probably relates to this ancient "ethic," for—like the physician who becomes aware of patient sensitivity only after he himself gets painfully ill—most doctors have never paid a dollar for medical care, let alone experienced the sometimes crushing blow of medical bills. One American physician had his child operated on by a famous surgeon in Canada, whose national border did not block "professional courtesy." The privilege is even stretched to include free laboratory tests whenever it can be arranged.

The only important exception is psychoanalytic care, a sore point that has brought psychiatric and general-medicine groups into sharp conflict. The psychiatrist often receives medical courtesy from his colleagues, but finds it economically difficult to reciprocate because of his limited number of patients and the extensive time given to each patient, up to five hours a week for a decade. One New

York psychiatrist complains that it is "irksome" for him to accept professional courtesy, since he is "usually unable to reciprocate."

Many traditional medical ethics are moralism-gone-astray—protecting the doctor's guild at the expense of the patient. "Ethical" admonishments against patient-stealing, solicitation of patients and the criticizing of colleagues sound noble, but they can inhibit the doctor from doing necessary work or from offering candid medical opinion about another doctor that might be lifesaving for the patient.

Section 5 of the AMA's "Principles of Medical Ethics" states that the doctor "should not solicit patients." The AMA Judicial Council has decreed that a medical group opening a new building may hold "open house" without violating its spirit. However, a pediatrician is prohibited from sending valuable immunization reminders to *all* his patients. He may send it to "regular" patients, but not to those referred to him by other doctors, even though these youngsters may be in dire need of immunization. Antiquated protocol may also inhibit a physician from calling up a sick patient he has not seen in some time, lest he be guilty of "soliciting" or "patient-stealing" in case the patient has a new doctor.

The ethical admonition against disparaging other doctors or their treatment is another concrete block on the conspiratorial medical wall of silence. It defends the incompetent physician and hides the case of gross negligence. When faced with errors perpetrated by a prior physician, doctors are expert in not revealing the truth to patients. The method includes "not raising his eyebrows," as one physician states it, when faced with glaring evidence of another doctor's mistake. Medical ethics dictate that the doctor who made the mistake be informed, not the patient!

The distorted concept makes it "unethical" for a patient's own doctor to warn him that another physician he intends to use is a known incompetent. One doctor who was troubled that a patient intended to go to a surgeon noted for his "poor work" sought ethical advice on the matter. He was told that all he could do was offer substitute physicians, but that he could not criticize the patient's choice. "We know who the incompetent physicians are in our communities," says a Westchester (New York) internist, "but there is nothing we can do or say about it."

Patient-stealing is a common ethical complaint of one physician against another that serves the professional code but may be injurious to the patient and weaken his free choice of doctors. Typically, the complaint involves a patient referred from one doctor to another who has not been referred back to the original doctor, a serious charge that is soberly heard by the Board of Censors at medical societies. One Utah physician who is an internist in a group practice writes a medical publication that he "often find[s] it difficult to get referred patients to go back to their local GP's," because they like his care. His solution to maintaining the "ethics" of the situation: to charge them a higher fee to get rid of them!

Medical discipline forces the doctor to "return" referred patient to either an incompetent doctor or to a competent physician who lacks the specific training needed. It may be medically *de rigueur,* but it is shockingly "unethical" from a public viewpoint. In a typical situation described in a recent symposium, a patient was sent by the family physician to a cardiologist for a consultation. After making his diagnosis, the cardiologist realized that the case required care the family physician could not properly give—the impeccable handling of dangerous drugs such as digitalis and anticoagulants, therapies capable of creating digitalis toxicity and hemorrhage that might be more deadly than the cardiac condition. The "ethical" dilemma was: must he, as a skilled cardiologist, insist on handling the case himself for the safety of the patient, or must he return the sick patient to the GP?

According to an authoritative opinion the cardiologist is ethically *required to return the cardiac case to the GP.* He may call the doctor and hint: "Administering these drugs is a very technical matter. Perhaps you'd like me to take care of it?" If the family physician says "No," he must not only return the patient, but *must do nothing to let the patient know that the family doctor cannot, in his opinion, properly handle the case!* The "ethics" of the medical guild are served, but the patient may die as witness to its power.

It is these parapets of doctor-guild protection that the community will have to scale to bring him under proper disciplinary control. The doctor operates without supervision or auditing, within the sanctity of a degree and a license that may be a generation or more old. His private office embraces a multitude of secrets about his daily medical conduct. His patterns of work, his omissions, errors, negligence, ignorance and short cuts are known only to him, and he may not have either the intellectual capacity or integrity to see that his concept of medical practice is limited, perhaps even distorted.

Our medical disciplinary system is unconcerned about his actual practice of medicine. No one—patient, law or organized medicine—has at the present time the prerogative of overseeing or curtailing the doctor's work. Once granted the state's license to practice, he may do whatever his unknowing, trusting patients will permit him to. Unquestionably, no professional needs closer control and supervision than the Doctor of Medicine; no one receives it less.

"There is no question in my mind that the practice of medicine should be surveyed and audited," states prominent New York surgeon Dr. Samuel Standard. "Usually we think of quality control in terms of hospitals, but ninety percent of our care is administered by doctors in their office. That's where we should be sure to survey medical care. A physician may be in practice for forty years, and no one has ever looked over his shoulder to see what he is doing. When I testified recently before a Senate committee, I asked that we survey the individual doctor and the medical care he is dispensing in his office. Senator Anderson asked if that wasn't a touchy subject. I answered 'Yes,' but it is one that should be touched."

The laxity of control of the American physician and the care he administers has its origin, as we have viewed, in medical school. The Medical College Admission Test (MCAT), used to help select medical students, is the first failure of control, a predictive one. The MCAT scores of the graduating classes of twelve medical schools have been crosschecked against their academic class standings, with "variable to poor" results, according to Dr. Osler L. Peterson of Harvard Medical School.

Having been chosen somewhat arbitrarily, the student is challenged with a year or two of formal sciences, then virtually presented an M.D. without substantial further evidence of skill. The system seldom tightens its academic vise sufficiently to create real attrition, and some 92 to 93 percent of all students receive their medical degrees. During schooling, approximately half the students take a national examination honored by most states, the multiple-choice "National Boards." They take the exam in the second and fourth years, and receive their license to practice after a fifth-year examination when their internship is complete. The remainder, and the 12 percent who fail the "National Boards," take their state examinations to receive their coveted license to practice medicine. Are these significant steeplechases *similar to the rigorous state "bar" exams for law graduates?*

Quite the contrary, explains a member of the New York State Board of Medical Examiners, who helps create the examination according to state requirements. "Almost no graduate of an American medical college fails the licensing test, and the few that do generally pass it the next time," he points out. (98.3 percent pass the state licensing examinations the first time.) "The test is created from a pool of multiple-choice questions from the exams given by the National Board of Medical Examiners, which cover material they learned at medical school. The science questions have been pretested on second-year students. Since the license applicants have been away from it for a few years, I try to pick those questions that are less technical, and have more clinical orientation." This examiner adds that the more demanding essay questions have been eliminated (just as the bedside test has been eliminated by the National Boards), and there is no oral examination, no personal interview, nor is proof of ability to diagnose and treat sick patients required by the licensing law.

What guarantee of doctor proficiency is there in such a licensing exam? "The way it is presently set up there is no point in the licensing exam at all for American graduates," the doctor-examiner contends. "A lengthy oral examination takes time and costs money, but I believe that is the only way to test an applicant."

(The most stringent licensing requirements are set up for foreign doctors, who must first pass an ECFMG—Educational Council for Foreign Medical Graduates—examination before taking the states' license examinations. In addition, some states require between one and four years of American hospital training. While the American failure rate is low, the foreign graduates have a high attrition of almost one-third failure.)

Except for foreign graduates, the licensing function, as it now exists, is merely to confirm the medical school's grades, and *not* to further weed out the unsatisfactory medical material. This laxity of premature acceptance permeates the profession. Neither internship nor residency training has any attrition rate or medical hurdles that must be surmounted. Only board certification represents any test of medical acumen, and only one third of physicians have been awarded such certificates. It should prompt consternation to view how easily a practically inept young physician can walk upright through this wide medical mesh.

"We're going to have to come to grips with an adequate regulatory mechanism for doctors," says Dr. David M. Spain, a state medical examiner himself. "The knowledge explosion is so great, and the techniques of medicine so much more precise, and more dangerous, that more knowledge is an essential. It is not easier, but more difficult to practice medicine today than a generation or two ago." Dr. Robert E. Healy of Westchester County, New York, an official of his county medical society, concurs. "We will have to develop a system to take care of the poor doctor, especially as we get more government, union, and third-party involvement in medicine, and more criteria with which to measure the doctor."

How has medicine reacted to suggestions that the quality of medical effort be checked and discipline strengthened? Thus far the only acceptable discipline has been in hospitals, operating through staff appointments and tissue committees. Most physicians have not fought this, for such proceedings are secret, intraprofessional and nonlegal. An unwanted doctor can always find another, if less prestigious, hospital with which to affiliate if he is refused a staff position or has had it withdrawn. *This system is absolutely no protection against gross negligence or ignorance.*

The near-hysterical response to Dr. Ray E. Trussell's quality audit of care in New York hospitals is a pregnant inkling of medicine's nightmarish fear of being closely, perhaps publicly, audited after a glorious era of anarchic liberty. Speaking to his antagonists at the New York County Medical Society meeting, Dr. Trussell described the profession's immature reactions to his quality audit. "First—are those physicians who curse my secretaries in the Department of Hospitals over the telephone," he began. "I can only ask of such distinguished critics that they talk to me directly. Second —are the attacks issued by County Medical Society leaders before receiving the report. The public is indeed fortunate to have a medical profession with certain members who are so scientifically proficient that they can critique a 312-page document without reading it. One doctor, indirectly, has even attacked my wife, little realizing that we both feel I should not be Commissioner of Hospitals."

After the initial doctor histrionics had subsided, the New York County Medical Society, in typical reactive fashion, decided to enter the medical-audit field itself. It is surveying the quality of surgical care in two common operations in co-operation with Blue Cross. The society's journal, *New York Medicine*, has possibly petrified its members by since predicting that county societies may one day have grievance committees to hear complaints about the quality of a doctor's care, as well as his fees!

The feasibility of medical-quality checks, whether Dr. Peterson's North Carolina study, hospital audits such as the Trussell reports or the work of the CPHA group in Ann Arbor, Michigan, has been well demonstrated. The present laxity of doctor control can be rectified in several suggested ways, one of which is the *periodic "over the shoulder" survey of every private doctor while he is practicing*.

Compulsory continuing education of the doctor is another idea receiving serious consideration. Dr. Donald C. Walker, secretary of the New York State Board of Medical Examiners, confirms that there have been "informal talks" at the state level about this idea, and doctor re-examination, but that implementation is a "long way away." Suggestions for relicensing exams meet with violent opposition from physicians who can barely contemplate the thought of the loss of their license. "To have such a miserable harassment forced on us is an intolerable affront," protests an Ohio physician in the letters column of a medical periodical.

Some doctors, such as Dr. Healy, do believe there should be "some compulsion" in maintaining proficiency. "I think doctors should be required to attend hospital conferences, and if a test were limited to my field—internal medicine," he says, "I would be willing to re-establish my American Board of Internal Medicine certificate when necessary." The possibility of the ultimate check on incompetence: the legal inspection and grading of a doctor's work and records, *both in his office and in the hospital*, raises a specter of fear among physicians not unlike that which some subjects reportedly experience under hallucinogenic influences.

Both the necessity and practicality of checking on doctors are stressed by Dr. Osler Peterson of Harvard Medical School. He calls the "continued existence of unsatisfactory practice intolerable," demanding that it be "prevented or corrected." Using the pages of the *New England Journal of Medicine,* he makes a plea: "It is possible that the need for studies of the quality of medical care is greater in the United States than in other countries, where organization is different and medical responsibility is more compartmentalized. Studies of the quality of medical care can help identify where and under what circumstances problems exist."

Quality control of medicine has an honorable history that includes Florence Nightingale's simple statistic that recruits in the Knightsbridge barracks had a mortality rate five times as high as the population in surrounding Kensington borough. Dr. Louis Lasagna relates an early French contribution to quality survey of a medical procedure —that of bloodletting. Dr. P. C. A. Louis suggested the then-revolutionary idea of counting who gets well and who does not. Louis studied the effects of "bleeding" purges on seventy-eight cases of pneumonia, twenty-three inflammations of the throat and thirty-three cases of erysipelas (acute streptococcus infection). When he found no difference in the death rates between those bled and those not, it signaled the decline and subsequent demise of bloodletting. Contemporary quality studies, such as Dr. Trussell's in New York, focuses more on "cases," attempting to evaluate the incidence of "good" and "poor" treatment.

There has been no *legal, compulsory* investigation of doctor quality as yet, although the poignant words "gross incompetence" or "gross negligence" are *technically* in the disciplinary statutes of eighteen states. In the wake of the Trussell reports, New York has passed a law to permit the State Department of Health to conduct medical audits, but the statute is unused. We are still almost totally immersed in an uncontrolled medical anarchy in which medical misadventures occur without any reverberations from organized medicine, the doctor's colleagues or the law. They can also take place without *any* effects on the doctor's practice, and without leading to any change in his future method of operation.

The nation's first meaningful legislation against laxity has just become law in California, with watchful import for the future. California's Senate Fact-finding Committee on Public Health and Safety, chaired by Senator Walter W. Stiern, issued a report that stated the frustrating problem succinctly: "Neither the Board of Medical Examiners nor any other agency of government has authority to restrict the right to practice medicine of physicians who engage in unethical medical pactices or whose conduct amounts to gross negligence or gross incompetence, no matter how harmful to patients the physician's conduct may be. Patients can bring malpractice actions against such physicians, but that does not affect the physician's right to practice medicine."

As patients have learned, doctor incompetence comes in a multitude of invidious forms, some of which the California committee defines: "Failing to call in a consultant when such a procedure is needed, performing operations for which the physician's training is inadequate when qualified physicians are available, performing unnecessary operations, failing to carry out adequate diagnostic procedures prior to treatment or surgery, prescribing unnecessary or incorrect medication, failing to keep abreast of advances in medicine, fee-splitting, overcharging, and ordering excessive hospitalization."

Anticipating medicine's shrill protestations to the effect that it already exerts doctor discipline, the fact-finding report dismisses medical-society control as too little and too timid. "Expulsion, the most severe penalty which the society can invoke, need not affect the physician's practice. Moreover, social and economic pressures, fear of lawsuits, and the difficulty of obtaining evidence may inhibit a society from taking action except under extreme circumstances," states the California report.

The other supposed medical self-control, the hospital, is shown to be riddled with inadequacies and escape sanctuaries for the incompetent physician. "Neither law nor regulation sets standards for hospital medical staff organization," the report points out, making five critical comments: 1) There are no legal standards or regulations for medical staff organizations; 2) there is no legal supervision or review of surgery and medical care of patients in the hospital; 3) the Joint Commission on Accreditation certifies only half the hospitals in the state, and there is no legal requirement that a hospital must seek accreditation; 4) professionally incompetent doctors may work mostly in their offices rather than at the hospital; 5) if a physician loses his staff privilege at one hospital, he can continue to work in other hospitals.

California's trenchant Fact-finding Committee report has led to the enactment of Senate Bills No. 400, 403 and 405 and to a revolutionary concept in medical discipline. As of September, 1965, five official district review committees, each composed of five doctors appointed by the governor (and paid per diem), may hear cases of medical "gross incompetence" and "gross negligence." The committees are now able to discipline a doctor-offender with the full power of the law, including the ability to recommend revocation of his license.

The California law has also established new hospital discipline that requires the hospital to organize a formal medical staff, to restrict that staff to men "competent in their respective fields," and to hold periodic meetings to review their clinical experience. It also prohibits fee-splitting "under any guise whatsoever." Any member of the new district review committees, or a doctor he delegates, may inspect a hospital to see if it conforms to the new law.

These California committees, although perhaps overladen with doctor panelists, may become a model for national action against medical complacency and incompetence. The necessity for doctor regulation is not seriously debatable; the controversy should restrict itself to method. The profession has shown itself unwilling to police itself, and cynically efficient thus far in keeping the law from performing the job they themselves swore to undertake. It requires little prophetic ability to predict that this ingeniously contrived imbalance and its offspring—the conspiracy of medical laxity—will not be a permanent one.

Part VI *Conclusion*

Chapter XX

Which Way Caduceus?:
A Scheme for Tomorrow

It has become patently clear that by and large the contemporary American physician is not sufficiently equipped—scientifically, intellectually or humanely—for the challenges now being presented to him. Neither is the medical milieu in which he is trained and generally works conducive to stimulating his potential. The necessity for change, truly significant change, is apparent and urgent.

Most suggestions for change are glib socio-economic master visions parodying the propaganda on which they rest. The liberal-oriented mind has adapted the simplistic view that massive government intervention, even the ultimate, so-called socialized medicine, is the elixir for our time. The eighteenth-century rationale of organized medicine is equally dogged in its determination that the guild-maintained private medical practice should not be impeded by external regulation.

Both advocates have neglected the essential problem. The quality of medical care resides basically in two areas: the medical and philosophical—not economic or political—environment which society creates for the doctor, and the physician himself. Creating a more workable scheme for American medicine requires both an internally altered physician and an external environment unfettered by its current narrow guild interests, its consuming compulsion for medical secrecy, and its undeserved complacency.

Society can (and should) help pay for medicine with a stroke of the Presidential pen. The search for excellence in the doctor, however, is considerably more trying. The primary requirement for change is to alter the "man" within this contemporary physician. The traditional healer was constantly aware of his role as sage and comforter, whether as an Indian shaman with buffalo horn and incantation or as an early-twentieth-century American physician exhibiting a relatively superior education and comforting demeanor, and often ministering closely at the patient's bedside, much as did the clergy.

Today's physician feels liberated from much of this by his science. He marvels more at the wonders of artery grafts than he does at the miracle of birth or the enigma of why man dies when the species' life (apparently still three score and ten) has run its course despite all of medicine's frenetic attempts. As a scientist-technician-business-man he feels little spiritual authority, and exercises less in his practice. Yet to the patient the doctor's lack of moral stature is one of the erosive faults in medical care.

The patient has traditionally, and now futilely, insisted that his physician be a superior being, in learning, dedication and altruism. Why else should he allow another mortal to tamper so seriously with his body and submit himself so trustingly to his remedies? The contemporary physician annoys us because he is so much a part of this civilization: materialistic, hurried and uncontemplative. Yet the patient offers himself, the failure of medical "priestliness" notwithstanding. But the engagement often troubles the patient deeply, and he is insecure with his health in such too-mortal, even uncaring hands.

The return to a "spiritual" medical orientation is essential and should be accomplished without injuring our accumulated medical science, its present implementation or its growth. Patients desire the opportunity to be cared for by a more altruistic healer. No responsible community objects to the physician's legitimate desire for reasonable affluence and comfort. What has become objectionable to much of society is his often near-demonic compulsion to intrude his financial method and his concern for personal convenience and prerogatives into his medical activity.

Rather than assume that his rewards will be sufficient, or better, as has traditionally been true, the contemporary doctor has too often structured his professional activity, his mind and his energies to ensure those rewards. No reasonable plan for tomorrow's medicine can succeed until the doctor's concentration has been refocused— back onto his patients.

A beginning is possible through a new perspective toward the choosing and training of young physicians of higher motivation. The corruption of youthful motive by which many students, as we have seen, make a choice of medicine for materialistic reasons is tragic. The Peace Corps and other altruistic endeavors attract thousands of young men and women. Medical missionaries abroad devote their energies unstintingly to healing. Relatively lower paid medical-university careers attract some men of caliber, without particular hope for great material reward. Should the domestic practice of medicine be less of a magnet for those who seek to serve? Is caring for the health needs of an American family in a middle-class suburb any less anointed or less demanding a task than serving the under-developed of the world?

The creation of such an idealized young professional should not be a sophomoric exercise in which every emerging physician is expected to be fully dedicated to healing, nor one in which we will be shocked to learn that many of its members share our contemporary foibles. But with higher philosophical goals, calling for a doctor more analogous to the clergy, we should anticipate a higher percentage of self-sacrifice among its members.

Altering the physician into that image requires creative, constructive action, and several suggestions have already been proffered. The fact that only 4 percent of our baccalaureates even apply for medical training and that they represent a distorted sample of available youth has been demonstrated by Dr. Edwin F. Rosinski of the Medical College of Virginia. To attract a broader, more satisfactory sample of young men to medicine requires sufficient medical-school openings: the existence of perhaps 150 medical universities instead of the current 87, and the immediate enlargement of present medical-school enrollment by 15 percent, a program recently endorsed by a prominent California medical educator. Building the institutions, either under private auspices or by state governments with federal aid, requires merely the impetus of public concern, for the sums involved are relatively small.

Having provided an opportunity for twenty thousand medical-school freshmen a year, how is one to pull them away from physics, the arts, the clergy, advertising and business? How is one to tap the dedicated, the poor, the extremely bright? The answer has already been hinted at broadly: *a free tuition program for all* medical students, with berths open by nationwide competitive examination. If bulwarked with subsistence allowance, much as we provided for GI's, a quiet revolution in medical-school selection and attitude would ensue. At prohibitive cost? Tuition fees for every present medical student totals only $32,000,000 a year, a pittance that equals only 10 percent of our present federal contribution to medical colleges.

Such a scheme would shatter the strangling chain of personal financial investment in medical education which the young doctor often seeks to repay more than amply. It would also erase financial and social inequity in selection, attracting many who would not otherwise have considered medicine. It offers a gift from society that should be repaid in dedication and by a wider spectrum of intellect and outlook in the next generation of physicians.

(It should be borne in mind that any such reform of selection and tuition, with the anticipated near-doubling of the number of medical students, is unlikely until the AMA is *relieved* of its present quasi-official function as an "approver" of medical schools. In many states, medical licensing requires graduation from schools with the AMA imprimatur; the medical guild thus enjoys subtle control over such vital issues as doctor supply. The services of the AMA are not needed for such approval. The other approval agency, the AAMC—Association of American Medical Colleges—and the states themselves, are perfectly capable.)

A broader, classless choice of young men should have its salutary effect on doctor humanism. It would be negated, however, if the candidates were educated under the current medical-school curriculum. The importance of humane learning has too long been dismissed by medical curriculum makers. "We assume that young men entering medical school have been well-formed as people and have a background in the humanities," a medical-school dean naïvely commented recently. This neglect of the humanities, medical history, patient attitudes and philosophy has already been indicted by many medical educators, including Dr. Herbert Ratner of Loyola University and Dr. Frederic Robbins of Western Reserve.

In his lecture at an AMA convention, Dr. Dickinson W. Richards, emeritus professor of medicine at Columbia's College of Physicians and Surgeons, reminded his audience that young physicians should be taught as good humanists, a term meant to encompass "the reasonable balance of life . . . discovered in the early Greeks," the "vivid interest in all sides of life," much as engaged in by Benjamin Franklin, or the "responsiveness to all human passions," as evidenced by Shakespeare or Goethe.

It is obviously time that we infused such an enriching education of the humanities (not the pale substitute of psychology or psychiatry) into the medical schools by setting up departments to teach humanities and medical history, with responsibility for at least 10 percent of the student's time. Such a "faculty of healing" could stimulate today's unknowing doctor in the problems of patients, in the philosophy and past of healing, in the true role of the physician, and the mysteries of more-than-anatomy. This scholarly introduction to humane medicine might well instill a lifelong interest in the subject, making vestigial the medical practice that is physician- rather than patient-oriented, both physically and psychologically.

Any viable plan for change must also include radical therapy of the *physician as a clinician*. We have seen that in the *schema medica* of today, the doctor's clinical education has been criticized as often impoverished, his clinical thoroughness as excessively spotty, his desire for lifelong maintenance of knowledge and skills as less than noteworthy, and the extent of necessary medical supervision over him as virtually nil.

In medical college, considerably more time and ingenuity must be devoted to clinical medicine, the patient's concern, rather than to abstract medicine, the nourishing food of researchers. (Students planning to practice medicine, it has previously been suggested, should train under a curriculum separate from those seeking to do medical research.) The current emphasis is on the "basic" sciences rather than on clinical medicine, an educational theory that such instruction will virtually eliminate gross scientific error in healing. The modern doctor's common avoidance of applied scientific technique—from common tonsil removal to general diagnostic neglect —indicates the failure of that theory. As Dr. David Seegal of Columbia College of Physicians and Surgeons points out, clinical training seldom includes even *one* well supervised, graded physical examination of a patient during the four years of medical school.

Other critics intelligently insist that a reformed medical education for practicing physicians should involve less time on biochemistry and genetics, and more effort on applied science and pharmacology, clinical medicine from arthritis to herpes zoster. The men who teach, Dr. John Knowles of Massachusetts General Hospital and Harvard Medical School has reminded us, must be physician-clinicians of proven skill, not today's esoteric researchers. Initial attempts at reform, such as Albert Einstein College of Medicine's recent 10 percent reduction in basic-science curriculum, are noteworthy, but can only be meaningful if a true clinical reorientation follows swiftly in their path.

The concentration on clinical medicine—the diagnosis and treatment of patients—should also have a salutary effect on bringing the practicing doctor back into clinical research, in observing and recording, then suggesting how particular treatments for common conditions such as ulcers, arthritis, heart conditions, diabetes, etc., can be improved. Relinquishing that responsibility completely to grant-supported universities is a current waste of first-line medical personnel. A proper scheme for tomorrow would underwrite the work of practicing doctors who wish to research the apparently mundane but widespread human ailments they see in daily practice.

Clinical skills of young physicians receive an early trial in internship and residency, programs whose nonstandardization explains why mature practicing physicians are often unable to exhibit routine medical skills. (Observers are shocked by such failures as the inability to analyze the sputum of pneumonia victims, as already noted by medical-school faculty members.)

We have seen how in our oft-irrational system of medicine the thin white line of internes and residents, present in only one in every five hospitals, is made up according to their indicated skills—the generally inferior young practitioners being relegated to hospitals with poor teaching programs, which have passed through the loose AMA approval screen. In such a weak medical environment, the trainee's poor clinical habits can be hardened by time and failure of instruction. Sense can only be brought to clinical training of internes and residents by radical change—the creation of a *comprehensive, standardized course of study with rigorous examinations* (and eliminations) at various stages of interne and specialist training, and the more intelligent distribution of trainees where they are now needed.

We have witnessed incisive physician criticism of doctors' poor attempts to "keep up" with medical knowledge. Without such continual postgraduate education, the question of clinical competence becomes academic, in the most narrow sense. "Undergraduates are students for four years. Postgraduate physicians are students for forty years," the recently deceased Dr. Samuel A. Levine of Harvard Medical School reminded us, expressing virtual disbelief at the little attention paid by the research-minded medical establishment to the question of improving the average practitioner's clinical efficiency.

"The health of our society would profit greatly if nothing new were discovered for a while and more of those millions were spent in teaching physicians what is already known," Dr. Levine has stated. "It is not suggested that research should be stopped or decreased, but that greater emphasis be placed on better, and more widespread teaching of the diagnosis, prognosis, and treatment of disease in the light of present knowledge."

The change exultantly called for by Dr. Levine and others is a continuing medical education for all doctors of a higher dimension than present feeble attempts at "keeping up." An effective program must be well financed, expertly designed for practical use and taught by expert clinicians. Most vital, *compulsory lifelong attendance and satisfactory academic performance* should be extracted from all doctors.

If quality clinical performance is to be expected from the bulk of physicians, their sacred "freedom" from supervision must be drastically altered. Society has apparently erred in permitting physicians to establish their own professional checks on their colleagues' competence, a responsibility that has been met with near-cynical evasion. Under today's system of potential progressive incompetence resulting from failure of supervision, the inadequate medical student becomes the poor interne, evolves as an unskilled resident, maturing as the incompetent practicing physician.

Not only is the inadequate doctor not screened out by the profession, but once in private practice, all physicians are left to their own *unseen, unsupervised, unchecked* devices. Should he presume (as he often does) that his own ready mixture of "science" and "art" is truly medicine, the doctor can apply this makeshift poultice to patients *ad infinitum* without inspection or recourse from his profession or the state. Who knows what quality of tests, diagnostic practices, remedies and counsel a particular physician is proffering in the privacy of his medical offices, and whether it bears significant resemblance to intelligent, scientific medical practice?

The doctor of today has only been seriously challenged academically at two points in his career, and one of these is quite voluntary: (1) he must pass his basic-science courses in the first two years of medical school, and (2) he may seek to pass his "boards" *if* he seeks specialist certification, although—incredibly— it is not now necessary to his functioning as a specialist. The credential most familiar to laymen, the doctor's state license to practice medicine and surgery, is a professional near-joke. This generally multiple-choice charade is less trying than examinations given to medical students, a shocking truth attested to by students and state medical examiners. Present state licensing examinations are pegged to the minimum level of student competence, and designed so that virtually all physicians pass on their first test attempt.

The present permissiveness should be curtailed. The American patient deserves a more supervised medical environment: stringent licensing examinations (not multiple-choice!) that truly evaluate clinical skill and would cause attrition in increased medical ranks; exacting clinical tests of diagnostic and therapeutic ability at the completion of internship—exams whose failure should mean repeating the year's experience; and periodic examinations during hospital residency training to eliminate poorer specialist trainees. The present policy of actively "covering" for inadequate trainees must be repudiated. Similarly, society should insist that the physician who holds himself out as a "specialist" has already passed his professional "boards"—exams which are apparently now quite arbitrary and inconclusive.

For patient protection, the profession might consider regularly and traumatically separating 20 percent or more of their colleagues from medicine at various stages of training—the first year of medical school to twenty years after graduation. Rather than assume, for example, that the practitioner of medicine has maintained his academic proficiency, society should insist that practicing physicians be required to submit to relicensing examinations, perhaps every five years.

Dr. Ray Trussell of Columbia University School of Public Health and Administrative Medicine has demonstrated the feasibility of auditing the quality of doctor's surgical and medical care in the hospital setting. Dr. Osler Peterson of Harvard has demonstrated that it is equally possible to survey the quality of medicine dispensed by the private doctor in his office. The anomaly of present medical "control" is that such obviously necessary audits—forceful intrusions into the guarded privacy of the medical structure—are now the exception rather than the rule.

To look over the shoulder of the doctor wherever he practices, *especially in the sacrosanct confines of his private office,* would be an essential change in the method of tomorrow's medicine. In suggesting such a course, Dr. Samuel Standard of New York startled a congressional committee but helped stimulate an essential debate. Little reform can be accomplished until the benefits of medical knowledge can be brought to the patient with greater certainty—assurance that can only be provided by checking the doctor's day-to-day efforts.

The predominant sociological characteristic of American medicine is its chaos. Nowhere is it as pronounced as in the doctor's office, whose occupant often has only a peripheral connection to much of his profession through licensing, county medical organizations and guild customs. Because his scientific connection to medicine may be tenuous and haphazard, any mature scheme for tomorrow must include a medical arm to *ensure* that the physician examines his patients properly for cancer; that he uses modern heart diagnostic techniques; that he does not rely on outdated diabetes tests; that he actively manages patients with chronic illness; that he is not an iatrogenic carrier; that he does not carelessly prescribe potentially destructive drugs for minor ailments; that he reads essential medical journals; that he is trained to use (and owns) essential tools such as a proctoscope or refers his patients to the appropriate subspecialist; that he supervises full immunization for all his patients. Training, testing, informing and supervising the practicing physician—specialist or general practitioner—is properly the prime concern of a pragmatic medicine of tomorrow.

Surveyors should not only check individual-doctor proficiency, but sample nationally the state of diagnosis and therapy, both generally and of particular ailments. Doctors may at first feel that the intrusion is restrictive, but its control of competence, and the stimulus of bringing proven techniques into greater use in daily practice, should prove invaluable to the profession and the patient.

No modern scheme could hope to extricate medicine from its chaos without a well-ordered plan to handle medical emergencies, neglect of which has become patently obvious. Physician unavailability at odd hours and on weekends has been a goad in developing doctor-patient antagonism—and risking life needlessly. That symbol of physician indifference, the doctor's midweek day off, should be abolished or, at the very least, intelligently staggered so that only one fifth of the doctors in a particular community will be luxuriating at one time. The irresponsibility of a virtually "doctorless Wednesday" in an entire town need not be elaborated on.

The contemporary doctorless weekend should also be a vestige of a once-systemless medicine. A percentage of all physicians could maintain office hours on Saturday and Sunday on a rotating schedule. Similarly, assigning certain physicians in each community to evening call for emergencies would regain medical order at little hardship to any individual doctor. In the re-education of the American physician, it is hoped that the positive social and medical value of many house calls will be stressed. The doctor-patient relationship has also been a victim of anarchic medicine; in the re-establishment of order, it is possible that compassion and friendliness will improve as a natural by-product.

Doctor abdication of much emergency and after-hours coverage has pushed the patient to the hospital emergency room, whose medical nonstandardization has outraged such critics as Dr. Robert H. Kennedy of the American College of Surgeons. Complex reform, as we have already noted, is essential—especially the requirement that all hospitals establish and maintain emergency rooms with physicians on the premises twenty-four hours a day. The present system of a hospital volunteering or *refusing* to supply ambulance service for emergencies is an irrationality that should be corrected. Building superior emergency facilities without ambulances (such as Cornell Medical Center in New York) and maintaining inadequate emergency rooms with ambulance service is a chilling hallmark of contemporary medicine that calls for radical modification.

The hospital audits conducted by Dr. Trussell in New York City were greeted with frenzied outrage by the New York County Medical Society. Dr. Trussell has related that individual doctors even phoned to insult his secretaries. Such histrionics can hardly alter the essential value of hospital audits by a responsible medical agency, hopefully a group with as little hesitancy in publishing detrimental information as the courageous Columbia investigators. Tissue committees and mortality conferences run by the hospitals themselves have too often proved to be inadequate controls over medical and surgical care in our hospitals. Witness is offered by the second (1964) Trussell report: only 31 percent satisfactory care reported in general medical hospital cases.

The lack of control over the American hospital gnaws at the concept of near-uniform quality medicine. Hospitals now function with or without internes as *they* so decide; permit anyone *they* please to do surgery or complex specialty medicine; maintain emergency facilities and ambulances, *if* they deem it necessary; permit whatever extent of infection, unnecessary surgery, medication error, accidents and mortality they deem permissible or defensible. This excessive autonomy is an affront to medical excellence.

It is incredible that the one professional standard for hospitals, the Joint Commission on Accreditation of Hospitals, is both a voluntary and minimal standard. No plausible scheme for medicine could hope to succeed without a new *compulsory* system of hospital audit and control, which would establish high mandatory standards for staffing, consultation, medicine and surgery. Violation of its standards should trigger official sanction, public revelation and possible termination of the hospital license. A hospital-coordinating organization both imbued with zeal and buttressed by quasi-official power would be the best single antidote for currently demonstrated hospital laxity.

Since he practices almost exclusively within the hospital, the surgeon must be a prime subject for medical supervision. The practicing surgeon has not demanded it, but medical critique and statistics indicate the need for a professional check on his activities. Any physician, including the general practitioner (and the osteopath in thirty-nine states) may legally elect to do any variety of surgery, and many do. No plausible scheme for tomorrow could tolerate such permissiveness; only board-certified surgical specialists should be permitted this privilege. Once granted this privilege, *individual* surgeons should receive the same external supervision as the hospital—continuing audits of his cases, his index of unnecessary surgery, his success and errors. *(To encourage surgical caution, it might be well in every case of surgery to require an independent consultation from another qualified surgeon, with a written opinion testifying to the patient's need for the operation.)* These factors, and his training, should determine whether the surgeon is qualified to operate.

Similar professional control should be established for the hospital anesthetist, setting more rigid standards of training and supervision of his case records, while gradually eliminating the nurse anesthetist from the medical scene.

The opportunities for reform in the American hospital are, as we have witnessed, legion: proper distribution of internes and residents according to need rather than prestige desires of hospitals and trainees; compulsory medical consultation on the seriously ill rather than the currently abused "gentleman's agreement" which leaves consultation to the physician's discretion; establishment of at least a minimal full-time and part-time staff in all hospitals despite alarmist cries that it is "the corporate practice of medicine"; eventual affiliation of all institutions with medical universities; gradual elimination of proprietary profit-making hospitals; renewed study as to the advisability of maintaining municipal hospitals, considering the possibility of providing free care for the indigent in often-superior voluntary institutions.

In the area of detailed care, some central hospital agency must have quasi-official power to examine the infection rate; standardize transfusion procedure and reduce blood reactions; investigate widespread iatrogenic hazards; eliminate overmedication; control medication-dispensing to reduce serious error; reduce malpractice and negligence, and ensure more rigorous use of known diagnostic and therapeutic regimens. The doctorless hospital, with evening medical care virtually in the paramedical hands of nurses, must be eliminated. Fifty state laws requiring a licensed doctor on the premises of every hospital around the clock is vital legislation that has been overlooked by the laity and been onerously blocked by the medical profession.

Who is to provide the leadership for tomorrow's medicine? In an ambitious scheme of anti-chaos, who is to do the supervision? Is there, is the logical retort to extravagant hope for reform, any possibility of better-organized medicine, sociologically or scientifically? If so, what type of body would handle the thinking and enforcement?

There has been a recent upsurge of interest in so-called group practice of medicine as a panacea for medical ills. While this is a viable form of medicine, and can reach excellent standards in organizations with élan, including the famed Mayo, Cleveland, and Lahey clinics, many so-called groups are merely economic and convenience arrangements for the doctor or insurance protection schemes for the patient. Too often they contain none of the medical controls necessary for superior medicine.

In a proper scheme for tomorrow, the private practitioner, the community hospital, the medical university must become one, constantly supervising and consulting one another. The present Town-Gown dispute, in which the medical school scorns the doctor it spawned and the practitioner inveighs against the "impractical" residents of the medical ivory tower, must first be adjudicated. Having accomplished this, we might begin to consider a united medical community.

A new medical bureaucracy to dogmatize all medicine would be as frightening as current negligence. The larger medical community cannot center about government, although its financial help is needed. Its known bureaucratic efforts can be as stifling as doctor carelessness. The guild orientation of the American Medical Association makes it an equally poor choice as a medical co-ordinator.

The participants in any new complex are logically the private practicing doctor, the hospital and the medical university. Valuable adjuncts should include foundations, the U. S. Public Health Service, and such professional organizations as the American College of Physicians, the Joint Commission on Accreditation of Hospitals, the American College of Surgeons, the American Hospital Association, the AAMC, and the many specialty boards. Such a blend requires a center, and the logical choice may well be the local medical university and its sometimes-associated school of public health.

The *medicoversity* envisioned here is not the current, often self-aggrandizing, overisolated medical college, but one of the new (150 instead of the current 87) centers in which every physician will be an integrated part, as a lifelong student or teacher, or both. *This medicoversity, together with community physicians, could establish medical standards to be rigorously enforced in every doctor's office and in every hospital.*

Should such an organizational reform ever be implemented, the "medical area" should be small enough for effective personal contact with all practitioners, but large enough to plan utilization of physician talent and hospitals in the community. Its quasi-legal function of checking and supervising all local medical care—whether diagnosis and therapy in the many private offices or surgery in the hospitals—would have to be authorized by state statute for such a quiet revolution to succeed. Its administrative financial support could only come from one source: federal grants.

Its operation might be surprisingly uncomplex. A cardiology committee, for example, chosen by *all* heart specialists in the community, could determine reasonably high standards of performance in the diagnosis and treatment of ambulatory and hospitalized heart patients, standards (not dogma) then to be enforced by the "medical area." Such a committee would similarly advise on the teaching of proper cardiology techniques to medical students, internes and residents, supervise the postgraduate education of practicing physicians in cardiology, develop community diagnostic cardiology screenings.

Dozens of similar medical committees, whether on gastroenterology or pediatrics, should be part of each contemplated medical jurisdiction. Only doctors, not committees, can practice medicine, but the "area" would need to employ a staff of full-time physicians (on a rotating basis) to survey private practices and hospitals to ensure that standards are being maintained. The school or department of public health of the local medical school is perhaps the appropriate organization to supervise the surveyors and *regularly* publish public reports on doctor and hospital performance, much as in the manner of the Trussell and Peterson surveys. While details on medical failure in terms of diseases, infections, etc., should be revealed to the public, names of physicians (but perhaps not hospitals) should appropriately be withheld pending educational or disciplinary action.

To be an effective medical control, the "area" must have the power to discipline the doctor by withdrawing his medical privileges (hospital and/or surgical) and the ultimate—recommendation to suspend or revoke a medical license. Hospitals in the "area" would similarly be subject to discipline: institutions habitually failing to live up to rigid standards of performance should be closed. Hospital accreditation as a voluntary and minimal standard is a modern anachronism.

The public too might have an opportunity for participation in medical supervision. The concept has troubled the physician psyche, but should not be dismissed in planning for tomorrow. California has pioneered with the establishment of District Review Committees to hear patient complaints against physicians, and any future organizational plan would be well advised to include a lay member (perhaps appointed by the state governor) on its administrative boards, both regionally and in the community.

By integrating the local medical areas, we might contemplate the formation of a National Academy of Medicine, offering medicine a sense of professional orientation to replace its current guild mentality. (The AMA could be maintained for its "union" function, to guard fiercely the dollars-and-cents prerogatives of the American doctor.) Such an academy, which has already been proposed by physician-critics, would appropriately set national guide lines for medical education, establish numerical needs in various specialties, co-ordinate medical research, plan for hospital construction and growth.

A National Academy might be the first objective group to tackle forcefully some of the socio-economic problems gnawing at medicine today. Hopefully, it would find it possible to separate medical economics from medical necessity, perhaps by the establishment of nationwide voluntary health insurance schemes for hospitalization and physician fees. Such a quasi-public scheme set up along the lines of the American Red Cross (chartered by Congress, with a chairman appointed by the President) would have *no* medical or age exclusions, a single premium, and would eliminate at least the economic uncertainty from medicine. Current "Blue" plans are highly inadequate to the task.

The ultimate value of a national medical co-ordinating body whose primary interests are medical, and whose values are patient-oriented, can hardly be contemplated in today's medical environment. It could develop accurate statistical information—surgical mortality, infections, iatrogenic disease, results of treatments in the physician's office, drug efficacy, etc.—vital figures that we can now only estimate. It could alter the very nature of medicine by its simple insistence on quality—that, for example, the general practitioner become the nation's most intensely trained physician rather than its least equipped. It could initiate a dialogue of ethical concern, a continuing reminder that the human values of medicine have too often been submerged by its modern practitioners.

No specific plan for tomorrow can encompass all the potential for change or hold any near-monopoly on wisdom. But that change in the American physician and in the medical profession is essential can hardly be debated. The result of its metamorphosis will undoubtedly be the creative compromise of many concerned minds.

Utopians will continue to anticipate medical perfection, but it will eternally be just beyond their fingertips. The tragedy of contemporary medicine is not the failure of perfection. It is the doctor's satisfaction with current conditions which enervate his mentality and psyche as much as they do the health and well-being of his patients. His failure to understand his shortcomings, both scientific and social, makes him peculiarly liable to self-delusion and thus prompts inaction toward improvement. The patient faces a unique challenge today: to stimulate the reform and re-education of his doctor while absorbing the sophistication necessary for survival in the chaos of the physician's doing.

The many concerned physician-critics have become increasingly courageous and vocal, but it is still quite apparent that contemporary medical reform must spring from the public. If even a significant minority of the almost 200,000,000 American patients seek this change, tomorrow's doctor will become the healer we once assumed he was.

*Notes
and Bibliography*

Notes and Bibliography

Because of the volume of research material, only the most significant sources are noted in this appendix. Other statistical material, personal interviews and certain journal references are sufficiently described in the body of the book. Notes are arranged consecutively within each chapter and carry subject key in parentheses when necessary.

CHAPTER I

Gregg, Alan, M.D., *Challenges to Contemporary Medicine,* New York, Columbia University Press, 1956, p. 13 (quote by Professor Henderson).

Annis, Edward R., M.D., "Annis-Grams," *Travis County* (Texas) *Medical Society Journal,* July 1964, pp. 5, 18.

Robert W. Hodge, *et al.,* "Occupational Prestige in the United States, 1925–1963," *American Journal of Sociology,* November 1964, pp. 286–302.

Gregg, Alan, M.D., *For Future Doctors,* Chicago, The University of Chicago Press, 1957, p. 104 (quote on medical annoyance at criticism).

Medicine, interview with Herbert Ratner, M.D., by Donald McDonald, Center for the Study of Democratic Institutions, 1962, 67 pp.

Peterson, Osler L., M.D., *et al.,* "An Analytical Study of North Carolina General Practice," *Journal of Medical Education,* December 1956, Part II, 165 pp. (analysis of the performance of a sample of doctors).

"A Study of Medical and Hospital Care Received by a Sample of Teamster Families in the New York City Area, Late 1960," Chapter 7, Part D of *Prepayment for Medical and Dental Care in New York State,* a report of the School of Public Health and Administrative Medicine, Columbia University, October 1962, pp. 225–248 (first Trussell report).

A Study of the Quality of Hospital Care Secured by a Sample of Teamster Family Members in New York City, Columbia University School of Public Health and Administrative Medicine, 1964, 98 pp. (second Trussell report).

Cherkasky, Martin, M.D. Unpublished speech delivered at the American Public Health Association, Detroit, Michigan, November 13, 1961 (comment on Trussell report).

Mannix, Arthur James Jr., M.D., "Medicolegal Implications of Operating Room Deaths," *New York State Journal of Medicine,* March 1, 1960, pp. 683–687 (physician error in the operating room).

Stanley-Brown, Edward G., M.D., *et al.,* "An Analysis of Operative Deaths in Infants and Children," *Surgery, Gynecology & Obstetrics,* February 1962, pp. 137–142 (doctor error in pediatric surgery).

Stahlgren, Leroy H., M.D., "An Analysis of Factors Influencing Mortality Following Extensive Abdominal Operations Upon Geriatric Patients," *Surgery, Gynecology & Obstetrics,* September 1961, pp. 283–292 (error in geriatric surgery).

Guide Issue, Part II, August 1965, *Hospitals,* American Hospital Association, Chicago (statistics on hospitals).

Spain, David M., M.D., *The Complications of Modern Medical Practices,* New York, Grune & Stratton, 1963, 342 pp. (quote on iatrogenic disease).

"Gastric Freezing," a survey report of the AMA Department of Medical Physics and Rehabilitation, *Journal of the American Medical Association,* March 28, 1964, pp. 1032–1033.

Bean, William B., M.D., "Recent Setbacks in Medicine," *Northwest Medicine,* Vol. 55, 1956, pp. 157–160.

Pignataro, Frank P., M.D., "The Personality of the Physician," *Journal of the Student American Medical Association,* October 1956, pp. 21–25.

Demographic Yearbook, Statistical Office of the United Nations, New York, 1963, 1964, 1965 (statistics on life expectancy and infant mortality).

Vital Statistics of the United States, Vol. II, Sec. 5. U.S. Department of Health, Education, and Welfare, Public Health Service, National Vital Statistics Division (statistics on life expectancy).

Mortality by Occupation and Industry, Vital Statistics, Special Reports, Vol. 53, No. 2, September 1962, U.S. Department of Health, Education, and Welfare, Public Health Service (statistics on survival by occupation).

Brokerage Briefs, Bulletin 13, Life Accident and Health Agency Department, Travelers Insurance Company (figures on life of adults added since 1900; quoted from Institute of Life Insurance).

"Life Expectancy," editorial in *New England Journal of Medicine,* June 27, 1963 (comment on true meaning of life expectancy figures).

Mariyama, Iwao M., *The Change in Mortality Trend in the United States,* Office of Health Statistics Analysis, U.S. Public Health Service, 1964 (levelingoff of death rate).

Anderson, Odin W., and Rosen, George, M.D., *An Examination of the Concept of Preventive Medicine.* Health Information Foundation, Research Series, No. 12, New York, 1960 (material on low death rates).

Health Manpower Source Book, Section 10, Physicians' Age, Type of Practice and Location, U.S. Public Health Service, 1960 (statistics on physicians' age, number, etc.).

Helpern, Milton, M.D., "Inaugural Address," *New York Medicine,* November 20, 1962, pp. 3–8.

Donabedian, A., M.D., and Axelrod, S. J., "Organizing Medical Care Programs to Meet Health Needs," *Annals of the American Academy of Political and Social Science,* Spring 1963.

Ellis, John R., M.D., "MDs Must Be More Than Technicians," excerpts of speech to the Association of American Medical Colleges, *Medical World News,* November 22, 1963, pp. 166–167.

Key Facts on Health, Education, and Welfare, 1952 and 1962, Office of Program Analysis, U.S. Department of Health, Education, and Welfare, 8 pp. (remaining survival figures at age 65).

CHAPTER II

Garland, L. Henry, M.D., "Studies on the Accuracy of Diagnostic Procedures," *American Journal of Roentgenology*, July, 1959, pp. 25–38 (comment on diagnostic error; material on radiological error).

Peterson, Osler L., M.D., *et al.*, "An Analytical Study of North Carolina General Practice," *see* Chapter I (a study of physician competence).

Seegal, David, M.D., and Wertheim, Arthur R., M.D., "On the Failure to Supervise Students' Performance of Complete Physical Examination," *Journal of the American Medical Association*, May 12, 1962, pp. 476–477 (comments on diagnostic training, and quote by Dr. Lewis).

Wynder, Ernest L., M.D., "The Physician, the Patient, and Statistics," *JAMA*, December 28, 1963, p. 1150.

Sanders, Barkev S., Ph.D., *Completeness and Reliability of Diagnoses in Therapeutic Practice*, a paper presented at the Statistics Section of the American Public Health Association meeting, November 14, 1963.

Volume of Physicians' Visits; United States, July 1963—June 1964, National Center for Health Statistics, Series 10, No. 18, U.S. Department of Health, Education, and Welfare, Public Health Service (statistics on patient visits to doctors).

Schenthal, Joseph E., M.D., "Multiphasic Screening of the Well Patient," *JAMA*, January 2, 1960, pp. 1–4 (Tulane University Cancer Detection Clinic results).

Krantz, Goldie, "A Multiphasic Health Program—A Supplement to Health and Welfare Plans," *American Journal of Public Health*, December 1962, pp. 2087–2092.

Elsom, Kendall A., M.D., *et al.*, "Periodic Health Examination: Nature and Distribution of Newly Discovered Disease in Executives," *JAMA*, January 2, 1960, pp. 5–10.

Siegel, Gordon S., M.D., M.P.H., *Periodic Health Examination: Abstracts From the Literature*, Public Health Service Publication 1010, Department of Health, Education, and Welfare, 1963, 116 pp.

Kilpatrick, G.S., M.D., "Observer Error in Medicine," *Journal of Medical Education*, January 1963, pp. 38–42.

Sheeley, William F., M.D., guest editorial, *American Journal of Psychiatry*, December 1963, p. 604.

Rossman, Phillip L., M.D., "Organic Diseases Simulating Functional Disorders," *GP*, August 1963, pp. 78–83.

James, George, M.D., "The General Practitioner of the Future," *New England Journal of Medicine*, June 11, 1964, pp. 1286–1291.

Grant, Roald N., M.D., "Physical Examinations and Lifesaving," *Ca*, January-February, 1964 (figures on use of proctoscope).

Veenema, Ralph J., M.D., and Lattimer, John K., M.D., "Early Diagnosis of Carcinoma of the Prostate," *JAMA*, October 12, 1963, pp. 127–131.

Weinstein, Haskell J., M.D., "Lung Cancer: Diagnosis Today, Not Tomorrow," *Medical Tribune*, August 23, 1963.

Russell, William O., M.D., "Cytology for Early Diagnosis of Lung Cancer," *Medical Tribune,* November 5, 1963.

Gilbertsen, Victor A., M.D., "X-ray Examination of the Chest; An Unsatisfactory Method of Detection of Early Lung Cancer in Asymptomatic Individuals," *JAMA,* June 22, 1964, p. 1082.

"Anemia—A Sign," editorial in *New England Journal of Medicine,* April 18, 1963.

O'Donnell, Walter E., M.D., Day, Emerson, M.D., and Venet, Louis, M.D., *Early Detection and Diagnosis of Cancer,* St. Louis, The C. V. Mosby Company, 1962, pp. 55–60 (details on breast examination for cancer).

Prevent Blindness: Screen for Glaucoma, Public Health Service Publication No. 932, U.S. Department of Health, Education, and Welfare, 14 pp.

"Diabetes Detection," editorial in *New England Journal of Medicine,* November 10, 1962.

Heart Disease in Adults, National Center for Health Statistics, Series 11, No. 6, Public Health Service, U.S. Department of Health, Education, and Welfare, September 1964, 43 pp.

"Two Step Test Called Best," *Medical World News,* April 10, 1964, pp. 56–57.

"The Electrocardiogram: A Reappraisal," editorial in *JAMA,* July 13, 1964, pp. 148–149.

Zinn, Willard J., M.D., and Cosby, Richard S., M.D., "Myocardial Infarction; II. A Re-evaluation of the Diagnostic Accuracy of the Electrocardiogram," *American Journal of Medicine,* February 1950, pp. 170–179.

Chodosh, Sanford, M.D., and Segal, Maurice, S., M.D., "Current Concepts: Chronic Bronchitis," *New England Journal of Medicine,* April 23, 1964, pp. 894–896.

Roberts, Albert, M.D., Division of Chronic Diseases, Public Health Service, speech before International Congress on Diseases, Mexico City, October 13, 1964 (statistics on death from chronic pulmonary emphysema).

Stollerman, Gene H., M.D., "Sore Throat—A Diagnostic and Therapeutic Dilemma," *JAMA,* July 13, 1964, pp. 145–146.

Massell, Benedict F., M.D., *et al.,* "Home Cultures As An Aid in the Diagnosis of Streptococcal Respiratory Infection," *New England Journal of Medicine,* September 17, 1964, pp. 581–585.

Alvarez, Walter, M.D., "The Need for Repeating Tests," editorial in *Modern Medicine,* September 28, 1964, pp. 93–95.

Sterling, Theodor, Ph.D., University of Cincinnati Medical Computing Center, report at the Conference on Data Acquisition, University of Rochester Medical Center, August 1963 (details on computer diagnosis of *placenta praevia*).

"Automation and Medicine," editorial in *Medical Tribune,* August 5, 1963 (comment on computer diagnosis).

CHAPTER III

"Patients Speak Out," *Medical Economics,* April 20, 1964, pp. 49–106 (survey of patient attitudes).

"Pulse of Medicine Report," *Medical Tribune,* January 18, 1963, p. 22 (survey of almost 1,000 doctors on house calls; statistics and opinions).

Medicine, interview with Dr. Herbert Ratner, *see* Chapter I (comment on pediatricians and GP's).

Kramer, Charles, *Medical Malpractice,* Practising Law Institute, New York, 1962, 70 pp.

Principles of Medical Ethics, American Medical Association, Chicago.

Cahn, Ira L., "For Shame," editorial in *Massapequa* (New York) *Post,* April 16, 1959.

Dichter, Ernest, Ph.D., "The Doctor's Human Relationships," *Medical Annals of the District of Columbia,* September 1958, pp. 493–494.

Plant, Marcus L., address at 15th Annual Advocacy Institute, University of Michigan, March 20, 1964.

Wegman, Myron E., M.D., address at science writing seminar, University of Michigan, May 14, 1964.

"Sophisticated Handling Called Key to Practice Two Generations Hence," *Medical Tribune,* January 11, 1963 (report on Atherton Bean address; text published in *Minnesota Medical Bulletin*).

Truman, Stanley R., M.D., "Report to the Board of Trustees of the American Medical Association of the Committee on Medical Practices," *Northwest Medicine,* August 1955, pp. 844–859.

Potter, Stephen, "Doctorship (M.D. Manship), Patientship, and the Health Ploy," pp. 290–308 in *Three-upmanship,* New York, Holt, Rinehart and Winston, 1962.

Evans, Lester J., M.D., 3rd of the William W. Cook Lectures, University of Michigan, November 15, 1963.

Yanof, Zale, M.D., "Personal Physician," *JAMA,* February 15, 1964; October 12, 1964.

Bean, William Bennett, M.D., "Careers in Medicine," *The Pharos,* Alpha Omega Alpha, May 1957.

"Osler's Master-word," *Annals of Internal Medicine,* November 1963, p. 765.

Ratner, Herbert, M.D., address given at West Side Medical Center, November 19–23, 1950 (comments on medical ideals).

CHAPTER IV

"Hospital Discharges and Length of Stay: Short-stay Hospitals, United States, 1958–1960," health statistics from the U.S. National Health Survey, Series B, No. 32, Table 25, p. 38 (number of tonsillectomy and/or adenoidectomy operations).

"Tonsillectomy and Adenoidectomy," editorial in *Canadian Medical Association Journal,* December 28, 1963, pp. 1334–1335 (statistics on death from tonsillectomy, plus report on the Dr. McKee study).

Bean, William B., M.D., "The Natural History of Error (Surgical Error: Lo the Poor Tonsils!)," *Transactions of the Association of American Physicians,* Vol. lxxii, 1959, pp. 40–55.

Austrian, Robert, M.D., "The Current Status of Bacteremic Pneumococcal Pneumonia. Re-evaluation of an Underemphasized Clinical Problem," *Transactions of the Association of American Physicians,* Vol. lxxvi, 1963, pp. 117–125.

Austrian, Robert, M.D., and Gold, Jerome, M.D., "Pneumococcal Bacteremia with Especial Reference to Bacteremic Pneumococcal Pneumonia," *Annals of Internal Medicine,* May 1964, pp. 757–776 (material on pneumonia vaccine; statistics on pneumococcus types and patients affected).

Louria, Donald B., M.D., and Brayton, Robert G., M.D., "The Efficacy of Penicillin Regimens," *JAMA,* December 14, 1963, pp. 987–990.

Schulman, Jonas A., M.D., *et al.,* "Errors and Hazards in the Diagnosis and Treatment of Bacterial Pneumonias," *Annals of Internal Medicine,* January 1965, pp. 41–58.

Reimann, Hobart A., M.D., "Current Problems of the Pneumonias," *Annals of Internal Medicine,* January 1962, pp. 144–154.

Feinstein, Alvan R., M.D., "Prophylaxis of Recurrent Rheumatic Fever," *JAMA,* February 8, 1965, pp. 451–454 (report on Irvington House study on rheumatic fever).

Alexson, Chloe G., M.D., *et al.,* "Experiences With Controlled Community Rheumatic Fever Prophylaxis Program," *American Journal of Public Health,* September 1964, pp. 1580–1587.

Eckmann, L., M.D., "Active and Passive Tetanus Immunization," *New England Journal of Medicine,* November 19, 1964, pp. 1088–1090.

"Human Antitoxin in Prophylaxis and Treatment of Tetanus," *Medical Letter on Drugs and Therapeutics,* February 12, 1965.

Goddard, James L., M.D., "Smallpox, Diphtheria, Tetanus, Pertussis, and Poliomyelitis Immunization," *JAMA,* March 28, 1964, pp. 1009–1012.

"A Rise in Tuberculosis," *Modern Medicine,* October 12, 1964, p. 54.

"Believer in TB Eradication: Dr. William B. Barclay," *Medical Tribune,* July 22, 1963.

"Vaccine Seems Effective in Control and Elimination of Tuberculosis," *JAMA,* November 1964, p. 35.

"Re-emphasis on Tuberculosis," editorial in *JAMA,* June 21, 1965, p. 1088.

Doege, Theodore C., M.D., "Tuberculosis Mortality in the United States, 1900–1960," *JAMA,* June 21, 1965, pp. 1045–1048.

Hanzel, George D., M.D., and Rogers, Kenneth D., M.D., "Multiple-Puncture and Mantoux Tuberculin Tests in High School Students," *JAMA,* December 21, 1964, pp. 1038–1042.

Barclay, William R., M.D., "BCG—A Neglected Weapon Against TB," *Medical Tribune,* March 27, 1964.

Rusk, Howard A., M.D., "Price of Human Life," *New York Times,* December 13, 1964, p. 80 (comment on "stroke").

"Gastric Freezing," Survey report of AMA Department of Medical Physics and Rehabilitation in *JAMA,* March 28, 1964, pp. 1032–1033.

Bernhard, William F., M.D., "Current Concepts: Hyperbaric Oxygenation," *New England Journal of Medicine,* September 10, 1964, pp. 562–564.

Anderson, Banks, Jr., M.D., *et al.,* "Dysbarism Among Hyperbaric Personnel," *JAMA,* December 21, 1964, pp. 1043–1045 (Duke University report on hazard to personnel).

Murray, Joseph E., M.D., *et al.,* "Third Report of the Human Kidney Transplant Registry," *Transplantation,* March 1965, pp. 294–302 (statistics on survival after transplantations of kidneys).

Elkinton, J. Russell, M.D., "Moral Problems in the Use of Borrowed Organs, Artificial and Transplanted," editorial in *Annals of Internal Medicine,* February 1964.

Kirsner, Joseph B., M.D., "Facts and Fallacies of Current Medical Therapy for Uncomplicated Duodenal Ulcer," *JAMA,* February 8, 1964, pp. 423–428.

Hirschowitz, Basil I., M.D., "Management of Peptic Ulcer," *GP,* March 1965, pp. 113–123.

Ulcers, Public Health Service Publication No. 280, U.S. Department of Health, Education, and Welfare, 1962.

Roth, Harold P., M.D., *et al.,* "Patients' Beliefs About Peptic Ulcer and Its Treatment," *Annals of Internal Medicine,* January 1962, pp. 72–80.

Welch, Claude E., M.D., "Abdominal Surgery," *New England Journal of Medicine,* October 15, 1964, pp. 829–833; October 22, 1964, pp. 885–890.

Hardy, James D., M.D., "Problems Associated With Gastric Surgery: A Review of 604 Consecutive Patients With Annotation," *American Journal of Surgery,* November 1964, pp. 699–716.

Moore, Francis D., M.D., "Surgery In Search of a Rationale," *American Journal of Surgery,* March 1963, pp. 304–312.

"Safety First in Ulcer Surgery," *Medical World News,* March 15, 1963, p. 119 (report on Spokane vagotomy survey).

Small, Wilfred T., M.D., and Ashraf, Mian, M.D., "Pyloroplasty and Vagotomy for Duodenal Ulcer: A Review of a Hundred and Ten Cases," *New England Journal of Medicine,* March 25, 1965, pp. 619–621 (report on reduced mortality with vagotomy at Memorial Hospital, Worcester, Massachusetts).

"Glomectomy for Asthma Is Opposed By Most of Thoracic Surgeons Polled," *Medical Tribune,* February 24, 1965 (report on speech by Dr. C. Thomas Read before Society of Thoracic Surgeons).

Marschke, Gerald, M.D., *et al.,* "Carotid-Body Removal in Asthma," *JAMA,* February 1, 1965, p. 397 (study done at the University of California Center for the Health Sciences).

Segal, Maurice S., M.D., and Dulfano, Mauricio J., M.D., "Glomectomy in the Treatment of Chronic Bronchial Asthma," *New England Journal of Medicine,* January 14, 1965, pp. 58–63 (Tufts University Lung Station report on failure of glomectomy).

"Science and Art," editorial in *Medical Tribune,* April 15, 1963.

"Surgeons Give Criteria For Aortic Aneurysm Operation," *Medical World News,* April 26, 1963.

Ellis, F. Henry, M.D., *et al.,* "Results of Open Operation for Acquired Mitral-Valve Disease," *New England Journal of Medicine,* April 29, 1965, pp. 869–874.

Eiseman, B., M.D., and Spencer, F. C., M.D., "The Occasional Open-Heart Surgeon," editorial in *Circulation* (American Heart Association), February 1965, pp. 161–162.

"Confidence Limits For Proportions or Percentages," *The Record,* Commission on Professional and Hospital Activities, December 18, 1962.

Muench, Hugo, M.D., "Statistics of Ruptured Aneurysm," letter to *New England Journal of Medicine,* December 17, 1964, p. 1325.

Moore, George E., M.D., "How To Achieve Surgical Results By Really Trying," Editorial in *Surgery, Gynecology & Obstetrics,* April 1963, pp. 497–498.

Shindell, Sidney, M.D., LL.B., "Hypotheses and Conclusions," Part 5 of "Statistics, Science, and Sense," *JAMA,* November 30, 1963, pp. 849–853.

Spink, Wesley W., M.D., "The Training of the Physician: Continuing Education—Whose Responsibility?" *New England Journal of Medicine,* October 15, 1964, pp. 827–828.

Dryer, Bernard V., M.D., "A Nationwide Plan for Continuing Medical Education: Pros and Cons," *JAMA,* July 6, 1964.

Beaton, Lindsay E., M.D., "A Doc Ain't Never Thru," *JAMA,* July 6, 1964, pp. 40–42.

Education for the Health Professions, New York State Committee on Medical Education, Board of Regents, New York State Education Department, Albany, N.Y., June 1963, 114 pp.

Shepherd, Glen R., M.D., "Continuing Education Courses for Physicians," *JAMA,* August 10, 1964, pp. 423–506.

The Physician's Continuing Education, American Heart Association, 1961, 47 pp.

Miller, George, M.D., "The Continuing Education of Physicians," *New England Journal of Medicine,* August 8, 1963, pp. 295–299.

Page, Irvine H., M.D., "Our Antiquated Administrative Systems," *Modern Medicine,* June 22, 1964, pp. 77–79.

McKittrick, Leland S., M.D., "Graduate Education in Preparation for Surgical Specialties," *JAMA,* November 16, 1964, pp. 583–585.

Wescoe, W. Clarke, M.D., "The Town-Gown Syndrome: Pathology," *JAMA,* November 23, 1963, pp. 785–786.

Ellis, Laurence B., M.D., "The Training of the Physician: Continuing Education-Postgraduate Medical Institute," *New England Journal of Medicine,* October 22, 1964, pp. 883–885.

CHAPTER V

"Postoperative Wound Infections," supplement to *Annals of Surgery,* August 1964, 192 pp. (report on surgical infection by National Academy of Sciences—National Research Council).

"Influence of Ultraviolet Light on Postoperative Infection," editorial in *JAMA,* August 17, 1964, pp. 574–575.

Klein, Jerome O., M.D., *et al.,* "Oxacillin Treatment of Severe Staphylococcal Infections," *New England Journal of Medicine,* December 5, 1963, pp. 1215–1225 (use of oxacillin in staph infection).

Eickhoff, Theodore C., M.D., Kislak, Jay Ward, M.D., and Finland, Maxwell, M.D., "Clinical Evaluation of Nafcillin in Patients with Severe Staphylococcal Disease," *New England Journal of Medicine,* April 8, 1965, pp. 699–707.

Lavine, Daniel, M.D., *et al.,* "Staphylococcus of a Newly Recognized Bacteriophage Type: Report of a Hospital Outbreak," *JAMA,* June 14, 1965, pp. 935–938 (report of staph outbreak at San Francisco General Hospital).

"New Hospital Staphylococci," editorial in *JAMA,* June 14, 1965, p. 994.

Moran, John M., M.D., "A Clinical and Bacteriological Study of Infections Associated With Venous Cutdown," *New England Journal of Medicine,* March 18, 1965, pp. 554–559.

"Hands Held Top Factor in Transmitting Staph," *Medical Tribune,* March 17, 1965.

Ginsberg, Frances, R.N., "Disposable Gloves May Best Ensure Asepsis," *Modern Hospital,* June 1965, p. 134.

Levenson, Stanley M., "Application of the Technology of the Germfree Laboratory to Special Problems of Patient Care," *American Journal of Surgery,* May 1964, pp. 710–722.

Hurst, Valerie, Ph.D., *et al.,* "Five-Year Follow-Up of an Outbreak of Staphylococcal Infection in a Hospital Nursery," *New England Journal of Medicine,* March 4, 1964, pp. 517–519 (infection spread out of the University of California nursery).

Bethune, D. W., *et al.,* "Dispersal of Staphylococcus Aureus by Patients and Surgical Staff," *Lancet,* February 27, 1965.

Robert D. Dripps, M.D., *et al.,* "The Role of Anesthesia in Surgical Mortality," *JAMA,* October 21, 1961, pp. 261–266.

Dillon, John B., M.D., "Things As They Are," *JAMA,* December 14, 1964, pp. 123–125.

Saidman, Lawrence J., M.D., *et al.*, "Hyperthermia During Anesthesia," *JAMA*, December 21, 1964, pp. 1029–1032.

Weaver, Daniel C., M.D., "Preventing Aspiration Deaths During Anesthesia," *JAMA*, June 15, 1964, pp. 971–974.

Clark, Richard B., M.D., and Maier, Eugene S., M.D., "Effects of Previous and Concomitant Drug Therapy on Surgery and Anesthesia," *GP*, January 1964, pp. 106–111.

Beecher, Henry K., M.D., *et al.*, "The Anesthetist As a Physician," *JAMA*, April 6, 1964, pp. 49–55.

Second Trussell report, *see* Chapter I.

Strumia, Max M., M.D., "A Guide to Rational Blood Transfusion," editorial in *Annals of Internal Medicine*, November 1963, pp. 770–771.

Sussman, Leon N., M.D., "Blood Transfusion Accidents," *Trauma*, February 1960, pp. 86–109.

Hirsh, Bernard D., LL.B., "3000 Die Yearly From Blood Transfusions . . . and the Physician Could Be Blamed," *New Medical Materia*, September 1961, p. 73.

Binder, Lee S., M.D., Ginsberg, Victor, M.D., and Harmel, Merel H., M.D., "A Six Year Study of Incompatible Blood Transfusion," *Surgery, Gynecology & Obstetrics*, January 1959, pp. 19–34.

Myers, Robert S., M.D., "One Pint Transfusions May Not Be Worth The Risk," *Modern Hospital*, November 1960.

"Prevention of High Fatality in Serum Hepatitis," editorial in *JAMA*, September 28, 1963.

Mirick, George S., M.D., Ward, Robert, M.D., and McCollum, M.D., "Modification of Post-Transfusion Hepatitis by Gamma Globulin," *New England Journal of Medicine*, July 8, 1965, pp. 60–65 (statistics on transfusion hepatitis rate in studies in Baltimore, Los Angeles and New Haven).

Hampers, Constantine, L., M.D., Prager, David, M.D., and Senior, John R., M.D., "Post-Transfusion Anicteric Hepatitis," *New England Journal of Medicine*, October 8, 1964, pp. 748–754 (statistics on transfusion hepatitis rate in a Philadelphia hospital study).

Grady, George F., M.D., and Chalmers, Thomas C., M.D., "Risk of Post-Transfusion Viral Hepatitis," *New England Journal of Medicine*, August 13, 1964, pp. 337–342 (report on low hepatitis rate in Boston teaching hospitals; statistics on Chicago, Cincinnati, New Jersey, Baltimore hepatitis studies).

Young, Lawrence E., M.D., "Complications of Blood Transfusion," *Annals of Internal Medicine*, July 1964, pp. 136–146.

Safren, Miriam Aronstein, Ph.D., and Chapanis, Alphonse, Ph.D., "A Critical Incident Study of Hospital Medication Errors," *Hospitals*, Part I: May 1, 1960; Part II: May 16, 1960 (report on medication errors in 1100 bed hospital by Johns Hopkins researchers).

Barker, Kenneth N., and McConnell Warren E., Ph.D., "How To Detect Medication Errors," *Modern Hospital*, July 1962, pp. 95–106 (disguised survey of medication errors in a Florida hospital).

Snedeker, Lendon, M.D., "Hazards to Health," *New England Journal of Medicine*, June 20, 1963, pp. 1401–1402.

Parrish, Henry M., M.P.H., and Weil, Thomas P., "Patient Accidents Occurring in Hospitals: Epidemiologic Study of 614 Accidents," *New York State Journal of Medicine*, March 15, 1958, pp. 838–846 (report of accidents at a hospital in New York over one-year period).

Stone, Eric P., M.D., "What Is A Reasonable 'Standard Rate' for Patient Accidents?" *Hospitals*, October 16, 1962, pp. 43–46, 114 (study of accidents a Philadelphia Hospital study).

Sparling, J. Frederick, M.D., "Measuring Medical Care Quality: A Comparative Study," *Hospitals,* March 16, 1962, pp. 1962–1968 (unnecessary appendectomies in several Baltimore hospitals).

Lawton, W. E., M.D., *et al.,* "The Tissue Committee v. The Normal Appendix," *West Virginia Medical Journal,* November 1955, pp. 345–348.

Eisele, C. Wesley, M.D., *et al.,* "Can The Practice of Internal Medicine Be Evaluated?" *Annals of Internal Medicine,* January 1956, pp. 144–161 (disparity of care at fifteen Michigan hospitals).

"Surgeon, Spare That Uterus," *GP,* April 1953, p. 31.

Doyle, James C., M.D., "Unnecessary Hysterectomies: Study of 6,248 Operations in Thirty Hospitals During 1948," *JAMA,* January 31, 1953, pp. 360–365.

"Hysterectomy Trends," *The Record,* Commission on Professional and Hospital Activities, March 25, 1965.

A. W. Diddle, M.D., *et al.,* "Gynecological Surgery in Five Non-teaching Hospitals," *Obstetrics and Gynecology,* February, 1953, pp. 197–203 (survey of unnecessary surgery in Virginia, Kentucky and Tennessee).

Medical Care Chart Book, 2nd ed., Bureau of Public Health Economics, University of Michigan, School of Public Health, 1964.

Thorek, Max, M.D., *Surgical Errors and Safeguards,* 5th ed., Philadelphia, J. B. Lippincott Company, 1960, 652 pp.

Slee, V. N., M.D., "Streamlining the Tissue Committee," *Bulletin, American College of Surgeons,* November-December 1959, p. 519 (survey of seven common operations).

Anderson, Odin W., and Feldman, Jacob J., "Distribution of Patients Hospitalized for Surgery in the United States: From July 1952 to July 1953," *Bulletin, American College of Surgeons,* September–October, 1958.

"The Characteristics of Hospitals and Physicians Used for Medical Care by New Jersey Physicians and Their Families, 1955–1958," Part A, Chapter 7, *Prepayment for Medical and Dental Care in New York State,* School of Public Health and Administrative Medicine, Columbia University, 1962, pp. 177–188 (survey of 469 New Jersey doctors).

Truman Committee report, *see* Chapter III.

Koontz, Amos R., M.D., "The Recurrent Hernia," *Hospital Medicine,* September 1964, pp. 19–23.

Zollinger, Robert M., M.D., and Williams, Roger D., M.D., "Cholecystectomy," *JAMA,* October 12, 1964.

Dowdy, Gerald S., Jr., M.D., and Waldron, George W., M.D., "Stumbling Blocks in Gallbladder Surgery," *GP,* May 1964, pp. 84–88.

"Surgical Congress Given Advice for Decreasing Postoperative Infection," *Medical Tribune,* June 3, 1963.

Dinsmore, Harold P., M.D., "Pitfalls in Colon Surgery," *West Virginia Medical Journal,* December 1961, pp. 439–442.

Lorhan, Paul H., M.D., and Shelby, Edwin A., M.D., "Factors Influencing Mortality in Hip Fractures," *American Journal of Surgery,* November 1964, pp. 645–648.

Win, M. Shein, M.D., "Late Complications of Surgery," letter to *New England Journal of Medicine,* April 22, 1965, p. 864.

Phillips, Otto C., M.D., and Ott, Harold A., M.D. "Doctors Call for Better OB Anesthesia," *Modern Hospital,* January 1964, pp. 105–108.

Rosenfield, A.B., M.D., "Maternal Mortality Studies in Nursing Anesthesia," *Hospitals,* February 16, 1964, p. 80–93.

"Delivery Procedures: 152 PAS Hospitals," *The Record,* Commission on Professional and Hospital Activities, October 1, 1963 (statistics on artificial induction of labor).

"Perinatal Mortality Rates in Michigan Hospitals," *The Record,* Commission on Professional and Hospital Activities, June 1, 1964 (figures on infant mortality in thirty-five Michigan hospitals).

Guide Issue, August 1, 1965, *Hospitals* (statistics on number of accredited hospitals, internes, residents, etc.).

Appel, James Z., M.D., "Trends in Accreditation," *Hospitals,* February 16, 1963 (comment on minimal nature of JCAH standards).

Means, James H., M.D., "Homo Medicus Americanus," *Daedalus,* Fall 1963, pp. 701–723 (comment on lack of consultation in modern medicine).

Standards for Hospital Accreditation, Joint Commission on Accreditation of Hospitals, Chicago, December 1, 1960.

Standards for Hospital Accreditation, Joint Commission on Accreditation of Hospitals, Chicago, December 5, 1953.

"Policies in Staffing Hospitals Satisfy 80% of MDs Queries," Pulse of Medicine Report, *Medical Tribune,* April 11–12, 1964, p. 15 (survey on full-time doctors).

Kennedy, Robert H., M.D., "Give The Emergency Room The Status It Deserves," editorial in *Hospitals,* March 16, 1957, pp. 35–36.

Skudder, Paul A., M.D., McCarroll, James R., M.D., and Wade, Preston A., M.D., "Hospital Emergency Facilities, A Survey," *Bulletin, American College of Surgeons,* March-April 1961.

Kennedy, Robert H., M.D., "Guidlines for an Effective Emergency Department," *Hospitals,* June 16, 1963.

Errera, Paul, M.D., and Dye, Mary C., M.S.N., "Emotional Steam Clouds Emergency Care," *Modern Hospital,* February 1965, pp. 87–92.

"Standards for Emergency Department in Hospitals," *Bulletin, American College of Surgeons,* May–June, 1963.

Hodgins, Eric, *Episode—Report on the Accident Inside My Skull,* New York, Atheneum, 1964.

Freidson, Eliot, and Feldman, Jacob J., *The Public Looks at Hospitals,* Health Information Foundation, Research Series 4, 1961, 22 pp.

Lambertsen, Eleanor C., R.N., Ed.D., "More Simple Courtesy Would Quiet Critics of Nursing Care," *Modern Hospital,* February 1965, p. 138.

French, Edward W., M. D., "The Shortage of Personnel in Care of the Sick," editorial in *Medical Tribune,* February 14, 1964.

CHAPTER VI

Spain, David M., M.D., *The Complications of Modern Medical Practices,* see Chapter I.

Barr, David P., M.D., "Hazards of Modern Diagnosis and Therapy—The Price We Pay," *JAMA,* December 10, 1955, pp. 1452–1456.

Moser, Robert H., M.D., "Diseases of Medical Progress," *New England Journal of Medicine,* September 27, 1956, pp. 606–614.

Schimmel, Elihu M., M.D., "The Hazards of Hospitalization," *Annals of Internal Medicine,* January 1964, pp. 100–110.

Cluff, Leighton, M.D., *Epidemiological Study of Adverse Drug Reactions,* unpublished report from Department of Medicine, The Johns Hopkins University School of Medicine and Johns Hopkins Hospital, 1965, 14 pp. and tables.

MacDonald, Murdo G., M.D., and MacKay, Bruce R., M.D., "Adverse Drug Reactions: Experience of Mary Fletcher Hospital During 1962," *JAMA*, December 21, 1964, pp. 1071–1074.

Perloff, J. K., M.D., "Cardiac Catheterization—Current Concepts," *GP*, April 1963, pp. 96–109.

Fonkalsrud, Eric W., M.D., and Clatworthy, H. William, Jr., M.D., "Accidental Perforation of the Colon and Rectum in Newborn Infants," *New England Journal of Medicine*, May 27, 1965, pp. 1097–1100.

Lurie, Paul R., M.D., and Grajo, Maria Z., M.D., "Accidental Cardiac Puncture During Right Heart Catheterization," *Pediatrics*, February 1962, pp. 283–294.

Levy, Morris J., M.D., and Lillehei, C. Walton, M.D., Ph.D., "Percutaneous Direct Cardiac Catheterization," *New England Journal of Medicine*, August 6, 1964, pp. 273–283.

Sanford, Jay P., M.D., "Hospital-acquired Urinary Tract Infections," *Annals of Internal Medicine*, May 1964, pp. 903–913.

Kass, Edward H., M.D., "Indwelling Catheter and Infection of Urinary Tract," *JAMA*, October 12, 1963, p. 173.

Cox, Clair E., M.D., and Hinman, Frank, Jr., M.D., "Retention Catheterization and the Bladder Defense Mechanism," *JAMA*, January 18, 1965, pp. 171–174.

Levin, Jack, M.D., "The Incidence and Prevention of Infection After Urethral Catheterization," *Annals of Internal Medicine*, May 1964, pp. 914–922.

"The Control of Urethral Catheter Infections," *Medical Letter on Drugs and Therapeutics*, November 23, 1962.

Chayet, Neil L., "Law-Medicine Notes: Malpractice—A Recent Case," *New England Journal of Medicine*, January 7, 1965, pp. 35–36 (details on $725,000 award involving radiodye).

Wennberg, John E., M.D., *et al.*, "Renal Toxicity of Oral Cholecystographic Media," *JAMA*, November 2, 1963, pp. 461–466 (danger of bunamiodyl sodium in gall bladder X-ray visualization).

Cooper, David R., M.D., "Cardiac Arrest on the Myelographic Tilt Table," *JAMA*, February 29, 1964, p. 674.

Seltzer, Ronald A., M.D., *et al.*, "Radiation Exposure from Radioisotopes in Pediatrics," *New England Journal of Medicine*, July 9, 1964, pp. 84–90 (comment on whole-body dosage to children).

Chadwick, Donald R., M.D., release from U.S. Department of Health, Education, and Welfare, March 8, 1964 (comment on radiation exposure in diagnostic use of X-rays; material on Dr. Hempelmann's study on danger of thymus radiation treatment).

Blatz, Hanson, "Common Causes of Excessive Patient Exposure in Diagnostics Radiology," *New England Journal of Medicine*, December 3, 1964, pp. 1184–1189.

Garland, L. Henry, M.D., "Safer Diagnostic X-rays," editorial in *Medical Tribune*, January 17, 1964.

Hanson, Daniel J., M.D., "Intramuscular Injection Injuries and Complications," *GP*, January 1963, pp. 109–115.

Keyes, John W., M.D., "Iatrogenic Heart Disease," unpublished paper.

Soffer, Alfred, M.D., "Iatrogenic Aspects of Digitalis Intoxication," *JAMA*, June 14, 1965, pp. 987–988.

"Choice of Digitalis Drugs," *Medical Letter on Drugs and Therapeutics*, September 14, 1962.

Kowal, Samuel J., M.D., "Iatrogenic Heart Disturbances," Chapter 16 of *The Complications of Modern Medical Practices*, pp. 197–205 (material on digitalis toxicity). *See* Chapter I.

Dooley, Donald M., M.D., and Perlmutter, Irwin, M.D., "Spontaneous Intracranial Hematomas in Patients Receiving Anticoagulation Therapy," *JAMA*, February 8, 1964, pp. 396–398.

Klingensmith, William, M.D., and Oles, Patrick, M.D., "Surgical Complications of Dicumarol Therapy," *American Journal of Surgery*, November 1964, pp. 640–644.

"Anticoagulants in Coronary Artery Disease," *Medical Letter on Drugs and Therapeutics*, August 28, 1964.

Moschos, Christos B., M.D., *et al.*, "Controlled Study of the Effective Level of Long-Term Anticoagulation," *JAMA*, November 30, 1964, pp. 799–804.

"Emotional Reactions to Long-Term Anticoagulant Therapy," editorial in *JAMA*, December 7, 1964, p. 930.

"Clinical Uses of Heparin," *Medical Letter on Drugs and Therapeutics*, March 13, 1964.

"Phenindione—A Hazardous Anticoagulant," *Medical Letter on Drugs and Therapeutics*, August 2, 1963.

Cohen, Sheldon B., M.D., "Brain Damage Due to Penicillin," *JAMA*, December 7, 1963, pp. 899–902.

Altemeier, William, M.D., *et al.*, "Staphylococcal Enterocolitis Following Antibiotic Therapy," *Annals of Surgery*, June 1963.

Johnstone, Frederick R. C., M.D., "An Assessment of Prophylactic Antibiotics in General Surgery," *Surgery, Gynecology & Obstetrics*, January 1963.

Erslev, Allan J., M.D., "Drug-Induced Blood Dyscrasias," *JAMA*, May 11, 1964, pp. 531–532.

Brown, George R., M.D., "Toxic Effects of Chloramphenicol on Bone Marrow," letter to the *New England Journal of Medicine*, April 8, 1965, p. 752.

Feingold, David S., M.D., "Antimicrobial Chemotherapeutic Agents: The Nature of Their Action and Selective Toxicity (Concluded)," *New England Journal of Medicine*, October 31, 1963, pp. 957–964.

"Chloramphenicol and Urinary Tract Infections," *Medical Letter on Drugs and Therapeutics*, June 21, 1963.

Schreiner, George E., M.D., "Toxic Nephropathy: Adverse Renal Effects Caused by Drugs and Chemicals," *JAMA*, March 8, 1965, pp. 849–850 (report on damage to kidneys).

"Toxic Drugs and The Liver," editorial in *New England Journal of Medicine*, November 8, 1962, p. 991.

"Caution in the Use of Tetracycline," editorial in *JAMA*, April 20, 1964, p. 315.

Dowling, Harry F., M.D. and Lepper, Mark H., M.D., "Hepactic Reactions to Tetracycline," *JAMA*, April 20, 1964, pp. 307–309.

Schultz, J.C., M.D., *et al.*, "Fatal Liver Disease After Intravenous Administration of Tetracycline in High Dosage," *New England Journal of Medicine*, November 7, 1963, pp. 999–1004 (report on death of pregnant women).

Cohlan, Sidney Q., M.D. "Growth Inhibition of Prematures Receiving Tetracycline," *American Journal of Diseases of Children*, May 1963, pp. 453–461.

Beutler, Ernest, M.D., "Drug-Induced Blood Dyscrasias," *JAMA*, July 13, 1964, pp. 143–144 (drugs causing hemolytic anemia).

"Principal Toxic, Allergic, and Other Adverse Effects of Antimicrobial Agents," *Medical Letter on Drugs and Therapeutics*, August 27, 1965 (list of reactions).

"Enteric Potassium Now Linked as Causal Factor With Intestinal Lesions," *Medical Tribune*, December 28, 1964.

Baker, Daniel R., M.D., *et al.*, "Small-Bowel Ulceration Apparently Associated With Thiazide and Potassium Therapy," *JAMA,* November 16, 1964, pp. 586–590.

"Iatrogenic Ulcers," editorial in *JAMA,* November 16, 1964, p. 681.

Morgenstern, Leon, M.D., *et al.,* "The Circumferential Small-Bowel Ulcer," *JAMA,* February 22, 1965, pp. 637–640.

Boley, Scott J., M.D., *et al.,* "Experimental Evaluation of Thiazides and Potassium as a Cause of Small-Bowel Ulcer," *JAMA,* May 31, 1965, pp. 763–768.

Perera, George A., M.D., address to Symposium on Adverse Drug Reactions, 1965 AMA Convention, New York City (comment on physiological action of drugs).

"Steroid Therapy and Infection," editorial in *JAMA,* November 9, 1963.

Goldstein, Elliot, M.D., and Rambo, Oscar N., M.D., "Cryptococcal Infection Following Steroid Therapy," *Annals of Internal Medicine,* January 1962, pp. 114–120.

Holley, Howard L., M.D., and Hogan, Robert S., M.D., "Present-Day Management of Rheumatoid Arthritis," *GP,* July 1964, pp. 115–125.

Cohen, Albert M., M.D., "Myopathy As a Manifestation of Endocrine Disorders or Drug Therapy," *GP,* May 1964, pp. 89–91.

Irby, Robert, M.D., "Cataracts in Rheumatoid Arthritis Patients Treated with Corticosteroids," *GP,* January 1964, pp. 92–97.

"FDA Issues A Warning to Physicians On Ophthalmic Use of Corticosteroids," *Medical Tribune,* June 10, 1963.

"Drugs Influencing Sexual Desire and Performance: Topical Ophthalmic Steroids and Glaucoma," *Medical Letter on Drugs and Therapeutics,* June 7, 1963.

Henkind, Paul, M.D., "Ocular Complications of Drug Treatment of Rheumatic Disorders," *Annals of Physical Medicine,* August 1964, pp. 258–262, 277.

Lloyd, L.A., M.D., and Hiltz, J.W., M.D., "Ocular Complications of Chloroquine Therapy," *Canadian Medical Association Journal,* March 6, 1965, p. 508.

Essig, Carl F., M.D., address to AMA Symposium on Non-Narcotic Addiction, June 22, 1965 (comments on addictive ability of seven popular nonbarbiturate sedative-hypnotic drugs).

McCormick, T. C., Jr., M.D., "Treatment of Meprobamate Withdrawal Syndrome," *GP,* March 1964, p. 86.

Hollister, Leo E., M.D., and Kosek, Jon C., M.D., "Sudden Death During Treatment With Phenothiazine Derivatives," *JAMA,* June 21, 1965, pp. 1035–1038.

"Irreversible Side Effects of Phenothiazines," editorial in *JAMA,* January 25, 1965, pp. 333–334.

Waitzkin, Leo, M.D., and MacMahon, H. Edward, M.D., "Hepatic Injury Found During Chronic Chlorpromazine Therapy," *Annals of Internal Medicine,* February 1962, pp. 220–232.

Hollister, Leo E., M.D., "Adverse Reactions to Phenothiazines," *JAMA,* July 27, 1964, pp. 311–313.

"Ocular Changes in Chlorpromazine Therapy," editorial in *JAMA,* June 7, 1965, p. 907.

Greiner, A.C., M.D., and Berry, K., M.D., "Skin Pigmentation and Corneal and Lens Opacities With Prolonged Chlorpromazine Therapy," *Canadian Medical Association Journal,* March 14, 1964, pp. 663–665.

Zelickson, Alvin S., M.D., "A New and Unusual Reaction to Chlorpromazine," *JAMA,* April 27, 1964, pp. 394–396 (report on pigmentation changes).

Utz, David C., M.D., *et al.,* "Retroperitoneal Fibrosis in Patients Taking Methysergide," *JAMA,* March 22, 1965, pp. 983–985 (fibrous tissue associated with migraine headache treatment).

"A Special Advisory Committee on Aminopyrine and Dipyrone," press release (HEW-C53) from Food and Drug Administration, September 17, 1964.

Eknoyan, Garabed, M.D., and Matson, James L., M.D., "Acute Renal Failure Caused by Aminopyrine," *JAMA,* December 7, 1964, pp. 934–935.

Hordern, Anthony, M.D., "The Antidepressant Drugs," *New England Journal of Medicine,* June 3, 1965, pp. 1159–1168 (survey of antidepressants and reactions).

"Aminopyrine and Dipyrone," *Medical Letter on Drugs and Therapeutics,* December 18, 1964.

Rubenstein, A. H., M.B., *et al.,* "Acetophenetidin Nephritis and Papillary Necrosis," *Archives of Internal Medicine,* March 1964, pp. 378–393.

Rapoport, A., M.D., *et al.,* "Renal Damage Associated With Chronic Phenacetin Overdose," *Annals of Internal Medicine,* December 1962, pp. 970–980.

Report on Acetophenetidin (Phenacetin), by Ad Hoc Scientific Advisory Committee on Possible Nephrotoxicity Associated With Abuse of Phenacetin-Containing Preparations. Submitted to the Commissioner of the Food and Drug Administration of the Department of Health, Education, and Welfare, April 23, 1964.

"Analgesic Abuse and the Kidney—A Commentary," editorial in *JAMA,* October 19, 1964, pp. 238–239.

Reynolds, Telfer B., M.D., "Phenacetin Nephritis," guest editorial in *Medical Tribune,* January 18, 1963.

Fordham, Christopher C., III, M.D., "Headache Powders and Renal Disease," *Archives of Internal Medicine,* March 1964, pp. 395–400.

Schreiner, George E., M.D., "The Nephrotoxicity of Analgesic Abuse," guest editorial in *Annals of Internal Medicine,* December 1962, pp. 1047–1050.

CHAPTER VII

Beecher, Henry K., M.D., address delivered at a symposium on "Problems and Complexities of Clinical Research," Augusta, Michigan, April 1965.

Blumgart, Herrman L., M.D., "Caring for the Patient," *New England Journal of Medicine,* February 27, 1964, pp. 449–456.

Mitscherlich, A., and Mielke, F., *Doctors of Infamy, the Story of the Nazi Medical Crimes,* New York, Schuman, 1949.

Leys, Duncan, M.B., "Ethical Standards in Clinical Research," letter to *Lancet,* November 14, 1953, p. 1044.

Fisher, D. A., M.D., and Panos, T. C., M.D., " 'Due Caution' and Radioiodine in Children," guest editorial in *American Journal of Diseases of Children,* June 1962, pp. 729–737 (comment on dangers from radioisotopes given to children).

Spach, Madison S., M.D., and Capp, M. Paul, M.D., "Radiation Exposure in Children," *American Journal of Diseases of Children,* June 1962, pp. 750–758 (dangers of medical radiation, measured without endangering children).

Waksman, Byron, M.D., letter to *New England Journal of Medicine,* May 7, 1964, p. 1019 (comment on inadvisability of thymus experiment).

Beecher, Henry K., M.D., "Ethics and Experimental Therapy," editorial in *JAMA,* November 30, 1963, pp. 858–859.

Jefferson, E., M.B., "Retrolental Fibroplasia," *Archives of Disease in Childhood,* August 1952, pp. 329–336 (proof of high-oxygen involvement in RLF obtained without danger to infants).

Forrester, R. M., M.B., *et al.,* "Oxygen and Retrolental Fibroplasia," *Lancet,* August 7, 1954, pp. 258–260.

"Decision Difficult," editorial in *Medical Tribune,* July 20, 1964 (comment on inadvisability of non-human heart transplant).

"Tissue Transplantation," editorial in *New England Journal of Medicine,* October 1, 1964, pp. 738–739 (impracticality of non-human transplant to man).

Robin, Eugene D., M.D., "Rapid Scientific Advances Bring New Ethical Questions," *JAMA,* August 24, 1964, pp. 624–625 (ethics of transplantation examined).

Grant, Roald M., M.D., "Therapeutic Intent," *Ca,* March-April 1964 (experimentation on cancer patients).

Beecher, Henry K., M.D., "Experimentation in Man," *JAMA,* January 31, 1959, pp. 461–477 (suggestion that experimenter first use himself as a subject; other comments).

————, "Some Fallacies and Errors in the Application of Consent in Human Experimentation," editorial in *Clinical Pharmacology and Therapeutics,* March-April 1962, pp. 141–145.

Ladimer, Irving, "Human Experimentation: Medicolegal Aspects," *New England Journal of Medicine,* July 4, 1957, pp. 18–24.

"Human Experimentation: Code of Ethics of the World Medical Association," *British Medical Journal,* July 18, 1964, pp. 177–180 (Declaration of Helsinki).

Bean, William Bennett, M.D., "A Testament of Duty: Some Strictures of Moral Responsibilities in Clinical Research," *Journal of Laboratory and Clinical Medicine,* Vol. 39, 1952, pp. 3–10.

Guttentag, Otto E., M.D., "The Problem of Experimentation on Human Beings: The Physician's Point of View," *Science,* February 27, 1953, pp. 207–210.

"B.M.A. Body Agrees Provisionally on Code for Human Experimentation," *Medical Tribune,* August 2, 1963.

"British Code of Research," editorial in *Medical Tribune,* August 5, 1963.

"Ethics of Human Experimentation," editorial in *British Medical Journal,* July 18, 1964, pp. 135–136.

"Responsibility in Investigations on Human Subjects: Statement by Medical Research Council," *British Medical Journal,* July 18, 1964, p. 178 (B.M.A. Code on Human Experimentation).

"Judgment Difficult," editorial in *New England Journal of Medicine,* August 29, 1963, pp. 479–480 (comment on use of children in experiments).

"The Ethics of Human Experimentation," *New England Journal of Medicine,* May 7, 1964, pp. 1014–1015 (comment on parental consent).

CHAPTER VIII

Hodge, Robert W., *et al.,* "Occupational Prestige in the United States, 1925–1963," *American Journal of Sociology,* November 1964, pp. 286–302 (physician rank in status).

Feldman, Jacob J., "What Americans Think About Their Medical Care," address presented at Annual Meeting of the American Statistical Association, Chicago, December 27–30, 1958.

Churchill, Edward D., M.D., "Should I Study Medicine?" *New England Journal of Medicine,* March 7, 1963, pp. 537–539.

Shaw, Bernard, *The Doctor's Dilemma,* Baltimore, Penguin Books, 1965 (original edition, London, 1906).

What Americans Think of the Medical Profession, Ben Gaffin and Associates, Inc., Chicago, 1955, 68 pp. (AMA-sponsored survey of public opinion of doctors and the profession).

Cahal, Mac F., "What the Public Thinks of the Family Doctor—Folklore and Facts," *GP,* February 1962, pp. 146–157 (results of Opinion Research Corporation survey).

———, "The Image," *JAMA,* July 20, 1963, pp. 183–187 (results of Opinion Research Corporation survey).

Koos, Earl A., " 'Metropolis'—What City Americans Think of Their Medical Services," *American Journal of Public Health,* December, 1955, pp. 1551–1557.

"Many MDs Not Happy About Their Public Image," Pulse of Medicine Report, *Medical Tribune,* June 13–14, 1964 (survey of 1100 doctors on physicians' public image).

Pellegrino, Edmund D., M.D., "Medicine, History, and the Idea of Man," *Annals of the American Academy of Political and Social Science,* March 1963, pp. 9–20.

Pignataro, Frank P., M.D., "The Personality of the Physician," *see* Chapter I.

Bradford, Charles H., M.D., *Medical Aims and Ideals,* address to annual meeting of the Massachusetts Medical Society, *New England Journal of Medicine,* May 23, 1963, pp. 1147–1150.

Yanof, Zale, M.D., "The Personal Physician," *JAMA,* April 20, 1964, p. 306.

Bloom, Samuel W., "The Process of Becoming a Physician," *Annals of the American Academy of Political and Social Science,* March 1963, pp. 77–87.

Miller, Richard C., M.D., "Humility and Compassion—Why Hast Thou Forsaken Us?" *GP,* October 1964, pp. 213–215.

Prinzmetal, Myron, M.D., "The Way to Understanding," *Medical Tribune,* February 1, 1963.

"Most Physicians in Poll Favor a GOP President," Pulse of Medicine Report, *Medical Tribune,* July 11–12, 1964.

Wagner, Mazie Earle, Ph.D., *et al.,* "Comparative Longevity of Physicians and General Population of White Males," *New York State Medical Journal,* July 15, 1964, pp. 1849–1850 (longevity of physicians).

"The Doctor's Health," *Patterns of Disease,* Parke, Davis & Company, Detroit, May–June 1965 (survey report on physician's health, vacations, life expectancy, etc.).

Duffy, John C., M.D., and Littin, Edward M., M.D., "Psychiatric Morbidity of Physicians," *JAMA,* September 28, 1964, pp. 989–992.

Davidson, Henry A., M.D., address to senior medical students at Indiana University School of Medicine (comment on declining doctor prestige).

CHAPTER IX

"Physicians' Economic Health: Excellent," *Medical Economics,* December 13, 1965, pp. 75–127 (survey of physicians earnings).

Cahal, Mac F., "Automated Management Systems," *GP,* May 1965, pp. 175–180.

"Rising Health Costs Analyzed," *Medical World News,* April 12, 1963, pp. 101–102 (U.S. Public Health Service survey on medical costs).

Medical Care Financing and Utilization, Health Economics Series, No. 1, Public Health Service, U. S. Department of Health, Education, and Welfare, 1963, 260 pp. (full text of above survey).

Harris, Seymour E., *The Economics of American Medicine,* New York, Macmillan, 1964, 494 pp.

Somers, Herman M., and Somers, Anne R. *Doctors, Patients and Health Insurance,* Washington, D.C., Brookings Institution, 1961, 576 pp.

"The Doctor and the Welfare Patient," *Modern Medicine,* December 7, 1964, pp. 14–16 (nationwide survey on payments to doctors by welfare departments).

Robbins, Frederick C., M.D., "Special Responsibilities of the Medical School in the Education of Physicians to Serve the Individual and the Community," *Research and Medical Education,* Association of American Medical Colleges, Evanston, Illinois, 1962, pp. 225–226.

CHAPTER X

Lasagna, Louis, M.D., *The Doctors' Dilemmas,* New York, Harper & Brothers, 1962, 306 pp.

Flexner, Abraham, *Medical Education in the United States and Canada,* Bulletin No. 4, Carnegie Foundation for the Advancement of Teaching, 1910.

"Spur to Teaching Is Held Needed for Future Care," *Medical Tribune,* May 10, 1963 (comment by Professor Joseph C. Hinsey of New York Hospital-Cornell Medical Center).

Brown, Willis E., M.D., "Who Teaches the Neophyte?" *JAMA,* January 25, 1964, pp. 287–290.

Compere, Clinton L., M.D., address to American Academy of Orthopaedic Surgeons, Chicago, February 1964.

"Effective Medical Teachers: Born or Made?" *Journal of Medical Education,* January 1963, p. 46 (comment on neglect of teaching at medical school).

Miller, George E., M.D., "The Effect of Research Emphasis on Medical Students and Medical Curricula: The Challenge to Medical Education," *Research and Medical Education,* Report of the Ninth Teaching Institute, Association of American Medical Colleges, Evanston, Illinois, 1961, pp. 57–67.

Robbins, Frederick C., M.D., "Special Responsibilities of the Medical School in the Education of Physicians to Serve the Individual and the Community," *Research and Medical Education,* Report of the Ninth Teaching Institute, AAMC, 1961, pp. 221–226.

Knowles, John H., M.D., "The Balanced Biology of the Teaching Hospital," *New England Journal of Medicine,* Part I: August 22, 1963, pp. 401–406; Conclusion: August 29, 1963, pp. 450–455.

Levine, Samuel A., M.D., "Our Neglect of General Internists and Practitioners in Teaching Hospitals," *JAMA,* October 26, 1964, pp. 286–288.

Garb, Solomon, M.D., "Planning a New Medical College," *Journal of Medical Education,* October 1962, pp. 1133–1135.

Richards, Dickinson W., M.D., "Objectives of a Medical Education in Our Decade," *JAMA,* November 30, 1963, pp. 845–848.

Miller, George E., M.D., "The Institute Discussion: Students and Curriculum," *Research and Medical Education,* Report of the Ninth Teaching Institute, AAMC, 1961, pp. 87–94.

Findley, Thomas, M.D., "The New Curriculum—Four Years or Ten?" *JAMA,* August 10, 1964, p. 518.

Montagu, Ashley, Ph.D., "Anthropology and Medical Education," *JAMA,* February 16, 1963, pp. 577–583.

Gregg, Alan, M.D., *Challenges to Contemporary Medicine,* New York, Columbia University Press, 1956, p. 117 (comment on cadaver in medical education).

Rutstein, David D., M.D., "Physicians for Americans: Two Medical Curricula," *Medical Education and Medical Care,* Report of the Eighth Teaching Institute, AAMC, 1960, pp. 129–138.

"Medical Education: Goal Argued: Practitioner or Scientist?" *Medical Tribune,* June 17, 1963 (comments of Dr. Dwight Wilbur made at Western Forum on Medical Education).

McKeown, Thomas, M.B., "The Responsibility of Medical Education for Initiating Change," *Medical Education and Medical Care,* Report of the Eighth Teaching Institute, AAMC, pp. 150–159.

White, K. L., M.D., and Williams, T. F., M.D., "Ecology of Medical Care," *New England Journal of Medicine,* November 2, 1961, pp. 885–892.

Rammelkamp, Charles H., Jr., M.D., and Chester, Edward M., M.D., "A New Approach to Teaching Ambulatory Medicine," *New England Journal of Medicine,* August 13, 1964, pp. 349–351.

Comroe, Julius H., Jr., M.D., "Objectives of Medical Education: The Effect of Research Emphasis on These," *Research and Medical Education,* Report of the Ninth Teaching Institute, AAMC, 1961, pp. 17–21.

Ratnoff, O.D., "Going to Medical School in Great Britain," from *Pre-Med,* quoted in *JAMA,* October 19, 1964, p. 234.

Gregg, Alan, M.D., *Challenges to Contemporary Medicine,* New York, Columbia University Press, 1956, pp. 118–119 (comment on physician stereotype).

"Physician-to-Population Ratio," editorial in *Medical Tribune,* March 7, 1966.

Rusk, Howard A., M.D., "Manpower for Health: The President's Plans and Their Effect on Present Critical Shortage of Doctors," *New York Times,* January 17, 1965.

"How Many More Medical Schools?" *Datagrams,* Association of American Medical Colleges, January 1960.

"Physician Supply and the Talent Pool: A National Problem," *Datagrams,* Association of American Medical Colleges, June 1962.

Rosinki, Edwin F., "Social Class of Medical Students: A Look at an Untapped Pool of Possible Medical School Applicants," *JAMA,* July 12, 1965, pp. 95–98.

Darley, Ward, M.D., "Physicians for the Future," *Journal of the National Medical Association,* November 1962, pp. 645–651 (statistics on medical manpower available).

"Current Trends in Career Choices Among Medical Graduates," *Datagrams,* Association of American Medical Colleges, March 1962 (percent of internes entering general practice and various specialties).

"Financial Aid to Medical Students," *Datagrams,* Association of American Medical Colleges, March 1960 (cost of four years of medical education).

Perera, George A., M.D., "All in Good Time," *Journal of Medical Education,* May 1964.

Ham, Thomas Hale, M.D., "Medical Education at Western Reserve University," *New England Journal of Medicine,* November 1, 1962, pp. 916–923.

Stokes, Joseph III, M.D., Blodgett, Frederick M., M.D., and Rutstein, David D., M.D., "An Experiment in the Teaching of Family Medicine," *Journal of Medical Education*, July 1963, pp. 539–546 (description of Harvard family medicine plan).

Cooper, John A. D., M.D., and Prior, Moody, "A New Program in Medical Education at Northwestern University," *Journal of Medical Education*, January 1961, pp. 80–90.

Keefer, Chester S., "Experiment with the Medical-School Curriculum at Boston University," *New England Journal of Medicine*, August 20, 1964, p. 401.

Lee, Peter V., M.D., *Medical Schools and the Changing Times: Nine Cases on Experimentation in Medical Education, 1950–1960*, Association of American Medical Colleges, 1962, 90 pp.

Stokes, Joseph III, M.D.; Cliff, Norman; Roche, Charles V.; Rutstein, David D., M.D., "The Effect of a Course in Family Medicine on Medical Student Skills and Attitudes," *Journal of Medical Education*, July 1963, pp. 547–554.

Culver, Perry J., M.D., "Premedical Education and the Selection of Medical Students," *New England Journal of Medicine*, July 11, 1963, pp. 78–84.

Blumgart, Herrman L., M.D., "Preparation for Medical School and Recruitment of Candidates," *New England Journal of Medicine*, July 30, 1964, pp. 238–242.

Willard, William R., M.D., "The Development of the Medical School as a Community Resource," *American Journal of Public Health*, July 1964, pp. 1041–1048.

CHAPTER XI

Stead, Eugene, A., Jr., M.D., "Postgraduate Medical Education in the Hospital," *New England Journal of Medicine*, August 1, 1963, pp. 240-244.

Cross, Roland R., Jr., M.D., "My Answer to the Moonlighting Problem," *RISS* (National Magazine for Residents, Internes, and Senior Students), May 1963, pp. 37–41.

Bonnemaison, Manuel F., M.D., "A South American Looks at a North American Residency," *JAMA*, November 2, 1963, pp. 503–504.

"Medical Education in the United States," supplement in *JAMA*, November 16, 1964, pp. 620–637 (section on internship and residency programs: location, enrollments, etc.).

Knowles, John H., M.D., "The Balanced Biology of the Teaching Hospital," *see* Chapter X.

Harvey, John Collins, M.D., "House Officer Training—Higher Education or Vocational Apprenticeship?" *JAMA*, September 7, 1963, pp. 764–768.

"A Consideration of Residency Training," editorial in *New England Journal of Medicine*, September 10, 1964, pp. 573–574.

Ebert, Richard V., M.D., "The Residency (I)," *New England Journal of Medicine*, September 10, 1964, pp. 547–549.

Burnett, C. H., M.D., *et al.*, "The Residency (II)," *New England Journal of Medicine*, September 10, 1964, pp. 550–552 (comments by community practitioners in North Carolina on residency deficiencies).

Willard, William R., M.D., "Achievement of Reasoned Goals for the First Hospital Year," *JAMA,* July 27, 1964, pp. 279–282.

Campbell, James A., M.D., "The Internship: Origins, Evolution, and Confusion," *JAMA,* July 27, 1964, pp. 273–278.

Peterson, Osler L., M.D., *et al.,* "Appraisal of Medical Students' Abilities as Related to Training and Careers After Graduation," *New England Journal of Medicine,* November 28, 1963, pp. 1174–1182.

Peterson, Osler L., M.D., "Teaching Diagnostic Skills," *New England Journal of Medicine,* November 2, 1964, pp. 1046–1047.

CHAPTER XII

(Source of number of GP's is 1964 survey by AMA. Of the 174,974 physicians in private practice, 45,175 are full-time general practitioners; 23,169 are general practitioners with some speciality practice. Full-time GP's were reduced 26 percent in ranks since 1960, while full-time specialists in private practice rose 14 percent, from 93,680 to 106,630.)

Peterson, Osler L., M.D., *et al.,* "An Analytical Study of North Carolina General Practice," *see* Chapter I.

Clute, Kenneth F., M.D., *The General Practitioner,* Toronto, University of Toronto Press, 1963, 566 pp. (study of general practitioners in two Canadian provinces).

Ingegno, Alfred P., M.D., "Twilight of General Practice," *Medical Economics,* May 7, 1962, pp. 49–55.

"Twilight of General Practice? The Hell You Say!" *Medical Economics,* December 3, 1962, pp. 73–83 (GP's answer Dr. Ingegno).

Foster, G. R., M.D., "The Crisis in General Practice," *JAMA,* March 14, 1964, pp. 109–112.

"Alexander Complex," *GP,* July 1964, pp. 181–182 (editorial comment on remarks by Robert S. Alexander, Ph.D., of Albany Medical College).

DeTar, John S., M.D., "Professors Can Ruin Private Medicine," *Medical Economics,* January 29, 1962, pp. 23–26.

Voy, Robert, M.D., address to the American Academy of General Practice, at Kansas City (reported in *GP,* October 1963).

Cahal, Mac F., "The Image," *JAMA, see* Chapter VIII (results of Opinion Research Center survey).

"The Characteristics of Hospital and Physicians Used for Medical Care by New Jersey Physicians and Their Families, 1955–58," Chapter 7, Part A of *Prepayment for Medical and Dental Care in New York State,* School of Public Health and Administrative Medicine, Columbia University, October 1962, pp. 177–188 (report of near-unanimous choice of specialists by New Jersey physicians seeking care for self or family).

"GPs Won't Become Specialists," *Medical World News,* April 26, 1963, pp. 38–39 (vote to turn down family-practice specialty board).

Baldwin, Richard D., M.D., "General Practice: A Concept and Its Challenges," *GP,* November 1963, pp. 181–189.

James, George, M.D., MPH, "The General Practitioner of the Future," *see* Chapter II.

Young, Lawrence E., M.D., "Education and Roles of Personal Physicians in Medical Practice," *JAMA*, March 21, 1964, p. 927.

Hunt, John H., M.D., "General Practice in the World Today," *GP*, November 1964, pp. 203–223.

"The Vanishing American," editorial in *Medical Tribune*, January 13, 1964.

Bean, William B., M.D., "Opportunity for Research in General Practice," *JAMA*, February 20, 1954, pp. 639–642.

"The Family Physician," editorial in *New England Journal of Medicine*, June 11, 1964, pp. 1311–1312.

Bower, Anthony D., M.D., "General Practice—An Analysis and Some Suggestions," *New England Journal of Medicine*, September 26, 1963, pp. 667–673.

"General Practice of Medicine Held in Need of a Revolution," *Medical Tribune*, January 23–24, 1965.

Silver, George A., M.D., *A Report on the Family Health Maintenance Demonstration,* Cambridge, Harvard University Press, 1963, 359 pp.

"Training Program for Family Practice," editorial in *New England Journal of Medicine*, January 17, 1963 (family medicine fellowship at Harvard Medical School).

CHAPTER XIII

Schade, George H., M.D., *et al.*, "Pediatrics as a Career," *New Physician*, July 1962, pp. 210–214.

"Congenital Defects on Rise Says Physician," release from University of Michigan on address by Dr. Donald C. Smith of their School of Public Health, October 30, 1963.

McKay, R. James, Jr., M.D., "Dissatisfactions with Pediatrics," guest editorial in *New Physician*, July 1962, pp. 208–209 (result of survey on pediatrician dissatisfaction).

Richmond, Julius B., M.D., "Opportunities and Training for a Career in Academic Pediatrics," *New Physician*, July 1962, pp. 219–221.

Shaw, Edward B., M.D., "Training for Pediatric Practice," *New Physician*, pp. 222–225.

"Opportunities and Training in Pediatric Subspecialties," *New Physician*, July 1962, pp. 236–243.

Stitt, Pauline G., M.D., "U.S. Ranks Eleventh in the Care of Infants," *Modern Hospital*, January 1964, p. 81.

McKay, R. James, M.D., and Lucey, Jerold F., M.D., "Neonatology," *New England Journal of Medicine*, June 11, 1964, pp. 1292–1298.

Keitel, Hans G., M.D., "The Need for Neonatology," guest editorial in *Medical Tribune*, January 1, 1963.

————, "A Neonatologic Challenge," letter to the *Medical Tribune*, April 1, 1963.

CHAPTER XIV

Bean, William B., M.D., "The Endeavor of Internal Medicine, 1859–1959," *AMA Archives of Internal Medicine,* December 1959, pp. 851–861.

Adams, Wright, M.D., "Internal Medicine Under Stress," *JAMA,* December 7, 1963, pp. 934–937.

Second Trussell report, *see* Chapter I.

Kroeger, Hilda J., M.D., MPH, *et al.,* "The Office Practice of Internists: 1. The Feasibility of Evaluating Quality of Care," *JAMA,* August 2, 1965, pp. 371–376.

"What Is an Internist?" editorial, *GP,* July 1963, p. 79.

Bean, William B., M.D., "Graduate Education for General Practice From the Viewpoint of Internal Medicine," *JAMA,* April 27, 1957, pp. 1592–1593.

Bates, Richard C., M.D., "The Internist: An Interpretive Portrait," *Medical Economics,* March 9, 1964, pp. 109–155.

CHAPTER XV

Focus on Research, National Osteopathic Foundation, Chicago, 20 pp. (description of osteopathic theory and history).

A Statistical Study of the Osteopathic Profession, Membership and Statistics Department, American Osteopathic Association, Chicago, May 1964, 22 pp.

Focus on Osteopathic Hospitals, American Osteopathic Association, 20 pp.

Mills, Lawrence W., *The Osteopathic Profession and Its Colleges,* American Osteopathic Association, Booklet No. 20, 36 pp. (history of profession and training of students, including curriculum of osteopathic colleges).

"Educational Standards for Osteopathic Colleges," *Journal of the American Osteopathic Association,* January 1962, pp. 404–407.

Educational Supplement (reprinted from January 1965 *Journal of AOA*), Office of Education, American Osteopathic Association, 28 pp.

Pearson, H. Dale, D. O., "Advisory Board for Osteopathic Specialists and Boards of Certification," *Journal of the American Osteopathic Association,* April 1964, pp. 745–780 (details on osteopathic specialties and their requirements).

Abstract of Laws and Regulations Governing the Practice of Osteopathy, American Osteopathic Association, 1964, 24 pp.

Annual Report of the Osteopathic Profession, American Osteopathic Association, 1964.

"Policy on Osteopaths," *JAMA,* November 17, 1962, p. 779 (clarification of medical profession's policy on osteopaths; description of California merger).

Pollock, Wayne, M.D., "The Present Relationship of Osteopathy and Scientific Medicine," *World Medical Journal,* September 1962, pp. 337–339.

"D.O.s to Stress Difference from M.D.s," *Modern Medicine,* August 3, 1964, p. 18.

White Paper: AOA-AMA Relationships, American Osteopathic Association, 20 pp. (detailed description of osteopathic profession's stand on merger and affiliation with medical doctors).

CHAPTER XVI

American Medical Association: Basic Facts About the American Medical Association . . . Its History . . . Its Purpose . . . Its Accomplishments, American Medical Association, Chicago, 1964, 20 pp.

Freymann, John Gordon, M.D., "Leadership in American Medicine," *New England Journal of Medicine,* April 2, 1964, pp. 710–720 (AMA history and commentary).

"The American Medical Association: Power, Purpose, and Politics in Organized Medicine," comment, *Yale Law Journal,* May 1954, pp. 938–1022.

Polissar, Jan, M.D., letter to *New England Journal of Medicine,* September 26, 1963.

Nadas, Alexander S., M.D., "Certain AMA Policies," letter to *New England Journal of Medicine,* July 11, 1963.

Burrow, James G., *AMA: Voice of American Medicine,* Baltimore, The Johns Hopkins Press, 1963, 430 pp.

Principles of Medical Ethics, American Medical Association, Chicago.

O'Rourke, Paul F., M.D., "Enemy of the People," *Harvard Medical Alumni Bulletin,* Fall 1961, pp. 36–41 (partial account of Dr. O'Rourke's experience).

Daily, Edwin F., M.D., "The Health Insurance Plan of Greater New York," *Ontario Medical Review,* June 1961.

Action of the House of Delegates of the American Medical Association on the Report of the Commission on Medical Care Plans, American Medical Association, Atlantic City, June 8–12, 1959, 15 pp. and tables.

AMPAC Offers You The Impact of an Effective, Coordinated National Political Action Program, American Medical Political Action Committee, Chicago.

How the Opinion Maker Makes Opinion in Politics, American Medical Political Action Committee.

Working Within the Party, Political Education Series, Pamphlet No. 4, American Medical Political Action Committee.

The Medical PAC Structure, Political Education Series, Pamphlet No. 5, American Medical Political Action Committee.

Mazzarella, V., M.D., letter to *New England Journal of Medicine,* September 26, 1963.

Page, Irvine H., M.D., "Needed—National Academy of Medicine," editorial in *Modern Medicine,* July 20, 1964, pp. 77–79.

CHAPTER XVII

Bean, William B., M.D., "Recent Setbacks in Medicine," *Northwest Medicine,* February 1956.

Cluff, Leighton E., M.D., *et al.,* "Studies on the Epidemiology of Adverse Drug Reactions," *JAMA,* June 15, 1964, pp. 976–983 (patients admitted to public medical service of Johns Hopkins Hospital for reason of drug-induced sickness).

Dowling, Harry F., M.D., "How Do Practicing Physicians Use New Drugs?" *JAMA,* July 27, 1963, pp. 233–236.

Modell, Walter, M.D., "The Drug Explosion," editorial in *Clinical Pharmacology and Therapeutics,* January-February 1961, pp. 1–7.

Spain, David M., M.D., *The Complications of Modern Medical Practices, see* Chapter I.

Wilkins, Lawson, M.D., "Modern Materia Medica," *American Journal of Diseases of Children,* November 1962, pp. 449–456.

"Toxic Drugs," editorial in *New England Journal of Medicine,* July 16, 1964, pp. 157–158 (comment on prescribing for symptomatic relief).

Alvarez, Walter C., M.D., "A Drug or a Chemical Can Cause the Disease," editorial in *Modern Medicine,* August 31, 1964.

Shirkey, Harry C., M.D., "Drug Dosage for Infants and Children," *JAMA,* August 9, 1965, pp. 443–446.

"Drug Dosage for Infants and Children," *Medical Letter on Drugs and Therapeutics,* January 1, 1965.

The Fond du Lac Study, 1955, American Medical Association, Chicago.

Dichter, Ernest, "The Doctor's Psychology and Selling," *Drug and Cosmetic Industry,* August 1965.

May, Charles D., M.D., "Selling Drugs by 'Educating' Physicians," *Journal of Medical Education,* January 1961, p. 1.

"Drug Samples Available for MDs Are Kept and Used by Majority," Pulse of Medicine Report, *Medical Tribune,* September 27, 1963.

"References Used in Drugs Advertisements," *Medical Letter on Drugs and Therapeutics,* July 5, 1963.

GP, editorial, June 1964, p. 75 (comment on physicians' owning drug stores).

"The Development of New Drugs," editorial in *New England Journal of Medicine,* February 21, 1963.

Modell, Walter, M.D., "Hazards of New Drugs," *Science,* March 22, 1963, pp. 1180–1185.

Modell, Walter, M.D., "Safety in New Drugs," *JAMA,* October 12, 1964, pp. 141–144.

CHAPTER XVIII

"1963 Professional-Liability Survey," *JAMA,* September 14, 1964, pp. 859–866 (prepared by the Law Department of the AMA from sampling of 14,616 doctors nationwide. Statistics on malpractice claims).

"Your Professional Liability: 131 Questions and Answers," *JAMA,* September 7, 1963, pp. 789–806.

Shindell, Sidney, M.D., " 'Epidemiology' of Professional Liability Losses," *JAMA,* November 30, 1964.

Kramer, Charles, *Medical Malpractice,* Practising Law Institute, New York, 1962, 70 pp.

Kramer, Charles, "Reply to 'Medical Professional Liability,' " draft of an answer to Bernard D. Hirsh of the Law Department of the AMA.

Julien, Alfred S., "Medical Malpractice from the Plaintiff's Viewpoint," speech given before the Tennessee Bar Association, June 8, 1961.

Appellate Division, Superior Court of New Jersey, 1954, 30 N.J. Super., *Steiginga v. Thron* (decision and comments of Justice Clapp).

News Letter, American Trial Lawyers Association, Watertown, Massachusetts (case material from various monthly editions, 1963–1965).

Journal of the American Trial Lawyers Association (previously NAACA Law Journal), Vols. 26–31, Boston, 1960–1965 (case material from various annual editions).

Louisell, David W., and Williams, Harold, *Trial of Medical Malpractice Cases,* Matthew Bender & Company, Albany, New York, 1960, 1022 pp. (plus current supplements).

Lambert, Thomas F., Jr., "Conspiracy of Silence of Medical Profession," *NACCA Law Journal,* Vol. 30, 1964, pp. 93–97 (discussion of difficulty in obtaining expert witness, and principle of *res ipsa loquitur*).

Cahal, Mac F., "Medicolegal Case Studies: Breach of Contract," *GP,* November 1963, pp. 177–179 (promise to cure).

Chayet, Neil L., "Law-Medicine Notes: Abandonment of the Patient," *New England Journal of Medicine,* June 3, 1965, pp. 1172–1173 (case histories and discussion).

Cahal, Mac F., "Medicolegal Trends: Abandonment," *GP,* June 1965, pp. 181–182.

"Physician Liable Because of Failure to Warn Patient of Dangers of Gold Injections," *Citation,* Law Department, American Medical Association, October 15, 1965.

Chayet, Neil L., "Law-Medicine Notes: Hospital Responsibility for Medical Care," *New England Journal of Medicine,* March 3, 1966, pp. 507–508.

CHAPTER XIX

Shaw, Bernard, *The Doctor's Dilemma, see* Chapter VIII.

Truman, Stanley R., M.D., "Report to the Board of Trustees of the American Medical Association of the Committee on Medical Practices," *see* Chapter III.

"Disciplinary Action in the Medical Profession," Judicial Council of the American Medical Association, *JAMA,* December 21, 1964, pp. 1077–1078.

"Medical Disciplinary Actions, 1962," Judicial Council of the American Medical Association, *JAMA,* October 5, 1963, pp. 78–79.

Shindell, Sidney, M.D., "A Survey of the Law of Medical Practice: 1. The Legal Status of the Physician," *JAMA,* August 16, 1965, pp. 601–606.

"A Physician Looks at Review Committees," *Health Insurance Trends,* Health Insurance Council, New York, March 1965.

"Medical Licensure Statistics for 1964," *JAMA,* June 7, 1965, pp. 855–904 (statistics on passing of state licensing examinations; licensing of foreign graduates; National Board examinations, etc.).

"California Medical Examiners Get More Disciplinary Power," *Medical Tribune,* October 13, 1965.

Report of the Senate Factfinding Committee on Public Health and Safety, Senate of the State of California, February 1965, 56 pp. (material leading to new California medical disciplinary laws; Senator Walter W. Stiern, committee chairman).

"Legal Sanctions Held Needed to Control Incompetent MDs," *Medical Tribune,* March 14, 1966 (comment by Dr. James J. Regan).

Peterson, Osler L., M.D., "Evaluation of the Quality of Medical Care," *New England Journal of Medicine,* December 5, 1963, pp. 1238–1245.

Peterson, Osler, L., M.D., *et al.,* "Appraisal of Medical Students' Abilities as Related to Training and Careers After Graduation," *see* Chapter XI (report on MCAT test prediction of medical-school performance; comment on awarding M.D. after demonstrating minimum competence).

Index

Index

Abandonment cases, 84, 89, 91, 92-93, 525-27

Abdominal aortic aneurysm, 135-36

Abortion, 540

Accident-prone environment of hospitals, 183-85

Accreditation, hospital, 217-18, 220, 569

Acetophenetidin, 280-81

Adenoidectomy, 102

Administrators, hospital, 414

Adrenal exhaustion, 271

Adriani, Dr. John, 116, 117

Aides, doctors', 78, 80, 90-92, 227, 350, 351

Air Force, U. S., 405-06

Alexander, Robert S., 424

Allen, Dr. Garrott, 178

Allen, Dr. John, 365

Alvarez, Dr. Walter C., 66, 490

Ambulance service, 229-30, 565

American Academy of General Practice, 111, 144, 148, 216, 322, 358, 427, 429, 431

American Association of Medical Assistants, 91

American Board of Internal Medicine, 443, 448

American Board of Surgery, 204

American Collectors Association, 350

American College of Cardiology, 131

American College of Obstetricians, 210

American College of Physicians, 216, 568

American College of Surgeons, 189, 203, 204, 205, 216, 225, 228, 229, 429, 516, 568

American Diabetes Association, 54, 55

American Heart Association, 63, 144, 503

American Hospital Association, 217, 568

American Medical Association (AMA), 3, 19, 21, 63, 84, 92, 94, 95, 111, 144, 148, 220, 279, 318, 320-21, 336, 359, 393, 394, 404, 413, 451, 456, 457, 458, 459, 460, 463-82, 493, 499, 503, 509, 515, 536, 537, 545, 546, 560, 568, 569

American Medical Political Action Committee (AMPAC), 337, 471, 479-81

American Medical Union, 468

American Medical Women's Association, 224

American Osteopathic Association, 453, 458

American Red Cross, 569

American Society of Anesthesiology, 165

American Society of Internal Medicine, 358, 442, 448

American Trial Lawyers Association, 526

Anderson, Odin W., 16

Anderson, Clinton, 548

Anesthesia mortality, 162-73, 207, 208, 273-74

Anesthesiologists, 162, 164-65, 169, 171, 172-73

Angina pectoris, 59

Angiograms, 246-47

Annis, Dr. Edward R., 4, 205, 471

Antibiotics, 105, 106, 108, 152, 153, 155, 261-67, 487-88

Anticholinergics, 124-25

Anticoagulants, 259-61

Antidepressants, 278, 489

Antihypertensive drugs, 269

Appel, Dr. James Z., 217

Appendectomies, 189-90, 211

Archambault, George F., 179

Armed Forces Institute of Pathol-ogy, U. S., 137

Arnold, Matthew, 491

Aspergillosis, 263

Aspiration of vomitus, 164, 167-69

Aspirin, 279, 281

Assembly-line medicine, 77-79

Associated Credit Bureaus of America, 351

Association of American Medical Colleges (AAMC), 383, 389, 394, 459, 478, 479, 560

Atchley, Dr. Dana, 429

Atomic Energy Commission, 291

Austrian, Dr. Robert, 106, 108

Automation, 97

Avedis, Dr., 21

Axelrod, Dr. S. J., 21

Babcock, Dr. Kenneth B., 159, 194, 218

Bacteria, hospital, 151-62

Baldwin, Dr. Richard D., 428

Bane Committee report, 394

Banting, Sir Frederick Grant, 56

Barclay, Dr. William R., 113

Barker, Kenneth, 180, 181, 183

Barr, Dr. David, 237, 240, 258, 266, 267, 284

Bates, Dr. Richard C., 448

Bauer, Dr. Raymond B., 132, 133

BCG (Bacille Calmette Guerin), 112-13

Bean, Atherton, 94

Bean, Dr. William Bennett, 11, 97, 103, 141, 309, 310-11, 483

Beaton, Dr. Lindsay E., 143, 147, 318, 337

Becker *v.* Janinski, 84

Bed falls in hospitals, 183-85

Beecher, Dr. Henry K., 165, 171, 287, 288, 298, 304, 306, 309, 310
Bennett, Wallace F., 480
Bernhard, Dr. William F., 116
Best, Dr. Charles Herbert, 56
Beyer, Dr. Karl H., Jr., 485
Bierce, Ambrose, 143
Bigley, Dr. Robert, 407
Binder, Dr. Lee, 176
Biomathematics, 70-72
Biopsy, 244-45, 294, 295
Birch Society, John, 337, 338
Black and Skaggs Associates, 354, 358
Blackmore, Dr. Richard, 329
Blatz, Hanson, 251-53
Blood groups and types, 174-75
Blood-transfusion accidents, 173-79
Bloom, Sol, 327
Blue Cross, 74, 189, 215, 404, 473, 475, 550, 569
Blue Shield, 98, 358, 405, 473, 475, 541, 542, 543, 569
Blumgart, Dr. Herrman L., 288, 308
Bonnemaison, Dr. Manuel F. E., 412, 413
Bradford, Dr. Charles H., 319, 325
Brain, Sir Russell, 26
Brand-name drugs, 508
Breast cancer, 51-52, 65
Brightmire, Paul W., 520-21
British Medical Association, 311
British Medical Research Council, 304
Bronchitis, chronic, 60-62
Bronchoscope, 240
Brown, Edmund G. (Pat), 470
Brown, Dr. Willis E., 376, 382-83
Brudzynski, Dr. C., 171
Bugbee, Dr. Lawrence M., 90
Buhler, Dr. Victor B., 68

Bureau of the Census, 111
Business expenses, doctors', 346
Businessmen, doctors as, 335-36, 343-66
Button, Dr. John C., 458

Cahn, Ira L., 86-87
Calcium, radioactive (Ca-45), 291
"Calculated risk," 283
Campanella, Joseph W., 531
Campbell, Dr. James A., 411
Canadian Hospital Association, 195
Candidiasis, 263
Cartwright, Dr. G. E., 283
Catheterization, 241-44, 288, 292-93, 303
Cerebral vascular disease, 114
Cervical cancer, 45, 48–49
Chadwick, Dr. Donald R., 249
Chapanis, Dr. A., 183
Chayet, Neil L., 527
Cherkasky, Dr. Martin, 7, 8, 19, 500
Chester, Dr. Edward, 389
Childbirth, 207-11, 212
Child medical care, *see* Pediatricians
Chiropractors, 450, 458, 459
Chloramphenicol, 263, 264-66, 298, 492
Chloroquine, 272
Chlorpromazine, 276-77
Chodosh, Dr. Sanford, 60
Cholecystectomy, 200-01
Cholecystogram, 201
Cholecystostomy, 200
Cholera, 142
Cholesterol, 259
Churchill, Dr. Edward D., 319

Cirrhosis, 236
Clatworthy, Dr. H. William, 202
Cleanliness, surgical, 156-58
Cleveland Clinic, 75, 161, 567
Cline, Dr. John, 457
Cloxacillin, 152, 487
Cluff, Dr. Leighton, 161, 238, 255, 256, 257, 258, 283, 285, 485
Clute, Dr. Kenneth R., 420
Code of Human Experimentation, 312-13
Coleman, Dr. Frank, 480-81
Collection agencies, 352
Collection of bills, 349-54
Collection letters, 350-51, 361
College of American Pathologists, 68
Colleges, medical, *see* Schools, medical
Colon surgery, 201
Commerce Department, U. S., 345
Commission on Drug Safety, 492
Commission on Heart Disease, Cancer and Stroke, President's, 114
Commission on Professional and Hospital Activities (CPHA), 102, 176, 211-12
Compere, Dr. Clinton L., 383
Computer diagnosis, 70-72
Comroe, Dr. Julius, 390
Condit, George W., 356, 363
Consent form, human experimentation, 305-06
Consultants, management, 354-56, 363
Consultation, 218-19
Continuing medical education, 143-48
Controlled experiment, 296-99, 307
Conventions, medical, 144-45
Cooper, Dr. David R., 247, 248

Corticosteroids, 269-71
Cortisone, 269, 270, 271, 281
Cost of medical education, 398-99
Council on Medical Education and Hospitals, AMA, 21, 479
County hospitals, 220-22
County medical societies, 463-64, 465, 472, 476-77
"Covering" doctor, 88-89
Credit cards, 353-54
Credit checks, 354
Creery, Dr. C. D., 242
Crosby, Dr. Edwin L., 397
Cross, Dr. Roland R., 405
Crowley, Dr. Daniel F., Jr., 349
Curran, William J., 516
Cyclopropane, 166
Cystoscope, 240

Darley, Dr. Ward, 397
Davidson, Dr. Henry A., 342
Davis, Gordon, 226
Davis, Dr. Hugh J., 48
Davis, Dr. Nathan Smith, 468
Day, Dr. Emerson, 46, 49, 50
Death certificates, 162-63
Death rate, 16
DeBakey, Dr. Michael, 110, 135
D'Eloia, Dr. Angelo S., 469-70
Delp, Dr. Mahlon, 449
Demerol, 339
Desautels, Dr. Robert E., 243
Descartes, René, 324
Detail men, *see* Drug salesmen
DeTar, Dr. John S., 82, 319, 424
Deterling, Dr. Ralph A., Jr., 122
Diabetes, 8, 54-56, 450-51
Diagnosis, medical, 7-8, 23-75; early, importance of, 45-46, 49, 52, 74

Dichter, Dr. Ernest, 93, **97**
Digitalis, 258-59, 293
Dillof, Henry H., 521
Dillon, Dr. John B., 165
Dineen, Dr. Peter, 156
Director of medical education
(DME), 414-15
Disciplining of doctors, 472, 534-
53
Dithiazanine, 492-93
Diuretics, 267-68, 488
Doctor-caused illnesses, *see* Iatro-
genic disease
Doctorless hospitals, 222-24
Doctor-patient relations, 79-99
Dominick, Peter, 480
Dooley, Dr. Donald M., 260
Dorman, Dr. Gerald D., 20
Dowell, Dr. Donald M., 364
Dowling, Dr. Harry F., 484, 491,
494-95, 514
Doyle, Arthur Conan, 329
Doyle, Dr. James C., 190, 191
Dripps, Dr. Robert D., 162, 163
Drug advertisements, 483, 493-
94, 495-96, 499-503, 508-09,
513
Drug industry, *see* Pharmaceuti-
cal industry
Drug reactions, 255-83
Drug salesmen, 493-94, 496, 497-
98, 504, 508
Drugstores, 497, 499, 503-04, 506
Dryer, Dr. Bernard V., 142
Dye, Mary C., 226

Eden, Murray, 71
Edsall, Dr. Geoffrey, 111

Education, medical, 369-401;
continuing, 143-48; postgradu-
ate, 145-48, 402-16, 483; *see
also* Schools, medical; Training
programs
Eichenwald, Dr. Heinz F., 160
Electrocardiogram examination,
56, 57-59, 70, 74
Elkinton, Dr. J. Russell, 121, 122
Ellis, Dr. John R., 21
Ellis, Dr. Laurence B., 147
Elson, Dr. K. A., 35
Emergency house calls, 86-88
Emergency-panel system, 87, 88
Emergency rooms, hospital, 215,
225-29, 414, 526, 564-65
Emotional climate of hospitals,
230-33
Emphysema, pulmonary, 61-62
Endoscopy, 240-41
Epstein, Dr. Robert, 171
Errera, Dr. Paul, 226
Ertel, Dr. Paul Y., 60
Esselstyn, Dr. Caldwell B., 477
Essig, Dr. Carl F., 275
Evans, Dr. Lester J., 16, 97
Evening hours practice, 84-85
Ether, 162, 166
Ethics, medical, 544-46
Experimentation, human, 286-
313; Code of, 312-13

Face masks, surgeon's, 156
Fairchild, Dr. John P., 161
Family doctor, *see* General prac-
titioners
Farber, Dr. Seymour M., 50
Farmers Union Medical Service,
475

Federal Trade Commission, 352
Fees, in anesthesia, 172; doctors',
    360-66, 422, 542-43, 545; in-
    ternists', 442, 445; splitting of,
    349, 429
Feigen, Dr. Gerald M., 334
Feinstein, Dr. Alvan, 109
Feldman, Dr. Herman E., 183
Feldman, Jacob J., 318, 322
Fernandez-Herlihy, Dr. Luis, 272
Fike, Dr. Winston W., 273
Findley, Dr. Thomas, 374
Finland, Dr. Maxwell, 153, 511
Fishbein, Dr. Morris, 24, 466
Flexner, Abraham, 13, 100, 371-
    72
Flexner reforms, 13, 372, 373,
    408, 415, 456
Fluoroscopes, 250, 252-53, 292
Flying Physicians Association,
    332
Fond du Lac Study, 493, 496
Fontana, Dr. Robert S., 50
Food and Drug Administration,
    278, 279, 280, 310, 484, 495,
    496, 498, 511, 513, 523
Fopeano, Dr. John V., 327
Foreign physicians, unlicensed,
    223
Foreman, Dr. Forrest H., 359
Foster, Dr. G. R., Jr., 424, 431
Fountain Committee, 484, 495
Fraad, Dr. Lewis, 435
Franklin, Dr. Trevor, 487
Fraser, Dr. C. G., 271
Freedman, George I., 507
Free tuition program, 559
Freidson, Elliott, 28
French, Dr. W. Edward, 233
Freymann, Dr. John, 465, 474
Friedman, Dr. Eli A., 28, 410
Frohman, Dr. I. P., 93
Frossmann, Dr. Werner, 303
Fuchsberg, Jacob D., 519, 522,
    529-30, 532

"Functional" illness, 38-40
Furadantin, 493, 495-96

Gaffin Associates, Ben, 320, 493,
    509
Galen, 123, 328
Gall bladder surgery, 200-01
Garb, Dr. Solomon, 386
Garland, Dr. L. Henry, 26, 36-37,
    64
Gas gangrene, 115
Gastrectomy, 128-29
Gates, Frederick C., 371
Gearing, Donald F., 349, 354,
    357, 360
Gellis, Dr. Sydney S., 438
General practitioners, 19, 26-27,
    73, 78, 84, 87, 207, 340, 348,
    361, 362, 396, 419-31, 566; as
    surgeons, 204-05
Geneva Code of the World Med-
    ical Association, 98, 308
Gerald, Sister Mary M., 179
Gershon-Cohen, Dr. J., 65
Ghost surgery, 205-07
Gifts to doctors, 504-05
Gilbertson, Dr. Victor A., 46, 50
Ginsberg, Frances, 156, 160, 195
Gladstone, Dr. Sidney A., 49
Glaser, Herman B., 526
Glaucoma, 53-54
Glover, Dr. J. A., 105
Goddard, Dr. James L., 112
Goldberger, Dr. Joseph, 303-04
Goldenberg, Dr. Ira S., 156
Good, Dr. Robert, 105
Goodman, Dr. Louis, 488
Goulder, Dr. L. Lynton, 338
Government hospitals, 212, 220-
    22

Grady, Dr., 178
Grajo, Dr. Mario, 242
Grant, Dr. Roald N., 47, 300-01
Greenbrier Clinic, 75
Greengold, Dr. Myron C., 359
Gregg, Dr. Alan, 5, 375, 392
Gregg, Dr. N. M., 142
Gregory, Dr. James, 219
Gresham, Perry, 329
Griem, Dr. Melvin, 249
Groom, Dr. Dale, 60
Gross, Dr. Robert E., 5, 202
Group Health Association, 473, 475-76
Group medical practice, 17, 356-58, 359, 401, 469
Guilds, doctor, 320
Guttentag, Dr. O. E., 309, 310
Guttmacher, Dr. Alan F., 192, 208, 211
Gynecological surgery, 192-93

Hagebush, Dr. Omer E., 68
Hahnemann, Dr. Samuel, 457
Halothane, 166
Halstead, Dr. James A., 319
Halstead, Dr. William Stewart, 51
Hammurabic code, 320
Hamwi, Dr. George J., 55
Hanson, Dr. Daniel J., 253
Harding, Dr. Harry B., 152
Hardyment, Dr. A. F., 282
Harris, John J., 528-29
Harrison, Dr. Tinsley R., 375
Hartford, Maj. Gen. Thomas J., 221
Hass, Dr. Albert, 61
Hawley, Dr. Paul R., 204
Health, doctors', 339
Health Information Foundation, 204, 232, 321

Health Insurance Plan (HIP), 469, 473-74, 476, 477, 528
Health screenings, multiphasic, 35
Healy, Dr. Robert E., 549
Heart disease, 56-60, 62-63, 71; iatrogenic, 254-55
Hellerstein, Dr. Herman K., 145-46
Helpern, Dr. Milton, 17
Hematologists, 179
Hempelmann, Dr. Louis, 249
Henderson, Lawrence J., 3
Hepatitis, 177-78
Hernia, 150-51, 198-200
Herrick, Ronald and Richard, 119
Hildick-Smith, Dr. G., 156
Hinkle, Dr. Lawrence E., 58
Hinsey, Joseph C., 382
Hippocrates, 4, 24, 110, 123, 320, 326, 390
Hippocratic oath, 287, 305, 307, 308
Hirsch, Bernard D., 519
Hirschowitz, Dr. Basil I., 123, 126, 127
History-taking, 27-29, 74
Hoag, Dr. J. Marshall, 455
Hodgins, Eric, 231
Hogan, Dr. Robert, 271
Holley, Dr. Howard, 271
Hollister, Dr. Leo E., 276, 489
Homeopaths, 457
Hospital infection, 151-62, 211
Hospitals, 10, 149-233, 565-67; homeopathic, 457; osteopathic, 452; pediatric, 438; *see also* County hospitals; Government hospitals; Municipal hospitals; Proprietary hospitals; Voluntary hospitals
House calls, 18, 81-82, 83-84, 85-88, 340
Housekeeping, hospital, 161-62
House staff, hospital, 213, 403

Hudson, Dr. Phoebe, 82

Human experimentation, 286-313; Code of, 312-13

Humphrey, Hubert, 246

Hunt, Dr. Thomas C., 125

Hunter, Dr. John, 303

Hussey, Dr. Hugh H., 495

Hutton, Dr. Margaret M., 439

Hyperbaric oxygen therapy, 115-17

Hypertensive heart disease, 56

Hyperthermia, 166-67

Hyperuricemia, 267

Hypochondriacs, 41-42

Hypodermic needles, 253-54

Hypoxemia, 171

Hysterectomy, 176, 190-92

Iatrogenic (doctor-caused) disease, 10-11, 234-85

Idealism, medical, failure of, 98-99

Illinois Welfare Agency, 365

Image, the doctor's, 3-4, 317-19, 350

"Imaginary" ailments, 42

Imipramine, 278

Immunization, general, 111-13

Impetigo, 159

Income of general practitioners, 419-20, 422, 423; of internes, 404, 406; of physicians, 17, 345-49

Income-tax evasion, 540

Incorporated doctors, 359-60

Infant mortality, 15, 160-61, 207, 212, 438

Information, sharing with patient, 93-95

Ingegno, Dr. Alfred P., 232, 421, 422

Injections, 92, 235, 236, 254

Insulin therapy, 56, 150

Insurance, hospital, see Blue Cross; Blue Shield; Commercial insurance; Malpractice insurance; Medicare

Intellectuality, doctor's, dearth of, 329-31

Internal Revenue Service, 359, 360

Internes, 181, 213, 220, 221, 284, 402-16, 419, 505, 561-62

Internists, 30, 73, 87, 97, 361, 362, 363, 441-49; see also Specialists

Intramuscular injections, 92, 254

Intravenous injections, 91, 235, 236, 254

Investments, doctors', 334-36

Iodine, 131, 290

Iproniazid, 278

Irby, Dr. Robert, 272

Isotopes, radioactive, 290–91

Ivy, Dr. Andrew C., 309

James, Dr. George, 45

Jaundice, 166, 289

Jefferson, Dr. E., 297

Johnson, Dr. O. J., 536

Johnson, Dr. Willard P., 133

Johnstone, Dr. Frederick R. C., 264

Joint Commission on Accreditation of Hospitals, 21, 162, 216-18, 220, 552, 566, 568

Judd, Dr. Walter H., 336

Julien, Alfred S., 519

Kaiser Foundation Health Plan, 75
Kass, Dr. E. H., 242
Keitel, Dr. Hans G., 439-40
Kelly, Professor E. Lowell, 398
Kennedy, Dr. Robert H., 225, 226, 227, 229, 565
Kerrin, Dr. Joseph F., 338
Keyes, Dr. John W., 254, 255
Killion, Raymond F., 543
Kilpatrick, Dr. G. S., 36
King, Cecil R., 471
King, Dr. John F., 250
Kirsner, Dr. Joseph B., 123, 124, 125, 127
Kline, Dr. Nathan, 274
Klingensmith, Dr. William, 260
Knight, Dr. Douglas, 330
Knowles, Dr. John, 369, 375, 377, 384, 385, 387, 389, 392, 393, 410, 413, 561
Kolff, Dr. William, 119
Koontz, Dr. Amos R., 199
Koos, Earl, 323
Kosek, Dr. John C., 276
Kowal, Dr. Samuel J., 258, 259
Kramer, Charles, 83, 515, 516-17, 520, 523
Krosnick, Dr. Arthur, 387

Laboratory diagnosis, 24, 63, 65-69, 72, 363
Labor induction, 209-10
Lahey Clinic, 75, 567
Lahvis, Dr. Paul, 132
Lambert, Tom, 525
Lambertsen, Eleanor, 210, 232
Landess, Dr. Ben, 476-77
Larynx, cancer of the, 52
Lasagna, Dr. Louis C., 370, 488, 510, 551

Lasker, Mrs. Albert T., 113
Lasser, J. K., 360
Lattimer, Dr. John K., 47
Leader, Dr. Abel J., 472-73
Lederer, Dr. Francis, 145
Lee, Dr. Edwin A., 145
Lee, Dr. Richard, 465
Lembcke, Dr. Paul, 105
Lenz, Dr. W., 281
Leukemia, 249, 251, 487
Levin, Dr. Jack, 244
Levine, Dr. Samuel A., 37, 385, 562
Lewis, Dr. Howard P., 30
Lewison, Dr. Edward F., 51
Leys, Dr. Duncan, 289, 301, 304, 309
Liberman, Dr. George, 216
Librium, 277, 489, 506
Licensing of doctors, 20, 548-49, 563
Lidocaine, 273
Life expectancy, 14-16
Lillehei, Dr. C. Walton, 242
Liston, Dr. Edward, 424
Little, Dr. David M., Jr., 168, 169
Liver disease, 166
Louis, Dr. P. C. A., 551
Louria, Dr. Donald B., 107, 264
Lung cancer, 48, 49-50
Lung transplant, 301-02, 303
Lurie, Dr. Paul R., 242
Lyons, Dr. Champ, 111
Lyons, Dr. Richard H., 404

MacMahon, Dr. Edward, 276
Malformations of children, congenital, 281-82
Malpractice insurance, 463-64, 529

Malpractice suits, 12, 51, 87, 90, 127, 171, 173, 195, 245, 253, 265, 351, 360, 491, 515-33, 551

Mammography, 65

Mangi, Dr. Charles C., 455, 456

Manheimer, Dr. Stephen, 222

Manipulation, osteopathic, 450, 452, 453-54, 455-56, 457, 460

Mannix, Dr. Arthur James, Jr., 9

Mantoux test, 112

Mariyama, Dr. Iwao M., 16

Mark, Dr. Lester C., 131, 168

Markovitz, Dr. Andrew S., 466

Markowitz, Dr. Martin, 424

Martin, William F., 351

Massachusetts House of Representatives, 10

Master, Dr. Arthur M., 58

May, Dr. Charles D., 484, 486, 495, 499, 500, 502, 507, 509-10

Mayo Clinic, 50, 75, 134, 135, 279, 339, 567

Mazzarella, Dr. Vincent, 481

Mazzia, Dr. Valentino D. B., 170

McConnell, Dr. Warren E., 180

McCormick, Dr. T. C., 275

McDonald, Dr. Glen W., 55

McGanity, Dr. William J., 210

McGovern, George, 480

McKay, Dr. R. James, Jr., 436

McKee, Dr. W. J. E., 104

McKeown, Dr. Thomas, 389

McKittrick, Dr. Leland S., 146, 412-13

Means, Dr. James H., 218, 219

Mechanical probes, 240-41

Meclizine, 282

Medical College Admission Test, 548

Medical-computer revolution, 69-72

Medical Letter, 501-03, 512

Medicare program, 336, 338, 463, 469, 470, 471, 475, 477, 481

Medication errors, 179-83

Meetings, medical, 144-45

Menguy, Dr. René B., 280

Menninger Foundation, 339

Mepivacaine, 273

Meprobamate, 275, 489

Methacholine, 492

Methicillin, 107, 152, 264, 487

Midwife, 211

Milch, Dr. Elmer, 317-18

Miles, Dr. Robert M., 197

Milk-alkali syndrome, 124

Miller, Dr. George E., 145, 370, 384, 387, 391

Miller, Dr. Richard C., 327, 328

Mills, Don H., 529

Missionaries, medical, 558

Mitral-valve surgery, 134-35

Modell, Dr. Walter, 386, 485, 496, 500, 507, 509, 510, 511

Monitors, electronic, 170-71

Montagu, Ashley, 375

Moonlighting, medical, 405

Moore, Dr. Francis D., 126, 128

Moore, Dr. George E., 138, 139, 488

Moore, Dr. Robert A., 395

Morehead, Dr. M. A., 7

Morton, William T. G., 162

Muench, Dr. Hugo, 137

Multiple Patient Processing, 79

Municipal hospitals, 220-22

Murphy, George, 480

Murphy, Dr. James D., 431

Murray, Dr. Joseph, 120

Muschenheim, Dr. Carl, 113

Myelograms, 247-48

Myers, Dr. J. Arthur, 53

Myers, Dr. Robert S., 20, 176-77, 205, 220

Myocardial infarction, 36-37, 56, 57, 58

Nadas, Dr. Alexander, 467
Nafcillin, 153
Nakayama, Dr. Komei, 130
Narcotic addiction, physicians', 339-40, 538-39
National Academy of Medicine, proposed, 482, 569
National Academy of Sciences, 152
National Association of Retail Druggists, 504
National Board of Medical Examiners, 548
National Bureau of Economic Research, 358
National Cash Register Company, 353
National Disease and Therapeutic Index, 345, 506
National Health Education Committee, 113
National Health Survey, 102
National Institutes of Health, 93, 291
National Kidney Disease Foundation, 120
National Opinion Research Center, 4, 317, 318, 321
National Research Council, 152
National Stroke Congress, 247
National Tuberculosis Association, 113
National Vital Statistics, 16
Negligence in hospitals, 149-51, 159, 173, 184; *see also* Disciplining of doctors; Malpractice suits
Niswander, Dr. Kenneth, 209
Nitrogen narcosis, 117
Novak, Thomas M., 346
Nuremberg code, 293
Nuremberg tribunal, 289, 307-08
Nurses and nursing care, 79, 90, 91, 92, 149, 160, 165, 180-81, 182, 183, 208, 210, 221, 223, 231, 232-33, 253, 254, 566

Obstetricians, 207-10, 340
Oles, Dr. Patrick, 260
Omnipotence, medical, myth of, 95-97, 122
Open-heart surgery, 134-35
Ophthalmoscopy, 57, 420
Opinion Research Corporation, 322, 425, 426
Organ transplantation, 118-21, 140, 301-03
O'Rourke, Dr. Paul, 470-71
Osler, Sir William, 98, 330, 371, 387, 388, 485
Osteopaths, 450-60, 566
Otolaryngologists, 103
Ott, Dr. Harold A., 208
Oxacillin, 107, 152, 153, 264, 487

Page, Dr. Irvine H., 146, 481
Painkillers, 278-81
Pamine, 493
Papanicolaou, Dr. George, 48
Papaverine injection, 181
Paperwork, hospital, 227, 231, 233; *see also* Records, medical
Pappworth, Dr. M. H., 288
Pap smear test, 48-49, 74, 192, 208
Parnate, 278
Parrish, Dr. Henry M., 184, 185
Pastor, Dr. Bernard H., 61, 62
Pathologists, 69, 179
Patient-doctor relations, 79-99
Patient-stealing, 546-47

Patterson, Dr. Robert J., 209
Pearson, Dr. Homer L., 326
Pediatricians, 26, 82, 84, 87, 293, 340, 432-40
Pellagra, 304
Pellegrino, Dr. Edmund D., 324
Penicillin, 106, 107, 109, 180, 236, 261-63, 487
Peptic ulcers, 115
Perera, Dr. George A., 269, 399
Perkins, Dr. Anna W., 83
Perlmutter, Dr. Irwin, 260
Perloff, Dr. J. K., 242
Permissible experimentation, 305-06
Personal physician, need for, 97
Peterson, Dr. Osler L., 7, 27, 415-16, 420, 548, 550-51, 563
Pharmaceutical industry, 484, 485, 488, 489, 494, 495, 497, 499, 500, 504-08, 509, 511, 513
Pharmacology, 510
Pharr, Dr. Samuel L., 50
Phenothiazine tranquilizers, 169, 275, 277, 489
Phenybutazone, 486-87
Philipsborn, Dr. Herbert F., Jr., 438
Phillips, Dr. Otto C., 208
Physical examination, 29-31, 43, 73-75
Pickney, Dr. Edward R., 144
Pignataro, Dr. Frank P., 12, 19, 325
Pipberger, Dr. Hubert V., 70
Pittinger, Dr. Charles B., 116
Pius XII, Pope, 310
Placebo benefits, 130, 279
Plant, Marcus L., 94
Plato, 320, 381
PMX (Preventive Medical Examination) Group, 75
Pneumonia, 31-32, 105-09, 211, 270, 455, 460

Pneumonia, vaccine, 108
Polissar, Dr. Jan, 467, 503
Political life, doctor's, 336-38
Politz, Alfred, 17
Polycythemia, 236
Postgraduate education, 146-48, 402-16, 483
Potter, Stephen, 96-97
Price, Dr. Julian, 11
Prinzmetal, Dr. Myron, 329, 391
Procaine, 273
Proctoscope, use of, 46-47, 240
Proetz, Dr. Arthur W., 141-42
Progesterone, 281
Promotion mailing pieces, drugs, 505-06, 513
Proprietary hospitals, 150, 212, 213-16
Proprietary Hospital Code, 215-16
Prosser, Dean William L., 85
Prostate carcinoma, 47
Prostatectomies, 136
Psychochemicals, 274-78, 488-89
Psychological diagnosis, 38-40
Psychoneurotic diagnosis, 38-44
Psychosomatic ailments, 40
Public Health Service, U. S., 15, 34, 52, 54, 56, 57, 75, 137, 165, 179, 238, 291, 395, 457, 568

Quinn, Dr. William F., 20, 539

Radiation, 248-53, 292
Radiodyes, 245-46
Radioisotopes, 65

Radiologists, 63, 64, 139

Radiology, 64-65, 227

Rammelkamp, Dr. Charles H., Jr., 389

Randall, Dr. H. T., 51

Rappleye, Dr. Willard C., 382

Ratner, Dr. Herbert, 5, 21, 83, 98-99, 390, 437, 545, 560

Ravin, Dr. Mark, 171

Read, Dr. C. Thomas, 130

Read, Dr. William, 142

Records, medical, 223, 528-29; *see also* Paperwork

Rectal examination, 47

Registry in Human Kidney Transplantation, 120

Registry of Blood Dyscrasias, 267

Regulation, medical, 20-21

Rehabilitation, 114

Reimann, Dr. Hobart A., 106

Reinhold, Dr. John G., 67

Reserpine, 169

Residents, 213, 221, 284, 380, 402-16, 419, 505, 561-62

Res ipsa, 524-25

Respiratory ailments, 61-62, 104, 455

Retirement benefits, doctors', 358, 359

Retrolental fibroplasia (RLF), 296-97

Reuther, Walter, 471

Reynolds, Dr. Telfer B., 280

Rh factor, 438, 439

Rheumatic fever, 109-10

Rheumatic heart disease, 56, 62-63, 109

Ribicoff, Abraham, 480, 481

Richards, Dr. Dickinson W., 386, 560

Richardson, Dr. Fred M., 148

Rickles, Dr. Nathan K., 327

Ritvo, Miriam, 233

Robb, Inez, 230-31

Robbins, Dr. Frederick C., 365-66, 376, 384, 392, 560

Robin, Dr. Eugene D., 303

Rockefeller, Nelson, 143, 457

Rockefeller Institute, 371

Rodman, Dr. Theodore, 61, 62

Roentgen, Wilhelm, 245

Rogatz, Dr. Peter, 25, 409

Rogoff, Dr. A. S., 82

Rorie, Dr. Ronald, 423

Rosen, Dr. George, 16, 373

Rosenberg, Dr. Benjamin, 261

Rosenthal, Dr. Roy, 113

Rosinski, Edwin F., 391, 397, 559

Ross-Loos Clinic, 475

Rossman, Dr. Philip L., 39, 42-44

Roth, Dr. James L. A., 279

Rourke, Dr. Anthony J. J., 220

Rubber gloves, surgeon's, 156

Rubenstein, Dr. A. H., 280

Rush, Dr. Benjamin, 102

Rusk, Dr. Howard A., 114, 394

Russell, Dr. William O., 49, 50, 53

Rutstein, Dr. David, 370, 375-76, 387, 396

Safren, Miriam, 183

Sage Foundation, Russell, 28

Salinger, Pierre, 480

Salk, Dr. Jonas, 117

Salter, Andrew, 41

Sample drugs, 498-99

Sampson, Dr. John J., 58

Sanders, Barkev S., 33, 34, 35, 37

Sanford, Dr. Jay P., 242

Saunders, Dr. John B. deC., 395

Schaeffer, Dr. Morris, 67, 69

Schimmel, Dr. Elihu M., 237-38, 239, 240, 244, 258, 283

Schlicke, Dr. C. P., 128

Schlossberg, Eli, 183
Schmeiser, Dr. Steve, Jr., 87
Schools, medical, 4, 27, 147, 328, 369-401, 468, 478-79, 559, 561; osteopathic, 452, 456, 457-58, 458-59
Schreiner, Dr. George E., 266
Schulman, Dr. Jonas A., 107
Schultz, Dr. J. C., 266
Schuman, Dr. Stanley H., 268
Sciatic nerve, 253
Scroggins, Clayton I., 351
Seegal, Dr. David, 30, 561
Segal, Dr. Maurice S., 60
Selzer, Dr. Arthur, 242
Senior, Dr. John R., 178
Septicemia, 154
Shadid, Dr. Michael, 475
Shank, Dr. Robert E., 536
Shaw, George Bernard, 319, 534
Shedders, staphylococcus, 158-59
Sheeley, Dr. William F., 39
Shindell, Dr. Sidney, 139, 515
Shirkey, Dr. Harry C., 492
Shortage of doctors, 349, 396-97, 399
Shortliffe, Dr. E., 225
Silver, Dr. George A., 19, 25, 41
Slaughter, Dr. Frank G., 329
Slee, Dr. Virgil, 193
Smith, Dr. Marcus J., 65
Smith, Dr. Robert E., 116
Snedeker, Dr. L., 183
Snow, John, 142
Socialized medicine, 5, 364
Social Security, 359, 360, 466, 469, 481
Soffer, Dr. Alfred, 259
"Sons of Aesculapius," 320
Sore throat, 62-63; *see also* Strep throat
Spain, Dr. David M., 10, 234, 235, 237, 244, 245, 247, 248, 249, 268, 273, 485, 549
Sparling, Dr. J. Frederick, 189

Sparteine sulfate, 210
Specialists, 19, 30, 77, 348, 361; *see also* Internists
Spink, Dr. Wesley W., 142
Sponges, misplaced, 195-96
Sputum cytology technique, 48, 50
Sputum smear test, 107
Staff meetings, hospital, 219-20
Stahlgren, Dr. Leroy H., 9, 203
Standard, Dr. Samuel, 326, 329, 384, 465, 547, 564
Stanley-Brown, Dr. Edward G., 9
Staphylococcus infection, 151-62, 286-87
State medical societies, 463-64
Statistics in medical literature, 139-40
Status, doctor's loss of, 318-28
Stead, Dr. Eugene A., Jr., 403
Steinhaus, Dr. John, 274
Stephen, Dr. C. Ronald, 171
Stern, Dr. Aaron M., 60
Sternlieb, Dr. I., 148
Steroids, 77, 169, 269-73, 486
Stethoscope, 59-60
Stetler, Joseph, 536
Stevens, Rev. John, 230
Stiern, Walter W., 551
Still, Dr. Andrew Taylor, 451, 452-53, 456, 458, 460
Stollerman, Dr. Gene H., 63
Stone, Dr. Eric, 184
Strang Clinic, 35, 46, 51, 64, 74, 250, 251
Strep throat, 62-63, 109, 299; *see also* Sore throat
Streptomycin, 281, 487
Stroke, cerebral, 114, 268
Strumia, Dr. Max, 177
Student American Medical Association, 19, 424, 473
Students, medical, 97, 369-401, 559-60
Sulfonamides, 267, 282

Sunshine, Dr. Irving, 273
Surgeons and surgery, 8-9, 129-37, 228, 348, 361, 566; by general practitioners, 428-29; ghost, 205-07; gynecological, 192-93; quality of, 197-98; unnecessary, 189-93
Surgical blunders, 193-97
Surgical infections, 154, 155, 158
Surgical "series," 299-300
Surgical technique, 198-204, 228
Suspicion, low index of, 31, 32
Sussman, Dr. Leon, 173, 174, 176, 179
Swanson, Dr. E. C., 398

Talton, Dr. Inger, 171
Taussig, Dr. Helen, 281
Telephone answering services, 85, 86, 87, 89-90
Telephone follow-up of patients, 97
"Telephone" visits, 345
Telinde, Dr. R. W., 191
Tetanus, 110-11, 116; immunization, 111
Tetracyclines, 106, 263, 266-67, 487, 492
Thalidomide, 255, 257, 281, 484, 512
Thermography, 65
Thiazides, 267
Thorek, Dr. Max, 193, 194, 196, 197
Thrombocytopenia, 267
Thymectomy, 294-95
Thymus gland, 294
Thyroid cancer, 249
Thyroxine, 290
Tine test, 112
Tofany, Dr. Victor J., 173

Tonometry, 54
Tonsillectomy, 36, 101-05
Tovey, John H., 51
Training programs, interne and resident, 21, 220, 221, 402-16, 444-45; surgical, 204-05
Tranquilizer drugs, 274-78, 488-89, 507
Transplantation of organs, 118-21, 140
Triacetyloleandomycin (TriA), 289-90
Trilling, Lionel, 392
Trimble, Dr. George X., 265
Tripanarol, 259
Truelove, Dr. S. C., 125
Truman, Harry S., 481
Truman, Dr. Stanley R., 94, 318
Truman Report, 95, 206, 536
Trussell, Dr. Ray E., 7, 213, 215, 221, 222, 223, 549-50, 551, 563, 565
Trussell Reports, 7, 8, 9, 171, 185, 192, 197, 203, 212, 213, 215, 217, 218, 437, 445-46, 447, 551, 565
Trust funds, 361
Tuberculin skin tests, 112, 113
Tuberculosis, 52-53, 112-14
Tullman, John J., 519, 524
Tumors, 191

Übermensch, 95-96, 308
Ulcers, 115, 122-29
Ulrich, John, 158
Undertakers, 229, 230
United Nations, 15
University-affiliated hospitals, 213
Unwarranted Claims, 122
Urinalysis, 29-30
Urinary-tract infections, 154-55

Vacations, doctors', 333; discontinuity of care during, 88
Veenema, Dr. Ralph J., 47
Veterans Administration, 365, 457
Vital Statistics, Bureau of, 137
Voluntary hospitals, 181, 212, 213, 214, 215, 216, 218, 463
Voy, Dr. Robert O., 424

Willard, Dr. William R., 413, 414
Williams, Dr. Roger D., 200, 201
Williams, Dr. William Carlos, 329, 330
Willson, Dr. J. Robert, 209
Wilson, Dr. Frank, 255
Win, Dr. M. Shein, 203
Wives of doctors, 340-41
World Medical Association, 98, 307, 308; Draft Code, 311
Wound disruption, 196-97
Wynder, Dr. Ernest L., 33

Waitzkin, Dr. Leo, 276
Waksman, Dr. Byron H., 294, 295
Walker, Dr. Donald C., 550
Wall, David L., 352
Warner, Dr. Homer, 71
Watrous, Dr. Willis G., 208
Wealth of doctors, 358
Weaver, Dr. Daniel C., 167, 168
Wegman, Dr. Myron E., 94
Weinstein, Dr. Haskell J., 49
Welch, Dr. Claude E., 126
Wertheim, Dr. Arthur R., 30
Wescoe, Dr. W. Clarke, 147
Wheeler, Dr. Charles B., 532
Wheeler, Dr. Warren, 467
White, Dr. Abraham, 381
White, Dr. K. L., 389
Whooping cough, 111-12
Wilbur, Dr. Dwight, 376
Wilens, Dr. Sigmund L., 66, 257
Wilkins, Dr. Lawson, 485

X-ray examination, 63-65, 74, 112, 228, 245, 247-53, 363

Yanof, Dr. Zale, 97, 326, 426
Yellow fever, 303
Young, Dr. Lawrence E., 131, 178-79

Ziegler, Dr. Carolyn H., 170
Zoghlin, Dr. Leon N., 428
Zollinger, Dr. Robert M., 200, 201

ABOUT THE AUTHOR: MARTIN L. GROSS is a writer, lecturer, teacher and social critic. His first book, *The Brain Watchers* (Random House, 1962), an analysis of psychological testing in schools and industry, drew wide critical acclaim and national attention, and has stimulated a continuing debate in the field of psychology. "A book that could hardly be bettered," commented C. Northcote Parkinson.

Publication of *The Brain Watchers* led to an investigation of psychological testing and its invasion of privacy in the two houses of Congress, at both of which Mr. Gross testified as a witness in 1965. As a result of these hearings, the Civil Service Commission voluntarily withdrew the use of psychological tests among federal employees.

Mr. Gross is also the author of many penetrating articles on national affairs, education and health published in such major national publications as *Life, The New Republic, Look,* etc. He has received citations from the American Heritage Foundation and the National Education Association for his writings. Mr. Gross has lectured at many universities and is currently a member of the faculty at the New School for Social Research in New York. During 1963–64 Mr. Gross was host and moderator of a WNBC discussion program covering a variety of contemporary subjects.

Mr. Gross is a native New Yorker and resides in Manhattan with his wife and two children. He graduated from City College of New York and did graduate work at Columbia University. During World War II he served as a navigator in the U. S. Army Air Corps.

The Doctors represents over three years of extensive research in the field of American medicine and the activities of the American physician.

40438

Gross

The doctors

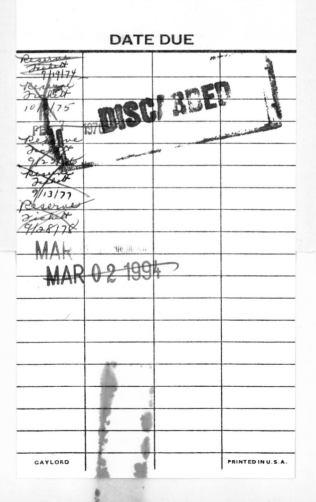

DATE DUE

Reserve
Ticket
9/19/74

Reserve
Ticket
10/1/75

FEB 7 1976 DISCARDED

Reserve
Ticket
9/23/76

Reserve
Ticket
9/13/77

Reserve
Ticket
4/28/78

MAR

MAR 0 2 1994

GAYLORD   PRINTED IN U.S.A.